MW00615650

Student Solutions Manual for McKeague's
Intermediate Algebra: Concepts with Applications

Prepared by

Ross Rueger

Department of Mathematics
College of the Sequoias
Visalia, California

Student Solutions Manual for McKeague's
Intermediate Algebra: Concepts with Applications

Ross Rueger

Publisher: XYZ Textbooks

Sales: Amy Jacobs, Richard Jones, Bruce Spears, Rachael Hillman

Cover Design: Rachel Hintz

ISBN-13: 978-1-63098-038-2 / ISBN-10: 1-63098-038-2
XYZ Textbooks

For product information and technology assistance, contact us at
XYZ Textbooks, 1-877-745-3499

For permission to use material from this text or product,
e-mail: **info@mathtv.com**

1339 Marsh Street
San Luis Obispo, CA 93401
USA

For your course and learning solutions, visit **www.xyztextbooks.com**

Printed in the United States of America

Contents

Preface

This *Student Solutions Manual* contains complete solutions to all odd-numbered exercises, and complete solutions to all review/test exercises, of *Intermediate Algebra: Concepts with Applications* by Charles P. McKeague. I have attempted to format solutions for readability and accuracy, and apologize to you for any errors that you may encounter. If you have any comments, suggestions, error corrections, or alternative solutions please feel free to send me an email (address below).

Please use this manual with some degree of caution. Be sure that you have attempted a solution, and re-attempted it, before you look it up in this manual. Mathematics can only be learned by *doing*, and not by observing! As you use this manual, do not just read the solution but work it along with the manual, using my solution to check your work. If you use this manual in that fashion then it should be helpful to you in your studying.

I would like to thank Staci Truelson, Amy Jacobs, and Patrick McKeague at XYZ Textbooks for their help with this project and for getting back to me with corrections so quickly. Producing a manual such as this is a team effort, and this is an excellent team to work with.

I wish to express my appreciation to Pat McKeague for asking me to be involved with this textbook. His books continue to refine the subject of intermediate algebra, and you will find the text very easy to read and understand. I especially appreciate his efforts through XYZ Textbooks to make textbooks affordable for students to purchase.

Good luck!

Ross Rueger
College of the Sequoias
rossrueger@gmail.com

January, 2015

Chapter 0
Real Numbers and Algebraic Expressions

0.1 The Real Numbers

1. Labeling the point:

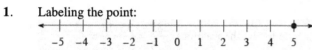

3. Labeling the point:

5. Labeling the point:

7. Labeling the point:

9. Converting the fraction: $\dfrac{3}{4} \cdot \dfrac{6}{6} = \dfrac{18}{24}$

11. Converting the fraction: $\dfrac{1}{2} \cdot \dfrac{12}{12} = \dfrac{12}{24}$

13. Converting the fraction: $\dfrac{5}{8} \cdot \dfrac{3}{3} = \dfrac{15}{24}$

15. Converting the fraction: $\dfrac{3}{5} \cdot \dfrac{12}{12} = \dfrac{36}{60}$

17. Converting the fraction: $\dfrac{11}{30} \cdot \dfrac{2}{2} = \dfrac{22}{60}$

19. Converting the fraction: $-\dfrac{5}{6} \cdot \dfrac{10}{10} = -\dfrac{50}{60}$

21. The opposite is -10, the reciprocal is $\dfrac{1}{10}$, and the absolute value is 10.

23. The opposite is $-\dfrac{3}{4}$, the reciprocal is $\dfrac{4}{3}$, and the absolute value is $\dfrac{3}{4}$.

25. The opposite is $-\dfrac{11}{2}$, the reciprocal is $\dfrac{2}{11}$, and the absolute value is $\dfrac{11}{2}$.

27. The opposite is 3, the reciprocal is $-\dfrac{1}{3}$, and the absolute value is 3.

29. The opposite is $\dfrac{2}{5}$, the reciprocal is $-\dfrac{5}{2}$, and the absolute value is $\dfrac{2}{5}$.

31. The opposite is $-x$, the reciprocal is $\dfrac{1}{x}$, and the absolute value is $|x|$.

33. Writing without absolute values: $|-2| = 2$

35. Writing without absolute values: $\left|-\dfrac{3}{4}\right| = \dfrac{3}{4}$

37. Writing without absolute values: $|\pi| = \pi$

39. Writing without absolute values: $-|4| = -4$

41. Writing without absolute values: $-|-2| = -2$

43. Writing without absolute values: $-\left|-\dfrac{3}{4}\right| = -\dfrac{3}{4}$

45. The correct statement is: $-5 < -3$

47. The correct statement is: $-3 > -7$

49. The correct statement is: $|-4| > -|-4|$

51. The correct statement is: $7 > -|-7|$

53. The correct statement is: $-\dfrac{3}{4} < -\dfrac{1}{4}$

55. The correct statement is: $-\dfrac{3}{2} < -\dfrac{3}{4}$

57. Simplifying: $|8 - 2| = |6| = 6$

59. Simplifying: $\left|5 \cdot 2^3 - 2 \cdot 3^2\right| = |5 \cdot 8 - 2 \cdot 9| = |40 - 18| = |22| = 22$

61. Simplifying: $|7 - 2| - |4 - 2| = |5| - |2| = 5 - 2 = 3$

63. Simplifying: $10 - |7 - 2(5 - 3)| = 10 - |7 - 2(2)| = 10 - |7 - 4| = 10 - |3| = 10 - 3 = 7$

65. Simplifying:
$$\begin{aligned}
15 - |8 - 2(3 \cdot 4 - 9)| - 10 &= 15 - |8 - 2(12 - 9)| - 10 \\
&= 15 - |8 - 2(3)| - 10 \\
&= 15 - |8 - 6| - 10 \\
&= 15 - |2| - 10 \\
&= 15 - 2 - 10 \\
&= 3
\end{aligned}$$

67. Factoring: $266 = 14 \cdot 19 = 2 \cdot 7 \cdot 19$ 69. Factoring: $111 = 3 \cdot 37$

71. Factoring: $369 = 9 \cdot 41 = 3^2 \cdot 41$

73. Reducing the fraction: $\dfrac{165}{385} = \dfrac{3 \cdot 55}{7 \cdot 55} = \dfrac{3}{7}$ 75. Reducing the fraction: $\dfrac{385}{735} = \dfrac{35 \cdot 11}{35 \cdot 21} = \dfrac{11}{21}$

77. Reducing the fraction: $\dfrac{111}{185} = \dfrac{37 \cdot 3}{37 \cdot 5} = \dfrac{3}{5}$ 79. Reducing the fraction: $\dfrac{75}{135} = \dfrac{15 \cdot 5}{15 \cdot 9} = \dfrac{5}{9}$

81. Reducing the fraction: $\dfrac{6}{8} = \dfrac{2 \cdot 3}{2 \cdot 4} = \dfrac{3}{4}$ 83. Reducing the fraction: $\dfrac{200}{5} = \dfrac{40 \cdot 5}{1 \cdot 5} = 40$

85. The perimeter is: $P = 4(1 \text{ in.}) = 4$ in.

   The area is: $A = (1 \text{ in.})^2 = 4 \text{ in.}^2$

87. The perimeter is: $P = 2(1.5 \text{ in.}) + 2(0.75 \text{ in.}) = 3 + 1.5 = 4.5$ in.

   The area is: $A = (1.5 \text{ in.})(0.75 \text{ in.}) = 1.125 \text{ in.}^2$

89. The perimeter is: $P = 4 \text{ cm} + 3.5 \text{ cm} + 2.75 \text{ cm} = 10.25 \text{ cm}$

   The area is: $A = \dfrac{1}{2}(4 \text{ cm})(2.5 \text{ cm}) = 5 \text{ cm}^2$

91. A loss of 8 yards corresponds to –8 on the number line. The total yards lost is 6 + (–8) = –2 yards.

93. This temperature is –64°F. The new temperature is –54 + 10 = –44°F.

95. The wind chill is –15°F.

97. This is –100 feet. The new depth is –100 – 5 = –105 feet.

99. The perimeter is: $P = 2(8.5 \text{ in.}) + 2(11 \text{ in.}) = 17 + 22 = 39$ in.

   The area is: $A = (8.5 \text{ in.})(11 \text{ in.}) = 93.5 \text{ in.}^2$

101. Finding the calories burned: $2(544) + 299 = 1{,}088 + 299 = 1{,}387$ calories

103. Finding the difference in calories burned: $3(653) - 3(435) = 1{,}959 - 1{,}305 = 654$ more calories

105. Two numbers are 20 and –20.

107. No, the absolute value of a number cannot be negative.

109. The exit is 141 + 16 = 157.

111. You are either 20 miles north (141 + 20 = 161) or 20 miles south (141 – 20 = 121). So you are either at exit 121 or exit 161.

113. **a.** The number of entertainment applications is: $5(52) = 260$ apps

   b. The number of book applications is: $2.5(52) = 130$ apps. The statement is false.

   c. The number of game applications is: $16(52) = 832$ apps. The statement is true.

0.2 Properties of Real Numbers

1. Commutative property of addition

3. Commutative property of multiplication

5. Additive inverse property

7. Commutative property of addition

9. Associative and commutative properties of multiplication

11. Commutative and associative properties of addition

13. Distributive property

15. Multiplicative inverse property

17. Using the associative property: $4 + (2 + x) = (4 + 2) + x = 6 + x$

19. Using the associative property: $(a + 3) + 5 = a + (3 + 5) = a + 8$

21. Using the associative property: $5(3y) = (5 \cdot 3)y = 15y$

23. Using the associative property: $\frac{1}{3}(3x) = \left(\frac{1}{3} \cdot 3\right)x = x$

25. Using the associative property: $4\left(\frac{1}{4}a\right) = \left(4 \cdot \frac{1}{4}\right)a = a$

27. Using the associative property: $\frac{2}{3}\left(\frac{3}{2}x\right) = \left(\frac{2}{3} \cdot \frac{3}{2}\right)x = x$

29. Applying the distributive property: $3(x + 6) = 3 \cdot x + 3 \cdot 6 = 3x + 18$

31. Applying the distributive property: $2(6x + 4) = 2 \cdot 6x + 2 \cdot 4 = 12x + 8$

33. Applying the distributive property: $5(3a + 2b) = 5 \cdot 3a + 5 \cdot 2b = 15a + 10b$

35. Applying the distributive property: $\frac{1}{3}(4x + 6) = \frac{1}{3} \cdot 4x + \frac{1}{3} \cdot 6 = \frac{4}{3}x + 2$

37. Applying the distributive property: $\frac{1}{5}(10 + 5y) = \frac{1}{5} \cdot 10 + \frac{1}{5} \cdot 5y = 2 + y$

39. Applying the distributive property: $(5t + 1)8 = 5t \cdot 8 + 1 \cdot 8 = 40t + 8$

41. Applying the distributive property: $3(3x + y - 2z) = 3 \cdot 3x + 3 \cdot y - 3 \cdot 2z = 9x + 3y - 6z$

43. Applying the distributive property: $10(0.3x + 0.7y) = 10 \cdot 0.3x + 10 \cdot 0.7y = 3x + 7y$

45. Applying the distributive property: $100(0.06x + 0.07y) = 100 \cdot 0.06x + 100 \cdot 0.07y = 6x + 7y$

47. Applying the distributive property: $3\left(x + \frac{1}{3}\right) = 3 \cdot x + 3 \cdot \frac{1}{3} = 3x + 1$

49. Applying the distributive property: $2\left(x - \frac{1}{2}\right) = 2 \cdot x - 2 \cdot \frac{1}{2} = 2x - 1$

51. Applying the distributive property: $x\left(1 + \frac{2}{x}\right) = x \cdot 1 + x \cdot \frac{2}{x} = x + 2$

53. Applying the distributive property: $a\left(1 - \frac{3}{a}\right) = a \cdot 1 - a \cdot \frac{3}{a} = a - 3$

55. Applying the distributive property: $8\left(\frac{1}{8}x + 3\right) = 8 \cdot \frac{1}{8}x + 8 \cdot 3 = x + 24$

57. Applying the distributive property: $6\left(\frac{1}{2}x - \frac{1}{3}y\right) = 6 \cdot \frac{1}{2}x - 6 \cdot \frac{1}{3}y = 3x - 2y$

59. Applying the distributive property: $12\left(\frac{1}{4}x + \frac{2}{3}y\right) = 12 \cdot \frac{1}{4}x + 12 \cdot \frac{2}{3}y = 3x + 8y$

61. Applying the distributive property: $20\left(\frac{2}{5}x + \frac{1}{4}y\right) = 20 \cdot \frac{2}{5}x + 20 \cdot \frac{1}{4}y = 8x + 5y$

63. Applying the distributive property: $3(5x+2)+4 = 15x+6+4 = 15x+10$

65. Applying the distributive property: $4(2y+6)+8 = 8y+24+8 = 8y+32$

67. Applying the distributive property: $5(1+3t)+4 = 5+15t+4 = 15t+9$

69. Applying the distributive property: $3+(2+7x)4 = 3+8+28x = 28x+11$

71. Adding the fractions: $\dfrac{2}{5}+\dfrac{1}{15} = \dfrac{2}{5}\cdot\dfrac{3}{3}+\dfrac{1}{15} = \dfrac{6}{15}+\dfrac{1}{15} = \dfrac{7}{15}$

73. Adding the fractions: $\dfrac{17}{30}+\dfrac{11}{42} = \dfrac{17}{30}\cdot\dfrac{7}{7}+\dfrac{11}{42}\cdot\dfrac{5}{5} = \dfrac{119}{210}+\dfrac{55}{210} = \dfrac{174}{210} = \dfrac{29}{35}$

75. Adding the fractions: $\dfrac{9}{48}+\dfrac{3}{54} = \dfrac{9}{48}\cdot\dfrac{9}{9}+\dfrac{3}{54}\cdot\dfrac{8}{8} = \dfrac{81}{432}+\dfrac{24}{432} = \dfrac{105}{432} = \dfrac{35}{144}$

77. Adding the fractions: $\dfrac{25}{84}+\dfrac{41}{90} = \dfrac{25}{84}\cdot\dfrac{15}{15}+\dfrac{41}{90}\cdot\dfrac{14}{14} = \dfrac{375}{1260}+\dfrac{574}{1260} = \dfrac{949}{1260}$

79. Simplifying: $\dfrac{3}{14}+\dfrac{7}{30} = \dfrac{3}{14}\cdot\dfrac{15}{15}+\dfrac{7}{30}\cdot\dfrac{7}{7} = \dfrac{45}{210}+\dfrac{49}{210} = \dfrac{94}{210} = \dfrac{47}{105}$

81. Simplifying: $32\left(\dfrac{3}{4}\right)-16\left(\dfrac{3}{4}\right)^2 = 32\left(\dfrac{3}{4}\right)-16\left(\dfrac{9}{16}\right) = 24-9 = 15$

83. Simplifying the expression: $5a+7+8a+a = (5a+8a+a)+7 = 14a+7$

85. Simplifying the expression: $2(5x+1)+2x = 10x+2+2x = 12x+2$

87. Simplifying the expression: $3+4(5a+3)+4a = 3+20a+12+4a = 24a+15$

89. Simplifying the expression: $5x+3(x+2)+7 = 5x+3x+6+7 = 8x+13$

91. Simplifying the expression: $5(x+2y)+4(3x+y) = 5x+10y+12x+4y = 17x+14y$

93. Simplifying the expression: $5b+3(4b+a)+6a = 5b+12b+3a+6a = 17b+9a$

95. Solving the equation:

$$x+\dfrac{x}{4} = 15$$
$$4\left(x+\dfrac{x}{4}\right) = 4(15)$$
$$4x+x = 60$$
$$5x = 60$$
$$x = 12$$

97. Finding the difference: $814-47 = 767$ acres

99. Finding the percent: $\dfrac{47}{4{,}217} \approx 0.011 = 1.1\%$

101.   **a.**   The decrease was the largest from 2006 to 2008.
     b.   The rate of increase from 2000 to 2002 was negative.
     c.   The number of millionaires was the lowest in 2002.

103. Applying the distributive property: $x(x+8) = x\cdot x+x\cdot 8 = x^2+8x$

105. Applying the distributive property: $x(y-4) = x\cdot y-x\cdot 4 = xy-4x$

107. This statement is false (if x is negative).   **109.** This statement is false (if x is positive).

111. This statement is true.   **113.** This statement is false (if $x = 0$).

115. This statement is false (if $x = 0$).

Landmark Review

1. Converting the fraction: $\dfrac{3}{5} \cdot \dfrac{3}{3} = \dfrac{9}{15}$

2. Converting the fraction: $\dfrac{2}{3} \cdot \dfrac{5}{5} = \dfrac{10}{15}$

3. Converting the fraction: $\dfrac{2}{1} \cdot \dfrac{15}{15} = \dfrac{30}{15}$

4. Converting the fraction: $\dfrac{1}{1} \cdot \dfrac{15}{15} = \dfrac{15}{15}$

5. The opposite is –5, the reciprocal is $\dfrac{1}{5}$, and the absolute value is 5.

6. The opposite is $\dfrac{1}{2}$, the reciprocal is -2, and the absolute value is $\dfrac{1}{2}$.

7. Simplifying: $\left|2 \times 3^2 - 4 \times 2^3\right| = \left|2 \times 9 - 4 \times 8\right| = \left|18 - 32\right| = \left|-14\right| = 14$

8. Simplifying: $14 - \left|4(3-4) - 13\right| = 14 - \left|4(-1) - 13\right| = 14 - \left|-4 - 13\right| = 14 - \left|-17\right| = 14 - 17 = -3$

9. Reducing the fraction: $\dfrac{50}{75} = \dfrac{25 \cdot 2}{25 \cdot 3} = \dfrac{2}{3}$

10. Reducing the fraction: $\dfrac{52}{65} = \dfrac{13 \cdot 4}{13 \cdot 5} = \dfrac{4}{5}$

11. Reducing the fraction: $\dfrac{48}{80} = \dfrac{16 \cdot 3}{16 \cdot 5} = \dfrac{3}{5}$

12. Reducing the fraction: $\dfrac{42}{56} = \dfrac{14 \cdot 3}{14 \cdot 4} = \dfrac{3}{4}$

13. Adding the fractions: $\dfrac{4}{10} + \dfrac{1}{15} = \dfrac{4}{10} \cdot \dfrac{3}{3} + \dfrac{1}{15} \cdot \dfrac{2}{2} = \dfrac{12}{30} + \dfrac{2}{30} = \dfrac{14}{30} = \dfrac{2 \cdot 7}{2 \cdot 15} = \dfrac{7}{15}$

14. Adding the fractions: $\dfrac{1}{12} + \dfrac{5}{16} = \dfrac{1}{12} \cdot \dfrac{4}{4} + \dfrac{5}{16} \cdot \dfrac{3}{3} = \dfrac{4}{48} + \dfrac{15}{48} = \dfrac{19}{48}$

15. Adding the fractions: $\dfrac{2}{5} + \dfrac{3}{8} = \dfrac{2}{5} \cdot \dfrac{8}{8} + \dfrac{3}{8} \cdot \dfrac{5}{5} = \dfrac{16}{40} + \dfrac{15}{40} = \dfrac{31}{40}$

16. Adding the fractions: $\dfrac{1}{2} + \dfrac{3}{4} = \dfrac{1}{2} \cdot \dfrac{2}{2} + \dfrac{3}{4} = \dfrac{2}{4} + \dfrac{3}{4} = \dfrac{5}{4}$

17. Simplifying: $4x + 3 + 2x + 5 + x = 7x + 8$

18. Simplifying: $2y + 3(y - 3) + 8 = 2y + 3y - 9 + 8 = 5y - 1$

19. Simplifying: $2a + 3(4a + 3) + 5a + 4 = 2a + 12a + 9 + 5a + 4 = 19a + 13$

20. Simplifying: $5 + 2(3x + 2y) + 6(x + y) = 5 + 6x + 4y + 6x + 6y = 12x + 10y + 5$

0.3 Arithmetic with Real Numbers

1. Finding the sum: $6 + (-2) = 6 - 2 = 4$

3. Finding the sum: $-6 + 2 = -4$

5. Finding the difference: $-7 - 3 = -7 + (-3) = -10$

7. Finding the difference: $-7 - (-3) = -7 + 3 = -4$

9. Finding the difference: $\dfrac{3}{4} - \left(-\dfrac{5}{6}\right) = \dfrac{3}{4} + \dfrac{5}{6} = \dfrac{3}{4} \cdot \dfrac{3}{3} + \dfrac{5}{6} \cdot \dfrac{2}{2} = \dfrac{9}{12} + \dfrac{10}{12} = \dfrac{19}{12}$

11. Finding the difference: $\dfrac{11}{42} - \dfrac{17}{30} = \dfrac{11}{42} \cdot \dfrac{5}{5} - \dfrac{17}{30} \cdot \dfrac{7}{7} = \dfrac{55}{210} - \dfrac{119}{210} = -\dfrac{64}{210} = -\dfrac{32}{105}$

13. Subtracting: $-3 - 5 = -8$

15. Subtracting: $-4 - 8 = -12$

17. Subtracting: $-3x - 4x = -7x$

19. The number is 13, since $5 - 13 = -8$.

21. Computing the value: $-7 + (2 - 9) = -7 + (-7) = -14$

23. Simplifying the value: $(8a + a) - 3a = 9a - 3a = 6a$

25. Finding the product: $3(-5) = -15$

27. Finding the product: $-3(-5) = 15$

29. Finding the product: $2(-3)(4) = -6(4) = -24$

31. Finding the product: $-2(5x) = -10x$

33. Finding the product: $-\dfrac{1}{3}(-3x) = \dfrac{3}{3}x = x$

35. Finding the product: $-\dfrac{2}{3}\left(-\dfrac{3}{2}y\right) = \dfrac{6}{6}y = y$

37. Finding the product: $-2(4x-3)=-8x+6$ 39. Finding the product: $-\dfrac{1}{2}(6a-8)=-3a+4$

41. Simplifying: $1(-2)-2(-16)+1(9)=-2+32+9=39$

43. Simplifying: $1(1)-3(-2)+(-2)(-2)=1+6+4=11$

45. Simplifying: $-4(0)(-2)-(-1)(1)(1)-1(2)(3)=0+1-6=-5$

47. Simplifying: $1[0-(-1)]-3(2-4)+(-2)(-2-0)=1(1)-3(-2)-2(-2)=1+6+4=11$

49. Simplifying: $3(-2)^2+2(-2)-1=3(4)+2(-2)-1=12-4-1=7$

51. Simplifying: $2(-2)^3-3(-2)^2+4(-2)-8=2(-8)-3(4)+4(-2)-8=-16-12-8-8=-44$

53. Simplifying: $\dfrac{0-4}{0-2}=\dfrac{-4}{-2}=2$ 55. Simplifying: $\dfrac{-4-4}{-4-2}=\dfrac{-8}{-6}=\dfrac{4}{3}$

57. Simplifying: $\dfrac{-6+6}{-6-3}=\dfrac{0}{-9}=0$ 59. Simplifying: $\dfrac{2-4}{2-2}=\dfrac{-2}{0}$, which is undefined

61. Simplifying: $\dfrac{3-(-1)}{-3-3}=\dfrac{4}{-6}=-\dfrac{2}{3}$ 63. Simplifying: $\dfrac{-3^2+9}{-4-4}=\dfrac{-9+9}{-8}=0$

65. Simplifying: $3(5x+4)-x=15x+12-x=14x+12$ 67. Simplifying: $6-7(3-m)=6-21+7m=7m-15$

69. Simplifying: $7-2(3x-1)+4x=7-6x+2+4x=-2x+9$

71. Simplifying: $5(3y+1)-(8y-5)=15y+5-8y+5=7y+10$

73. Simplifying: $4(2-6x)-(3-4x)=8-24x-3+4x=-20x+5$

75. Simplifying: $10-4(2x+1)-(3x-4)=10-8x-4-3x+4=-11x+10$

77. Simplifying: $3x-5(x-3)-2(1-3x)=3x-5x+15-2+6x=4x+13$

79. $\dfrac{4}{0}$ is undefined 81. Dividing: $\dfrac{0}{-3}=0\cdot\left(-\dfrac{1}{3}\right)=0$

83. Dividing: $-\dfrac{3}{4}\div\dfrac{9}{8}=-\dfrac{3}{4}\cdot\dfrac{8}{9}=-\dfrac{2}{3}$ 85. Dividing: $-8\div\left(-\dfrac{1}{4}\right)=-8\cdot\left(-\dfrac{4}{1}\right)=32$

87. Dividing: $-40\div\left(-\dfrac{5}{8}\right)=-40\cdot\left(-\dfrac{8}{5}\right)=64$ 89. Dividing: $\dfrac{4}{9}\div(-8)=\dfrac{4}{9}\cdot\left(-\dfrac{1}{8}\right)=-\dfrac{1}{18}$

91. Simplifying: $\dfrac{3(-1)-4(-2)}{8-5}=\dfrac{-3+8}{3}=\dfrac{5}{3}$

93. Simplifying: $8-(-6)\left[\dfrac{2(-3)-5(4)}{-8(6)-4}\right]=8+6\left(\dfrac{-6-20}{-48-4}\right)=8+6\left(\dfrac{-26}{-52}\right)=8+6\left(\dfrac{1}{2}\right)=8+3=11$

95. Simplifying: $6-(-3)\left[\dfrac{2-4(3-8)}{1-5(1-3)}\right]=6-(-3)\left[\dfrac{2-4(-5)}{1-5(-2)}\right]=6-(-3)\left(\dfrac{2+20}{1+10}\right)=6-(-3)\left(\dfrac{22}{11}\right)=6+6=12$

97. Completing the table:

a	b	Sum $a+b$	Difference $a-b$	Product ab	Quotient a/b
3	12	15	-9	36	$\frac{1}{4}$
-3	12	9	-15	-36	$-\frac{1}{4}$
3	-12	-9	15	-36	$-\frac{1}{4}$
-3	-12	-15	9	36	$\frac{1}{4}$

99. Completing the table:

x	$3(5x-2)$	$15x-6$	$15x-2$
-2	-36	-36	-32
-1	-21	-21	-17
0	-6	-6	-2
1	9	9	13
2	24	24	28

101. **a.** Evaluating when $a = 3$ and $b = -6$: $-\dfrac{b}{2a} = -\dfrac{-6}{2(3)} = -\dfrac{-6}{6} = 1$

     b. Evaluating when $a = -2$ and $b = 6$: $-\dfrac{b}{2a} = -\dfrac{6}{2(-2)} = -\dfrac{6}{-4} = \dfrac{3}{2}$

     c. Evaluating when $a = -1$ and $b = -2$: $-\dfrac{b}{2a} = -\dfrac{-2}{2(-1)} = -\dfrac{-2}{-2} = -1$

     d. Evaluating when $a = -0.1$ and $b = 27$: $-\dfrac{b}{2a} = -\dfrac{27}{2(-0.1)} = -\dfrac{27}{-0.2} = 135$

103. Using a calculator: $\dfrac{1.380}{0.903} \approx 1.5282$

105. Using a calculator: $\dfrac{1}{2}(-0.1587) \approx -0.0794$

107. Using a calculator: $\dfrac{1}{2}\left(\dfrac{1.2}{1.4} - 1\right) \approx -0.0714$

109. Using a calculator: $\dfrac{(6.8)(3.9)}{7.8} = 3.4$

111. Using a calculator: $\dfrac{0.0005(200)}{(0.25)^2} = 1.6$

113. Using a calculator: $-500 + 27(100) - 0.1(100)^2 = -500 + 2,700 - 1,000 = 1,200$

115. Using a calculator: $-0.05(130)^2 + 9.5(130) - 200 = -845 + 1,235 - 200 = 190$

117. **a.** Finding the ratio: $\dfrac{4,050}{59,424} \approx 0.068$ stores per mi^2

     b. Finding the ratio: $\dfrac{9,143}{268,580} \approx 0.034$ stores per mi^2

     c. Georgia has a higher concentration of convenience stors.

119. **a.** Finding the difference: 1:44:19 − 1:44:75 = −0:00:56

     b. Finding the difference: 1:45:65 − 1:45:68 = −0:00:03

     c. Finding the difference: 1:44:19 − 1:45:68 = −0:01:49

121. Finding the ratio: $\dfrac{16,094}{4,217} \approx 3.8$ times larger

123. Solving the equation:

$$4x + 109 = 4,217$$
$$4x = 4,108$$
$$x = 1,027$$

Golden Gate Park has an area of 1,027 acres.

0.4 Exponents and Scientific Notation

1. Evaluating: $4^2 = 4 \cdot 4 = 16$

3. Evaluating: $-4^2 = -(4 \cdot 4) = -16$

5. Evaluating: $-0.3^3 = -(0.3 \cdot 0.3 \cdot 0.3) = -0.027$

7. Evaluating: $2^5 = 2 \cdot 2 \cdot 2 \cdot 2 \cdot 2 = 32$

9. Evaluating: $\left(\dfrac{1}{2}\right)^3 = \dfrac{1}{2} \cdot \dfrac{1}{2} \cdot \dfrac{1}{2} = \dfrac{1}{8}$

11. Evaluating: $\left(\dfrac{5}{6}\right)^2 = \dfrac{5}{6} \cdot \dfrac{5}{6} = \dfrac{25}{36}$

13. Evaluating: $\left(\dfrac{1}{10}\right)^4 = \dfrac{1}{10} \cdot \dfrac{1}{10} \cdot \dfrac{1}{10} \cdot \dfrac{1}{10} = \dfrac{1}{10,000}$

15. Evaluating: $\left(-\dfrac{5}{6}\right)^2 = \left(-\dfrac{5}{6}\right)\left(-\dfrac{5}{6}\right) = \dfrac{25}{36}$

17. Evaluating: $\left(-\dfrac{3}{7}\right)^2 = \left(-\dfrac{3}{7}\right)\left(-\dfrac{3}{7}\right) = \dfrac{9}{49}$

19. Using properties of exponents: $x^5 \cdot x^4 = x^{5+4} = x^9$

21. Using properties of exponents: $\left(2^3\right)^2 = 2^{3 \cdot 2} = 2^6 = 64$

23. Using properties of exponents: $-3a^2\left(2a^4\right) = -6a^{2+4} = -6a^6$

25. Using properties of exponents: $\left(4x^2\right)^2 = 4^2\left(x^2\right)^2 = 16x^4$

27. Writing with positive exponents: $3^{-2} = \dfrac{1}{3^2} = \dfrac{1}{9}$

29. Writing with positive exponents: $(-2)^{-5} = \dfrac{1}{(-2)^5} = -\dfrac{1}{32}$

31. Writing with positive exponents: $\left(\dfrac{3}{4}\right)^{-2} = \left(\dfrac{4}{3}\right)^2 = \dfrac{16}{9}$

33. Writing with positive exponents: $\left(\dfrac{1}{3}\right)^{-2} + \left(\dfrac{1}{2}\right)^{-3} = 3^2 + 2^3 = 9 + 8 = 17$

35. Multiplying: $8x^3 \cdot 10y^6 = 80x^3y^6$

37. Multiplying: $8x^3 \cdot 9y^3 = 72x^3y^3$

39. Multiplying: $3x \cdot 5y = 15xy$

41. Multiplying: $4x^6y^6 \cdot 3x = 12x^7y^6$

43. Multiplying: $27a^6c^3 \cdot 2b^2c = 54a^6b^2c^4$

45. Multiplying: $12x^3y^4 \cdot 3xy^2 = 36x^4y^6$

47. Dividing: $\dfrac{10x^5}{5x^2} = 2x^{5-2} = 2x^3$

49. Dividing: $\dfrac{20x^3}{5x^2} = 4x^{3-2} = 4x$

51. Dividing: $\dfrac{8x^3y^5}{-2x^2y} = -4x^{3-2}y^{5-1} = -4xy^4$

53. Dividing: $\dfrac{4x^4y^3}{-2x^2y} = -2x^{4-2}y^{3-1} = -2x^2y^2$

55. Simplifying: $\dfrac{x^{-1}}{x^9} = x^{-1-9} = x^{-10} = \dfrac{1}{x^{10}}$

57. Simplifying: $\dfrac{a^4}{a^{-6}} = a^{4-(-6)} = a^{4+6} = a^{10}$

59. Simplifying: $\dfrac{t^{-10}}{t^{-4}} = t^{-10-(-4)} = t^{-10+4} = t^{-6} = \dfrac{1}{t^6}$

61. Simplifying: $\left(\dfrac{x^5}{x^3}\right)^6 = \left(x^{5-3}\right)^6 = \left(x^2\right)^6 = x^{12}$

63. Simplifying: $\dfrac{\left(x^5\right)^6}{\left(x^3\right)^4} = \dfrac{x^{30}}{x^{12}} = x^{30-12} = x^{18}$

65. Simplifying: $\dfrac{\left(x^{-2}\right)^3\left(x^3\right)^{-2}}{x^{10}} = \dfrac{x^{-6}x^{-6}}{x^{10}} = \dfrac{x^{-12}}{x^{10}} = x^{-12-10} = x^{-22} = \dfrac{1}{x^{22}}$

67. Simplifying: $\dfrac{5a^8b^3}{20a^5b^{-4}} = \dfrac{5}{20}a^{8-5}b^{3-(-4)} = \dfrac{1}{4}a^3b^7 = \dfrac{a^3b^7}{4}$

69. Simplifying: $\dfrac{\left(3x^{-2}y^8\right)^4}{\left(9x^4y^{-3}\right)^2} = \dfrac{81x^{-8}y^{32}}{81x^8y^{-6}} = x^{-8-8}y^{32+6} = x^{-16}y^{38} = \dfrac{y^{38}}{x^{16}}$

71. Simplifying: $\left(\dfrac{8x^2y}{4x^4y^{-3}}\right)^4 = \left(2x^{2-4}y^{1+3}\right)^4 = \left(2x^{-2}y^4\right)^4 = 16x^{-8}y^{16} = \dfrac{16y^{16}}{x^8}$

73. Simplifying: $\left(\dfrac{x^{-5}y^2}{x^{-3}y^5}\right)^{-2} = \left(x^{-5+3}y^{2-5}\right)^{-2} = \left(x^{-2}y^{-3}\right)^{-2} = x^4y^6$

75. Simplifying: $\left(\dfrac{ab^{-3}c^{-2}}{a^{-3}b^0c^{-5}}\right)^0 = 1$ 77. Simplifying: $\left(\dfrac{x^2}{x^{-3}}\right)^0 = 1$

79. Writing in scientific notation: $378{,}000 = 3.78 \times 10^5$ 81. Writing in scientific notation: $4{,}900 = 4.9 \times 10^3$

83. Writing in scientific notation: $0.00037 = 3.7 \times 10^{-4}$ 85. Writing in scientific notation: $0.00495 = 4.95 \times 10^{-3}$

87. Writing in expanded form: $5.34 \times 10^3 = 5{,}340$ 89. Writing in expanded form: $7.8 \times 10^6 = 7{,}800{,}000$

91. Writing in expanded form: $3.44 \times 10^{-3} = 0.00344$ 93. Writing in expanded form: $4.9 \times 10^{-1} = 0.49$

95. Simplifying: $\left(4 \times 10^{10}\right)\left(2 \times 10^{-6}\right) = 8 \times 10^{10-6} = 8 \times 10^4$

97. Simplifying: $\dfrac{8 \times 10^{14}}{4 \times 10^5} = 2 \times 10^{14-5} = 2 \times 10^9$

99. Simplifying: $\dfrac{\left(5 \times 10^6\right)\left(4 \times 10^{-8}\right)}{8 \times 10^4} = \dfrac{20 \times 10^{-2}}{8 \times 10^4} = \dfrac{20}{8} \times 10^{-2-4} = 2.5 \times 10^{-6}$

101. Simplifying: $\dfrac{\left(2.4 \times 10^{-3}\right)\left(3.6 \times 10^{-7}\right)}{\left(4.8 \times 10^6\right)\left(1 \times 10^{-9}\right)} = \dfrac{8.64 \times 10^{-10}}{4.8 \times 10^{-3}} = \dfrac{8.64}{4.8} \times 10^{-10+3} = 1.8 \times 10^{-7}$

103. Simplifying: $\dfrac{2.00 \times 10^8}{3.98 \times 10^6} = \dfrac{2.00}{3.98} \times 10^2 \approx 50$

105. Using a calculator: $10^{-4.1} \approx 7.9 \times 10^{-5}$

107. a. Using the rule for order of operations: $3 \cdot 5 + 4 = 15 + 4 = 19$
    b. Using the rule for order of operations: $3(5+4) = 3 \cdot 9 = 27$
    c. Using the rule for order of operations: $3 \cdot 5 + 3 \cdot 4 = 15 + 12 = 27$

109. a. Using the rule for order of operations: $6 + 3 \cdot 4 - 2 = 6 + 12 - 2 = 16$
    b. Using the rule for order of operations: $6 + 3(4-2) = 6 + 3 \cdot 2 = 6 + 6 = 12$
    c. Using the rule for order of operations: $(6+3)(4-2) = 9 \cdot 2 = 18$

111. a. Using the rule for order of operations: $(5+7)^2 = 12^2 = 144$
    b. Using the rule for order of operations: $5^2 + 7^2 = 25 + 49 = 74$
    c. Using the rule for order of operations: $5^2 + 2 \cdot 5 \cdot 7 + 7^2 = 25 + 70 + 49 = 144$

113. a. Using the rule for order of operations: $2 + 3 \cdot 2^2 + 3^2 = 2 + 3 \cdot 4 + 9 = 2 + 12 + 9 = 23$
    b. Using the rule for order of operations: $2 + 3\left(2^2 + 3^2\right) = 2 + 3(4+9) = 2 + 3 \cdot 13 = 2 + 39 = 41$
    c. Using the rule for order of operations: $(2+3)\left(2^2 + 3^2\right) = (5)(4+9) = 5 \cdot 13 = 65$

115. Writing in scientific notation: $630{,}000{,}000 = 6.3 \times 10^8$ seconds

117. Multiplying to find the distance: $\left(1.7 \times 10^6 \text{ light-years}\right)\left(5.9 \times 10^{12} \text{ miles/light-year}\right) \approx 1.003 \times 10^{19}$ miles

119. **a.** Writing in scientific notation: $4,204,000 = 4.204 \times 10^6$ viewers

     b. Writing in scientific notation: $7,995,000 = 7.995 \times 10^6$ viewers

     c. Writing in scientific notation: $6,761,000 = 6.761 \times 10^6$ viewers

121. Finding the distance: $\left(4.2 \text{ light-years}\right)\left(5.9 \times 10^{12} \text{ miles/light-year}\right) = 2.478 \times 10^{13}$ miles

123. Finding the time: $\dfrac{4.13 \times 10^{17} \text{ miles}}{5.9 \times 10^{12} \text{ miles/year}} = 70,000$ years

125. **a.** Writing in scientific notation: $800,000,000,000 = 8.0 \times 10^{11}$

     b. Dividing to find the average: $\dfrac{8.0 \times 10^{11} \text{ dollars}}{1.8 \times 10^8 \text{ people}} \approx \$4.444 \times 10^3 = \$4,444$

127. Completing the table:

Unit	Exponential Form	Scientific Form
Kilobyte	$2^{10} = 1,024$	1.024×10^3
Megabyte	$2^{20} \approx 1,048,000$	1.048×10^6
Gigabyte	$2^{30} \approx 1,074,000,000$	1.074×10^9
Terabyte	$2^{40} \approx 1,099,500,000,000$	1.0995×10^{12}

129. Simplifying: $x^{m-4} x^{m+9} x^{-2m} = x^{m-4+m+9-2m} = x^5$

131. Simplifying: $\left(y^m\right)^{-4} \left(y^3\right)^m \left(y^{m+6}\right) = y^{-4m} \cdot y^{3m} \cdot y^{m+6} = y^{-4m+3m+m+6} = y^6$

133. Simplifying: $\dfrac{x^{n-3}}{x^{n-7}} = x^{n-3-(n-7)} = x^{n-3-n+7} = x^4$

135. Simplifying: $x^{2b-3} x^{5-8b} x^{-4-3b} = x^{2b-3+5-8b-4-3b} = x^{-9b-2}$

137. Simplifying: $\left(x^{4m-1}\right)^3 \left(x^{m+2}\right)^4 = x^{12m-3} \cdot x^{4m+8} = x^{12m-3+4m+8} = x^{16m+5}$

139. Simplifying: $\dfrac{x^{2b-6}}{x^{5b+2}} = x^{2b-6-(5b+2)} = x^{2b-6-5b-2} = x^{-3b-8}$

141. Simplifying: $\dfrac{\left(x^{4m-3}\right)^4}{\left(x^{2m+1}\right)^3} = \dfrac{x^{16m-12}}{x^{6m+3}} = x^{16m-12-(6m+3)} = x^{16m-12-6m-3} = x^{10m-15}$

143. Simplifying: $\left(\dfrac{x^{-3a+2}}{x^{-5a-4}}\right)^3 = \dfrac{x^{-9a+6}}{x^{-15a-12}} = x^{-9a+6-(-15a-12)} = x^{-9a+6+15a+12} = x^{6a+18}$

Chapter 0 Review

1. Converting the fraction: $\dfrac{2}{3} \cdot \dfrac{12}{12} = \dfrac{24}{36}$

2. Converting the fraction: $\dfrac{7}{9} \cdot \dfrac{4}{4} = \dfrac{28}{36}$

3. The correct statement is: $-4 < 9$

4. The correct statement is: $-6 < -3$

5. The correct statement is: $5 > 3$

6. The correct statement is: $-\dfrac{2}{3} < -\dfrac{1}{6}$

7. Simplifying: $|7 - 12 \div 3| = |7 - 4| = |3| = 3$

8. Simplifying: $|9 - 12| - |3 - 11| = |-3| - |-8| = 3 - 8 = -5$

9. Simplifying: $13 - |7(2 - 5)| = 13 - |7(-3)| = 13 - |-21| = 13 - 21 = -8$

10. Simplifying: $7 + |5 \cdot 3 - 7| - 6 = 7 + |15 - 7| - 6 = 7 + |8| - 6 = 7 + 8 - 6 = 9$

11. Reducing the fraction: $\dfrac{252}{468} = \dfrac{36 \cdot 7}{36 \cdot 13} = \dfrac{7}{13}$

12. Reducing the fraction: $\dfrac{208}{496} = \dfrac{16 \cdot 13}{16 \cdot 31} = \dfrac{13}{31}$

13. Simplifying: $3(2x + 5) - 4x = 6x + 15 - 4x = 2x + 15$

14. Simplifying: $5x - 5 + 2x + 7 = 7x + 2$

15. Simplifying: $3x + 2(3x + 2y) + 4y = 3x + 6x + 4y + 4y = 9x + 8y$

16. Simplifying: $4a + 3(2b + 4) - 8 = 4a + 6b + 12 - 8 = 4a + 6b + 4$

17. Simplifying: $4y + 2(2x - 4) - 2y = 4y + 4x - 8 - 2y = 4x + 2y - 8$

18. Simplifying: $16\left(\dfrac{5}{8}x + \dfrac{1}{4}\right) - 2 = 16 \cdot \dfrac{5}{8}x + 16 \cdot \dfrac{1}{4} - 2 = 10x + 4 - 2 = 10x + 2$

19. Adding the fractions: $\dfrac{9}{14} + \dfrac{7}{24} = \dfrac{9}{14} \cdot \dfrac{12}{12} + \dfrac{7}{24} \cdot \dfrac{7}{7} = \dfrac{108}{168} + \dfrac{49}{168} = \dfrac{157}{168}$

20. Adding the fractions: $\dfrac{9}{16} + \dfrac{12}{36} = \dfrac{9}{16} \cdot \dfrac{9}{9} + \dfrac{12}{36} \cdot \dfrac{4}{4} = \dfrac{81}{144} + \dfrac{48}{144} = \dfrac{129}{144} = \dfrac{3 \cdot 43}{3 \cdot 48} = \dfrac{43}{48}$

21. Simplifying: $3 - (5 - x) + 3x = 3 - 5 + x + 3x = 4x - 2$

22. Simplifying: $(6 - 3x) - (2x - 4) = 6 - 3x - 2x + 4 = -5x + 10$

23. Simplifying: $3x - 4(2x - 3) - 12 = 3x - 8x + 12 - 12 = -5x$

24. Simplifying: $\dfrac{3(-2) - 4(4)}{6 - 4} = \dfrac{-6 - 16}{6 - 4} = \dfrac{-22}{2} = -11$

25. Using properties of exponents: $\left(-2x^2\right)^{-2} = (-2)^{-2}\left(x^2\right)^{-2} = \dfrac{1}{(-2)^2\left(x^2\right)^2} = \dfrac{1}{4x^4}$

26. Using properties of exponents: $\left(3x^2y^2\right)^3 = (3)^3\left(x^2\right)^3\left(y^2\right)^3 = 27x^6y^6$

27. Using properties of exponents: $\left(\dfrac{2}{3}\right)^{-3} = \left(\dfrac{3}{2}\right)^3 = \dfrac{27}{8}$

28. Using properties of exponents: $2x^4y \cdot -2xy^4 = -4x^5y^5$

29. Using properties of exponents: $-3x^2y \cdot 7x^5y^2 = -21x^7y^3$

30. Using properties of exponents: $\dfrac{36a^5b}{6a^2b^4} = 6a^{5-2}b^{1-4} = 6a^3b^{-3} = \dfrac{6a^3}{b^3}$

31. Using properties of exponents: $\dfrac{24a^6b^3}{-30ab^4} = -\dfrac{4}{5}a^{6-1}b^{3-4} = -\dfrac{4}{5}a^5b^{-1} = -\dfrac{4a^5}{5b}$

32. Using properties of exponents: $\left(\dfrac{7a^4b}{14a^6b^5}\right)^{-2} = \left(\dfrac{1}{2a^2b^4}\right)^{-2} = \left(2a^2b^4\right)^2 = 4a^4b^8$

33. Writing in scientific notation: $482{,}000 = 4.82 \times 10^5$

34. Writing in scientific notation: $7,280,000 = 7.28 \times 10^6$

35. Writing in scientific notation: $0.00421 = 4.21 \times 10^{-3}$

36. Writing in scientific notation: $0.0526 = 5.26 \times 10^{-2}$

37. Writing in expanded form: $6.29 \times 10^{-3} = 0.00629$

38. Writing in expanded form: $3.29 \times 10^3 = 3,290$

39. Writing in expanded form: $6.31 \times 10^{-2} = 0.0631$

40. Writing in expanded form: $4.82 \times 10^7 = 48,200,000$

41. Simplifying: $\dfrac{\left(3.6 \times 10^7\right)\left(2 \times 10^{-4}\right)}{2.4 \times 10^6} = \dfrac{7.2 \times 10^3}{2.4 \times 10^6} = \dfrac{7.2}{2.4} \times 10^{3-6} = 3.0 \times 10^{-3}$

42. Simplifying: $\dfrac{\left(4 \times 10^{-6}\right)\left(1.6 \times 10^4\right)}{\left(3.2 \times 10^9\right)\left(1 \times 10^{-7}\right)} = \dfrac{6.4 \times 10^{-2}}{3.2 \times 10^2} = \dfrac{6.4}{3.2} \times 10^{-2-2} = 2.0 \times 10^{-4}$

Chapter 0 Test

1. Converting the fraction: $\dfrac{1}{2} \cdot \dfrac{9}{9} = \dfrac{9}{18}$

2. Converting the fraction: $\dfrac{5}{6} \cdot \dfrac{3}{3} = \dfrac{15}{18}$

3. The correct statement is: $-6 < -4$

4. The correct statement is: $7 < 9$

5. The correct statement is: $3 > -6$

6. The correct statement is: $-\dfrac{6}{7} < -\dfrac{2}{5}$

7. Simplifying: $|9 - 16 \div 8| = |9 - 2| = |7| = 7$

8. Simplifying: $|7 - 10| - |3 - 5| = |-3| - |-2| = 3 - 2 = 1$

9. Simplifying: $16 - |3(2 - 6)| = 16 - |3(-4)| = 16 - |-12| = 16 - 12 = 4$

10. Simplifying: $6 + |3 \cdot 2 - 4| - 3 = 6 + |6 - 4| - 3 = 6 + |2| - 3 = 6 + 2 - 3 = 5$

11. Reducing the fraction: $\dfrac{192}{312} = \dfrac{24 \cdot 8}{24 \cdot 13} = \dfrac{8}{13}$

12. Reducing the fraction: $\dfrac{162}{459} = \dfrac{27 \cdot 6}{27 \cdot 17} = \dfrac{6}{17}$

13. Simplifying: $4(3x + 2) - 6 = 12x + 8 - 6 = 12x + 2$

14. Simplifying: $6x - 3 + 4x + 5 = 10x + 2$

15. Simplifying: $4x + 3(2x + 4y) - 6y = 4x + 6x + 12y - 6y = 10x + 6y$

16. Simplifying: $3a + 2(5b + 4) - 1 = 3a + 10b + 8 - 1 = 3a + 10b + 7$

17. Simplifying: $6y + 3(x + 3) - 4y = 6y + 3x + 9 - 4y = 3x + 2y + 9$

18. Simplifying: $18\left(\dfrac{5}{6}y - \dfrac{2}{3}x\right) - 5y = 18 \cdot \dfrac{5}{6}y - 18 \cdot \dfrac{2}{3}x - 5y = 15y - 12x - 5y = 10y - 12x$

19. Adding the fractions: $\dfrac{7}{18} + \dfrac{7}{9} = \dfrac{7}{18} + \dfrac{7}{9} \cdot \dfrac{2}{2} = \dfrac{7}{18} + \dfrac{14}{18} = \dfrac{21}{18} = \dfrac{3 \cdot 7}{3 \cdot 6} = \dfrac{7}{6}$

20. Adding the fractions: $\dfrac{7}{12} + \dfrac{13}{34} = \dfrac{7}{12} \cdot \dfrac{17}{17} + \dfrac{13}{34} \cdot \dfrac{6}{6} = \dfrac{119}{204} + \dfrac{78}{204} = \dfrac{197}{204}$

21. Simplifying: $4 - (2x - 7) + 4x = 4 - 2x + 7 + 4x = 2x + 11$

22. Simplifying: $(5 - 4x) - (3 - 2x) = 5 - 4x - 3 + 2x = -2x + 2$

23. Simplifying: $5x - 3(2x + 4) + 15 = 5x - 6x - 12 + 15 = -x + 3$

24. Simplifying: $\dfrac{(8)(-9) - (6)(-2)}{-(12 - 8)} = \dfrac{-72 + 12}{-4} = \dfrac{-60}{-4} = 15$

25. Using properties of exponents: $\left(-3x^4\right)^{-3} = (-3)^{-3}\left(x^4\right)^{-3} = \dfrac{1}{(-3)^3\left(x^4\right)^3} = -\dfrac{1}{27x^{12}}$

26. Using properties of exponents: $\left(4x^2y\right)^3 = (4)^3\left(x^2\right)^3(y)^3 = 64x^6y^3$

27. Using properties of exponents: $\left(\dfrac{5}{9}\right)^{-2} = \left(\dfrac{9}{5}\right)^2 = \dfrac{81}{25}$

28. Using properties of exponents: $-5x^2y \cdot -7x^3y = 35x^5y^2$

29. Using properties of exponents: $-6xy^3 \cdot 3x^{-2}y^4 = -18x^{-1}y^7 = -\dfrac{18y^7}{x}$

30. Using properties of exponents: $\dfrac{18a^4b}{3ab^3} = 6a^{4-1}b^{1-3} = 6a^3b^{-2} = \dfrac{6a^3}{b^2}$

31. Using properties of exponents: $\dfrac{18a^5b^9}{24a^7b^4} = \dfrac{3}{4}a^{5-7}b^{9-4} = \dfrac{3}{4}a^{-2}b^5 = \dfrac{3b^5}{4a^2}$

32. Using properties of exponents: $\left(\dfrac{3x^{-2}y}{9xy^2}\right)^{-3} = \left(\dfrac{1}{3x^3y}\right)^{-3} = \left(3x^3y\right)^3 = 27x^9y^3$

33. Writing in scientific notation: $12,530,000 = 1.253 \times 10^7$

34. Writing in scientific notation: $0.0052 = 5.2 \times 10^{-3}$

35. Writing in scientific notation: $6,320 = 6.32 \times 10^3$

36. Writing in scientific notation: $0.00034 = 3.4 \times 10^{-4}$

37. Writing in expanded form: $5.26 \times 10^{-3} = 0.00526$

38. Writing in expanded form: $4.9 \times 10^5 = 490,000$

39. Writing in expanded form: $6.3 \times 10^{-4} = 0.00063$

40. Writing in expanded form: $7.8 \times 10^4 = 78,000$

41. Simplifying: $\dfrac{\left(1.4 \times 10^7\right)\left(6.5 \times 10^{-4}\right)}{7.0 \times 10^2} = \dfrac{9.1 \times 10^3}{7.0 \times 10^2} = \dfrac{9.1}{7.0} \times 10^{3-2} = 1.3 \times 10^1$

42. Simplifying: $\dfrac{\left(1.8 \times 10^7\right)\left(6.8 \times 10^6\right)}{\left(2.4 \times 10^9\right)\left(3.0 \times 10^{-4}\right)} = \dfrac{12.24 \times 10^{13}}{7.2 \times 10^5} = \dfrac{12.24}{7.2} \times 10^{13-5} = 1.7 \times 10^8$

Chapter 1
Linear Equations and Inequalities in One Variable

1.1 Linear Equations

1. Substituting $x = -1$: $-3(-1) + 2 = 3 + 2 = 5$. Yes, -1 is a solution to the equation.

3. Substituting $x = 1$: $4(1) - 5 = 4 - 5 = -1 \neq -9$. No, 1 is not a solution to the equation.

5. Substituting $x = -1$:
$$2(-1) + 1 = -2 + 1 = -1 \qquad 3(-1) - 4 = -3 - 4 = -7$$
No, -1 is not a solution to the equation.

7. Substituting $x = 6$: $\dfrac{6}{2} + 1 = 3 + 1 = 4$. Yes, 6 is a solution to the equation.

9. Substituting $x = -12$:
$$\frac{-12}{3} + 1 = -4 + 1 = -3 \qquad \frac{-12}{4} = -3$$
Yes, -12 is a solution to the equation.

11. Substituting $x = 2$:
$$3(2 - 2) + 1 = 3(0) + 1 = 0 + 1 = 1 \qquad 2(2) - 4 = 4 - 4 = 0$$
No, 2 is not a solution to the equation.

13. Solving the equation:
$$\begin{aligned} 7y - 4 &= 2y + 11 \\ 5y - 4 &= 11 \\ 5y &= 15 \\ y &= 3 \end{aligned}$$

15. Solving the equation:
$$\begin{aligned} -\frac{2}{5}x + \frac{2}{15} &= \frac{2}{3} \\ 15\left(-\frac{2}{5}x + \frac{2}{15}\right) &= 15\left(\frac{2}{3}\right) \\ -6x + 2 &= 10 \\ -6x &= 8 \\ x &= -\frac{4}{3} \end{aligned}$$

17. Solving the equation:
$$\begin{aligned} 0.14x + 0.08(10{,}000 - x) &= 1{,}220 \\ 0.14x + 800 - 0.08x &= 1{,}220 \\ 0.06x + 800 &= 1{,}220 \\ 0.06x &= 420 \\ x &= 7{,}000 \end{aligned}$$

19. Solving the equation:
$$\begin{aligned} 5(y + 2) - 4(y + 1) &= 3 \\ 5y + 10 - 4y - 4 &= 3 \\ y + 6 &= 3 \\ y &= -3 \end{aligned}$$

21. Solving the equation:
$$\begin{aligned} -3 - 4x &= 15 \\ -4x &= 18 \\ x &= -\frac{9}{2} \end{aligned}$$

23. Solving the equation:
$$\begin{aligned} 0 &= 6{,}400a + 70 \\ -70 &= 6{,}400a \\ a &= -\frac{70}{6{,}400} = -\frac{7}{640} \end{aligned}$$

25. Solving the equation:
$$5(2x+1)=12$$
$$10x+5=12$$
$$10x=7$$
$$x=\frac{7}{10}$$

27. Solving the equation:
$$100P=2,400$$
$$P=\frac{2,400}{100}=24$$

29. Solving the equation:
$$5\left(-\frac{19}{15}\right)+5y=9$$
$$-\frac{19}{3}+5y=9$$
$$5y=\frac{46}{3}$$
$$y=\frac{46}{15}$$

31. Solving the equation:
$$4x+(x-2)\cdot 3=8$$
$$4x+3x-6=8$$
$$7x-6=8$$
$$7x=14$$
$$x=2$$

33. Solving the equation:
$$15-3(x-1)=x-2$$
$$15-3x+3=x-2$$
$$-3x+18=x-2$$
$$-4x+18=-2$$
$$-4x=-20$$
$$x=5$$

35. Solving the equation:
$$2(20+x)=3(20-x)$$
$$40+2x=60-3x$$
$$40+5x=60$$
$$5x=20$$
$$x=4$$

37. Solving the equation:
$$0.08x+0.09(9,000-x)=750$$
$$0.08x+810-0.09x=750$$
$$-0.01x+810=750$$
$$-0.01x=-60$$
$$x=6,000$$

39. Solving the equation:
$$3x-6=3(x+4)$$
$$3x-6=3x+12$$
$$-6=12$$
Since this statement is false, there is no solution.

41. Solving the equation:
$$2(4t-1)+3=5t+4+3t$$
$$8t-2+3=8t+4$$
$$8t+1=8t+4$$
$$1=4$$
Since this statement is false, there is no solution.

43. Solving the equation:
$$7(x+2)-4(2x-1)=18-x$$
$$7x+14-8x+4=18-x$$
$$-x+18=-x+18$$
$$18=18$$
Since this statement is true, the solution is all real numbers.

45. Solving the equation:
$$-0.0035A+70=-35$$
$$-0.0035A=-105$$
$$A=\frac{-105}{-0.0035}$$
$$A=30,000$$
The altitude is 30,000 feet.

47. Substituting $x = 40$: $P = 15 + 0.434(40) = 32.36$ psi

49. Solving the equation:
$$15 + 0.434x = 104.5$$
$$0.434x = 89.5$$
$$x = \frac{89.5}{0.434}$$
$$x \approx 206$$
The depth is approximately 206 feet.

51. Substituting $x = 2{,}000$: $P = 15 + 0.434(2{,}000) = 883$ psi

53. Solving the equation:
$$x \cdot 42 = 21$$
$$x = \frac{21}{42} = \frac{1}{2}$$

55. Solving the equation:
$$25 = 0.4x$$
$$x = \frac{25}{0.4} = 62.5$$

57. Solving the equation:
$$12 - 4y = 12$$
$$-4y = 0$$
$$y = 0$$

59. Solving the equation:
$$525 = 900 - 300p$$
$$-375 = -300p$$
$$p = \frac{-375}{-300} = \frac{5}{4}$$

61. Solving the equation:
$$486.7 = 78.5 + 31.4h$$
$$408.2 = 31.4h$$
$$h = \frac{408.2}{31.4} = 13$$

1.2 Formulas

1. Substituting $x = 0$:
$$3(0) - 4y = 12$$
$$-4y = 12$$
$$y = -3$$

3. Substituting $x = 4$:
$$3(4) - 4y = 12$$
$$12 - 4y = 12$$
$$-4y = 0$$
$$y = 0$$

5. Substituting $y = 0$:
$$2x - 3 = 0$$
$$2x = 3$$
$$x = \frac{3}{2}$$

7. Substituting $y = 5$:
$$2x - 3 = 5$$
$$2x = 8$$
$$x = 4$$

9. Substituting $y = -\frac{6}{5}$:
$$x - 2\left(-\frac{6}{5}\right) = 4$$
$$x + \frac{12}{5} = 4$$
$$x = \frac{8}{5}$$

11. Substituting $x = 160$ and $y = 0$:
$$0 = a(160 - 80)^2 + 70$$
$$-70 = a(80)^2$$
$$6{,}400a = -70$$
$$a = -\frac{70}{6{,}400} = -\frac{7}{640}$$

13. Substituting $p = 1.5$: $R = (900 - 300 \cdot 1.5)(1.5) = (450)(1.5) = 675$

15.
a. Substituting $x = 100$: $P = -0.1(100)^2 + 27(100) + 1{,}700 = -1{,}000 + 2{,}700 + 1{,}700 = 3{,}400$

b. Substituting $x = 170$: $P = -0.1(170)^2 + 27(170) + 1{,}700 = -2{,}890 + 4{,}590 + 1{,}700 = 3{,}400$

17. **a.** Substituting $t = \frac{1}{4}$: $h = 16 + 32\left(\frac{1}{4}\right) - 16\left(\frac{1}{4}\right)^2 = 16 + 8 - 1 = 23$

    b. Substituting $t = \frac{7}{4}$: $h = 16 + 32\left(\frac{7}{4}\right) - 16\left(\frac{7}{4}\right)^2 = 16 + 56 - 49 = 23$

19. Substituting $d = 30$, $r = 12$, and $t = 3$:
$$30 = (12 - c) \cdot 3$$
$$30 = 36 - 3c$$
$$-6 = -3c$$
$$c = 2$$

21. Substituting $x = 5$ and $y = 15$:
$$15 = k(5)$$
$$k = 3$$

23. Substituting $P = 48$ and $V = 50$:
$$50 = \frac{k}{48}$$
$$k = 50 \cdot 48 = 2{,}400$$

25. Substituting $x = 2$:
$$5(2) - 3y = -15$$
$$10 - 3y = -15$$
$$-3y = -25$$
$$y = \frac{25}{3}$$

27. Substituting $x = -\frac{1}{5}$:
$$5\left(-\frac{1}{5}\right) - 3y = -15$$
$$-1 - 3y = -15$$
$$-3y = -14$$
$$y = \frac{14}{3}$$

29. Solving for r:
$$d = rt$$
$$r = \frac{d}{t}$$

31. Solving for t:
$$d = (r + c)t$$
$$t = \frac{d}{r + c}$$

33. Solving for l:
$$A = lw$$
$$l = \frac{A}{w}$$

35. Solving for t:
$$I = prt$$
$$t = \frac{I}{pr}$$

37. Solving for T:
$$PV = nRT$$
$$T = \frac{PV}{nR}$$

39. Solving for x:
$$y = mx + b$$
$$y - b = mx$$
$$x = \frac{y - b}{m}$$

41. Solving for F:
$$C = \frac{5}{9}(F - 32)$$
$$\frac{9}{5}C = F - 32$$
$$F = \frac{9}{5}C + 32$$

43. Solving for v:
$$h = vt + 16t^2$$
$$h - 16t^2 = vt$$
$$v = \frac{h - 16t^2}{t}$$

45. Solving for d:
$$A = a + (n - 1)d$$
$$A - a = (n - 1)d$$
$$d = \frac{A - a}{n - 1}$$

47. Solving for y:

$$2x + 3y = 6$$
$$3y = -2x + 6$$
$$y = \frac{-2x+6}{3}$$
$$y = -\frac{2}{3}x + 2$$

49. Solving for y:

$$-3x + 5y = 15$$
$$5y = 3x + 15$$
$$y = \frac{3x+15}{5}$$
$$y = \frac{3}{5}x + 3$$

51. Solving for y:

$$2x - 6y + 12 = 0$$
$$-6y = -2x - 12$$
$$y = \frac{-2x-12}{-6}$$
$$y = \frac{1}{3}x + 2$$

53. Solving for x:

$$ax + 4 = bx + 9$$
$$ax - bx + 4 = 9$$
$$ax - bx = 5$$
$$x(a-b) = 5$$
$$x = \frac{5}{a-b}$$

55. Solving for h:

$$S = \pi r^2 + 2\pi rh$$
$$2\pi rh = S - \pi r^2$$
$$h = \frac{S - \pi r^2}{2\pi r}$$

57. Solving for x:

$$-3x + 4y = 12$$
$$-3x = -4y + 12$$
$$x = \frac{-4y+12}{-3} = \frac{4}{3}y - 4$$

59. Solving for x:

$$ax + 3 = cx - 7$$
$$ax - cx = -10$$
$$x(a-c) = -10$$
$$x = -\frac{10}{a-c}$$

61. Solving for y:

$$x = 2y - 3$$
$$2y = x + 3$$
$$y = \frac{x+3}{2} = \frac{1}{2}x + \frac{3}{2}$$

63. Solving for y:

$$y - 3 = -2(x+4)$$
$$y - 3 = -2x - 8$$
$$y = -2x - 5$$

65. Solving for y:

$$y - 3 = -\frac{2}{3}(x+3)$$
$$y - 3 = -\frac{2}{3}x - 2$$
$$y = -\frac{2}{3}x + 1$$

67. Solving for y:

$$y - 4 = -\frac{1}{2}(x+1)$$
$$y - 4 = -\frac{1}{2}x - \frac{1}{2}$$
$$y = -\frac{1}{2}x + \frac{7}{2}$$

69. **a.** Solving for y:

$$\frac{y+1}{x-0} = 4$$
$$y + 1 = 4(x-0)$$
$$y + 1 = 4x$$
$$y = 4x - 1$$

b. Solving for y:

$$\frac{y+2}{x-4} = -\frac{1}{2}$$
$$y + 2 = -\frac{1}{2}(x-4)$$
$$y + 2 = -\frac{1}{2}x + 2$$
$$y = -\frac{1}{2}x$$

c. Solving for y:
$$\frac{y+3}{x-7}=0$$
$$y+3=0(x-7)$$
$$y+3=0$$
$$y=-3$$

71. Solving for y:
$$\frac{x}{8}+\frac{y}{2}=1$$
$$8\left(\frac{x}{8}+\frac{y}{2}\right)=8(1)$$
$$x+4y=8$$
$$4y=-x+8$$
$$y=-\frac{1}{4}x+2$$

73. Solving for y:
$$\frac{x}{5}+\frac{y}{-3}=1$$
$$15\left(\frac{x}{5}+\frac{y}{-3}\right)=15(1)$$
$$3x-5y=15$$
$$-5y=-3x+15$$
$$y=\frac{3}{5}x-3$$

75. a. Solving the equation:
$$-4x+5=20$$
$$-4x=15$$
$$x=-\frac{15}{4}$$

b. Substituting $x=3$: $-4x+5=-4(3)+5=-7$

c. Solving for y:
$$-4x+5y=20$$
$$5y=4x+20$$
$$y=\frac{4}{5}x+4$$

d. Solving for x:
$$-4x+5y=20$$
$$-4x=-5y+20$$
$$x=\frac{5}{4}y-5$$

77. Finding the weight: $W=\dfrac{(6\cdot5)(30)(4)}{2,000}=\dfrac{9}{5}$ tons

79. Let c represent the rate of the current. The equation is:
$$2(15-c)=18$$
$$30-2c=18$$
$$-2c=-12$$
$$c=6$$
The speed of the current is 6 mph.

81. Let w represent the rate of the wind. The equation is:
$$4(258-w)=864$$
$$1032-4w=864$$
$$-4w=-168$$
$$w=42$$
The speed of the wind is 42 mph.

83. The distance traveled by the rider is the circumference: $C=\pi(65)\approx(3.14)(65)\approx204.1$ feet

Finding the rate: $\dfrac{204.1\text{ feet}}{30\text{ seconds}}\approx6.8$ feet per second

85. Finding the size: $S=\dfrac{480\cdot216\cdot30\cdot150}{35,000}\approx13,330$ KB

87. Finding the cost in grams: 50 million rupees $\cdot\dfrac{1\text{ gram}}{1.4\text{ rupees}}\approx35.7$ million grams

89. Substituting $n=1$, $y=7$, and $z=15$:
$$x^1+7^1=15^1$$
$$x+7=15$$
$$x=8$$

91. For Shar, $M=220-46=174$ and $R=60$: $T=R+0.6(M-R)=60+0.6(174-60)=128.4$ beats per minute

For Sara, $M=220-26=194$ and $R=60$: $T=R+0.6(M-R)=60+0.6(194-60)=140.4$ beats per minute

93. Translating into symbols: $2x-3$

95. Translating into symbols: $x+y=180$

97. Solving the equation:

$$x + 2x = 90$$
$$3x = 90$$
$$x = 30$$

99. Solving the equation:

$$2(2x - 3) + 2x = 45$$
$$4x - 6 + 2x = 45$$
$$6x - 6 = 45$$
$$6x = 51$$
$$x = \frac{51}{6} = 8.5$$

101. Solving the equation:

$$0.06x + 0.05(10{,}000 - x) = 560$$
$$100\big(0.06x + 0.05(10{,}000 - x)\big) = 100(560)$$
$$6x + 5(10{,}000 - x) = 56{,}000$$
$$6x + 50{,}000 - 5x = 56{,}000$$
$$x + 50{,}000 = 56{,}000$$
$$x = 6{,}000$$

103. Solving the equation for x:

$$\frac{x}{a} + \frac{y}{b} = 1$$
$$ab\left(\frac{x}{a} + \frac{y}{b}\right) = ab(1)$$
$$bx + ay = ab$$
$$bx = -ay + ab$$
$$x = -\frac{a}{b}y + a$$

105. Solving the equation for a:

$$\frac{1}{a} + \frac{1}{b} = \frac{1}{c}$$
$$abc\left(\frac{1}{a} + \frac{1}{b}\right) = abc\left(\frac{1}{c}\right)$$
$$bc + ac = ab$$
$$bc = ab - ac$$
$$bc = a(b - c)$$
$$a = \frac{bc}{b - c} \qquad (b \neq c)$$

1.3 Applications

1. Let w represent the width and $2w$ represent the length. Using the perimeter formula:

$$2w + 2(2w) = 60$$
$$2w + 4w = 60$$
$$6w = 60$$
$$w = 10$$

The dimensions are 10 feet by 20 feet.

3. Let s represent the side of the square. Using the perimeter formula:

$$4s = 28$$
$$s = 7$$

The length of each side is 7 feet.

5. Let x represent the shortest side, $x + 3$ represent the medium side, and $2x$ represent the longest side. Using the perimeter formula:

$$x + x + 3 + 2x = 23$$
$$4x + 3 = 23$$
$$4x = 20$$
$$x = 5$$

The shortest side is 5 inches.

7. Let w represent the width and $2w - 3$ represent the length. Using the perimeter formula:

$$2w + 2(2w - 3) = 18$$
$$2w + 4w - 6 = 18$$
$$6w - 6 = 18$$
$$6w = 24$$
$$w = 4$$

The width is 4 meters.

9. Let w represent the width and $2w$ represent the length. Using the perimeter formula:
$$2w + 2(2w) = 48$$
$$2w + 4w = 48$$
$$6w = 48$$
$$w = 8$$
The width is 8 feet and the length is 16 feet. Finding the cost: $C = 1.75(32) + 2.25(16) = 56 + 36 = 92$

The cost to build the pen is $92.00.

11. Let b represent the amount of money Eric had at the beginning of the trip. Using the percent increase:
$$b + 0.50b = 300$$
$$1.5b = 300$$
$$b = 200$$
Eric had $200.00 at the beginning of the trip.

13. Let c represent the cost for the bookstore. Using the markup equation:
$$c + 0.33c = 115$$
$$1.33c = 115$$
$$c \approx 86.47$$
The cost to the bookstore was approximately $86.47.

15. Let R represent the 3-D screening receipts (which are 70% of the revenue). The amount is:
$$0.70(116.3) = \$81.41 \text{ million}$$

The receipts from 3-D screenings were approximately $81.41 million.

17. Let x represent one angle and $8x$ represent the other angle. Since the angles are supplementary:
$$x + 8x = 180$$
$$9x = 180$$
$$x = 20$$
The two angles are 20° and 160°.

19. **a.** Let x represent one angle and $4x - 12$ represent the other angle. Since the angles are complementary:
$$x + 4x - 12 = 90$$
$$5x - 12 = 90$$
$$5x = 102$$
$$x = 20.4$$
$$4x - 12 = 4(20.4) - 12 = 69.6$$

The two angles are 20.4° and 69.6°.

b. Let x represent one angle and $4x - 12$ represent the other angle. Since the angles are supplementary:
$$x + 4x - 12 = 180$$
$$5x - 12 = 180$$
$$5x = 192$$
$$x = 38.4$$
$$4x - 12 = 4(38.4) - 12 = 141.6$$

The two angles are 38.4° and 141.6°.

21. Let x represent the smallest angle, $3x$ represent the largest angle, and $3x - 9$ represent the third angle. The equation is:
$$x + 3x + 3x - 9 = 180$$
$$7x - 9 = 180$$
$$7x = 189$$
$$x = 27$$
The three angles are 27°, 72° and 81°.

23. Let x represent the largest angle, $\frac{1}{3}x$ represent the smallest angle, and $\frac{1}{3}x+10$ represent the third angle.

The equation is:
$$\frac{1}{3}x+x+\frac{1}{3}x+10=180$$
$$\frac{5}{3}x+10=180$$
$$\frac{5}{3}x=170$$
$$x=102$$

The three angles are $34°$, $44°$ and $102°$.

25. Let x represent the measure of the two base angles, and $2x+8$ represent the third angle. The equation is:
$$x+x+2x+8=180$$
$$4x+8=180$$
$$4x=172$$
$$x=43$$

The three angles are $43°$, $43°$ and $94°$.

27. Let x represent the amount invested at 8% and $9,000-x$ represent the amount invested at 9%. The equation is:
$$0.08x+0.09(9,000-x)=750$$
$$0.08x+810-0.09x=750$$
$$-0.01x+810=750$$
$$-0.01x=-60$$
$$x=6,000$$

Donna invested $6,000 at 8% and $3,000 at 9%.

29. Let x represent the amount borrowed at 12% and $15,000-x$ represent the amount borrowed at 10%. The equation is:
$$0.12x+0.10(15,000-x)=1,600$$
$$0.12x+1,500-0.10x=1,600$$
$$0.02x+1,500=1,600$$
$$0.02x=100$$
$$x=5,000$$

Bill borrowed $5,000 at 12% and $10,000 at 10%.

31. Let x represent the amount borrowed at 8% and $6,000-x$ represent the amount borrowed at 9%. The equation is:
$$0.08x+0.09(6,000-x)=500$$
$$0.08x+540-0.09x=500$$
$$-0.01x+540=500$$
$$-0.01x=-40$$
$$x=4,000$$

Stacy borrowed $4,000 at 8% and $2,000 at 9%.

33. Let x represent the number of father tickets sold and $75-x$ the number of son tickets sold. The equation is:
$$5(x)+3.50(75-x)=307.50$$
$$5x+262.5-3.5x=307.5$$
$$1.5x+262.5=307.5$$
$$1.5x=45$$
$$x=30$$
$$75-x=45$$

There were 30 fathers tickets and 45 sons tickets sold.

35. The total money collected is: $1204 − $250 = $954

Let *x* represent the amount of her sales (not including tax). Since this amount includes the tax collected, the equation is:

$$x + 0.06x = 954$$
$$1.06x = 954$$
$$x = 900$$

Charlotte's sales were $900, so the sales tax is: $0.06(900) = $54

37. Completing the table:

t	0	¼	1	⁷⁄₄	2
h	0	7	16	7	0

39. Completing the table:

Speed (miles per hour)	Distance (miles)
20	10
30	15
40	20
50	25
60	30
70	35

41. Completing the table:

Time (hours)	Distance upstream (miles)	Distance downstream (miles)
1	6	14
2	12	28
3	18	42
4	24	56
5	30	70
6	36	84

43. Completing the table:

Year	Sales (billions of dollars)
2005	7
2006	7.5
2007	8
2008	8.6
2009	9.2

45. Completing the table:

w (ft)	*l* (ft)	*A* (ft²)
2	22	44
4	20	80
6	18	108
8	16	128
10	14	140
12	12	144

47. Completing the table:

Age (years)	Maximum Heart Rate (beats per minute)
18	202
19	201
20	200
21	199
22	198
23	197

49. Completing the table:

Maximum Heart Rate (beats per minute)	Training Heart Rate (beats per minute)
60	144
62	144.8
64	145.6
68	147.2
70	148
72	148.8

51. Graphing the inequality:

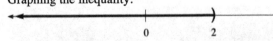

53. Graphing the inequality:

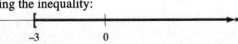

55. Solving the equation:

$$-2x - 3 = 7$$
$$-2x = 10$$
$$x = -5$$

57. Solving the equation:

$$3(2x - 4) - 7x = -3x$$
$$6x - 12 - 7x = -3x$$
$$-x - 12 = -3x$$
$$-12 = -2x$$
$$x = 6$$

Landmark Review

1. Solving the equation:

$$4x + 3 = 15$$
$$4x = 12$$
$$x = 3$$

2. Solving the equation:

$$3(y - 2) - 2(2y - 2) = 1$$
$$3y - 6 - 4y + 4 = 1$$
$$-y - 2 = 1$$
$$-y = 3$$
$$y = -3$$

3. Solving the equation:

$$\frac{2}{3}x + \frac{3}{5} = \frac{2}{15}$$
$$15\left(\frac{2}{3}x + \frac{3}{5}\right) = 15\left(\frac{2}{15}\right)$$
$$10x + 9 = 2$$
$$10x = -7$$
$$x = -\frac{7}{10}$$

4. Solving the equation:

$$0.2x + 0.3 = 0.5$$
$$10(0.2x + 0.3) = 10(0.5)$$
$$2x + 3 = 5$$
$$2x = 2$$
$$x = 1$$

5. Substituting $x = 0$:

$$5(0) + 3y = 15$$
$$0 + 3y = 15$$
$$3y = 15$$
$$y = 5$$

6. Substituting $x = -3$:

$$5(-3) + 3y = 15$$
$$-15 + 3y = 15$$
$$3y = 30$$
$$y = 10$$

7. Substituting $x = 1$:

$$5(1) + 3y = 15$$
$$5 + 3y = 15$$
$$3y = 10$$
$$y = \frac{10}{3}$$

8. Substituting $x = 4$:

$$5(4) + 3y = 15$$
$$20 + 3y = 15$$
$$3y = -5$$
$$y = -\frac{5}{3}$$

9. Solving for y:

$$3x + 4y = 5$$
$$4y = -3x + 5$$
$$y = -\frac{3}{4}x + \frac{5}{4}$$

10. Solving for c:

$$d = (r + c)t$$
$$\frac{d}{t} = r + c$$
$$c = \frac{d}{t} - r$$

11. Solving for r:

$$A = p + prt$$
$$A - p = prt$$
$$r = \frac{A - p}{pt}$$

12. Solving for x:

$$5x - 3y = 15$$
$$5x = 3y + 15$$
$$x = \frac{3}{5}y + 3$$

13. Completing the table:

t	0	$\frac{1}{4}$	1	$\frac{5}{4}$	2
h	0	15	48	55	64

14. Completing the table:

t	5	7	9	11
h	14	10	7.78	6.36

1.4 Interval Notation and Linear Inequalities

1. Solving the inequality:

$$2x \le 3$$
$$x \le \frac{3}{2}$$

Graphing the solution set:

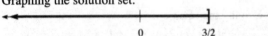

3. Solving the inequality:

$$\frac{1}{2}x > 2$$
$$x > 4$$

Graphing the solution set:

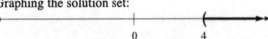

5. Solving the inequality:

$$-5x \le 25$$
$$x \ge -5$$

Graphing the solution set:

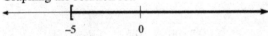

7. Solving the inequality:

$$-\frac{3}{2}x > -6$$
$$-3x > -12$$
$$x < 4$$

Graphing the solution set:

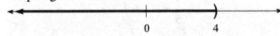

9. Solving the inequality:

$$-12 \le 2x$$
$$x \ge -6$$

Graphing the solution set:

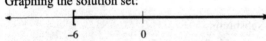

11. Solving the inequality:

$$-1 \ge -\frac{1}{4}x$$
$$x \ge 4$$

Graphing the solution set:

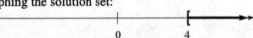

13. Solving the inequality:

$$-3x + 1 > 10$$
$$-3x > 9$$
$$x < -3$$

Graphing the solution set:

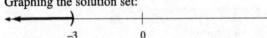

15. Solving the inequality:

$$\frac{1}{2} - \frac{m}{12} \le \frac{7}{12}$$
$$12\left(\frac{1}{2} - \frac{m}{12}\right) \le 12\left(\frac{7}{12}\right)$$
$$6 - m \le 7$$
$$-m \le 1$$
$$m \ge -1$$

Graphing the solution set:

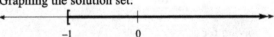

17. Solving the inequality:

$$\frac{1}{2} \ge -\frac{1}{6} - \frac{2}{9}x$$
$$18\left(\frac{1}{2}\right) \ge 18\left(-\frac{1}{6} - \frac{2}{9}x\right)$$
$$9 \ge -3 - 4x$$
$$12 \ge -4x$$
$$x \ge -3$$

Graphing the solution set:

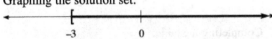

19. Solving the inequality:

$$-40 \le 30 - 20y$$
$$-70 \le -20y$$
$$y \le \frac{7}{2}$$

Graphing the solution set:

21. Solving the inequality:

$$\frac{2}{3}x - 3 < 1$$
$$\frac{2}{3}x < 4$$
$$2x < 12$$
$$x < 6$$

Graphing the solution set:

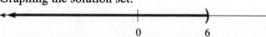

25. Solving the inequality:

$$4 - \frac{1}{2}x < \frac{2}{3}x - 5$$
$$6\left(4 - \frac{1}{2}x\right) < 6\left(\frac{2}{3}x - 5\right)$$
$$24 - 3x < 4x - 30$$
$$-7x < -54$$
$$x > \frac{54}{7}$$

Graphing the solution set:

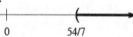

29. Solving the inequality:

$$3 - \frac{x}{5} < 5 - \frac{x}{4}$$
$$20\left(3 - \frac{x}{5}\right) < 20\left(5 - \frac{x}{4}\right)$$
$$60 - 4x < 100 - 5x$$
$$x < 40$$

Graphing the solution set:

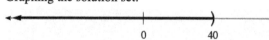

33. Solving the inequality:

$$-(a+1) - 4a \le 2a - 8$$
$$-a - 1 - 4a \le 2a - 8$$
$$-5a - 1 \le 2a - 8$$
$$-7a \le -7$$
$$a \ge 1$$

The solution set is $[1, \infty)$.

23. Solving the inequality:

$$10 - \frac{1}{2}y \le 36$$
$$-\frac{1}{2}y \le 26$$
$$y \ge -52$$

Graphing the solution set:

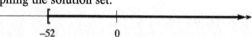

27. Solving the inequality:

$$0.03x - 0.4 \le 0.08x + 1.2$$
$$100(0.03x - 0.4) \le 100(0.08x + 1.2)$$
$$3x - 40 \le 8x + 120$$
$$-5x \le 160$$
$$x \ge -32$$

Graphing the solution set:

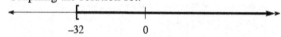

31. Solving the inequality:

$$2(3y + 1) \le -10$$
$$6y + 2 \le -10$$
$$6y \le -12$$
$$y \le -2$$

The solution set is $(-\infty, -2]$.

35. Solving the inequality:

$$\frac{1}{3}t - \frac{1}{2}(5 - t) < 0$$
$$6\left(\frac{1}{3}t - \frac{1}{2}(5 - t)\right) < 6(0)$$
$$2t - 3(5 - t) < 0$$
$$2t - 15 + 3t < 0$$
$$5t - 15 < 0$$
$$5t < 15$$
$$t < 3$$

The solution set is $(-\infty, 3)$.

37. Solving the inequality:

$$-2 \le 5 - 7(2a+3)$$
$$-2 \le 5 - 14a - 21$$
$$-2 \le -16 - 14a$$
$$14 \le -14a$$
$$a \le -1$$

The solution set is $(-\infty, -1]$.

39. Solving the inequality:

$$-\frac{1}{3}(x+5) \le -\frac{2}{9}(x-1)$$
$$9\left[-\frac{1}{3}(x+5)\right] \le 9\left[-\frac{2}{9}(x-1)\right]$$
$$-3(x+5) \le -2(x-1)$$
$$-3x - 15 \le -2x + 2$$
$$-x - 15 \le 2$$
$$-x \le 17$$
$$x \ge -17$$

The solution set is $[-17, \infty)$.

41. Solving the inequality:

$$5(x-2) - 7(x+1) \le -4x + 3$$
$$5x - 10 - 7x - 7 \le -4x + 3$$
$$-2x - 17 \le -4x + 3$$
$$2x - 17 \le 3$$
$$2x \le 20$$
$$x \le 10$$

The solution set is $(-\infty, 10]$.

43. Solving the inequality:

$$\frac{2}{3}x - \frac{1}{3}(4x-5) < 1$$
$$2x - 1(4x-5) < 3$$
$$2x - 4x + 5 < 3$$
$$-2x + 5 < 3$$
$$-2x < -2$$
$$x > 1$$

The solution set is $(1, \infty)$.

45. Solving the inequality:

$$20x + 9,300 > 18,000$$
$$20x > 8,700$$
$$x > 435$$

The solution set is $(435, \infty)$.

47. Solving the inequality:

$$0.04x + 0.06(1,200 - x) \ge 54$$
$$4x + 6(1,200 - x) \ge 5,400$$
$$4x + 7,200 - 6x \ge 5,400$$
$$-2x + 7,200 \ge 5,400$$
$$-2x \ge -1,800$$
$$x \le 900$$

The solution set is $(-\infty, 900]$.

49.

a. Evaluating when $x = 0$: $-\frac{1}{2}x + 1 = -\frac{1}{2}(0) + 1 = 1$

b. Solving the equation:
$$-\frac{1}{2}x + 1 = -7$$
$$-\frac{1}{2}x = -8$$
$$x = 16$$

c. Substituting $x = 0$: $-\frac{1}{2}x + 1 = -\frac{1}{2}(0) + 1 = 1$

No, 0 is not a solution to the inequality.

d. Solving the inequality:
$$-\frac{1}{2}x + 1 < -7$$
$$-\frac{1}{2}x < -8$$
$$x > 16$$

51. Let x represent the width and $3x$ represent the length. Solving the inequality:
$$2(x) + 2(3x) \ge 48$$
$$2x + 6x \ge 48$$
$$8x \ge 48$$
$$x \ge 6$$
The width is at least 6 meters.

53. Let x, $x + 2$, and $x + 4$ represent the three sides. Solving the inequality:
$$x + x + 2 + x + 4 > 24$$
$$3x + 6 > 24$$
$$3x > 18$$
$$x > 6$$
The shortest side is greater than 6 inches (and is even).

55. The inequality is $t \geq 100$.

57. Let x represent the number of tickets they sell. To make a profit, the inequality is:
$$7.50x > 1500$$
$$x > 200$$
They will make a profit if they sell more than 200 tickets, and they will lose money if they sell less than 200 tickets.

59. **a.** Solving the inequality:
$$900 - 300p \geq 300$$
$$-300p \geq -600$$
$$p \leq 2.00$$
They should charge at most $2.00.

b. Solving the inequality:
$$900 - 300p > 600$$
$$-300p > -300$$
$$p < 1.00$$
They should charge less than $1.00.

c. Solving the inequality:
$$900 - 300p < 525$$
$$-300p < -375$$
$$p > 1.25$$
They should charge more than $1.25.

d. Solving the inequality:
$$900 - 300p \leq 375$$
$$-300p \leq -525$$
$$p \geq 1.75$$
They should charge at least $1.75.

61. **a.** Solving the inequality:
$$0.36x + 15.9 < 17$$
$$0.36x < 1.1$$
$$x < 3.06$$
The years were 1983 and earlier.

b. Solving the inequality:
$$0.36x + 15.9 > 20$$
$$0.36x > 4.1$$
$$x > 11.39$$
The years were 1991 and later.

63. Solving the inequality:
$$46,400 + 2,800t \geq 90,000$$
$$2,800t \geq 43,600$$
$$t \geq 15.6$$
A mathematics major should expect to work 15.6 years to be earning at least $90,000 per year.

65. Solving the inequality:
$$41,500 + 3,050t > 46,400 + 2,800t$$
$$41,500 + 250t > 46,400$$
$$250t > 4,900$$
$$t > 19.6$$
A government major should expect to work 19.6 years to be earning more than a mathematics major.

67. Solving the inequality:
$$2x - 1 \geq 3$$
$$2x \geq 4$$
$$x \geq 2$$

69. Solving the inequality:
$$-2x > -8$$
$$x < 4$$

71. Solving the inequality:
$$-3 > 4x + 1$$
$$4x < -4$$
$$x < -1$$

73. Solving the inequality:
$$-4x + 3 < 15$$
$$-4x < 12$$
$$x > -3$$

75. Solving the inequality:

$$ax + b < c$$
$$ax < c - b$$
$$x < \frac{c-b}{a}$$

77. Solving the inequality:

$$\frac{x}{a} + \frac{y}{b} < 1$$
$$ab\left(\frac{x}{a} + \frac{y}{b}\right) < ab(1)$$
$$bx + ay < ab$$
$$bx < -ay + ab$$
$$x < -\frac{a}{b}y + a$$

79. Solving the inequality:

$$ax + b < cx + d$$
$$ax - cx < d - b$$
$$x(a-c) < d - b$$
$$x > \frac{d-b}{a-c}$$

Note this inequality was reversed since $a < c$, thus $a - c$ is a negative number.

81. Solving the inequality:

$$\frac{x}{a} + \frac{1}{b} < \frac{x}{c} + \frac{1}{d}$$
$$abcd\left(\frac{x}{a} + \frac{1}{b}\right) < abcd\left(\frac{x}{c} + \frac{1}{d}\right)$$
$$bcdx + acd < abdx + abc$$
$$bcdx - abdx < abc - acd$$
$$bdx(c-a) < ac(b-d)$$
$$x < \frac{ac(b-d)}{bd(c-a)}$$

1.5 Sets and Compound Inequalities

1. This statement is true.

3. This statement is false.

5. This statement is true.

7. This statement is true.

9. The set is $A \cup B = \{0,1,2,3,4,5,6\}$.

11. The set is $A \cap B = \{2,4\}$.

13. The set is $A \cup (B \cap C) = \{0,1,2,3,4,5,6\}$.

15. The set is $\{0,2\}$.

17. The set is $\{0,1,2,3,4,5,6,7\}$.

19. The set is $\{1,2,4,5\}$.

21. **a.** The set is $A = \{-2,-1,0\}$.

  b. The set is $B = \{0,1,2\}$.

  c. The set is $A \cup B = \{-2,-1,0,1,2\}$.

  d. The set is $A \cap B = \{0\}$.

23. **a.** The set is $A = \{4,5\}$.

  b. The set is $B = \{-5,-4\}$.

  c. The set is $A \cup B = \{-5,-4,4,5\}$.

  d. The set is $A \cap B = \varnothing$.

25. Sketching a Venn diagram:

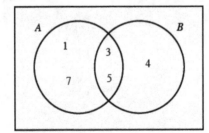

27. The interval notation is $(-\infty, 1)$.

29. The interval notation is $[3, \infty)$.

31. The interval notation is $(-\infty, \infty)$.

33. The interval notation is $(-\infty, -1) \cup (5, \infty)$:

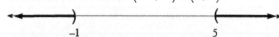

35. The interval notation is $(1, 5)$:

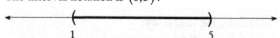

37. The interval notation is $(0, 7]$:

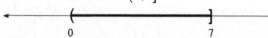

39. The interval notation is $(-\infty, 2) \cup (4, \infty)$:

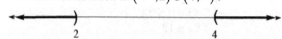

41. The interval notation is $(-1, 3)$:

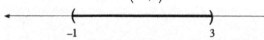

43. The interval notation is $(-3, -2]$:

45. The interval notation is $[-3, 2)$:

47. Solving the inequality:

$$-2 \le m - 5 \le 2$$
$$3 \le m \le 7$$

The solution set is $[3, 7]$. Graphing the solution set:

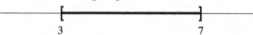

49. Solving the inequality:

$$-40 < 20a + 20 < 20$$
$$-60 < 20a < 0$$
$$-3 < a < 0$$

The solution set is $(-3, 0)$. Graphing the solution set:

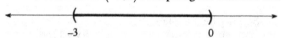

51. Solving the inequality:

$$0.5 \le 0.3a - 0.7 \le 1.1$$
$$1.2 \le 0.3a \le 1.8$$
$$4 \le a \le 6$$

The solution set is $[4, 6]$. Graphing the solution set:

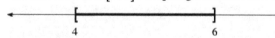

53. Solving the inequality:

$$3 < \frac{1}{2}x + 5 < 6$$
$$-2 < \frac{1}{2}x < 1$$
$$-4 < x < 2$$

The solution set is $(-4, 2)$. Graphing the solution set:

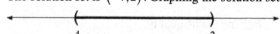

55. Solving the inequality:

$$4 < 6 + \frac{2}{3}x < 8$$
$$-2 < \frac{2}{3}x < 2$$
$$-6 < 2x < 6$$
$$-3 < x < 3$$

The solution set is $(-3, 3)$. Graphing:

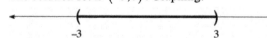

57. Solving the inequality:

$$-2 < -\frac{1}{2}x + 1 < 1$$
$$-4 < -x + 2 < 2$$
$$-6 < -x < 0$$
$$6 > x > 0$$

The solution set is $(0, 6)$. Graphing:

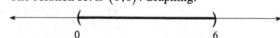

59. Solving the inequality:

$$-\frac{1}{2} \le \frac{3x+1}{2} \le \frac{1}{2}$$
$$-1 \le 3x + 1 \le 1$$
$$-2 \le 3x \le 0$$
$$-\frac{2}{3} \le x \le 0$$

61. Solving the inequality:

$$-1.5 \le \frac{2x-3}{4} \le 3.5$$
$$-6 \le 2x - 3 \le 14$$
$$-3 \le 2x \le 17$$
$$-\frac{3}{2} \le x \le \frac{17}{2}$$

The solution set is $\left[-\frac{2}{3}, 0\right]$. Graphing:

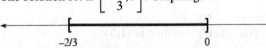

The solution set is $\left[-\frac{3}{2}, \frac{17}{2}\right]$. Graphing:

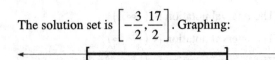

63. Solving the inequality:
$$-\frac{3}{4} \le \frac{4x-3}{2} \le 1.5$$
$$-3 \le 8x - 6 \le 6$$
$$3 \le 8x \le 12$$
$$\frac{3}{8} \le x \le \frac{3}{2}$$

The solution set is $\left[\frac{3}{8}, \frac{3}{2}\right]$. Graphing:

65. Solving the inequality:
$$x + 5 \le -2 \qquad \text{or} \qquad x + 5 \ge 2$$
$$x \le -7 \qquad \text{or} \qquad x \ge -3$$

The solution set is $(-\infty, -7] \cup [-3, \infty)$. Graphing the solution set:

67. Solving the inequality:
$$5y + 1 \le -4 \qquad \text{or} \qquad 5y + 1 \ge 4$$
$$5y \le -5 \qquad \text{or} \qquad 5y \ge 3$$
$$y \le -1 \qquad \text{or} \qquad y \ge \frac{3}{5}$$

The solution set is $(-\infty, -1] \cup \left[\frac{3}{5}, \infty\right)$. Graphing the solution set:

69. Solving the inequality:
$$2x + 5 < 3x - 1 \qquad \text{or} \qquad x - 4 > 2x + 6$$
$$-x + 5 < -1 \qquad \text{or} \qquad -x - 4 > 6$$
$$-x < -6 \qquad \text{or} \qquad -x > 10$$
$$x > 6 \qquad \text{or} \qquad x < -10$$

The solution set is $(-\infty, -10) \cup (6, \infty)$. Graphing the solution set:

71. Solving the inequality:
$$3x + 1 < -8 \qquad \text{or} \qquad -2x + 1 \le -3$$
$$3x < -9 \qquad \text{or} \qquad -2x \le -4$$
$$x < -3 \qquad \text{or} \qquad x \ge 2$$

The solution set is $(-\infty, -3) \cup [2, \infty)$. Graphing the solution set:

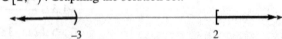

73. Writing as an inequality: $-2 < x \le 4$

75. Writing as an inequality: $x < -4$ or $x \ge 1$

77. **a.** Solving the inequality:

$$95 \le \frac{9}{5}C + 32 \le 113$$
$$63 \le \frac{9}{5}C \le 81$$
$$315 \le 9C \le 405$$
$$35° \le C \le 45°$$

b. Solving the inequality:

$$68 \le \frac{9}{5}C + 32 \le 86$$
$$36 \le \frac{9}{5}C \le 54$$
$$180 \le 9C \le 270$$
$$20° \le C \le 30°$$

c. Solving the inequality:

$$-13 \le \frac{9}{5}C + 32 \le 14$$
$$-45 \le \frac{9}{5}C \le -18$$
$$-225 \le 9C \le -90$$
$$-25° \le C \le -10°$$

d. Solving the inequality:

$$-4 \le \frac{9}{5}C + 32 \le 23$$
$$-36 \le \frac{9}{5}C \le -9$$
$$-180 \le 9C \le -45$$
$$-20° \le C \le -5°$$

79. For adults, the inequality is $0.72 - 0.11 \le r \le 0.72 + 0.11$, or $0.61 \le r \le 0.83$. The survival rate for adults is between 61% and 83%. For juveniles, the inequality is $0.13 - 0.07 \le r \le 0.13 + 0.07$, or $0.06 \le r \le 0.20$. The survival rate for juveniles is between 6% and 20%.

81. Solving the equation:

$$2a - 1 = -7$$
$$2a = -6$$
$$a = -3$$

83. Solving the equation:

$$\frac{2}{3}x - 3 = 7$$
$$\frac{2}{3}x = 10$$
$$x = 15$$

85. Solving the equation:

$$x - 5 = x - 7$$
$$-5 = -7$$

The equation has no solution $(\varnothing)$.

87. Solving the equation:

$$x - 5 = -x - 7$$
$$2x - 5 = -7$$
$$2x = -2$$
$$x = -1$$

89. Solving the inequality:

$$-c < ax + b < c$$
$$-c - b < ax < c - b$$
$$\frac{-c - b}{a} < x < \frac{c - b}{a}$$

91. Solving the inequality:

$$-d < \frac{ax + b}{c} < d$$
$$-cd < ax + b < cd$$
$$-cd - b < ax < cd - b$$
$$\frac{-cd - b}{a} < x < \frac{cd - b}{a}$$

1.6 Absolute Value Equations

1. Solving the equation:
$$|x| = 4$$
$$x = -4, 4$$

3. Solving the equation:
$$2 = |a|$$
$$a = -2, 2$$

5. The equation $|x| = -3$ has no solution, or $\varnothing$.

7. Solving the equation:
$$|a| + 2 = 3$$
$$|a| = 1$$
$$a = -1, 1$$

9. Solving the equation:

$$|y| + 4 = 3$$
$$|y| = -1$$

The equation $|y| = -1$ has no solution, or $\varnothing$.

11. Solving the equation:

$$|a - 4| = \frac{5}{3}$$
$$a - 4 = -\frac{5}{3}, \frac{5}{3}$$
$$a = \frac{7}{3}, \frac{17}{3}$$

13. Solving the equation:

$$\left|\frac{3}{5}a + \frac{1}{2}\right| = 1$$
$$\frac{3}{5}a + \frac{1}{2} = -1, 1$$
$$\frac{3}{5}a = -\frac{3}{2}, \frac{1}{2}$$
$$a = -\frac{5}{2}, \frac{5}{6}$$

15. Solving the equation:

$$60 = |20x - 40|$$
$$20x - 40 = -60, 60$$
$$20x = -20, 100$$
$$x = -1, 5$$

17. Since $|2x + 1| = -3$ is impossible, there is no solution, or $\varnothing$.

19. Solving the equation:

$$\left|\frac{3}{4}x - 6\right| = 9$$
$$\frac{3}{4}x - 6 = -9, 9$$
$$\frac{3}{4}x = -3, 15$$
$$3x = -12, 60$$
$$x = -4, 20$$

21. Solving the equation:

$$\left|1 - \frac{1}{2}a\right| = 3$$
$$1 - \frac{1}{2}a = -3, 3$$
$$-\frac{1}{2}a = -4, 2$$
$$a = -4, 8$$

23. Solving the equation:

$$|2x - 5| = 3$$
$$2x - 5 = -3, 3$$
$$2x = 2, 8$$
$$x = 1, 4$$

25. Solving the equation:

$$|4 - 7x| = 5$$
$$4 - 7x = -5, 5$$
$$-7x = -9, 1$$
$$x = -\frac{1}{7}, \frac{9}{7}$$

27. Solving the equation:

$$\left|3 - \frac{2}{3}y\right| = 5$$
$$3 - \frac{2}{3}y = -5, 5$$
$$-\frac{2}{3}y = -8, 2$$
$$-2y = -24, 6$$
$$y = -3, 12$$

29. Solving the equation:

$$|3x + 4| + 1 = 7$$
$$|3x + 4| = 6$$
$$3x + 4 = -6, 6$$
$$3x = -10, 2$$
$$x = -\frac{10}{3}, \frac{2}{3}$$

31. Solving the equation:

$$|3 - 2y| + 4 = 3$$
$$|3 - 2y| = -1$$

Since this equation is impossible, there is no solution, or $\varnothing$.

32. Solving the equation:

$$|8 - 7y| + 9 = 1$$
$$|8 - 7y| = -8$$

Since this equation is impossible, there is no solution, or $\varnothing$.

33. Solving the equation:

$$3+|4t-1|=8$$
$$|4t-1|=5$$
$$4t-1=-5,5$$
$$4t=-4,6$$
$$t=-1,\frac{3}{2}$$

35. Solving the equation:

$$\left|9-\frac{3}{5}x\right|+6=12$$
$$\left|9-\frac{3}{5}x\right|=6$$
$$9-\frac{3}{5}x=-6,6$$
$$-\frac{3}{5}x=-15,-3$$
$$-3x=-75,-15$$
$$x=5,25$$

37. Solving the equation:

$$5=\left|\frac{2x}{7}+\frac{4}{7}\right|-3$$
$$\left|\frac{2x}{7}+\frac{4}{7}\right|=8$$
$$\frac{2x}{7}+\frac{4}{7}=-8,8$$
$$2x+4=-56,56$$
$$2x=-60,52$$
$$x=-30,26$$

39. Solving the equation:

$$2=-8+\left|4-\frac{1}{2}y\right|$$
$$\left|4-\frac{1}{2}y\right|=10$$
$$4-\frac{1}{2}y=-10,10$$
$$-\frac{1}{2}y=-14,6$$
$$y=-12,28$$

41. Solving the equation:

$$|3(x+1)|-4=-1$$
$$|3(x+1)|=3$$
$$3(x+1)=-3,3$$
$$x+1=-1,1$$
$$x=-2,0$$

43. Solving the equation:

$$|1+3(2x-1)|=5$$
$$1+3(2x-1)=-5,5$$
$$3(2x-1)=-6,4$$
$$2x-1=-2,\frac{4}{3}$$
$$2x=-1,\frac{7}{3}$$
$$x=-\frac{1}{2},\frac{7}{6}$$

45. Solving the equation:

$$3=-2+\left|5-\frac{2}{3}a\right|$$
$$\left|5-\frac{2}{3}a\right|=5$$
$$5-\frac{2}{3}a=-5,5$$
$$-\frac{2}{3}a=-10,0$$
$$-2a=-30,0$$
$$a=0,15$$

47. Solving the equation:

$$6=|7(k+3)-4|$$
$$7(k+3)-4=-6,6$$
$$7(k+3)=-2,10$$
$$k+3=-\frac{2}{7},\frac{10}{7}$$
$$k=-\frac{23}{7},-\frac{11}{7}$$

49. Solving the equation:
$$|3a+1|=|2a-4|$$

$3a+1=2a-4$	or	$3a+1=-2a+4$
$a+1=-4$		$5a=3$
$a=-5$		$a=\frac{3}{5}$

51. Solving the equation:

$$\left| x - \frac{1}{3} \right| = \left| \frac{1}{2}x + \frac{1}{6} \right|$$

$$\begin{aligned} x - \frac{1}{3} &= \frac{1}{2}x + \frac{1}{6} \\ 6x - 2 &= 3x + 1 \\ 3x - 2 &= 1 \\ 3x &= 3 \\ x &= 1 \end{aligned} \qquad \text{or} \qquad \begin{aligned} x - \frac{1}{3} &= -\frac{1}{2}x - \frac{1}{6} \\ 6x - 2 &= -3x - 1 \\ 9x - 2 &= -1 \\ 9x &= 1 \\ x &= \frac{1}{9} \end{aligned}$$

53. Solving the equation:

$$\left| y - 2 \right| = \left| y + 3 \right|$$

$$\begin{aligned} y - 2 &= y + 3 \\ -2 &= -3 \\ y &= \text{impossible} \end{aligned} \qquad \text{or} \qquad \begin{aligned} y - 2 &= -y - 3 \\ 2y &= -1 \\ y &= -\frac{1}{2} \end{aligned}$$

55. Solving the equation:

$$\left| 3x - 1 \right| = \left| 3x + 1 \right|$$

$$\begin{aligned} 3x - 1 &= 3x + 1 \\ -1 &= 1 \\ x &= \text{impossible} \end{aligned} \qquad \text{or} \qquad \begin{aligned} 3x - 1 &= -3x - 1 \\ 6x &= 0 \\ x &= 0 \end{aligned}$$

57. Solving the equation:

$$\left| 0.03 - 0.01x \right| = \left| 0.04 + 0.05x \right|$$

$$\begin{aligned} 0.03 - 0.01x &= 0.04 + 0.05x \\ -0.06x &= 0.01 \\ x &= -\frac{1}{6} \end{aligned} \qquad \text{or} \qquad \begin{aligned} 0.03 - 0.01x &= -0.04 - 0.05x \\ 0.04x &= -0.07 \\ x &= -\frac{7}{4} \end{aligned}$$

59. Since $\left| x - 2 \right| = \left| 2 - x \right|$ is always true, the solution set is all real numbers.

61. Since $\left| \frac{x}{5} - 1 \right| = \left| 1 - \frac{x}{5} \right|$ is always true, the solution set is all real numbers.

63. Solving the equation:

$$\left| \frac{2}{3}b - \frac{1}{4} \right| = \left| \frac{1}{6}b + \frac{1}{2} \right|$$

$$\begin{aligned} \frac{2}{3}b - \frac{1}{4} &= \frac{1}{6}b + \frac{1}{2} \\ 8b - 3 &= 2b + 6 \\ 6b - 3 &= 6 \\ 6b &= 9 \\ b &= \frac{3}{2} \end{aligned} \qquad \text{or} \qquad \begin{aligned} \frac{2}{3}b - \frac{1}{4} &= -\frac{1}{6}b - \frac{1}{2} \\ 8b - 3 &= -2b - 6 \\ 10b - 3 &= -6 \\ 10b &= -3 \\ b &= -\frac{3}{10} \end{aligned}$$

65. Solving the equation:

$$\left| 0.1a - 0.04 \right| = \left| 0.3a + 0.08 \right|$$

$$\begin{aligned} 0.1a - 0.04 &= 0.3a + 0.08 \\ -0.2a - 0.04 &= 0.08 \\ -0.2a &= 0.12 \\ -20a &= 12 \\ a &= -\frac{3}{5} \end{aligned} \qquad \text{or} \qquad \begin{aligned} 0.1a - 0.04 &= -0.3a - 0.08 \\ 0.4a - 0.04 &= -0.08 \\ 0.4a &= -0.04 \\ 40a &= -4 \\ a &= -\frac{1}{10} \end{aligned}$$

67. **a.** Solving the equation:

$$4x - 5 = 0$$
$$4x = 5$$
$$x = \frac{5}{4}$$

b. Solving the equation:

$$|4x - 5| = 0$$
$$4x - 5 = 0$$
$$4x = 5$$
$$x = \frac{5}{4}$$

c. Solving the equation:

$$4x - 5 = 3$$
$$4x = 8$$
$$x = 2$$

d. Solving the equation:

$$|4x - 5| = 3$$
$$4x - 5 = -3, 3$$
$$4x = 2, 8$$
$$x = \frac{1}{2}, 2$$

e. Solving the equation:

$$|4x - 5| = |2x + 3|$$

$$4x - 5 = 2x + 3 \qquad \text{or} \qquad 4x - 5 = -2x - 3$$
$$2x - 5 = 3 \qquad\qquad\qquad\qquad 6x - 5 = -3$$
$$2x = 8 \qquad\qquad\qquad\qquad\quad 6x = 2$$
$$x = 4 \qquad\qquad\qquad\qquad\quad x = \frac{1}{3}$$

69. Solving the equation:

$$-60|x - 11| + 962 = 722$$
$$-60|x - 11| = -240$$
$$|x - 11| = 4$$
$$x - 11 = -4, 4$$
$$x = 7, 15$$

The revenue was \$722 million in 1987 and 1995.

71. Solving the inequality:

$$2x - 5 < 3$$
$$2x < 8$$
$$x < 4$$

73. Solving the inequality:

$$-4 \le 3a + 7$$
$$-11 \le 3a$$
$$a \ge -\frac{11}{3}$$

75. Solving the inequality:

$$4t - 3 \le -9$$
$$4t \le -6$$
$$t \le -\frac{3}{2}$$

77. Solving the inequality:

$$|x - a| = b$$
$$x - a = -b, b$$
$$x = a - b \text{ or } x = a + b$$

79. Solving the equation:

$$|ax + b| = c$$
$$ax + b = -c, c$$
$$ax = -b - c, -b + c$$
$$x = \frac{-b - c}{a} \text{ or } x = \frac{-b + c}{a}$$

81. Solving the equation:

$$\left|\frac{x}{a} + \frac{y}{b}\right| = 1$$
$$\frac{x}{a} + \frac{y}{b} = -1, 1$$
$$\frac{x}{a} = -\frac{y}{b} - 1, -\frac{y}{b} + 1$$
$$x = -\frac{a}{b}y - a \text{ or } x = -\frac{a}{b}y + a$$

1.7 Absolute Value Inequalities

1. Solving the inequality:

$|x| < 3$

$-3 < x < 3$

The solution set is $(-3, 3)$:

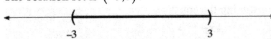

3. Solving the inequality:

$|x| \geq 2$

$x \leq -2$ or $x \geq 2$

The solution set is $(-\infty, -2] \cup [2, \infty)$:

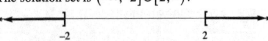

5. Solving the inequality:

$|x| + 2 < 5$

$|x| < 3$

$-3 < x < 3$

The solution set is $(-3, 3)$:

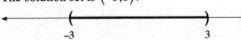

7. Solving the inequality:

$|t| - 3 > 4$

$|t| > 7$

$t < -7$ or $t > 7$

The solution set is $(-\infty, -7) \cup (7, \infty)$:

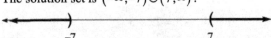

9. Since the inequality $|y| < -5$ is never true, the solution set is $\varnothing$:

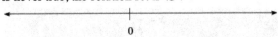

11. Since the inequality $|x| \geq -2$ is always true, the solution set is all real numbers, or $(-\infty, \infty)$:

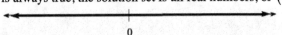

13. Solving the inequality:

$|x - 3| < 7$

$-7 < x - 3 < 7$

$-4 < x < 10$

The solution set is $(-4, 10)$:

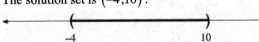

15. Solving the inequality:

$|a + 5| \geq 4$

$a + 5 \leq -4$ or $a + 5 \geq 4$

$a \leq -9$ or $a \geq -1$

The solution set is $(-\infty, -9] \cup [-1, \infty)$:

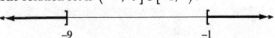

17. Solving the inequality:

$|x - 5| < 3$

$-3 < x - 5 < 3$

$2 < x < 8$

The solution set is $(2, 8)$:

19. Since the inequality $|a - 1| < -3$ is never true, the solution set is $\varnothing$:

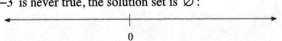

21. Solving the inequality:

$|2x - 4| < 6$

$-6 < 2x - 4 < 6$

$-2 < 2x < 10$

$-1 < x < 5$

The solution set is $(-1, 5)$:

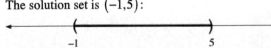

23. Solving the inequality:

$|3y + 9| \geq 6$

$3y + 9 \leq -6$ or $3y + 9 \geq 6$

$3y \leq -15$ $3y \geq -3$

$y \leq -5$ $y \geq -1$

The solution set is $(-\infty, -5] \cup [-1, \infty)$:

25. Solving the inequality:
$$|2k+3| \geq 7$$
$$2k+3 \leq -7 \qquad \text{or} \qquad 2k+3 \geq 7$$
$$2k \leq -10 \qquad\qquad\qquad 2k \geq 4$$
$$k \leq -5 \qquad\qquad\qquad k \geq 2$$
The solution set is $(-\infty,-5]\cup[2,\infty)$:

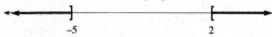

27. Solving the inequality:
$$|x-3|+2 < 6$$
$$|x-3| < 4$$
$$-4 < x-3 < 4$$
$$-1 < x < 7$$
The solution set is $(-1,7)$:

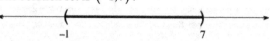

29. Solving the inequality:
$$|2a+1|+4 \geq 7$$
$$|2a+1| \geq 3$$
$$2a+1 \leq -3 \qquad \text{or} \qquad 2a+1 \geq 3$$
$$2a \leq -4 \qquad\qquad\qquad 2a \geq 2$$
$$a \leq -2 \qquad\qquad\qquad a \geq 1$$

The solution set is $(-\infty,-2]\cup[1,\infty)$:

31. Solving the inequality:
$$|3x+5|-8 < 5$$
$$|3x+5| < 13$$
$$-13 < 3x+5 < 13$$
$$-18 < 3x < 8$$
$$-6 < x < \frac{8}{3}$$
The solution set is $\left(-6,\frac{8}{3}\right)$:

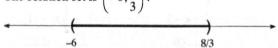

33. Solving the inequality:
$$|x-3| \leq 5$$
$$-5 \leq x-3 \leq 5$$
$$-2 \leq x \leq 8$$

The solution set is $[-2,8]$.

35. Solving the inequality:
$$|3y+1| < 5$$
$$-5 < 3y+1 < 5$$
$$-6 < 3y < 4$$
$$-2 < y < \frac{4}{3}$$
The solution set is $\left(-2,\frac{4}{3}\right)$.

37. Solving the inequality:
$$|a+4| \geq 1$$
$$a+4 \leq -1 \qquad \text{or} \qquad a+4 \geq 1$$
$$a \leq -5 \qquad\qquad\qquad a \geq -3$$

The solution set is $(-\infty,-5]\cup[3,\infty)$.

39. Solving the inequality:
$$|2x+5| > 2$$
$$2x+5 < -2 \qquad \text{or} \qquad 2x+5 > 2$$
$$2x < -7 \qquad\qquad\qquad 2x > -3$$
$$x < -\frac{7}{2} \qquad\qquad\qquad x > -\frac{3}{2}$$
The solution set is $\left(-\infty,-\frac{7}{2}\right)\cup\left(-\frac{3}{2},\infty\right)$.

41. Solving the inequality:
$$|-5x+3| \leq 8$$
$$-8 \leq -5x+3 \leq 8$$
$$-11 \leq -5x \leq 5$$
$$\frac{11}{5} \geq x \geq -1$$
The solution set is $\left[-1,\frac{11}{5}\right]$.

43. Solving the inequality:
$$|-3x+7| < 2$$
$$-2 < -3x+7 < 2$$
$$-9 < -3x < -5$$
$$3 > x > \frac{5}{3}$$
The solution set is $\left(\frac{5}{3},3\right)$.

45. Solving the inequality:

$$|5-x|>3$$

$$5-x<-3 \qquad \text{or} \qquad 5-x>3$$
$$-x<-8 \qquad\qquad\qquad -x>-2$$
$$x>8 \qquad\qquad\qquad x<2$$

The solution set is $(-\infty,2)\cup(8,\infty)$:

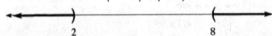

47. Solving the inequality:

$$\left|3-\frac{2}{3}x\right|\geq 5$$

$$3-\frac{2}{3}x\leq -5 \qquad \text{or} \qquad 3-\frac{2}{3}x\geq 5$$
$$-\frac{2}{3}x\leq -8 \qquad\qquad -\frac{2}{3}x\geq 2$$
$$-2x\leq -24 \qquad\qquad -2x\geq 6$$
$$x\geq 12 \qquad\qquad\qquad x\leq -3$$

The solution set is $(-\infty,-3]\cup[12,\infty)$:

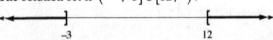

49. Solving the inequality:

$$\left|2-\frac{1}{2}x\right|>1$$

$$2-\frac{1}{2}x<-1 \qquad \text{or} \qquad 2-\frac{1}{2}x>1$$
$$-\frac{1}{2}x<-3 \qquad\qquad -\frac{1}{2}x>-1$$
$$x>6 \qquad\qquad\qquad x<2$$

The solution set is $(-\infty,2)\cup(6,\infty)$:

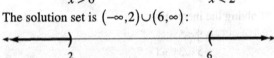

51. Solving the inequality:

$$\left|\frac{1}{3}x-2\right|>4$$

$$\frac{1}{3}x-2<-4 \qquad \text{or} \qquad \frac{1}{3}x-2>4$$
$$\frac{1}{3}x<-2 \qquad\qquad\qquad \frac{1}{3}x>6$$
$$x<-6 \qquad\qquad\qquad x>18$$

The solution set is $(-\infty,-6)\cup(18,\infty)$:

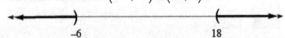

53. Solving the inequality:

$$|x-1|<0.01$$
$$-0.01<x-1<0.01$$
$$0.99<x<1.01$$

The solution set is $(0.99,1.01)$.

55. Solving the inequality:

$$|2x+1|\geq \frac{1}{5}$$

$$2x+1\leq -\frac{1}{5} \qquad \text{or} \qquad 2x+1\geq \frac{1}{5}$$
$$2x\leq -\frac{6}{5} \qquad\qquad\qquad 2x\geq -\frac{4}{5}$$
$$x\leq -\frac{3}{5} \qquad\qquad\qquad x\geq -\frac{2}{5}$$

The solution set is $\left(-\infty,-\frac{3}{5}\right]\cup\left[-\frac{2}{5},\infty\right)$.

57. Solving the inequality:

$$|3x-2|\leq \frac{1}{3}$$
$$-\frac{1}{3}\leq 3x-2\leq \frac{1}{3}$$
$$\frac{5}{3}\leq 3x\leq \frac{7}{3}$$
$$\frac{5}{9}\leq x\leq \frac{7}{9}$$

The solution set is $\left[\frac{5}{9},\frac{7}{9}\right]$.

59. Solving the inequality:

$$\left|\frac{3x+1}{2}\right|>\frac{1}{2}$$

$$\frac{3x+1}{2}<-\frac{1}{2} \qquad \text{or} \qquad \frac{3x+1}{2}>\frac{1}{2}$$
$$3x+1<-1 \qquad\qquad\qquad 3x+1>1$$
$$3x<-2 \qquad\qquad\qquad 3x>0$$
$$x<-\frac{2}{3} \qquad\qquad\qquad x>0$$

The solution set is $\left(-\infty,-\frac{2}{3}\right)\cup(0,\infty)$.

61. Solving the inequality:

$$\left|\frac{4-3x}{2}\right| \geq 1$$

$$\frac{4-3x}{2} \leq -1 \qquad \text{or} \qquad \frac{4-3x}{2} \geq 1$$

$$4-3x \leq -2 \qquad\qquad 4-3x \geq 2$$

$$-3x \leq -6 \qquad\qquad -3x \geq -2$$

$$x \geq 2 \qquad\qquad x \leq \frac{2}{3}$$

The solution set is $\left(-\infty, \frac{2}{3}\right] \cup [2, \infty)$.

63. Solving the inequality:

$$\left|\frac{3x-2}{5}\right| \leq \frac{1}{2}$$

$$-\frac{1}{2} \leq \frac{3x-2}{5} \leq \frac{1}{2}$$

$$-\frac{5}{2} \leq 3x-2 \leq \frac{5}{2}$$

$$-\frac{1}{2} \leq 3x \leq \frac{9}{2}$$

$$-\frac{1}{6} \leq x \leq \frac{3}{2}$$

The solution set is $\left[-\frac{1}{6}, \frac{3}{2}\right]$.

65. Solving the inequality:

$$\left|2x - \frac{1}{5}\right| < 0.3$$

$$-0.3 < 2x - 0.2 < 0.3$$

$$-0.1 < 2x < 0.5$$

$$-0.05 < x < 0.25$$

The solution set is $(-0.05, 0.25)$.

67. Solving the inequality:

$$\left|-2x + \frac{1}{2}\right| < \frac{1}{3}$$

$$-\frac{1}{3} < -2x + \frac{1}{2} < \frac{1}{3}$$

$$-\frac{5}{6} < -2x < -\frac{1}{6}$$

$$\frac{5}{12} > x > \frac{1}{12}$$

The solution set is $\left(\frac{1}{12}, \frac{5}{12}\right)$.

69. Writing as an absolute value inequality: $|x| \leq 4$

71. Writing as an absolute value inequality: $|x-5| \leq 1$

73. **a.** Evaluating when $x = 0$: $|5x+3| = |5(0)+3| = |3| = 3$

    b. Solving the equation:

$$|5x+3| = 7$$

$$5x+3 = -7, 7$$

$$5x = -10, 4$$

$$x = -2, \frac{4}{5}$$

    c. No, it is not a solution.

    d. Solving the inequality:

$$|5x+3| > 7$$

$$5x+3 < -7 \qquad \text{or} \qquad 5x+3 > 7$$

$$5x < -10 \qquad\qquad 5x > 4$$

$$x < -2 \qquad\qquad x > \frac{4}{5}$$

The solution set is $(-\infty, -2) \cup \left(\frac{4}{5}, \infty\right)$.

75. Solving the inequality:

$$|v - 455| < 23$$

$$-23 < v - 455 < 23$$

$$432 < v < 478$$

The copper fireworks wavelength fit into the blue color range.

77. Solving the inequality:

$$x - a < b$$
$$x < a + b$$

79. Solving the inequality:

$$ax - b > c$$
$$ax > b + c$$
$$x > \frac{b + c}{a}$$

81. Solving the inequality:

$$ax + b \le c$$
$$ax \le c - b$$
$$x \le \frac{c - b}{a}$$

83. Solving the inequality:

$$\left|\frac{x}{a} + \frac{1}{b}\right| > c$$

$$\frac{x}{a} + \frac{1}{b} < -c \qquad \text{or} \qquad \frac{x}{a} + \frac{1}{b} > c$$
$$bx + a < -abc \qquad\qquad bx + a > abc$$
$$bx < -a - abc \qquad\qquad bx > -a + abc$$
$$x < \frac{-a - abc}{b} \qquad\qquad x > \frac{-a + abc}{b}$$

85. Solving the inequality:

$$\left|(x + a)^2 - x^2\right| < 3a^2$$

$$-3a^2 < (x + a)^2 - x^2 < 3a^2$$
$$-3a^2 < x^2 + 2ax + a^2 - x^2 < 3a^2$$
$$-3a^2 < 2ax + a^2 < 3a^2$$
$$-4a^2 < 2ax < 2a^2$$
$$-2a < x < a$$

87. Solving the inequality:

$$\left|x - a^2\right| \le 2a^2$$

$$-2a^2 \le x - a^2 \le 2a^2$$
$$-a^2 \le x \le 3a^2$$

Chapter 1 Review

1. Solving the equation:

$$x - 4 = 7$$
$$x = 11$$

2. Solving the equation:

$$3y = -5$$
$$y = -\frac{5}{3}$$

3. Solving the equation:

$$2(x + 2) - 4(2x - 3) = 4(2x - 1)$$
$$2x + 4 - 8x + 12 = 8x - 4$$
$$-6x + 16 = 8x - 4$$
$$-14x = -20$$
$$x = \frac{10}{7}$$

4. Solving the equation:

$$-0.05x - 0.08 = 0.03 - 0.04(2x - 1)$$
$$-0.05x - 0.08 = 0.03 - 0.08x + 0.04$$
$$-0.05x - 0.08 = -0.08x + 0.07$$
$$0.03x = 0.15$$
$$x = 5$$

5. Substituting $x = 3$:

$$6(3) - 9y = 15$$
$$18 - 9y = 15$$
$$-9y = -3$$
$$y = \frac{1}{3}$$

6. Substituting $x = -2$:

$$6(-2) - 9y = 15$$
$$-12 - 9y = 15$$
$$-9y = 27$$
$$y = -3$$

7. Substituting $y = 0$:

$$-5x + 7(0) = 35$$
$$-5x + 0 = 35$$
$$-5x = 35$$
$$x = -7$$

8. Substituting $y = -5$:

$$-5x + 7(-5) = 35$$
$$-5x - 35 = 35$$
$$-5x = 70$$
$$x = -14$$

9. Solving for y:

$$5x - 10y = 20$$
$$-10y = -5x + 20$$
$$y = \frac{1}{2}x - 2$$

10. Solving for x:

$$ax + by = cx + dy$$
$$ax - cx = dy - by$$
$$x(a - c) = y(d - b)$$
$$x = \frac{y(d - b)}{a - c}$$

11. Solving for y:

$$5x - y = 5$$
$$-y = -5x + 5$$
$$y = 5x - 5$$

12. Solving for y:

$$6x - 3y = 15$$
$$-3y = -6x + 15$$
$$y = 2x - 5$$

13. Solving for y:

$$y - 2 = \frac{2}{3}(x + 6)$$
$$y - 2 = \frac{2}{3}x + 4$$
$$y = \frac{2}{3}x + 6$$

14. Solving for y:

$$y - 5 = \frac{1}{4}(12x + 8)$$
$$y - 5 = 3x + 2$$
$$y = 3x + 7$$

15. Let x represent the width and $2x$ represent the length. Using the perimeter formula:

$$2(x) + 2(2x) = 102$$
$$2x + 4x = 102$$
$$6x = 102$$
$$x = 17$$
$$2x = 34$$

The width is 17 in. and the length is 34 in.

16. Adding up the sides of the triangle:

$$x + 2x + (x + 4) = 24$$
$$4x + 4 = 24$$
$$4x = 20$$
$$x = 5 \text{ meters}$$

17. Let x and $6x + 5$ represent the two angles. Since they are supplementary:

$$x + 6x + 5 = 180$$
$$7x + 5 = 180$$
$$7x = 175$$
$$x = 25$$
$$6x + 5 = 155$$

The angles are $25°$ and $155°$.

18. Since the angles are complementary:

$$3x + (2x + 30) = 90$$
$$5x + 30 = 90$$
$$5x = 60$$
$$x = 12$$
$$3x = 36$$
$$2x + 30 = 54$$

The angles are $36°$ and $54°$.

19. The amount collected for the day is $\$1{,}021.40 - \$75 = \$946.40$. Since this amount includes the sales s plus the tax, the equation is:

$$s + 0.082s = 946.40$$
$$1.082s = 946.40$$
$$s \approx 874.68$$

The portion that is sales tax is: $0.082(874.20) \approx 71.72$. The sales tax collected is $\$71.72$.

	Dollars Invested at 9%	Dollars Invested at 11%
Dollars	x	$x+2,000$
Interest	$0.09(x)$	$0.11(x+2,000)$

20. Completing the table:

The equation is:
$$0.09(x)+0.11(x+2,000)=320$$
$$0.09x+0.11x+220=320$$
$$0.20x+220=320$$
$$0.20x=100$$
$$x=500$$
$$x+2,000=2,500$$

I have \$500 invested at 9% and \$2,500 invested at 11%.

21. Solving the inequality:

$$-3x<12$$
$$x>-4$$

The solution set is $(-4,\infty)$:

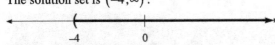

22. Solving the inequality:
$$-6-\frac{4}{3}x\ge 2$$
$$-\frac{4}{3}x\ge 8$$
$$-4x\ge 24$$
$$x\le -6$$

The solution set is $(-\infty,-6]$:

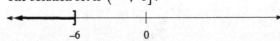

23. Solving the inequality:

$$1.5x-2.6\ge 0.5x+1.4$$
$$1.0x-2.6\ge 1.4$$
$$x\ge 4$$

The solution set is $[4,\infty)$:

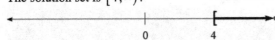

24. Solving the inequality:
$$3(5x-6)<6(3x+5)$$
$$15x-18<18x+30$$
$$-3x-18<30$$
$$-3x<48$$
$$x>-16$$

The solution set is $(-16,\infty)$:

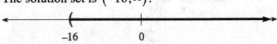

25. The set is $A\cap C=\{3\}$.

26. The set is $\{3,4\}$.

27. Solving the inequality:
$$-2\le \frac{2}{3}x-4\le 8$$
$$2\le \frac{2}{3}x\le 12$$
$$6\le 2x\le 36$$
$$3\le x\le 18$$
The solution set is $[3,18]$.

28. Solving the inequality:

$$
\begin{array}{lll}
x-5>3 & \text{or} & 2x-7<3 \\
x>8 & \text{or} & 2x<10 \\
x>8 & \text{or} & x<5
\end{array}
$$

The solution set is $(-\infty,5)\cup(8,\infty)$.

29. Solving the equation:

$$\left|\frac{1}{8}x - 4\right| = \frac{1}{2}$$
$$\frac{1}{8}x - 4 = -\frac{1}{2}, \frac{1}{2}$$
$$\frac{1}{8}x = \frac{7}{2}, \frac{9}{2}$$
$$x = 28, 36$$

30. Solving the equation:

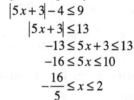

$$\left|\frac{3}{2}a + 7\right| = 4$$
$$\frac{3}{2}a + 7 = -4, 4$$
$$\frac{3}{2}a = -11, -3$$
$$3a = -22, -6$$
$$a = -\frac{22}{3}, -2$$

31. Solving the equation:

$$|4y - 5| - 3 = 10$$
$$|4y - 5| = 13$$
$$4y - 5 = -13, 13$$
$$4y = -8, 18$$
$$y = -2, \frac{9}{2}$$

32. Solving the equation:

$$\left|\frac{5}{6} - \frac{1}{9}x\right| + 5 = 2$$
$$\left|\frac{5}{6} - \frac{1}{9}x\right| = -3$$

Since this equation is impossible, there is no solution, or $\varnothing$.

33. Solving the inequality:

$$|3y - 4| \geq 2$$

$$3y - 4 \leq -2 \quad \text{or} \quad 3y - 4 \geq 2$$
$$3y \leq 2 \qquad\qquad 3y \geq 6$$
$$y \leq \frac{2}{3} \qquad\qquad y \geq 2$$

The solution set is $\left(-\infty, \frac{2}{3}\right] \cup [2, \infty)$:

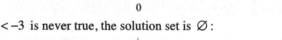

2/3   2

34. Solving the inequality:

$$|5x + 3| - 4 \leq 9$$
$$|5x + 3| \leq 13$$
$$-13 \leq 5x + 3 \leq 13$$
$$-16 \leq 5x \leq 10$$
$$-\frac{16}{5} \leq x \leq 2$$

The solution set is $\left[-\frac{16}{5}, 2\right]$:

-16/5   2

35. Since the inequality $|4x - 6| > -8$ is always true, the solution set is all real numbers, or $(-\infty, \infty)$:

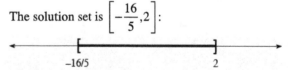

0

36. Since the inequality $|2 - 5t| < -3$ is never true, the solution set is $\varnothing$:

0

Chapter 1 Cumulative Review

1. Simplifying: $6^2 = 6 \cdot 6 = 36$

2. Simplifying: $|-5| = 5$

3. Simplifying: $4 \cdot (-3) + 7 = -12 + 7 = -5$

4. Simplifying: $3(4-5) = 3(-1) = -3$

5. Simplifying: $9 - 2 \cdot 4 + 1 = 9 - 8 + 1 = 2$

6. Simplifying: $(7-1)(5+4) = (6)(9) = 54$

7. Simplifying: $8 + 2(3+2) = 8 + 2(5) = 8 + 10 = 18$

8. Simplifying: $45 - 24 \div 8 + 3 = 45 - 3 + 3 = 45$

9. Simplifying: $-(4+1) - (8-11) = -5 - (-3) = -5 + 3 = -2$

10. Simplifying: $3(-4)^2 + 2(-3)^3 = 3(16) + 2(-27) = 48 - 54 = -6$

11. Simplifying: $\dfrac{-4-4}{-1-3} = \dfrac{-8}{-4} = 2$

12. Simplifying: $\dfrac{7(-2)+4}{9(-2)+6(2)} = \dfrac{-14+4}{-18+12} = \dfrac{-10}{-6} = \dfrac{5}{3}$

13. Reducing the fraction: $\dfrac{57}{76} = \dfrac{3 \cdot 19}{2 \cdot 2 \cdot 19} = \dfrac{3}{2 \cdot 2} = \dfrac{3}{4}$

14. Reducing the fraction: $\dfrac{129}{387} = \dfrac{3 \cdot 43}{3 \cdot 3 \cdot 43} = \dfrac{1}{3}$

15. Adding the fractions: $\dfrac{7}{28} + \dfrac{5}{12} = \dfrac{7}{28} \cdot \dfrac{3}{3} + \dfrac{5}{12} \cdot \dfrac{7}{7} = \dfrac{21}{84} + \dfrac{35}{84} = \dfrac{56}{84} = \dfrac{28 \cdot 2}{28 \cdot 3} = \dfrac{2}{3}$

16. Adding the fractions: $\dfrac{45}{56} + \dfrac{17}{21} = \dfrac{45}{56} \cdot \dfrac{3}{3} + \dfrac{17}{21} \cdot \dfrac{8}{8} = \dfrac{135}{168} + \dfrac{136}{168} = \dfrac{271}{168}$

17. Finding the difference: $4 - (-5) = 4 + 5 = 9$

18. Computing the value: $4(-7) - (-3) = -28 + 3 = -25$

19. The set is $A \cup C = \{1,3,5,6,7,8\}$.

20. The set is $A \cap B = \{3\}$.

21. The set is $\{9,12\}$.

22. The set is $\{5,6,7\}$.

23. Simplifying: $14\left(\dfrac{x}{7} + 1\right) = 14 \cdot \dfrac{x}{7} + 14 \cdot 1 = 2x + 14$

24. Simplifying: $4(3x-2) + 7 = 12x - 8 + 7 = 12x - 1$

25. Simplifying: $x\left(1 + \dfrac{3}{x}\right)\left(1 + \dfrac{3}{x}\right) = x\left(1 + \dfrac{6}{x} + \dfrac{9}{x^2}\right) = x + 6 + \dfrac{9}{x}$

26. Simplifying: $1,000(0.03x + 0.01y) = 1,000 \cdot 0.03x + 1,000 \cdot 0.01y = 30x + 10y$

27. Solving the equation:

$$3 - 6y = -9$$
$$-6y = -12$$
$$y = 2$$

28. Solving the equation:

$$3(2-x) = 4(1+3x)$$
$$6 - 3x = 4 + 12x$$
$$-15x = -2$$
$$x = \dfrac{2}{15}$$

29. Solving the equation:

$$6 - \dfrac{4}{3}a = -2$$
$$3\left(6 - \dfrac{4}{3}a\right) = 3(-2)$$
$$18 - 4a = -6$$
$$-4a = -24$$
$$a = 6$$

30. Solving the equation:

$$300x = 100x + 50$$
$$200x = 50$$
$$x = \dfrac{50}{200}$$
$$x = \dfrac{1}{4}$$

31. Solving the equation:

$$|x| + 3 = 5$$
$$|x| = 2$$
$$x = -2, 2$$

32. Solving the equation:

$$|5y+3| = 18$$
$$5y + 3 = -18, 18$$
$$5y = -21, 15$$
$$y = -\dfrac{21}{5}, 3$$

33. Solving for t:

$$1{,}550 = 50 + 50(0.3)t$$
$$1{,}550 = 50 + 15t$$
$$1{,}500 = 15t$$
$$t = 100$$

34. Solving for n:

$$15 = 3 + (n-1)(6)$$
$$15 = 3 + 6n - 6$$
$$15 = 6n - 3$$
$$6n = 18$$
$$n = 3$$

35. Solving for m:

$$y = mx + b$$
$$mx = y - b$$
$$m = \frac{y-b}{x}$$

36. Solving for r:

$$S = \frac{a}{1-r}$$
$$S - Sr = a$$
$$-Sr = a - S$$
$$Sr = S - a$$
$$r = \frac{S-a}{S}$$

37. Solving for F:

$$C = \frac{5}{9}(F-32)$$
$$9C = 5F - 160$$
$$5F = 9C + 160$$
$$F = \frac{9}{5}C + 32$$

38. Solving for x:

$$ax - 2 = bx + 3$$
$$ax - bx = 5$$
$$x(a-b) = 5$$
$$x = \frac{5}{a-b}$$

39. Let x and $4x + 5$ represent the two angles. Since they are complementary, the equation is:

$$x + 4x + 5 = 90$$
$$5x + 5 = 90$$
$$5x = 85$$
$$x = 17$$
$$4x + 5 = 73$$

The angles are 17° and 73°.

40. Let w represent the width and $3w$ represent the length. Using the perimeter formula:

$$2(w) + 2(3w) = 64$$
$$2w + 6w = 64$$
$$8w = 64$$
$$w = 8$$
$$3w = 24$$

The width is 8 feet and the length is 24 feet.

41. Solving the inequality:

$$500 + 200x > 300$$
$$200x > -200$$
$$x > -1$$

The solution set is $(-1, \infty)$.

42. Solving the inequality:

$$-\frac{1}{8} \le \frac{1}{16}x \le \frac{1}{4}$$
$$-2 \le x \le 4$$

The solution set is $[-2, 4]$.

43. Solving the inequality:

$$|3x-1| > 7$$

$3x - 1 < -7$	or	$3x - 1 > 7$
$3x < -6$		$3x > 8$
$x < -2$		$x > \dfrac{8}{3}$

The solution set is $(-\infty, -2) \cup \left(\dfrac{8}{3}, \infty\right)$:

44. Solving the inequality:

$$|4t-3| + 2 < 4$$
$$|4t-3| < 2$$
$$-2 < 4t - 3 < 2$$
$$1 < 4t < 5$$
$$\frac{1}{4} < t < \frac{5}{4}$$

The solution set is $\left(\dfrac{1}{4}, \dfrac{5}{4}\right)$:

45. Finding the difference: $6.7 - 3.9 = 2.8$ hours per day **46.** Finding the difference: $5.3 - 4.4 = 0.9$ hours per day

Chapter 1 Test

1. Solving the equation:

$$x + 4 = 3$$
$$x = -1$$

2. Solving the equation:

$$5y = -2$$
$$y = -\frac{2}{5}$$

3. Solving the equation:

$$4(3x-1) + 3(x-2) = 7x + 2$$
$$12x - 4 + 3x - 6 = 7x + 2$$
$$15x - 10 = 7x + 2$$
$$8x = 12$$
$$x = \frac{3}{2}$$

4. Solving the equation:

$$-0.07x - 0.02 = 0.05 - 0.03(4x+2)$$
$$-7x - 2 = 5 - 3(4x+2)$$
$$-7x - 2 = 5 - 12x - 6$$
$$-7x - 2 = -12x - 1$$
$$5x = 1$$
$$x = \frac{1}{5}$$

5. Substituting $x = 0$:

$$8(0) + 4y = 16$$
$$0 + 4y = 16$$
$$4y = 16$$
$$y = 4$$

6. Substituting $x = 2$:

$$8(2) + 4y = 16$$
$$16 + 4y = 16$$
$$4y = 0$$
$$y = 0$$

7. Substituting $y = 0$:

$$-3x + 9(0) = 21$$
$$-3x + 0 = 21$$
$$-3x = 21$$
$$x = -7$$

8. Substituting $y = 3$:

$$-3x + 9(3) = 21$$
$$-3x + 27 = 21$$
$$-3x = -6$$
$$x = 2$$

9. Solving for m:

$$y = mx + b$$
$$mx = y - b$$
$$m = \frac{y - b}{x}$$

10. Solving for F:

$$C = \frac{5}{9}(F - 32)$$
$$9C = 5F - 160$$
$$5F = 9C + 160$$
$$F = \frac{9}{5}C + 32$$

11. Solving for y:

$$7x - y = 2$$
$$-y = -7x + 2$$
$$y = 7x - 2$$

12. Solving for y:

$$4x - 5y = 10$$
$$-5y = -4x + 10$$
$$y = \frac{4}{5}x - 2$$

13. Solving for y:

$$y + 9 = \frac{1}{5}(x + 10)$$
$$y + 9 = \frac{1}{5}x + 2$$
$$y = \frac{1}{5}x - 7$$

14. Solving for y:

$$y - 7 = \frac{4}{3}(9x - 6)$$
$$y - 7 = 12x - 8$$
$$y = 12x - 1$$

15. Let x represent the width and $3x$ represent the length. Using the perimeter formula:

$$2(x)+2(3x)=72$$
$$2x+6x=72$$
$$8x=72$$
$$x=9$$
$$3x=27$$

The width is 9 in. and the length of 27 in.

16. Adding up the sides of the triangle:

$$x+4x+(x+3)=15$$
$$6x+3=15$$
$$6x=12$$
$$x=2 \text{ meters}$$

17. Let x and $3x+12$ represent the two angles. Since they are supplementary:

$$x+3x+12=180$$
$$4x+12=180$$
$$4x=168$$
$$x=42$$
$$3x+12=138$$

The angles are 42° and 138°.

18. Since the angles are complementary:

$$6x+9x=90$$
$$15x=90$$
$$x=6$$
$$6x=36$$
$$9x=54$$

The angles are 36° and 54°.

19. The amount collected for the day is $928.30 – $55 = $873.30. Since this amount includes the sales s plus the tax, the equation is:

$$s+0.065s=873.30$$
$$1.065s=873.30$$
$$s=820$$

The portion that is sales tax is: $0.065(820)=\$53.30$. The sales tax collected is $53.30.

20. Completing the table:

	Dollars Invested at 13%	Dollars Invested at 15%
Dollars	x	$x+1,000$
Interest	$0.13(x)$	$0.15(x+1,000)$

The equation is:

$$0.13(x)+0.15(x+1,000)=990$$
$$0.13x+0.15x+150=990$$
$$0.28x+150=990$$
$$0.28x=840$$
$$x=3,000$$
$$x+1,000=4,000$$

I have $3,000 invested at 13% and $4,000 invested at 15%.

21. Solving the inequality:

$$-4t \le 16$$
$$t \ge -4$$

The solution set is $[-4, \infty)$:

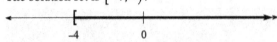

22. Solving the inequality:

$$-7 - \frac{3}{4}x \le 2$$
$$-\frac{3}{4}x \le 9$$
$$-3x \le 36$$
$$x \ge -12$$

The solution set is $[-12, \infty)$:

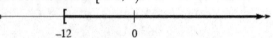

23. Solving the inequality:

$$1.2x + 1.5 < 0.6x + 3.9$$
$$0.6x + 1.5 < 3.9$$
$$0.6x < 2.4$$
$$x < 4$$

The solution set is $(-\infty, 4)$:

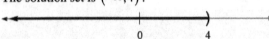

24. Solving the inequality:

$$2(3y - 2) > 5(y + 3)$$
$$6y - 4 > 5y + 15$$
$$y - 4 > 15$$
$$y > 19$$

The solution set is $(19, \infty)$. Graphing the solution set:

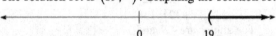

25. Solving the equation:

$$\left|\frac{1}{6}x - 2\right| = \frac{1}{3}$$
$$\frac{1}{6}x - 2 = -\frac{1}{3}, \frac{1}{3}$$
$$\frac{1}{6}x = \frac{5}{3}, \frac{7}{3}$$
$$x = 10, 14$$

26. Solving the equation:

$$\left|\frac{4}{7}a + 8\right| = 4$$
$$\frac{4}{7}a + 8 = -4, 4$$
$$\frac{4}{7}a = -12, -4$$
$$4a = -84, -28$$
$$a = -21, -7$$

27. Solving the equation:

$$|3y + 9| - 2 = 7$$
$$|3y + 9| = 9$$
$$3y + 9 = -9, 9$$
$$3y = -18, 0$$
$$y = -6, 0$$

28. Solving the equation:

$$\left|\frac{3}{4} - \frac{1}{17}x\right| + 4 = 3$$
$$\left|\frac{3}{4} - \frac{1}{17}x\right| = -1$$

Since this statement is false, there is no solution, or $\varnothing$.

29. Solving the inequality:

$$|4y+7|<3$$
$$-3<4y+7<3$$
$$-10<4y<-4$$
$$-\frac{5}{2}<y<-1$$

The solution set is $\left(-\frac{5}{2},-1\right)$:

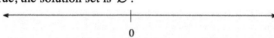

-5/2   -1

30. Solving the inequality:

$$|8x+4|-3\geq 9$$
$$|8x+4|\geq 12$$

$8x+4\leq -12$	or	$8x+4\geq 12$
$8x\leq -16$		$8x\geq 8$
$x\leq -2$		$x\geq 1$

The solution set is $(-\infty,-2]\cup[1,\infty)$:

-2   1

31. Since the inequality $|11x-8|\geq -6$ is always true, the solution set is all real numbers, or $(-\infty,\infty)$:

0

32. Since $|2-9t|<-7$ is never true, the solution set is $\varnothing$:

0

Chapter 2
Graphs of Equations, Inequalities, and Functions

2.1 Graphs of Equations

1. Plotting the points:

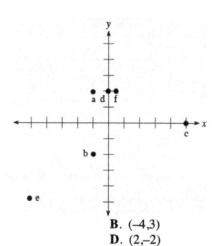

3. **A.** (4,1)   **B.** (–4,3)
    C. (–2,–5)   **D.** (2,–2)
    E. (0,5)   **F.** (–4,0)
    G. (1,0)

5. The correct chart is b.

7. Since the slope is $\dfrac{2}{3}$ and the y-intercept is –2, this is the graph of equation b.

9. The blue graph is shifted up 3, so its equation is $y = x + 3$.

11. The blue graph is shifted down 3, so its equation is $y = |x| - 3$.

13. Sketching the graphs:

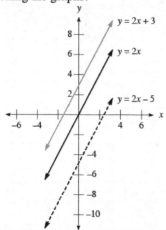

15. Sketching the graphs:

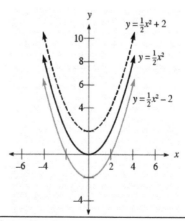

17. Graphing the line:

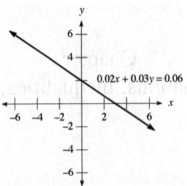

$$0.02x + 0.03y = 0.06$$

19. a. Graphing the line:

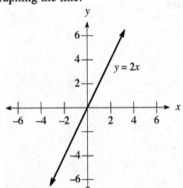

$$y = 2x$$

b. Graphing the line:

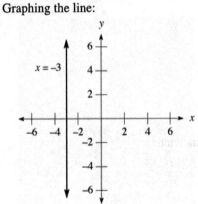

$$x = -3$$

c. Graphing the line:

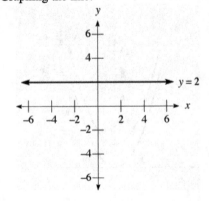

$$y = 2$$

21. a. Graphing the line:

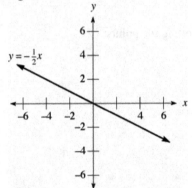

$$y = -\frac{1}{2}x$$

b. Graphing the line:

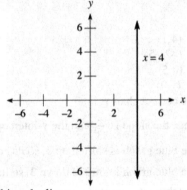

$$x = 4$$

c. Graphing the line:

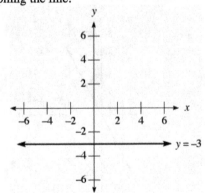

$$y = -3$$

23. The *x*-intercepts are (±3,0) and the *y*-intercept is (0,–9):

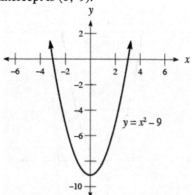

$y = x^2 - 9$

25. The *x*-intercept is (2,0) and the *y*-intercept is (0,–4):

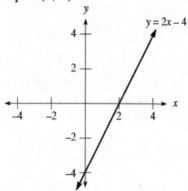

$y = 2x - 4$

27. The *x*-intercept is (–2,0) and the *y*-intercept is (0,1):

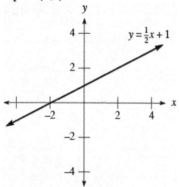

$y = \frac{1}{2}x + 1$

29. The *x*-intercept is (0,0) and the *y*-intercept is (0,0):

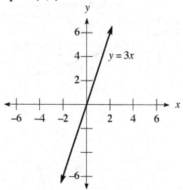

$y = 3x$

31. The x-intercepts are $(0,0)$ and $(1,0)$ and the y-intercept is $(0,0)$:

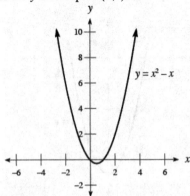

$y = x^2 - x$

33. The x-intercept is $(3,0)$ and the y-intercept is $(0,-3)$:

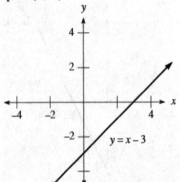

$y = x - 3$

35. **a.** Solving the equation:
$$4x + 12 = -16$$
$$4x = -28$$
$$x = -7$$

c. Substituting $x = 0$:
$$4(0) + 12y = -16$$
$$12y = -16$$
$$y = -\frac{4}{3}$$

d. Graphing the line:

b. Substituting $y = 0$:
$$4x + 12(0) = -16$$
$$4x = -16$$
$$x = -4$$

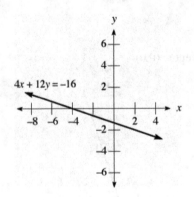

$4x + 12y = -16$

e. Solving for y:
$$4x + 12y = -16$$
$$12y = -4x - 16$$
$$y = -\frac{1}{3}x - \frac{4}{3}$$

37. **a.** Yes, the graph contains the point (2002, 5.75).
    b. No, the graph does not contain the point (2005, 5.5).
    c. Yes, the graph contains the point (2007, 6.75).

39. Constructing a line graph:

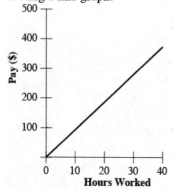

41. Constructing a bar chart:

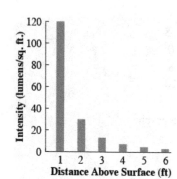

43. Constructing a line graph:

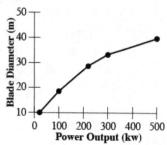

45. **a.** At 6:30 there are 60 people in line.   **b.** At 6:45 there are 70 people in line.
    c. At 7:30 there are 10 people in line.   **d.** There are 60 people in line at 6:30 and at 7:00.
    e. There is no one left in line about 20 minutes after the show starts.

47. Completing the table:

x	y
0	0
10	75
20	150

49. Completing the table:

x	y
0	0
$\frac{1}{2}$	3.75
1	7.5

1. Completing the table:

x	y
−2	−8
0	0
2	8
5	20

Sketching the graph:

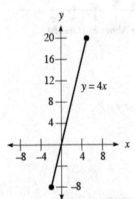

3. Completing the table:

x	y
0	100
5	80
10	60
15	40
20	20
25	0

Sketching the graph:

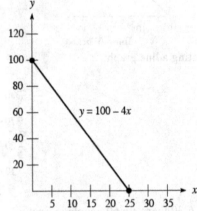

5. Completing the table:

x	y
0	1600
40	1200
80	800
120	400
160	0

Sketching the graph:

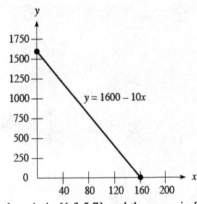

7. Completing the table:

x	y
0	40.0
25	102.5
50	165.0
75	227.5
100	290.0

Sketching the graph:

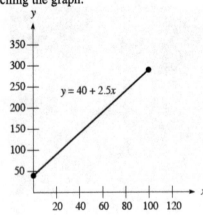

9. The domain is {1,3,5,7} and the range is {2,4,6,8}. This is a function.

11. The domain is {0,1,2,3} and the range is {4,5,6}. This is a function.

13. The domain is {a,b,c,d} and the range is {3,4,5}. This is a function.

15. The domain is {a} and the range is {1,2,3,4}. This is not a function.

17. The domain is {AAPL, DELL, MSFT, FB, GRPN} and the range is {$12, $29, $32, $562}.

19. The domain is {Atlanta, Chicago, Boston, Houston} and the range is {Braves, White Sox, Cubs, Red Sox, Astros}.

21. Yes, since it passes the vertical line test. **23.** No, since it fails the vertical line test.

25. No, since it fails the vertical line test. **27.** Yes, since it passes the vertical line test.

29. Yes, since it passes the vertical line test. **31.** Yes, since it passes the vertical line test.

33. The domain is $\{x \mid -5 \le x \le 5\} = [-5, 5]$ and the range is $\{y \mid 0 \le y \le 5\} = [0, 5]$.

35. The domain is $\{x \mid -5 \le x \le 3\} = [-5, 3]$ and the range is $\{y \mid y = 3\} = [3, 3]$.

37. The domain is all real numbers and the range is $\{y \mid y \ge -1\}$. This is a function.

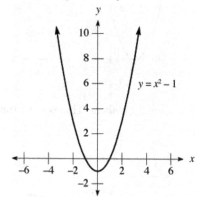

39. The domain is all real numbers and the range is $\{y \mid y \ge 4\}$. This is a function.

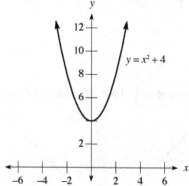

41. The domain is $\{x \mid x \ge -1\}$ and the range is all real numbers. This is not a function.

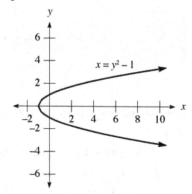

43. The domain is all real numbers and the range is $\{y \mid y \geq 0\}$. This is a function.

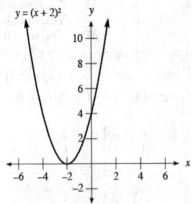

45. The domain is $\{x \mid x \geq 0\}$ and the range is all real numbers. This is not a function.

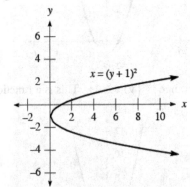

47. The domain is all real numbers and the range is $\{y \mid y \geq 2\}$. This is a function.

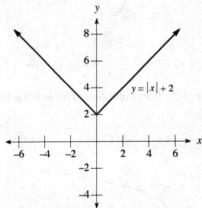

49. The domain is {2001,2003,2005,2007,2009} and the range is {5,10,40,80,160}.

51. **a.** The equation is $y = 8.5x$ for $10 \leq x \leq 40$.

b. Completing the table:

Hours Worked	Function Rule	Gross Pay ($)
x	$y = 8.5x$	y
10	$y = 8.5(10) = 85$	85
20	$y = 8.5(20) = 170$	170
30	$y = 8.5(30) = 255$	255
40	$y = 8.5(40) = 340$	340

c. Constructing a line graph:

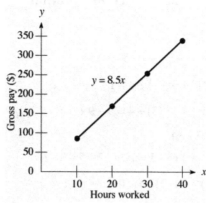

d. The domain is $\{x \mid 10 \le x \le 40\}$ and the range is $\{y \mid 85 \le y \le 340\}$.

e. The minimum is $85 and the maximum is $340.

53. **a.** The domain is {2008,2009,2010,2011,2012} and the range is {5.8,5.2-5.5,7.5,9.7,12.1}.
   b. The demand increased more in 2012.
   c. The demand decreased in 2009.

55. **a.** Figure III   **b.** Figure I
   c. Figure II   **d.** Figure IV

57. **a.** Substituting $t = 10$: $s = \dfrac{60}{10} = 6$ **b.** Substituting $t = 8$: $s = \dfrac{60}{8} = 7.5$

59. **a.** Substituting $x = 5$: $(5)^2 + 2 = 25 + 2 = 27$ **b.** Substituting $x = -2$: $(-2)^2 + 2 = 4 + 2 = 6$

61. Substituting $x = 2$: $y = (2)^2 - 3 = 4 - 3 = 1$ **63.** Substituting $x = 0$: $y = (0)^2 - 3 = 0 - 3 = -3$

65. Solving for x when $y = -3$:

$$x^2 - 3 = -3$$
$$x^2 = 0$$
$$x = 0$$

67. Solving for y:

$$\frac{8}{5} - 2y = 4$$
$$-2y = \frac{12}{5}$$
$$y = -\frac{6}{5}$$

69. Substituting $x = 0$ and $y = 0$:

$$0 = a(0 - 8)^2 + 70$$
$$0 = 64a + 70$$
$$64a = -70$$
$$a = -\frac{70}{64} = -\frac{35}{32}$$

2.3 Function Notation

1. Evaluating the function: $f(2) = 2(2) - 5 = 4 - 5 = -1$

3. Evaluating the function: $f(-3) = 2(-3) - 5 = -6 - 5 = -11$

5. Evaluating the function: $g(-1) = (-1)^2 + 3(-1) + 4 = 1 - 3 + 4 = 2$

7. Evaluating the function: $g(-3) = (-3)^2 + 3(-3) + 4 = 9 - 9 + 4 = 4$

9. Evaluating the function: $g(a) = a^2 + 3a + 4$

11. Evaluating the function: $f(a+6) = 2(x+6) - 5 = 2a + 12 - 5 = 2a + 7$

13. Evaluating the function: $f(0) = 3(0)^2 - 4(0) + 1 = 0 - 0 + 1 = 1$

15. Evaluating the function: $g(-4) = 2(-4) - 1 = -8 - 1 = -9$

17. Evaluating the function: $f(-1) = 3(-1)^2 - 4(-1) + 1 = 3 + 4 + 1 = 8$

19. Evaluating the function: $g\left(\dfrac{1}{2}\right) = 2\left(\dfrac{1}{2}\right) - 1 = 1 - 1 = 0$

21. Evaluating the function: $f(a) = 3a^2 - 4a + 1$

23. Evaluating the function: $f(a+2) = 3(a+2)^2 - 4(a+2) + 1 = 3a^2 + 12a + 12 - 4a - 8 + 1 = 3a^2 + 8a + 5$

25. $f(1) = 4$ 27. $g\left(\dfrac{1}{2}\right) = 0$

29. $g(-2) = 2$

31. Evaluating the function: $f[g(1)] = f(1) = 4$ 33. The value is $x = \dfrac{1}{2}$, since $g\left(\dfrac{1}{2}\right) = 0 = f(\pi)$.

35. Evaluating the function: $f(-4) = (-4)^2 - 2(-4) = 16 + 8 = 24$

37. First evaluate each function:
$$f(-2) = (-2)^2 - 2(-2) = 4 + 4 = 8 \qquad g(-1) = 5(-1) - 4 = -5 - 4 = -9$$
Now evaluating: $f(-2) + g(-1) = 8 - 9 = -1$

39. Evaluating the function: $2f(x) - 3g(x) = 2(x^2 - 2x) - 3(5x - 4) = 2x^2 - 4x - 15x + 12 = 2x^2 - 19x + 12$

41. Evaluating the function: $f[g(3)] = f[5(3) - 4] = f(11) = (11)^2 - 2(11) = 121 - 22 = 99$

43. First evaluate each function:
$$f[g(2)] = f[5(2) - 4] = f(6) = (6)^2 - 2(6) = 36 - 12 = 24$$
$$g[f(2)] = g[2^2 - 2(2)] = g(-4) = 5(-4) - 4 = -20 - 4 = -24$$
Now evaluating: $f[g(2)] - g[f(2)] = 24 - (-24) = 24 + 24 = 48$

45. Evaluating the function: $[f(-3)]^2 = [(-3)^2 - 2(-3)]^2 = (9 + 6)^2 = 15^2 = 225$

47. Evaluating the function: $f\left(\dfrac{1}{3}\right) = \dfrac{1}{\dfrac{1}{3} + 3} \cdot \dfrac{3}{3} = \dfrac{3}{1 + 9} = \dfrac{3}{10}$

49. Evaluating the function: $f\left(-\dfrac{1}{2}\right) = \dfrac{1}{-\dfrac{1}{2} + 3} \cdot \dfrac{2}{2} = \dfrac{2}{-1 + 6} = \dfrac{2}{5}$

51. Evaluating the function: $f(-1) = \dfrac{1}{-3+3} = \dfrac{1}{0}$, which is undefined

53. Evaluating the function: $g(-2) = \dfrac{1}{-2} + 1 = -\dfrac{1}{2} + 1 = \dfrac{1}{2}$

55.

    a. Evaluating the function: $f(a) - 3 = \left(a^2 - 4\right) - 3 = a^2 - 7$

    b. Evaluating the function: $f(a-3) = (a-3)^2 - 4 = a^2 - 6a + 9 - 4 = a^2 - 6a + 5$

    c. Evaluating the function: $f(x) + 2 = \left(x^2 - 4\right) + 2 = x^2 - 2$

    d. Evaluating the function: $f(x+2) = (x+2)^2 - 4 = x^2 + 4x + 4 - 4 = x^2 + 4x$

    e. Evaluating the function: $f(a+b) = (a+b)^2 - 4 = a^2 + 2ab + b^2 - 4$

    f. Evaluating the function: $f(x+h) = (x+h)^2 - 4 = x^2 + 2xh + h^2 - 4$

57. Graphing the function:

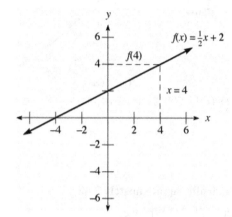

59. Finding where $f(x) = x$:

$$\dfrac{1}{2}x + 2 = x$$
$$2 = \dfrac{1}{2}x$$
$$x = 4$$

61. Graphing the function:

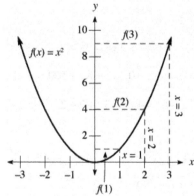

63. Evaluating: $V(3) = 150 \cdot 2^{3/3} = 150 \cdot 2 = 300$; The painting is worth \$300 in 3 years.

    Evaluating: $V(6) = 150 \cdot 2^{6/3} = 150 \cdot 4 = 600$; The painting is worth \$600 in 6 years.

65. **a.** This statement is true. **b.** This statement is false.
   c. This statement is true. **d.** This statement is false.
   e. This statement is true.

67. **a.** Evaluating: $V(3.75) = -3300(3.75) + 18000 = \$5,625$

   b. Evaluating: $V(5) = -3300(5) + 18000 = \$1,500$

   c. The domain of this function is $\{t \mid 0 \le t \le 5\}$.

   d. Sketching the graph:

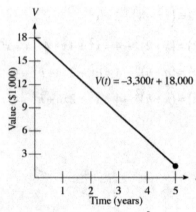

   e. The range of this function is $\{V(t) \mid 1,500 \le V(t) \le 18,000\}$.

   f. Solving $V(t) = 10000$:
$$-3300t + 18000 = 10000$$
$$-3300t = -8000$$
$$t \approx 2.42$$
   The copier will be worth \$10,000 after approximately 2.42 years.

69. **a.** Completing the table:

d (feet)	$f(d)$ (kWh/year)
0	0
5	332
10	1,328
15	2,988
20	5,312

   b. The range is $0 \le f(d) \le 5,312$.

71. Multiplying: $x(35 - 0.1x) = 35x - 0.1x^2$

73. Multiplying: $(4x - 3)(x - 1) = 4x^2 - 3x - 4x + 3 = 4x^2 - 7x + 3$

75. Simplifying: $(35x - 0.1x^2) - (8x + 500) = 35x - 0.1x^2 - 8x - 500 = -0.1x^2 + 27x - 500$

77. Simplifying: $(4x^2 + 3x + 2) - (2x^2 - 5x - 6) = 4x^2 + 3x + 2 - 2x^2 + 5x + 6 = 2x^2 + 8x + 8$

79. Simplifying: $4(2)^2 - 3(2) = 16 - 6 = 10$

81. Simplifying: $2(x - 3)^2 - 5(x - 3) = 2x^2 - 12x + 18 - 5x + 15 = 2x^2 - 17x + 33$

83. Simplifying: $-8(-3x + 1) + 2 = 24x - 8 + 2 = 24x - 6$

2.4 Algebra and Composition with Functions

1. Writing the formula: $(f+g)(x) = f(x) + g(x) = (4x-3) + (2x+5) = 6x+2$

3. Writing the formula: $(g-f)(x) = g(x) - f(x) = (2x+5) - (4x-3) = -2x+8$

5. Writing the formula: $(f \cdot g)(x) = f(x) \cdot g(x) = (4x-3)(2x+5) = 8x^2 + 14x - 15$

7. Writing the formula: $\left(\dfrac{g}{f}\right)(x) = \dfrac{g(x)}{f(x)} = \dfrac{2x+5}{4x-3}$

9. Writing the formula: $(f+g)(x) = f(x) + g(x) = (3x-5) + \left(\dfrac{5}{x}\right) = 3x - 5 + \dfrac{5}{x}$

11. Writing the formula: $(g-f)(x) = g(x) - f(x) = \left(\dfrac{5}{x}\right) - (3x-5) = \dfrac{5}{x} - 3x + 5$

13. Writing the formula: $(f \cdot g)(x) = f(x) \cdot g(x) = (3x-5)\left(\dfrac{5}{x}\right) = 15 - \dfrac{25}{x}$

15. Writing the formula: $\left(\dfrac{g}{f}\right)(x) = \dfrac{g(x)}{f(x)} = \dfrac{5/x}{3x-5} \cdot \dfrac{x}{x} = \dfrac{5}{3x^2 - 5x}$

17. Writing the formula: $(g+f)(x) = g(x) + f(x) = (x-2) + (3x-5) = 4x-7$

19. Writing the formula: $(g+h)(x) = g(x) + h(x) = (x-2) + \left(3x^2 - 11x + 10\right) = 3x^2 - 10x + 8$

21. Writing the formula: $(g-f)(x) = g(x) - f(x) = (x-2) - (3x-5) = -2x+3$

23. Writing the formula: $(f \cdot g)(x) = f(x) \cdot g(x) = (3x-5)(x-2) = 3x^2 - 11x + 10$

25. Writing the formula:
$$(f \cdot h)(x) = f(x) \cdot h(x)$$
$$= (3x-5)\left(3x^2 - 11x + 10\right)$$
$$= 9x^3 - 33x^2 + 30x - 15x^2 + 55x - 50$$
$$= 9x^3 - 48x^2 + 85x - 50$$

27. Writing the formula: $\left(\dfrac{h}{f}\right)(x) = \dfrac{h(x)}{f(x)} = \dfrac{3x^2 - 11x + 10}{3x-5} = \dfrac{(3x-5)(x-2)}{3x-5} = x-2$

29. Writing the formula: $\left(\dfrac{f}{h}\right)(x) = \dfrac{f(x)}{h(x)} = \dfrac{3x-5}{3x^2 - 11x + 10} = \dfrac{3x-5}{(3x-5)(x-2)} = \dfrac{1}{x-2}$

31. Writing the formula: $(f+g+h)(x) = f(x) + g(x) + h(x) = (3x-5) + (x-2) + \left(3x^2 - 11x + 10\right) = 3x^2 - 7x + 3$

33. Writing the formula:
$$(h + f \cdot g)(x) = h(x) + f(x) \cdot g(x)$$
$$= \left(3x^2 - 11x + 10\right) + (3x-5)(x-2)$$
$$= 3x^2 - 11x + 10 + 3x^2 - 11x + 10$$
$$= 6x^2 - 22x + 20$$
The domain is all real numbers, or $(-\infty, \infty)$.

35. Writing the formula: $\left(\dfrac{f+g}{h}\right)(x) = \dfrac{f(x) + g(x)}{h(x)} = \dfrac{3x-5+x-2}{3x^2 - 11x + 10} = \dfrac{4x-7}{3x^2 - 11x + 10} = \dfrac{4x-7}{(3x-5)(x-2)}$

The domain is all real numbers $x \neq \dfrac{5}{3}, 2$, or $\left(-\infty, \dfrac{5}{3}\right) \cup \left(\dfrac{5}{3}, 2\right) \cup (2, \infty)$.

37. Writing the formula: $\left(f^2\right)(x)=f(x)\cdot f(x)=(3x-5)(3x-5)=9x^2-30x+25$

The domain is all real numbers, or $(-\infty,\infty)$.

39. Writing the formula:
$$\begin{aligned}\left(f^2-g^2\right)(x)&=f(x)\cdot f(x)-g(x)\cdot g(x)\\&=(3x-5)(3x-5)-(x-2)(x-2)\\&=\left(9x^2-30x+25\right)-\left(x^2-4x+4\right)\\&=9x^2-30x+25-x^2+4x-4\\&=8x^2-26x+21\end{aligned}$$

The domain is all real numbers, or $(-\infty,\infty)$.

41. Evaluating: $(f+g)(2)=f(2)+g(2)=(2\cdot 2+1)+(4\cdot 2+2)=5+10=15$

43. Evaluating: $(f\cdot g)(3)=f(3)\cdot g(3)=(2\cdot 3+1)(4\cdot 3+2)=7\cdot 14=98$

45. Evaluating: $\left(\dfrac{h}{g}\right)(1)=\dfrac{h(1)}{g(1)}=\dfrac{4(1)^2+4(1)+1}{4(1)+2}=\dfrac{9}{6}=\dfrac{3}{2}$

47. Evaluating: $(f\cdot h)(0)=f(0)\cdot h(0)=(2(0)+1)\left(4(0)^2+4(0)+1\right)=(1)(1)=1$

49. Evaluating: $(f+g+h)(2)=f(2)+g(2)+h(2)=(2(2)+1)+(4(2)+2)+\left(4(2)^2+4(2)+1\right)=5+10+25=40$

51. Evaluating:
$$(h+f\cdot g)(3)=h(3)+f(3)\cdot g(3)=\left(4(3)^2+4(3)+1\right)+(2(3)+1)\cdot(4(3)+2)=49+7\cdot 14=49+98=147$$

53. **a.** Evaluating: $(f\circ g)(5)=f(g(5))=f(5+4)=f(9)=9^2=81$

b. Evaluating: $(g\circ f)(5)=g(f(5))=g\left(5^2\right)=g(25)=25+4=29$

c. Evaluating: $(f\circ g)(x)=f(g(x))=f(x+4)=(x+4)^2$

d. Evaluating: $(g\circ f)(x)=g(f(x))=g\left(x^2\right)=x^2+4$

55. **a.** Evaluating: $(f\circ g)(0)=f(g(0))=f(4\cdot 0-1)=f(-1)=(-1)^2+3(-1)=1-3=-2$

b. Evaluating: $(g\circ f)(0)=g(f(0))=g\left(0^2+3\cdot 0\right)=g(0)=4(0)-1=-1$

c. Evaluating: $(f\circ g)(x)=f(g(x))=f(4x-1)=(4x-1)^2+3(4x-1)=16x^2-8x+1+12x-3=16x^2+4x-2$

d. Evaluating: $(g\circ f)(x)=g(f(x))=g\left(x^2+3x\right)=4\left(x^2+3x\right)-1=4x^2+12x-1$

57. **a.** Evaluating: $(f\circ g)(3)=f(g(3))=f\left(\dfrac{3}{3}\right)=f(1)=(1)^2=1$

b. Evaluating: $(g\circ f)(3)=g(f(3))=g\left(3^2\right)=g(9)=\dfrac{3}{9}=\dfrac{1}{3}$

c. Evaluating: $(f\circ g)(x)=f(g(x))=f\left(\dfrac{3}{x}\right)=\left(\dfrac{3}{x}\right)^2=\dfrac{9}{x^2}$

d. Evaluating: $(g\circ f)(x)=g(f(x))=g\left(x^2\right)=\dfrac{3}{x^2}$

59. Evaluating each composition:

$$(f \circ g)(x) = f(g(x)) = f\left(\frac{x+4}{5}\right) = 5\left(\frac{x+4}{5}\right) - 4 = x + 4 - 4 = x$$

$$(g \circ f)(x) = g(f(x)) = g(5x-4) = \frac{5x-4+4}{5} = \frac{5x}{5} = x$$

Thus $(f \circ g)(x) = (g \circ f)(x) = x$.

61. Evaluating each composition:

$$(f \circ g)(x) = f(g(x)) = f\left(\frac{x}{3}-2\right) = 3\left(\frac{x}{3}-2\right) + 6 = x - 6 + 6 = x$$

$$(g \circ f)(x) = g(f(x)) = g(3x+6) = \frac{3x+6}{3} - 2 = x + 2 - 2 = x$$

Thus $(f \circ g)(x) = (g \circ f)(x) = x$.

63. Setting $f(x) = x$:

$$3x + 2 = x$$
$$2x + 2 = 0$$
$$2x = -2$$
$$x = -1$$

65. Setting $f(x) = x$:

$$7x + 8 = x$$
$$6x + 8 = 0$$
$$6x = -8$$
$$x = -\frac{4}{3}$$

67. Setting $f(x) = x$:

$$-4x + 2 = x$$
$$-5x + 2 = 0$$
$$-5x = -2$$
$$x = \frac{2}{5}$$

69. Setting $f(x) = x$:

$$\frac{1}{2}x - 1 = x$$
$$-\frac{1}{2}x - 1 = 0$$
$$-\frac{1}{2}x = 1$$
$$x = -2$$

71. Setting $f(x) = x$:

$$-\frac{3}{4}x + \frac{1}{2} = x$$
$$-\frac{7}{4}x + \frac{1}{2} = 0$$
$$-\frac{7}{4}x = -\frac{1}{2}$$
$$x = \frac{2}{7}$$

73.
a. Finding the revenue: $R(x) = x(11.5 - 0.05x) = 11.5x - 0.05x^2$

b. Finding the cost: $C(x) = 2x + 200$

c. Finding the profit: $P(x) = R(x) - C(x) = \left(11.5x - 0.05x^2\right) - (2x + 200) = -0.05x^2 + 9.5x - 200$

d. Finding the average cost: $\bar{C}(x) = \dfrac{C(x)}{x} = \dfrac{2x + 200}{x} = 2 + \dfrac{200}{x}$

75.
a. The function is $M(x) = 220 - x$.   **b.** Evaluating: $M(24) = 220 - 24 = 196$ beats per minute

c. The training heart rate function is: $T(M) = 62 + 0.6(M - 62) = 0.6M + 24.8$

Finding the composition: $T(M(x)) = T(220 - x) = 0.6(220 - x) + 24.8 = 156.8 - 0.6x$

Evaluating: $T(M(24)) = 156.8 - 0.6(24) \approx 142$ beats per minute

d. Evaluating: $T(M(36)) = 156.8 - 0.6(36) \approx 135$ beats per minute

e. Evaluating: $T(M(48)) = 156.8 - 0.6(48) \approx 128$ beats per minute

77. **a.** For coal, the function is: $f(x) = 94.80x$ For wind, the function is: $g(x) = 97.00x$

    b. Sketching the graphs:

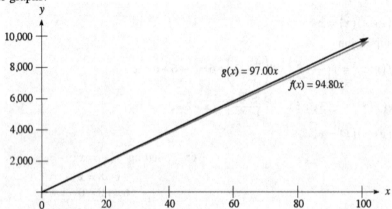

    c. Finding the increase: $h(x) = g(x) - f(x) = 97.00x - 94.80x = 2.20x$

79. **a.** For coal, the function is: $f(x) = 136.20x$ For wind, the function is: $g(x) = 97.00x$

    b. Sketching the graphs:

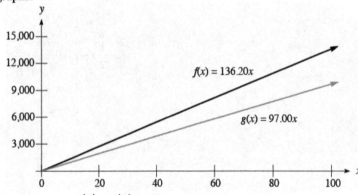

    c. Finding the increase: $h(x) = f(x) - g(x) = 136.20x - 97.00x = 39.20x$

81. Solving the equation:

$$x - 5 = 7$$
$$x = 12$$

83. Solving the equation:

$$5 - \frac{4}{7}a = -11$$
$$7\left(5 - \frac{4}{7}a\right) = 7(-11)$$
$$35 - 4a = -77$$
$$-4a = -112$$
$$a = 28$$

85. Solving the equation:

$$5(x-1) - 2(2x+3) = 5x - 4$$
$$5x - 5 - 4x - 6 = 5x - 4$$
$$x - 11 = 5x - 4$$
$$-4x = 7$$
$$x = -\frac{7}{4}$$

87. Solving for w:

$$P = 2l + 2w$$
$$P - 2l = 2w$$
$$w = \frac{P - 2l}{2}$$

89. Solving the inequality:

$$-5t \le 30$$
$$t \ge -6$$

The solution set is $[-6, \infty)$. Graphing:

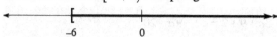

91. Solving the inequality:

$$1.6x - 2 < 0.8x + 2.8$$
$$0.8x - 2 < 2.8$$
$$0.8x < 4.8$$
$$x < 6$$

The solution set is $(-\infty, 6)$. Graphing:

93. Solving the equation:

$$\left| \frac{1}{4}x - 1 \right| = \frac{1}{2}$$
$$\frac{1}{4}x - 1 = -\frac{1}{2}, \frac{1}{2}$$
$$\frac{1}{4}x = \frac{1}{2}, \frac{3}{2}$$
$$x = 2, 6$$

95. Solving the equation:

$$|3 - 2x| + 5 = 2$$
$$|3 - 2x| = -3$$

Since this statement is false, there is no solution, or $\varnothing$.

Landmark Review

1. Sketching the graph:

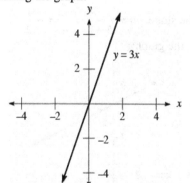

2. Sketching the graph:

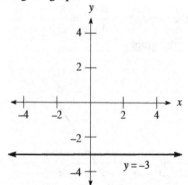

3. Sketching the graph:

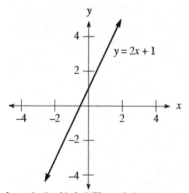

4. Sketching the graph:

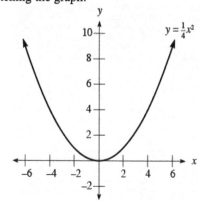

5. The domain is $\{1,3,4,7\}$ and the range is $\{2,3,9\}$. This is a function.

6. The domain is $\{0,1,3\}$ and the range is $\{2,3,4\}$. This is not a function.

7. The domain is $\{a,b,4,5\}$ and the range is $\{0,1,3\}$. This is a function.

8. The domain is {1} and the range is {0,2,3,5}. This is not a function.

9. Evaluating: $f(3) = 3(3) - 4 = 9 - 4 = 5$

10. Evaluating: $g(2) = (2)^2 + 3(2) + 2 = 4 + 6 + 2 = 12$

11. Evaluating: $f(a+1) = 3(a+1) - 4 = 3a + 3 - 4 = 3a - 1$

12. Evaluating: $g(a+3) = (a+3)^2 + 3(a+3) + 2 = a^2 + 6a + 9 + 3a + 9 + 2 = a^2 + 9a + 20$

13. Writing the expression: $(f+g)(x) = f(x) + g(x) = (2x+1) + (3x-5) = 5x - 4$

14. Writing the expression: $(g-f)(x) = g(x) - f(x) = (3x-5) - (2x+1) = 3x - 5 - 2x - 1 = x - 6$

15. Writing the expression: $(fg)(x) = f(x) \cdot g(x) = (2x+1)(3x-5) = 6x^2 - 7x - 5$

16. Writing the expression: $\left(\dfrac{g}{f}\right)(x) = \dfrac{g(x)}{f(x)} = \dfrac{3x-5}{2x+1}$

17. Writing the expression: $(f \circ g)(1) = f(g(1)) = f(3 \cdot 1 - 5) = f(-2) = 2(-2) + 1 = -3$

18. Writing the expression: $(g \circ f)(3) = g(f(3)) = g(2 \cdot 3 + 1) = g(7) = 3(7) - 5 = 16$

2.5 Slope and Average Rate of Change

1. The slope is $\dfrac{3}{2}$.

3. There is no slope (undefined).

5. The slope is $\dfrac{2}{3}$.

7. Finding the slope: $m = \dfrac{4-1}{4-2} = \dfrac{3}{2}$

   Sketching the graph:

   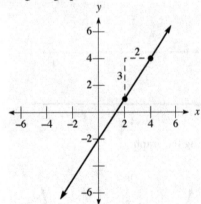

9. Finding the slope: $m = \dfrac{2-4}{5-1} = \dfrac{-2}{4} = -\dfrac{1}{2}$

   Sketching the graph:

   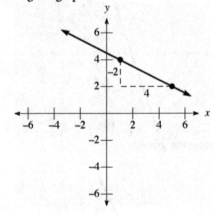

11. Finding the slope: $m = \dfrac{2-(-3)}{4-1} = \dfrac{2+3}{3} = \dfrac{5}{3}$

Sketching the graph:

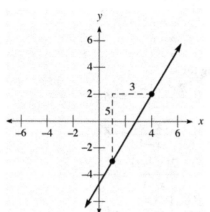

13. Finding the slope: $m = \dfrac{-9-(-4)}{5-2} = \dfrac{-9+4}{3} = -\dfrac{5}{3}$

Sketching the graph:

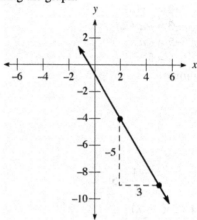

15. Finding the slope: $m = \dfrac{-1-5}{1-(-3)} = \dfrac{-6}{1+3} = \dfrac{-6}{4} = -\dfrac{3}{2}$

Sketching the graph:

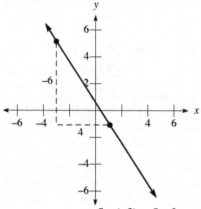

17. Finding the slope: $m = \dfrac{6-6}{2-(-4)} = \dfrac{0}{6} = 0$

Sketching the graph:

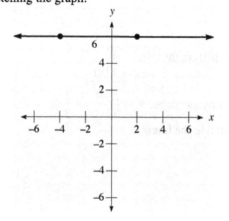

19. Finding the slope: $m = \dfrac{5-(-3)}{a-a} = \dfrac{5+3}{0}$, which is undefined

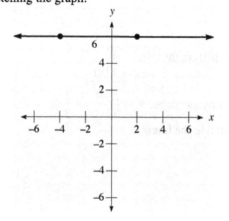

21. Using the slope formula:

$$\frac{3-6}{a-2}=-1$$
$$-3=-1(a-2)$$
$$-3=-a+2$$
$$-5=-a$$
$$a=5$$

23. Using the slope formula:

$$\frac{4b-b}{-1-2}=-2$$
$$3b=-2(-3)$$
$$3b=6$$
$$b=2$$

25. Solving for x:

$$\frac{x^2-4}{x-2}=5$$
$$\frac{(x+2)(x-2)}{x-2}=5$$
$$x+2=5$$
$$x=3$$

27. Solving for x:

$$\frac{2x^2+1-3}{x-1}=-6$$
$$\frac{2x^2-2}{x-1}=-6$$
$$\frac{2(x^2-1)}{x-1}=-6$$
$$\frac{2(x+1)(x-1)}{x-1}=-6$$
$$2x+2=-6$$
$$2x=-8$$
$$x=-4$$

29. Completing the table:

x	y
0	2
3	0

Finding the slope: $m=\dfrac{2-0}{0-3}=-\dfrac{2}{3}$

31. Completing the table:

x	y
0	-5
3	-3

Finding the slope: $m=\dfrac{-5-(-3)}{0-3}=\dfrac{-5+3}{-3}=\dfrac{2}{3}$

33. Graphing the line:

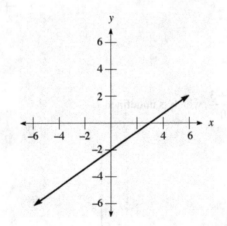

The slope is $m=\dfrac{2}{3}$.

35. Finding the slope of this line: $m=\dfrac{1-3}{-8-2}=\dfrac{-2}{-10}=\dfrac{1}{5}$. Since the parallel slope is the same, its slope is $\dfrac{1}{5}$.

37. Finding the slope of this line: $m=\dfrac{2-(-6)}{5-5}=\dfrac{8}{0}$, which is undefined

Since the perpendicular slope is a horizontal line, its slope is 0.

39. Finding the slope of this line: $m=\dfrac{-5-1}{4-(-2)}=\dfrac{-6}{6}=-1$. Since the parallel slope is the same, its slope is -1.

41. Finding the slope of this line: $m = \dfrac{-3-(-5)}{1-(-2)} = \dfrac{2}{3}$

Since the perpendicular slope is the negative reciprocal, its slope is $-\dfrac{3}{2}$.

43. **a.** Since the slopes between each successive pairs of points is 2, this could represent ordered pairs from a line.
    b. Since the slopes between each successive pairs of points is not the same, this could not represent ordered pairs from a line.

45. Finding the slope: $m = \dfrac{105-0}{6-0} = 17.5$ miles/hour

47. Finding the slope: $m = \dfrac{3600-0}{30-0} = 120$ feet/second

49. Finding the average rate of change: $\dfrac{f(4)-f(1)}{4-1} = \dfrac{\left(4^2+5\cdot 4\right)-\left(1^2+5\cdot 1\right)}{3} = \dfrac{36-6}{3} = \dfrac{30}{3} = 10$

51. Finding the average rate of change: $\dfrac{f(-1)-f(-3)}{-1-(-3)} = \dfrac{(5(-1)+6)-(5(-3)+6)}{2} = \dfrac{1-(-9)}{2} = \dfrac{10}{2} = 5$

53. Finding the average rate of change: $\dfrac{f(3)-f(-2)}{3-(-2)} = \dfrac{\left(3^2-3\cdot 3\right)-\left((-2)^2-3(-2)\right)}{5} = \dfrac{0-10}{5} = \dfrac{-10}{5} = -2$

55. Finding the average rate of change: $\dfrac{f(5)-f(1)}{5-1} = \dfrac{\left(2\cdot 5^2+3\right)-\left(2\cdot 1^2+3\right)}{4} = \dfrac{53-5}{4} = \dfrac{48}{4} = 12$

57. **a.** It takes 10 minutes for all the ice to melt.   **b.** It takes 20 minutes before the water boils.
    c. The slope of A is 20°C per minute.   **d.** The slope of C is 10°C per minute.
    e. It is changing faster during the first minute, since its slope is greater.

59. Computing the slope: $m = \dfrac{400-1}{2010-2004} = \dfrac{399}{6} = 66.5$

Between 2004 and 2010, the number of active Facebook users increased an average of 66.5 million users per year.

61. **a.** Computing the slope: $m = \dfrac{73-70}{2009-1999} = \dfrac{3}{10} = 0.3$

    The attendance for Major League Baseball increased by 0.3 million = 300,000 people per year from 1999 to 2009.

    b. Computing the slope: $m = \dfrac{73-80}{2009-2007} = \dfrac{-7}{2} = -3.5$

    The attendance for Major League Baseball decreased by 3.5 million people per year from 2007 to 2009.

63. **a.** Computing the slope: $m = \dfrac{100-25}{17-10} = \dfrac{75}{7} \approx 10.7$ kw/m

    b. Computing the slope: $m = \dfrac{225-100}{27-17} = \dfrac{125}{10} = 12.5$ kw/m

    c. Computing the slope: $m = \dfrac{300-225}{33-27} = \dfrac{75}{6} = 12.5$ kw/m

    d. Computing the slope: $m = \dfrac{500-300}{40-33} = \dfrac{200}{7} \approx 28.6$ kw/m

    e. Since the slopes increase, it is advantageous to build longer wind turbines.

65. **a.** Computing the slope: $m = \dfrac{7.5 - 5.35}{2010 - 2009} = \dfrac{2.15}{1} = 2.15$ GW/year

b. Computing the slope: $m = \dfrac{9.7 - 7.5}{2011 - 2010} = \dfrac{2.2}{1} = 2.20$ GW/year

c. Computing the slope: $m = \dfrac{12.1 - 9.7}{2012 - 2011} = \dfrac{2.4}{1} = 2.40$ GW/year

d. Since the slopes are relatively the same, global solar energy demand is increasing at a steady rate.

67. Simplifying: $\dfrac{3 - (-1)}{-3 - 3} = \dfrac{4}{-6} = -\dfrac{2}{3}$

69. Simplifying: $3\left(-\dfrac{2}{3}x + 1\right) = 3\left(-\dfrac{2}{3}x\right) + 3(1) = -2x + 3$

71. Solving for y:

$$2x + 3y = 6$$
$$3y = -2x + 6$$
$$y = \dfrac{-2x + 6}{3} = -\dfrac{2}{3}x + 2$$

73. Solving for y:

$$y + 1 = -\dfrac{2}{3}(x - 3)$$
$$y + 1 = -\dfrac{2}{3}x + 2$$
$$y = -\dfrac{2}{3}x + 1$$

75. Solving for y: $y = -\dfrac{4}{3}(3) + 5 = -4 + 5 = 1$

2.6 Linear Functions

1. Using the slope-intercept formula: $f(x) = -4x - 3$

3. Using the slope-intercept formula: $f(x) = -\dfrac{2}{3}x$

5. Using the slope-intercept formula: $f(x) = -\dfrac{2}{3}x + \dfrac{1}{4}$

7. **a.** The parallel slope will be the same, which is 3.

b. The perpendicular slope will be the negative reciprocal, which is $-\dfrac{1}{3}$.

9. **a.** First solve for y to find the slope:
$$3y + y = -2$$
$$y = -3x - 2$$
The parallel slope will be the same, which is –3.

b. The perpendicular slope will be the negative reciprocal, which is $\dfrac{1}{3}$.

11. **a.** First solve for y to find the slope:
$$2x + 5y = -11$$
$$5y = -2x - 11$$
$$y = -\dfrac{2}{5}x - \dfrac{11}{5}$$
The parallel slope will be the same, which is $-\dfrac{2}{5}$.

b. The perpendicular slope will be the negative reciprocal, which is $\dfrac{5}{2}$.

13. **a.** Since this equation is equivalent to $y = 3$, the slope is 0.

b. The perpendicular line is vertical, so its slope is undefined.

15. The slope is 3, the y-intercept is -2, and the perpendicular slope is $-\dfrac{1}{3}$.

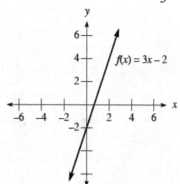

17. The slope is $\dfrac{2}{3}$, the y-intercept is -4, and the perpendicular slope is $-\dfrac{3}{2}$.

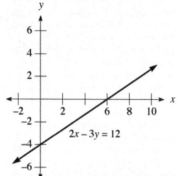

19. The slope is $-\dfrac{4}{5}$, the y-intercept is 4, and the perpendicular slope is $\dfrac{5}{4}$.

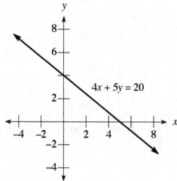

21. The slope is $\dfrac{1}{2}$ and the y-intercept is -4. Using the slope-intercept form, the equation is $f(x) = \dfrac{1}{2}x - 4$.

23. The slope is $-\dfrac{2}{3}$ and the y-intercept is 3. Using the slope-intercept form, the equation is $f(x) = -\dfrac{2}{3}x + 3$.

25. Using the point-slope formula:

$$y-(-5)=2(x-(-2))$$
$$y+5=2(x+2)$$
$$y+5=2x+4$$
$$f(x)=2x-1$$

27. Using the point-slope formula:

$$y-1=-\frac{1}{2}(x-(-4))$$
$$y-1=-\frac{1}{2}(x+4)$$
$$y-1=-\frac{1}{2}x-2$$
$$f(x)=-\frac{1}{2}x-1$$

29. Using the point-slope formula:

$$y-2=-3\left(x-\left(-\frac{1}{3}\right)\right)$$
$$y-2=-3\left(x+\frac{1}{3}\right)$$
$$y-2=-3x-1$$
$$f(x)=-3x+1$$

31. Using the point-slope formula:

$$y-2=\frac{2}{3}(x-(-4))$$
$$y-2=\frac{2}{3}(x+4)$$
$$y-2=\frac{2}{3}x+\frac{8}{3}$$
$$f(x)=\frac{2}{3}x+\frac{14}{3}$$

33. Using the point-slope formula:

$$y-(-2)=-\frac{1}{4}(x-(-5))$$
$$y+2=-\frac{1}{4}(x+5)$$
$$y+2=-\frac{1}{4}x-\frac{5}{4}$$
$$f(x)=-\frac{1}{4}x-\frac{13}{4}$$

35. Using the point-slope formula:

$$y-0=-\frac{2}{3}(x-(-4))$$
$$y=-\frac{2}{3}(x+4)$$
$$f(x)=-\frac{2}{3}x-\frac{8}{3}$$

37. First find the slope: $m=\dfrac{1-(-2)}{-2-3}=\dfrac{1+2}{-5}=-\dfrac{3}{5}$. Using the point-slope formula:

$$y-(-2)=-\frac{3}{5}(x-3)$$
$$5(y+2)=-3(x-3)$$
$$5y+10=-3x+9$$
$$3x+5y=-1$$

39. First find the slope: $m=\dfrac{\frac{1}{3}-\frac{1}{2}}{-4-(-2)}=\dfrac{-\frac{1}{6}}{-4+2}=\dfrac{-\frac{1}{6}}{-2}=\dfrac{1}{12}$. Using the point-slope formula:

$$y-\frac{1}{2}=\frac{1}{12}(x-(-2))$$
$$12\left(y-\frac{1}{2}\right)=1(x+2)$$
$$12y-6=x+2$$
$$x-12y=-8$$

41. First find the slope: $m = \dfrac{-1 - \left(-\dfrac{1}{5}\right)}{-\dfrac{1}{3} - \dfrac{1}{3}} = \dfrac{-1 + \dfrac{1}{5}}{-\dfrac{2}{3}} = \dfrac{-\dfrac{4}{5}}{-\dfrac{2}{3}} = \dfrac{4}{5} \cdot \dfrac{3}{2} = \dfrac{6}{5}$. Using the point-slope formula:

$$y - (-1) = \frac{6}{5}\left(x - \left(-\frac{1}{3}\right)\right)$$

$$y + 1 = \frac{6}{5}\left(x + \frac{1}{3}\right)$$

$$5(y + 1) = 6\left(x + \frac{1}{3}\right)$$

$$5y + 5 = 6x + 2$$

$$6x - 5y = 3$$

43. First find the slope: $m = \dfrac{\dfrac{1}{4} - \left(-\dfrac{1}{2}\right)}{\dfrac{1}{4} - \left(-\dfrac{1}{2}\right)} = \dfrac{\dfrac{1}{4} + \dfrac{1}{2}}{\dfrac{1}{4} + \dfrac{1}{2}} = \dfrac{\dfrac{3}{4}}{\dfrac{3}{4}} = 1$. Using the point-slope formula:

$$y - \frac{1}{4} = 1\left(x - \frac{1}{4}\right)$$

$$y - \frac{1}{4} = x - \frac{1}{4}$$

$$y = x$$

$$x - y = 0$$

45. Two points on the line are (0,–4) and (2,0). Finding the slope: $m = \dfrac{0 - (-4)}{2 - 0} = \dfrac{4}{2} = 2$

Using the slope-intercept form, the equation is $f(x) = 2x - 4$.

47. Two points on the line are (0,4) and (–2,0). Finding the slope: $m = \dfrac{0 - 4}{-2 - 0} = \dfrac{-4}{-2} = 2$

Using the slope-intercept form, the equation is $f(x) = 2x + 4$.

49. **a.** For the x-intercept, substitute $y = 0$:   For the y-intercept, substitute $x = 0$:

$$3x - 2(0) = 10 \qquad\qquad\qquad\qquad 3(0) - 2y = 10$$

$$3x = 10 \qquad\qquad\qquad\qquad\qquad -2y = 10$$

$$x = \frac{10}{3} \qquad\qquad\qquad\qquad\qquad\quad y = -5$$

b. Substituting $y = 1$:

$$3x - 2(1) = 10$$

$$3x - 2 = 10$$

$$3x = 12$$

$$x = 4$$

Another solution is (4,1). Other answers are possible.

c. Solving for y:

$$3x - 2y = 10$$

$$-2y = -3x + 10$$

$$f(x) = \frac{3}{2}x - 5$$

d. Substituting $x = 2$: $y = \dfrac{3}{2}(2) - 5 = 3 - 5 = -2$. No, the point (2,2) is not a solution to the equation.

51. **a.** Solving for x:

$$-2x+1=-3$$
$$-2x=-4$$
$$x=2$$

b. Substituting $y=0$:

$$-2x+0=-3$$
$$-2x=-3$$
$$x=\frac{3}{2}$$

c. Substituting $x=0$:

$$-2(0)+y=-3$$
$$y=-3$$

d. Sketching the graph:

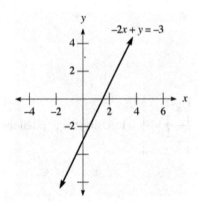

e. Solving for y:

$$-2x+y=-3$$
$$y=2x-3$$

53. **a.** The slope is $\frac{1}{2}$, the x-intercept is 0, and the y-intercept is 0.

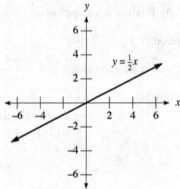

b. There is no slope, the x-intercept is 3, and there is no y-intercept.

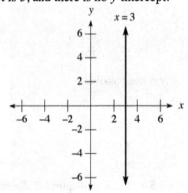

c.   The slope is 0, there is no x-intercept, and the y-intercept is -2.

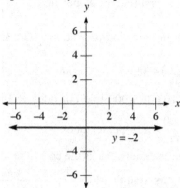

55.   First find the slope:
$$3x - y = 5$$
$$-y = -3x + 5$$
$$y = 3x - 5$$
So the slope is 3. Using $(-1,4)$ in the point-slope formula:
$$y - 4 = 3(x - (-1))$$
$$y - 4 = 3(x + 1)$$
$$y - 4 = 3x + 3$$
$$f(x) = 3x + 7$$

57.   First find the slope:
$$2x - 5y = 10$$
$$-5y = -2x + 10$$
$$y = \frac{2}{5}x - 2$$

So the perpendicular slope is $-\frac{5}{2}$. Using $(-4,-3)$ in the point-slope formula:
$$y - (-3) = -\frac{5}{2}(x - (-4))$$
$$y + 3 = -\frac{5}{2}(x + 4)$$
$$y + 3 = -\frac{5}{2}x - 10$$
$$f(x) = -\frac{5}{2}x - 13$$

59.   The perpendicular slope is $\frac{1}{4}$. Using $(-1,0)$ in the point-slope formula:
$$y - 0 = \frac{1}{4}(x - (-1))$$
$$y = \frac{1}{4}(x + 1)$$
$$f(x) = \frac{1}{4}x + \frac{1}{4}$$

61.   Using the points $(3,0)$ and $(0,2)$, first find the slope: $m = \frac{2 - 0}{0 - 3} = -\frac{2}{3}$

Using the slope-intercept formula, the equation is: $f(x) = -\frac{2}{3}x + 2$

63.   a.   Using the points (0,32) and (25,77), first find the slope: $m = \dfrac{77-32}{25-0} = \dfrac{45}{25} = \dfrac{9}{5}$

           Using the slope-intercept formula, the equation is: $F(C) = \dfrac{9}{5}C + 32$

       b.   Substituting $C = 30$: $F(30) = \dfrac{9}{5}(30) + 32 = 54 + 32 = 86°$

65.   a.   Substituting $n = 10{,}000$: $C(10{,}000) = 125{,}000 + 6.5(10{,}000) = \$190{,}000$

       b.   Finding the average cost: $\dfrac{\$190{,}000}{10{,}000} = \$19$ per textbook

       c.   Since each textbook costs \$6.50 in materials, this is the cost to produce the next textbook.

67.   Using the points (1934,1) and (1950,4), first find the slope: $m = \dfrac{4-1}{1950-1934} = \dfrac{3}{16} = 0.1875$

      Using the point-slope formula:
$$y - 1 = 0.1875(x - 1934)$$
$$y - 1 = 0.1875x - 362.625$$
$$y = 0.1875x - 361.625$$

69.   Using the points (0, 1800) and (4, 400), first find the slope: $m = \dfrac{400-1800}{4-0} = \dfrac{-1400}{4} = -350$

      Using slope-intercept formula: $V(t) = -350t + 1{,}800$

71.   a.   Using the points (10, 25) and (40, 500), first find the slope: $m = \dfrac{500-25}{40-10} = \dfrac{475}{30} = \dfrac{95}{6}$

           Using point-slope formula:
$$p - 25 = \frac{95}{6}(d - 10)$$
$$p - 25 = \frac{95}{6}d - \frac{475}{3}$$
$$p(d) = \frac{95}{6}d - \frac{400}{3}$$

       b.   Substituting $d = 50$: $p(50) = \dfrac{95}{6}(50) - \dfrac{400}{3} \approx 658.33$ kW

           The power output of a turbine with a blade diameter of 50 m would be 658.33 kW.

       c.   Finding when $p = 400$:
$$\frac{95}{6}d - \frac{400}{3} = 400$$
$$\frac{95}{6}d = \frac{1600}{3}$$
$$d = \frac{640}{19} \approx 33.68 \text{ m}$$

           A blade diameter of 33.68 m will produce a power output of 400 kW.

73.   Since $0 + 0 \le 4$ and $4 + 0 \le 4$, but $2 + 3 > 4$, the points (0,0) and (4,0) are solutions.

75.   Since $0 \le \dfrac{1}{2}(0)$ and $0 \le \dfrac{1}{2}(2)$, but $0 > \dfrac{1}{2}(-2)$, the points (0,0) and (2,0) are solutions.

2.7 Linear Inequalities

1. Graphing the solution set:

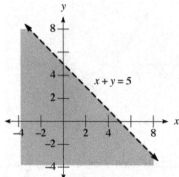

$x + y = 5$

3. Graphing the solution set:

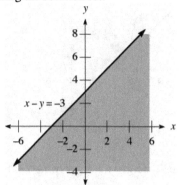

$x - y = -3$

5. Graphing the solution set:

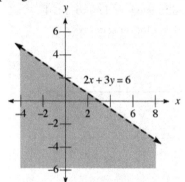

$2x + 3y = 6$

7. Graphing the solution set:

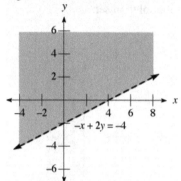

$-x + 2y = -4$

9. Graphing the solution set:

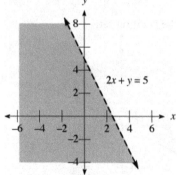

$2x + y = 5$

11. Graphing the solution set:

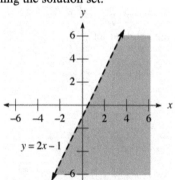

$y = 2x - 1$

13. Graphing the solution set:

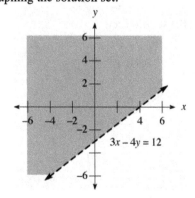

$3x - 4y = 12$

15. Graphing the solution set:

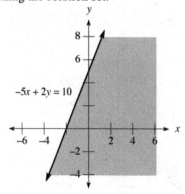

$-5x + 2y = 10$

17. Graphing the solution set:

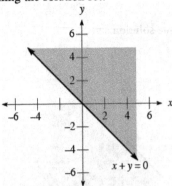

19. Graphing the solution set:

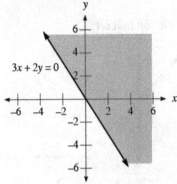

21. The inequality is $x + y > 4$, or $y > -x + 4$.

23. The inequality is $-x + 2y \leq 4$ or $y \leq \dfrac{1}{2}x + 2$.

25. The inequality is $x \geq 0$.

27. The inequality is $x > -2$.

29. Graphing the solution set:

31. The inequality is equivalent to $y \leq 4$.

Graphing the solution set:

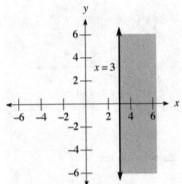

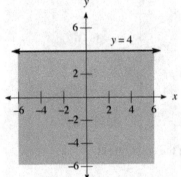

33. Graphing the solution set:

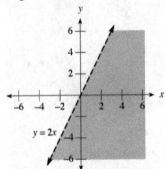

35. Graphing the solution set:

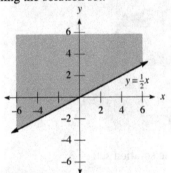

37. Graphing the solution set:

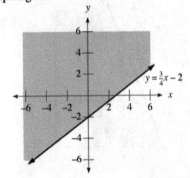

39. Graphing the solution set:

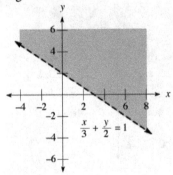

41. Graphing the solution set:

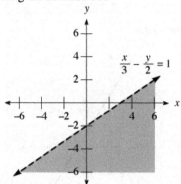

$$\frac{x}{3} - \frac{y}{2} = 1$$

43. Graphing the solution set:

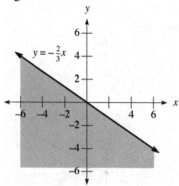

$$y = -\frac{2}{3}x$$

45. Graphing the solution set:

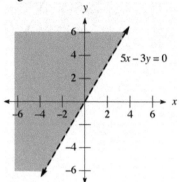

$$5x - 3y = 0$$

47. Graphing the solution set:

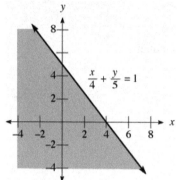

$$\frac{x}{4} + \frac{y}{5} = 1$$

49. Graphing the region:

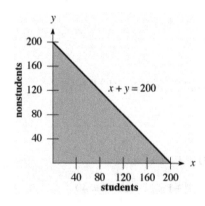

$$x + y = 200$$

51. Graphing the region:

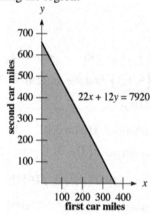

$$22x + 12y = 7920$$

Chapter 2 Review

1. Graphing the line:

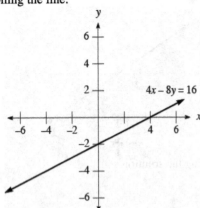

$4x - 8y = 16$

2. Graphing the line:

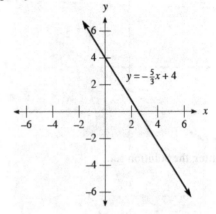

$y = -\frac{5}{3}x + 4$

3. Graphing the line:

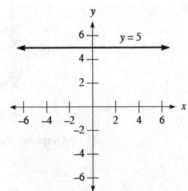

$y = 5$

4. The domain is $\{2,3\}$ and the range is $\{-4,0,1\}$. This is not a function.

5. The domain is $\{3,4,5\}$ and the range is $\{-3,0,2\}$. This is a function.

6. Evaluating: $f(2) = 3$

7. Evaluating: $f(5) + g(-2) = 0 + 0 = 0$

8. Evaluating the function: $f(0) = 3(0)^2 - 4(0) + 1 = 0 - 0 + 1 = 1$

9. Evaluating the function: $g(3) = 4(3) - 3 = 12 - 3 = 9$

10. Evaluating the function: $f\big(g(1)\big) = f(4(1) - 3) = f(1) = 3(1)^2 - 4(1) + 1 = 3 - 4 + 1 = 0$

11. Evaluating the function: $f\big(g(0)\big) = f(4(0) - 3) = f(-3) = 3(-3)^2 - 4(-3) + 1 = 27 + 12 + 1 = 40$

12. Evaluating the function: $(g \circ h)(-2) = g\big(h(-2)\big) = g(-2 + 5) = g(3) = (3)^2 + 4 = 9 + 4 = 13$

13. Evaluating the function: $(f + g)(-4) = f(-4) + g(-4) = \big[4(-4) - 3\big] + \big[(-4)^2 + 4\big] = -19 + 20 = 1$

14. Evaluating the function: $\left(\dfrac{g}{f}\right)(2) = \dfrac{g(2)}{f(2)} = \dfrac{(2)^2 + 4}{4(2) - 3} = \dfrac{4 + 4}{8 - 3} = \dfrac{8}{5}$

15. Evaluating the function:

$(g - fh)(-5) = g(-5) - f(-5) \cdot h(-5) = \big[(-5)^2 + 4\big] - \big[4(-5) - 3\big][-5 + 5] = 29 - (-23)(0) = 29$

16. Finding the slope: $m = \dfrac{8 - 3}{-4 - 6} = \dfrac{5}{-10} = -\dfrac{1}{2}$

17. Finding the slope: $m = \dfrac{7 - 2}{-5 - (-3)} = \dfrac{5}{-2} = -\dfrac{5}{2}$

18. Solving for y:

$$\frac{4-y}{4-5}=-1$$
$$\frac{4-y}{-1}=-1$$
$$4-y=1$$
$$-y=-3$$
$$y=3$$

19. Solving for x:

$$\frac{9-7}{x-(-3)}=\frac{1}{4}$$
$$\frac{2}{x+3}=\frac{1}{4}$$
$$x+3=8$$
$$x=5$$

20. Finding the slope: $m=\dfrac{4-(-3)}{-7-5}=\dfrac{7}{-12}=-\dfrac{7}{12}$

21. Solving for y:

$$\frac{3y-2y}{6-4}=-\frac{1}{2}$$
$$\frac{y}{2}=-\frac{1}{2}$$
$$2y=-2$$
$$y=-1$$

22. Using the slope-intercept formula, the equation is $y=-5x+4$.

23. Using the slope-intercept formula, the equation is $y=-7x-3$.

24. Solving for y:

$$4x-y=3$$
$$-y=-4x+3$$
$$y=4x-3$$

The slope is $m=4$ and the y-intercept is $b=-3$.

25. Solving for y:

$$4x-5y=10$$
$$-5y=-4x+10$$
$$y=\frac{4}{5}x-2$$

The slope is $m=\dfrac{4}{5}$ and the y-intercept is $b=-2$.

26. Using the point-slope formula:

$$y-5=3(x-3)$$
$$y-5=3x-9$$
$$y=3x-4$$

27. Using the point-slope formula:

$$y-5=\frac{3}{2}(x+2)$$
$$y-5=\frac{3}{2}x+3$$
$$y=\frac{3}{2}x+8$$

28. First find the slope: $m=\dfrac{4-0}{-2-3}=\dfrac{4}{-5}=-\dfrac{4}{5}$. Now using the point-slope formula:

$$y-0=-\frac{4}{5}(x-3)$$
$$y=-\frac{4}{5}x+\frac{12}{5}$$

29. First find the slope: $m=\dfrac{-5-2}{3-(-4)}=\dfrac{-7}{7}=-1$. Now using the point-slope formula:

$$y+5=-1(x-3)$$
$$y+5=-x+3$$
$$y=-x-2$$

30. First find the slope: $m = \dfrac{1-3}{4-(-2)} = \dfrac{-2}{6} = -\dfrac{1}{3}$. Now using the point-slope formula:

$$y - 1 = -\frac{1}{3}(x - 4)$$
$$y - 1 = -\frac{1}{3}x + \frac{4}{3}$$
$$y = -\frac{1}{3}x + \frac{7}{3}$$

31. First find the slope by solving for y:

$$3x + y = 5$$
$$y = -3x + 5$$

The parallel slope is also $m = -3$. Using the slope-intercept formula: $y = -3x + 4$

32. The perpendicular slope is $m = \dfrac{3}{2}$. Now using the point-slope formula:

$$y - 0 = \frac{3}{2}(x + 4)$$
$$y = \frac{3}{2}x + 6$$

33. Graphing the inequality:

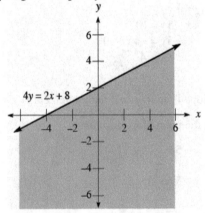

34. Graphing the inequality:

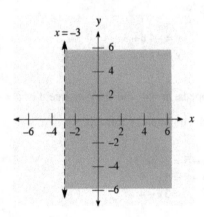

Chapter 2 Cumulative Review

1. Simplifying: $-6^2 = -6 \cdot 6 = -36$

2. Simplifying: $-|-4| = -(4) = -4$

3. Simplifying: $3^3 + 4^2 = 27 + 16 = 43$

4. Simplifying: $(4+9)^2 = 13^2 = 169$

5. Simplifying: $36 \div 12 \cdot 6 = 3 \cdot 6 = 18$

6. Simplifying: $108 \div 6 \cdot 3 = 18 \cdot 3 = 54$

7. Simplifying: $36 - 24 \div 6 + 2 = 36 - 4 + 2 = 34$

8. Simplifying: $36 - 24 \div (6 + 2) = 36 - 24 \div 8 = 36 - 3 = 33$

9. Evaluating when $x = 5$: $x^2 + 3x - 7 = (5)^2 + 3(5) - 7 = 25 + 15 - 7 = 33$

10. Evaluating when $x = 5$: $x^2 - 36 = (5)^2 - 36 = 25 - 36 = -11$

11. Simplifying: $\dfrac{108}{126} = \dfrac{2 \cdot 2 \cdot 3 \cdot 3 \cdot 3}{2 \cdot 3 \cdot 3 \cdot 7} = \dfrac{2 \cdot 3}{7} = \dfrac{6}{7}$

12. Simplifying: $\dfrac{252}{468} = \dfrac{2 \cdot 2 \cdot 3 \cdot 3 \cdot 7}{2 \cdot 2 \cdot 3 \cdot 3 \cdot 13} = \dfrac{7}{13}$

13. Adding: $\dfrac{7}{18} + \dfrac{7}{24} = \dfrac{7}{18} \cdot \dfrac{4}{4} + \dfrac{7}{24} \cdot \dfrac{3}{3} = \dfrac{28}{72} + \dfrac{21}{72} = \dfrac{49}{72}$

14. Subtracting: $\dfrac{7}{32} - \dfrac{5}{24} = \dfrac{7}{32} \cdot \dfrac{3}{3} - \dfrac{5}{24} \cdot \dfrac{4}{4} = \dfrac{21}{96} - \dfrac{20}{96} = \dfrac{1}{96}$

15. Evaluating: $-\dfrac{5}{4} + (7)\left(\dfrac{1}{4}\right) = -\dfrac{5}{4} + \dfrac{7}{4} = \dfrac{2}{4} = \dfrac{1}{2}$

16. Evaluating: $(8)\left(\dfrac{5}{6}\right) - \dfrac{7}{9} = \dfrac{20}{3} - \dfrac{7}{9} = \dfrac{60}{9} - \dfrac{7}{9} = \dfrac{53}{9}$

17. Simplifying: $12\left(\dfrac{2}{3}x - \dfrac{5}{6}y\right) = 12 \cdot \dfrac{2}{3}x - 12 \cdot \dfrac{5}{6}y = 8x - 10y$

18. Simplifying: $6\left(\dfrac{1}{3}x - \dfrac{3}{2}y\right) = 6 \cdot \dfrac{1}{3}x - 6 \cdot \dfrac{3}{2}y = 2x - 9y$

19. Solving the equation:

$$\dfrac{2}{3}x + 3 = -9$$
$$\dfrac{2}{3}x = -12$$
$$2x = -36$$
$$x = -18$$

20. Solving the equation:

$$\dfrac{1}{2}(4x - 7) + \dfrac{1}{6} = -1$$
$$6 \cdot \dfrac{1}{2}(4x - 7) + 6 \cdot \dfrac{1}{6} = 6 \cdot (-1)$$
$$3(4x - 7) + 1 = -6$$
$$12x - 21 + 1 = -6$$
$$12x - 20 = -6$$
$$12x = 14$$
$$x = \dfrac{7}{6}$$

21. Solving the equation:
$$-3 + 4(2x - 5) = 9$$
$$-3 + 8x - 20 = 9$$
$$8x - 23 = 9$$
$$8x = 32$$
$$x = 4$$

22. Solving the equation:
$$4x - (2x - 7) = -9$$
$$4x - 2x + 7 = -9$$
$$2x + 7 = -9$$
$$2x = -16$$
$$x = -8$$

23. Solving the equation:
$$|3x - 5| = 4$$
$$3x - 5 = -4, 4$$
$$3x = 1, 9$$
$$x = \dfrac{1}{3}, 3$$

24. Solving the equation:
$$|2x - 5| = 2x + 7$$
$$2x - 5 = -2x - 7 \quad \text{or} \quad 2x - 5 = 2x + 7$$
$$4x = -2 \qquad\qquad\qquad -5 = 12$$
$$x = -\dfrac{1}{2} \qquad\qquad\qquad \text{impossible}$$

This value checks in the original equation.

25. Solving for y:

$$y - 3 = -4(x - 2)$$
$$y - 3 = -4x + 8$$
$$y = -4x + 11$$

26. Solving for y:

$$y + 4 = \dfrac{3}{2}(4x - 6)$$
$$y + 4 = 6x - 9$$
$$y = 6x - 13$$

27. Solving the inequality:

$$|2x - 5| \le 9$$
$$-9 \le 2x - 5 \le 9$$
$$-4 \le 2x \le 14$$
$$-2 \le x \le 7$$

Graphing the solution set:

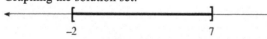

28. Solving for x:
$$|3x + 5| - 3 > 7$$
$$|3x + 5| > 10$$
$$3x + 5 < -10 \quad \text{or} \quad 3x + 5 > 10$$
$$3x < -15 \qquad\qquad\qquad 3x > 5$$
$$x < -5 \qquad\qquad\qquad x > \dfrac{5}{3}$$

Graphing the solution set:

29. Graphing the equation:

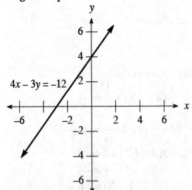

$4x - 3y = -12$

30. Graphing the equation:

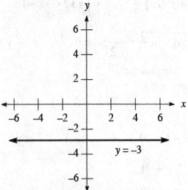

$y = -3$

31. Graphing the equation:

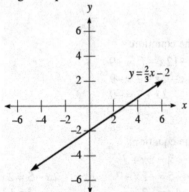

$y = \frac{2}{3}x - 2$

32. Graphing the equation:

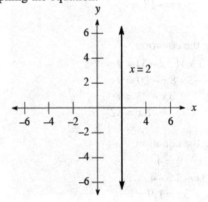

$x = 2$

33. Finding the slope: $m = \dfrac{-7-4}{5-(-6)} = \dfrac{-11}{11} = -1$

34. Solving for y:
$$\frac{y-2}{3+6} = \frac{2}{3}$$
$$\frac{y-2}{9} = \frac{2}{3}$$
$$y-2 = 6$$
$$y = 8$$

35. Since this line is vertical, its slope is undefined.

36. The slope-intercept form of the line is $y = -\dfrac{3}{5}x + 7$.

37. Solving for y:
$$3x - 6y = 12$$
$$-6y = -3x + 12$$
$$y = \frac{1}{2}x - 2$$

The slope is $m = \dfrac{1}{2}$ and the y-intercept is $b = -2$.

38. First find the slope using the points $(-3, 0)$ and $(0,6)$: $m = \dfrac{6-0}{0-(-3)} = \dfrac{6}{3} = 2$.

The slope-intercept form of the line is $y = 2x + 6$.

39. Solving for y:

$$3x - 6y = 4$$
$$-6y = -3x + 4$$
$$y = \frac{1}{2}x - \frac{3}{2}$$

Using the slope of $\dfrac{1}{2}$ in the point-slope formula:

$$y - 7 = \frac{1}{2}(x - 6)$$
$$y - 7 = \frac{1}{2}x - 3$$
$$y = \frac{1}{2}x + 4$$

40. Using the point-slope formula:

$$y - (-3) = \frac{5}{7}(x - 14)$$
$$y + 3 = \frac{5}{7}x - 10$$
$$y = \frac{5}{7}x - 13$$

41. Evaluating the function: $g(0) = 2(0) + 3 = 3$

42. Evaluating the function: $f(-1) + h(2) = \left[(-1)^2 + 5(-1)\right] + \left[3(2) - 1\right] = -4 + 5 = 1$

43. Evaluating the function: $(f \circ h)(3) = f[h(3)] = f(3(3) - 1) = f(8) = (8)^2 + 5(8) = 64 + 40 = 104$

44. Evaluating the function: $(f - g)(x) = f(x) - g(x) = (x^2 + 5x) - (2x + 3) = x^2 + 5x - 2x - 3 = x^2 + 3x - 3$

45. The domain is $\{-5, -2, 1\}$ and the range is $\{3, 4\}$. This relation is a function.

46. Finding the percent:

$$p \cdot 15 = 2.25$$
$$p = \frac{2.25}{15} = 0.15$$

The tip was 15% of the cost of the dinner.

47. Finding the amount: $0.082(200) = \$16.40$

Randy will pay $16.40 in sales tax.

48. The difference is: $9{,}143 - 5{,}768 = 3{,}375$. Expressed as a percent: $\dfrac{3{,}375}{5{,}768} \approx 58.5\%$

There are approximately 58.5% more convenience stores in Texas compared to California.

49. The difference is: $3{,}402 - 2{,}996 = 406$. Expressed as a percent: $\dfrac{406}{2{,}996} \approx 13.6\%$

There are approximately 13.6% more convenience stores in Michigan compared to Pennsylvania.

Chapter 2 Test

1. The x-intercept is 3, the y-intercept is –9, and the slope is 3.

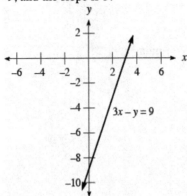

$3x - y = 9$

2. The x-intercept is 8, the y-intercept is 4, and the slope is $-\dfrac{1}{2}$.

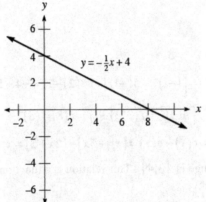

$y = -\frac{1}{2}x + 4$

3. The x-intercept is 10, the y-intercept is –6, and the slope is $\dfrac{3}{5}$.

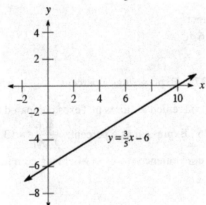

$y = \frac{3}{5}x - 6$

4. The *x*-intercept is –4, there is no *y*-intercept, and there is no slope.

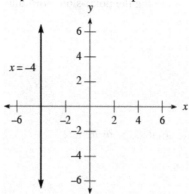

5. The domain is $\{0,2,6\}$ and the range is $\{-4,3,5\}$. This is a function.

6. The domain is all real numbers and the range is $\{y \mid y \geq 2\}$. This is a function.

7. The domain is $\{-6,0\}$ and the range is $\{5,7\}$. This is not a function.

8. The domain is all real numbers and the range is all real numbers. This is a function.

9. The domain is $\{x \mid -2 \leq x \leq 2\}$ and the range is $\{y \mid -1 \leq y \leq 2\}$.

10. The domain is $\{x \mid -2 \leq x \leq 2\}$ and the range is $\{y \mid -3 \leq y \leq 3\}$.

11. Evaluating the function: $f(0)+g(-3)=[0-5]+[2(-3)-5]=-5-11=-16$

12. Evaluating the function: $h(0)-g(0)=[0^2-5\cdot 0+6]-[2\cdot 0-5]=6+5=11$

13. Evaluating the function: $f\big(g(-1)\big)=f\big(2(-1)-5\big)=f(-7)=-7-5=-12$

14. Evaluating the function: $g\big(f(3)\big)=g(3-5)=g(-2)=2(-2)-5=-9$

15. Evaluating the function: $f(-3)+g(4)=-1+3=2$

16. Evaluating the function: $(f-g)(5)=f(5)-g(5)=2-3=-1$

17. Evaluating the function: $(g \circ f)(2)=g\big[f(2)\big]=g(1)=3$

18. Evaluating the function: $(f \circ g)(-7)=f\big[g(-7)\big]=f(2)=1$

19. Finding the slope: $m=\dfrac{0-2}{3-0}=\dfrac{-2}{3}=-\dfrac{2}{3}$

20. Finding the slope: $m=\dfrac{2-(-1)}{0-(-1)}=\dfrac{3}{1}=3$

21. The slope is $-\dfrac{3}{2}$ and the *y*-intercept is 3, so the slope-intercept form is $y=-\dfrac{3}{2}x+3$.

22. The slope is $\dfrac{1}{3}$ and the *y*-intercept is 1, so the slope-intercept form is $y=\dfrac{1}{3}x+1$.

23. Using the point-slope formula:
$$y-1=-3(x+6)$$
$$y-1=-3x-18$$
$$y=-3x-17$$

24. First find the slope: $m = \dfrac{2-8}{-3-6} = \dfrac{-6}{-9} = \dfrac{2}{3}$. Using the point-slope formula:

$$y - 8 = \frac{2}{3}(x - 6)$$
$$y - 8 = \frac{2}{3}x - 4$$
$$y = \frac{2}{3}x + 4$$

25. The perpendicular slope is $\dfrac{3}{2}$. Using the point-slope formula:

$$y - 1 = \frac{3}{2}(x - (-4))$$
$$y - 1 = \frac{3}{2}x + 6$$
$$y = \frac{3}{2}x + 7$$

26. First solve for y to find the slope:
$$4x - 2y = 3$$
$$-2y = -4x + 3$$
$$y = 2x - \frac{3}{2}$$

The parallel line will also have a slope of 2. Now using the slope-intercept formula: $y = 2x - 6$

27. The inequality is $y \geq -\dfrac{2}{3}x + 2$.

28. The inequality is $y < 2x + 4$.

29. Graphing the inequality:

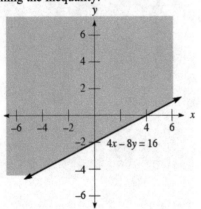

30. Graphing the inequality:

Chapter 3
Systems of Equations

3.1 Solving Linear Systems

1. The intersection point is (4,3).

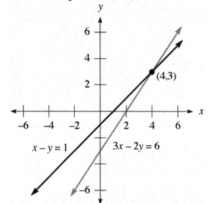

3. The intersection point is (–5,–6).

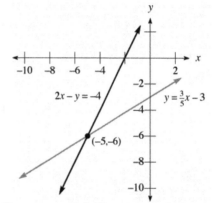

5. The intersection point is (4,2).

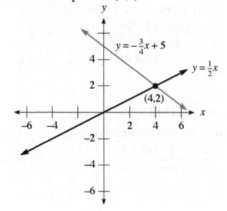

7. The lines are parallel. There is no solution to the system.

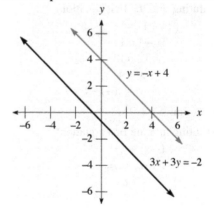

9. The intersection point is $(2,1)$.

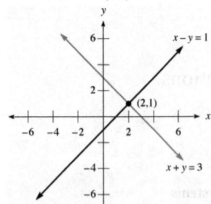

11. The intersection point is $(0,0)$.

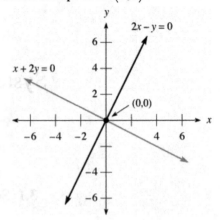

13. The intersection point is $(-4,6)$.

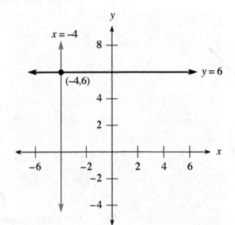

15. Substituting into the first equation:

$$x+(2x-1)=11$$
$$3x-1=11$$
$$3x=12$$
$$x=4$$
$$y=2(4)-1=7$$

The solution is $(4,7)$.

17. Substituting into the first equation:

$$x+(5x+2)=20$$
$$6x+2=20$$
$$6x=18$$
$$x=3$$
$$y=5(3)+2=17$$

The solution is $(3,17)$.

19. Substituting into the first equation:

$$-2x+(-4x+8)=-1$$
$$-6x+8=-1$$
$$-6x=-9$$
$$x=\frac{3}{2}$$
$$y=-4\left(\frac{3}{2}\right)+8=-6+8=2$$

The solution is $\left(\frac{3}{2},2\right)$.

21. Substituting into the first equation:

$$5x+4(-3x)=7$$
$$5x-12x=7$$
$$-7x=7$$
$$x=-1$$
$$y=-3(-1)=3$$

The solution is $(-1,3)$.

23. Solving the second equation for x:
$$x - 2y = -1$$
$$x = 2y - 1$$
Substituting into the first equation:
$$(2y - 1) + 3y = 4$$
$$5y - 1 = 4$$
$$5y = 5$$
$$y = 1$$
$$x = 2(1) - 1 = 1$$
The solution is $(1, 1)$.

25. Solving the first equation for x:
$$x - 5y = 17$$
$$x = 5y + 17$$
Substituting into the second equation:
$$2(5y + 17) + y = 1$$
$$10y + 34 + y = 1$$
$$11y + 34 = 1$$
$$11y = -33$$
$$y = -3$$
$$x = 5(-3) + 17 = 2$$
The solution is $(2, -3)$.

27. Solving the first equation for y yields $y = 2x - 5$. Substituting into the second equation:
$$4x - 2(2x - 5) = 10$$
$$4x - 4x + 10 = 10$$
$$10 = 10$$
Since this statement is true, the two lines coincide. The solution is $\{(x, y) \mid 2x - y = 5\}$.

29. Solving the second equation for x:
$$x + 3y = 12$$
$$x = -3y + 12$$
Substituting into the first equation:
$$-3(-3y + 12) - 9y = 7$$
$$9y - 36 - 9y = 7$$
$$-36 = 7$$
Since this statement is false, there is no solution to the system. The system is inconsistent.

31. Substituting into the first equation:
$$0.05x + 0.10(22 - x) = 1.70$$
$$0.05x + 2.2 - 0.10x = 1.70$$
$$-0.05x + 2.2 = 1.7$$
$$-0.05x = -0.5$$
$$x = 10$$
$$y = 22 - 10 = 12$$
The solution is $(10, 12)$.

33. Adding the two equations:
$$2x = 4$$
$$x = 2$$
Substituting into the first equation:
$$2 + y = 3$$
$$y = 1$$
The solution is $(2, 1)$.

35. Adding the two equations:
$$4x = -4$$
$$x = -1$$
Substituting into the first equation:
$$-1 + y = -1$$
$$y = 0$$
The solution is $(-1, 0)$.

37. Adding the two equations:
$$0 = 0$$
The lines coincide (the system is dependent).

39. To clear each equation of fractions, multiply the first equation by 6 and the second equation by 20:
$$3x + 2y = 78$$
$$8x + 5y = 200$$
Multiply the first equation by 5 and the second equation by –2:
$$15x + 10y = 390$$
$$-16x - 10y = -400$$
Adding yields:
$$-x = -10$$
$$x = 10$$
The solution is (10,24).

41. To clear each equation of fractions, multiply the first equation by 15 and the second equation by 6:
$$10x + 6y = -60$$
$$2x - 3y = -2$$
Multiply the second equation by 2:
$$10x + 6y = -60$$
$$4x - 6y = -4$$
Adding yields:
$$14x = -64$$
$$x = -\frac{32}{7}$$
Substituting into the second equation:
$$2\left(-\frac{32}{7}\right) - 3y = -2$$
$$-\frac{64}{7} - 3y = -2$$
$$-3y = \frac{50}{7}$$
$$y = -\frac{50}{21}$$
The solution is $\left(-\frac{32}{7}, -\frac{50}{21}\right)$.

43. Multiplying the first equation by 2:
$$6x - 2y = 8$$
$$2x + 2y = 24$$
Adding the two equations:
$$8x = 32$$
$$x = 4$$
Substituting into the first equation:
$$3(4) - y = 4$$
$$12 - y = 4$$
$$-y = -8$$
$$y = 8$$
The solution is $(4, 8)$.

45. Multiplying the second equation by –3:
$$5x - 3y = -2$$
$$-30x + 3y = -3$$
Adding the two equations:
$$-25x = -5$$
$$x = \frac{1}{5}$$
Substituting into the first equation:
$$5\left(\frac{1}{5}\right) - 3y = -2$$
$$1 - 3y = -2$$
$$-3y = -3$$
$$y = 1$$
The solution is $\left(\frac{1}{5}, 1\right)$.

47. Multiplying the second equation by 4:
$$11x - 4y = 11$$
$$20x + 4y = 20$$
Adding the two equations:
$$31x = 31$$
$$x = 1$$

Substituting into the second equation:

$$5(1) + y = 5$$
$$5 + y = 5$$
$$y = 0$$

The solution is $(1, 0)$.

49. Multiplying the first equation by 3:
$$9x + 3y = 15$$
$$2x - 3y = -2$$
Adding the two equations:
$$11x = 13$$
$$x = \frac{13}{11}$$

Substituting into the first equation:
$$3\left(\frac{13}{11}\right) + y = 5$$
$$\frac{39}{11} + y = 5$$
$$y = \frac{16}{11}$$

The solution is $\left(\frac{13}{11}, \frac{16}{11}\right)$.

51. Multiplying the second equation by 3:
$$3x - 5y = 7$$
$$-3x + 3y = -3$$
Adding the two equations:
$$-2y = 4$$
$$y = -2$$

Substituting into the second equation:

$$-x - 2 = -1$$
$$-x = 1$$
$$x = -1$$

The solution is $(-1, -2)$.

53. Multiplying the first equation by -2:
$$2x + 16y = 2$$
$$-2x + 4y = 13$$
Adding the two equations:
$$20y = 15$$
$$y = \frac{3}{4}$$

Substituting into the second equation:
$$-x - 8\left(\frac{3}{4}\right) = -1$$
$$-x - 6 = -1$$
$$-x = 5$$
$$x = -5$$

The solution is $\left(-5, \frac{3}{4}\right)$.

55. Multiplying the first equation by 2:
$$-6x - 2y = 14$$
$$6x + 7y = 11$$
Adding the two equations:
$$5y = 25$$
$$y = 5$$

Substituting into the first equation:

$$-3x - 5 = 7$$
$$-3x = 12$$
$$x = -4$$

The solution is $(-4, 5)$.

57. Multiplying the first equation by 3:
$$6x - 9y = 15$$
$$-6x + y = 4$$
Adding the two equations:
$$-8y = 19$$
$$y = -\frac{19}{8}$$

Substituting into the first equation:
$$2x - 3\left(-\frac{19}{8}\right) = 5$$
$$2x + \frac{57}{8} = 5$$
$$2x = -\frac{17}{8}$$
$$x = -\frac{17}{16}$$

The solution is $\left(-\frac{17}{16}, -\frac{19}{8}\right)$.

59. Multiply the second equation by 3:
$$x - 3y = 7$$
$$6x + 3y = -18$$
Adding yields:
$$7x = -11$$
$$x = -\frac{11}{7}$$
Substituting into the original second equation:
$$2\left(-\frac{11}{7}\right) + y = -6$$
$$-\frac{22}{7} + y = -6$$
$$y = -\frac{20}{7}$$
The solution is $\left(-\frac{11}{7}, -\frac{20}{7}\right)$.

61. Substituting into the first equation:
$$-\frac{1}{3}x + 2 = \frac{1}{2}x + \frac{1}{3}$$
$$6\left(-\frac{1}{3}x + 2\right) = 6\left(\frac{1}{2}x + \frac{1}{3}\right)$$
$$-2x + 12 = 3x + 2$$
$$-5x = -10$$
$$x = 2$$
Substituting into the first equation: $y = \frac{1}{2}(2) + \frac{1}{3} = 1 + \frac{1}{3} = \frac{4}{3}$. The solution is $\left(2, \frac{4}{3}\right)$.

63. Substituting into the first equation:
$$3\left(\frac{2}{3}y - 4\right) - 4y = 12$$
$$2y - 12 - 4y = 12$$
$$-2y - 12 = 12$$
$$-2y = 24$$
$$y = -12$$
Substituting into the second equation: $x = \frac{2}{3}(-12) - 4 = -8 - 4 = -12$. The solution is $(-12, -12)$.

65. Multiply the first equation by 2:
$$8x - 6y = -14$$
$$-8x + 6y = -11$$
$$0 = -25$$
Since this statement is false, there is no solution ($\varnothing$). The system is inconsistent.

67. Multiply the first equation by –20:

$$-60y - 20z = -340$$
$$5y + 20z = 65$$

Adding yields:

$$-55y = -275$$
$$y = 5$$

Substituting into the first equation:

$$3(5) + z = 17$$
$$15 + z = 17$$
$$z = 2$$

The solution is $y = 5, z = 2$.

69. Substitute into the first equation:

$$\frac{3}{4}x - \frac{1}{3}\left(\frac{1}{4}x\right) = 1$$
$$\frac{3}{4}x - \frac{1}{12}x = 1$$
$$\frac{2}{3}x = 1$$
$$x = \frac{3}{2}$$

Substituting into the second equation: $y = \frac{1}{4}\left(\frac{3}{2}\right) = \frac{3}{8}$. The solution is $\left(\frac{3}{2}, \frac{3}{8}\right)$.

71. To clear each equation of fractions, multiply the first equation by 12 and the second equation by 12:

$$3x - 6y = 4$$
$$4x - 3y = -8$$

Multiply the second equation by –2:

$$3x - 6y = 4$$
$$-8x + 6y = 16$$

Adding yields:

$$-5x = 20$$
$$x = -4$$

Substituting into the first equation:

$$3(-4) - 6y = 4$$
$$-12 - 6y = 4$$
$$-6y = 16$$
$$y = -\frac{8}{3}$$

The solution is $\left(-4, -\frac{8}{3}\right)$.

73. To clear each equation of fractions, multiply the first equation by 12 and the second equation by 20:

$8x - 9y = -2$

$15x - 4y = -2$

Multiply the first equation by −4 and the second equation by 9:

$-32x + 36y = 8$

$135x - 36y = -18$

Adding yields:

$103x = -10$

$$x = -\frac{10}{103}$$

Substituting into the second equation:

$$15\left(-\frac{10}{103}\right) - 4y = -2$$

$$-\frac{150}{103} - 4y = -2$$

$$-4y = -\frac{56}{103}$$

$$y = \frac{14}{103}$$

The solution is $\left(-\dfrac{10}{103}, \dfrac{14}{103}\right)$.

75. **a.** The car and truck would cost the same at 350 miles.

 b. The car is cheaper if Daniel drives more than 600 miles.

 c. The truck is cheaper if Daniel drives less than 100 miles.

 d. The problem is only dealing with positive numbers.

77. **a.** The cost to install the panels is: $0.50(400)(100) = \$20,000$

 b. The money saved by not purchasing electricity is: $0.15(400)(20) = \$1,200$

 Subtracting the initial cost, the function is: $f(t) = 1,200t - 20,000$

 c. Finding when the function is 0 (the break-even point):

$$1,200t - 20,000 = 0$$

$$1,200t = 20,000$$

$$t = \frac{50}{3} \approx 16.67 \text{ years}$$

79. a. Writing each cost as a linear function:

charter jet: $f(x) = 5,200(5) = 26,000$

business class: $g(x) = 1,300x$

b. Graphing the equations:

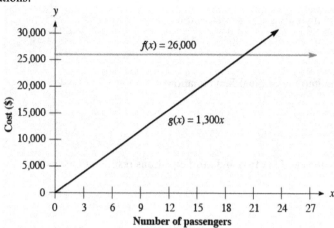

c. Computing the cost for 15 employees:

charter jet: $f(15) = \$26,000$

business class: $g(15) = 1,300(15) = \$19,500$

It is cheaper to purchase the tickets in business class.

d. Finding the break-even point:

$1,300x = 26,000$

$x = 20$

The charter jet would be cheaper if more than 20 employees were flying.

81. a. Writing the cost as a linear function:

Civic Hybrid: $f(x) = 22,600 + 0.095x$

Civix Ex: $g(x) = 18,710 + 0.14x$

b. Finding when the costs are equal:

$18,710 + 0.14x = 22,600 + 0.095x$

$0.045x + 18,710 = 22,600$

$0.045x = 3,890$

$x \approx 86,444$

The hybrid will be the cheaper alternative after 86,444 miles.

83. Simplifying: $2 - 2(6) = 2 - 12 = -10$

85. Simplifying: $(x + 3y) - 1(x - 2z) = x + 3y - x + 2z = 3y + 2z$

87. Solving the equation:

$-9y = -9$

$y = 1$

89. Solving the equation:

$3(1) + 2z = 9$

$3 + 2z = 9$

$2z = 6$

$z = 3$

91. Applying the distributive property: $2(5x - z) = 10x - 2z$

93. Applying the distributive property: $3(3x + y - 2z) = 9x + 3y - 6z$

3.2 Systems of Linear Equations in Three Variables

1. Adding the first two equations and the first and third equations results in the system:
$$2x + 3z = 5$$
$$2x - 2z = 0$$
Solving the second equation yields $x = z$, now substituting:
$$2z + 3z = 5$$
$$5z = 5$$
$$z = 1$$
So $x = 1$, now substituting into the original first equation:
$$1 + y + 1 = 4$$
$$y + 2 = 4$$
$$y = 2$$
The solution is $(1,2,1)$.

3. Adding the first two equations and the first and third equations results in the system:
$$2x + 3z = 13$$
$$3x - 3z = -3$$
Adding yields:
$$5x = 10$$
$$x = 2$$
Substituting to find z:
$$2(2) + 3z = 13$$
$$4 + 3z = 13$$
$$3z = 9$$
$$z = 3$$
Substituting into the original first equation:
$$2 + y + 3 = 6$$
$$y + 5 = 6$$
$$y = 1$$
The solution is $(2,1,3)$.

5. Adding the second and third equations:
$$5x + z = 11$$
Multiplying the second equation by 2:
$$x + 2y + z = 3$$
$$4x - 2y + 4z = 12$$
Adding yields:
$$5x + 5z = 15$$
$$x + z = 3$$
So the system becomes:
$$5x + z = 11$$
$$x + z = 3$$
Multiply the second equation by -1:
$$5x + z = 11$$
$$-x - z = -3$$
Adding yields:
$$4x = 8$$
$$x = 2$$
Substituting to find z:
$$5(2) + z = 11$$
$$z + 10 = 11$$
$$z = 1$$

Substituting into the original first equation:

$$2 + 2y + 1 = 3$$
$$2y + 3 = 3$$
$$2y = 0$$
$$y = 0$$

The solution is $(2,0,1)$.

7. Multiply the second equation by −1 and add it to the first equation:

$$2x + 3y - 2z = 4$$
$$-x - 3y + 3z = -4$$

Adding results in the equation $x + z = 0$. Multiply the second equation by 2 and add it to the third equation:

$$2x + 6y - 6z = 8$$
$$3x - 6y + z = -3$$

Adding results in the equation:

$$5x - 5z = 5$$
$$x - z = 1$$

So the system becomes:

$$x - z = 1$$
$$x + z = 0$$

Adding yields:

$$2x = 1$$
$$x = \frac{1}{2}$$

Substituting to find z:

$$\frac{1}{2} + z = 0$$
$$z = -\frac{1}{2}$$

Substituting into the original first equation:

$$2\left(\frac{1}{2}\right) + 3y - 2\left(-\frac{1}{2}\right) = 4$$
$$1 + 3y + 1 = 4$$
$$3y + 2 = 4$$
$$3y = 2$$
$$y = \frac{2}{3}$$

The solution is $\left(\frac{1}{2}, \frac{2}{3}, -\frac{1}{2}\right)$.

9. Multiply the first equation by 2 and add it to the second equation:

$$-2x + 8y - 6z = 4$$
$$2x - 8y + 6z = 1$$

Adding yields $0 = 5$, which is false. There is no solution (inconsistent system).

11. To clear the system of fractions, multiply the first equation by 2 and the second equation by 3:

$$x - 2y + 2z = 0$$
$$6x + y + 3z = 6$$
$$x + y + z = -4$$

Multiply the third equation by 2 and add it to the first equation:

$$x - 2y + 2z = 0$$
$$2x + 2y + 2z = -8$$

Adding yields the equation $3x + 4z = -8$. Multiply the third equation by −1 and add it to the second equation:

$$6x + y + 3z = 6$$
$$-x - y - z = 4$$

Adding yields the equation $5x + 2z = 10$. So the system becomes:
$$3x + 4z = -8$$
$$5x + 2z = 10$$
Multiply the second equation by –2:
$$3x + 4z = -8$$
$$-10x - 4z = -20$$
Adding yields:
$$-7x = -28$$
$$x = 4$$
Substituting to find z:
$$3(4) + 4z = -8$$
$$12 + 4z = -8$$
$$4z = -20$$
$$z = -5$$
Substituting into the original third equation:
$$4 + y - 5 = -4$$
$$y - 1 = -4$$
$$y = -3$$
The solution is $(4,-3,-5)$.

13. Multiply the first equation by –2 and add it to the third equation:
$$-4x + 2y + 6z = -2$$
$$4x - 2y - 6z = 2$$
Adding yields $0 = 0$, which is true. Since there are now less equations than unknowns, there is no unique solution (dependent system).

15. Multiply the second equation by 3 and add it to the first equation:
$$2x - y + 3z = 4$$
$$3x + 6y - 3z = -9$$
Adding yields the equation $5x + 5y = -5$, or $x + y = -1$.

Multiply the second equation by 2 and add it to the third equation:
$$2x + 4y - 2z = -6$$
$$4x + 3y + 2z = -5$$
Adding yields the equation $6x + 7y = -11$. So the system becomes:
$$6x + 7y = -11$$
$$x + y = -1$$
Multiply the second equation by –6:
$$6x + 7y = -11$$
$$-6x - 6y = 6$$
Adding yields $y = -5$. Substituting to find x:
$$6x + 7(-5) = -11$$
$$6x - 35 = -11$$
$$6x = 24$$
$$x = 4$$
Substituting into the original first equation:
$$2(4) - (-5) + 3z = 4$$
$$13 + 3z = 4$$
$$3z = -9$$
$$z = -3$$
The solution is $(4,-5,-3)$.

17. Adding the second and third equations results in the equation $x + y = 9$. Since this is the same as the first equation, there are less equations than unknowns. There is no unique solution (dependent system).

19. Adding the second and third equations results in the equation $4x + y = 3$. So the system becomes:

$$4x + y = 3$$
$$2x + y = 2$$

Multiplying the second equation by -1:

$$4x + y = 3$$
$$-2x - y = -2$$

Adding yields:

$$2x = 1$$
$$x = \frac{1}{2}$$

Substituting to find y:

$$2\left(\frac{1}{2}\right) + y = 2$$
$$1 + y = 2$$
$$y = 1$$

Substituting into the original second equation:

$$1 + z = 3$$
$$z = 2$$

The solution is $\left(\frac{1}{2}, 1, 2\right)$.

21. Multiply the third equation by 2 and adding it to the second equation:

$$6y - 4z = 1$$
$$2x + 4z = 2$$

Adding yields the equation $2x + 6y = 3$. So the system becomes:

$$2x - 3y = 0$$
$$2x + 6y = 3$$

Multiply the first equation by 2:

$$4x - 6y = 0$$
$$2x + 6y = 3$$

Adding yields:

$$6x = 3$$
$$x = \frac{1}{2}$$

Substituting to find y:

$$2\left(\frac{1}{2}\right) + 6y = 3$$
$$1 + 6y = 3$$
$$6y = 2$$
$$y = \frac{1}{3}$$

Substituting into the original third equation to find z:

$$\frac{1}{2} + 2z = 1$$
$$2z = \frac{1}{2}$$
$$z = \frac{1}{4}$$

The solution is $\left(\frac{1}{2}, \frac{1}{3}, \frac{1}{4}\right)$.

23. Multiply the first equation by –2 and add it to the second equation:

$$-2x - 2y + 2z = -4$$
$$2x + y + 3z = 4$$

Adding yields $-y + 5z = 0$. Multiply the first equation by –1 and add it to the third equation:

$$-x - y + z = -2$$
$$x - 2y + 2z = 6$$

Adding yields $-3y + 3z = 4$. So the system becomes:

$$-y + 5z = 0$$
$$-3y + 3z = 4$$

Multiply the first equation by –3:

$$3y - 15z = 0$$
$$-3y + 3z = 4$$

Adding yields:

$$-12z = 4$$
$$z = -\frac{1}{3}$$

Substituting to find y:

$$-3y + 3\left(-\frac{1}{3}\right) = 4$$
$$-3y - 1 = 4$$
$$-3y = 5$$
$$y = -\frac{5}{3}$$

Substituting into the original first equation:

$$x - \frac{5}{3} + \frac{1}{3} = 2$$
$$x - \frac{4}{3} = 2$$
$$x = \frac{10}{3}$$

The solution is $\left(\frac{10}{3}, -\frac{5}{3}, -\frac{1}{3}\right)$.

25. Multiply the third equation by –1 and add it to the first equation:

$$2x + 3y = -\frac{1}{2}$$
$$-3y - 2z = \frac{3}{4}$$

Adding yields the equation $2x - 2z = \frac{1}{4}$. So the system becomes:

$$2x - 2z = \frac{1}{4}$$
$$4x + 8z = 2$$

Multiply the first equation by 4:

$$8x - 8z = 1$$
$$4x + 8z = 2$$

Adding yields:

$$12x = 3$$

$$x = \frac{1}{4}$$

Substituting to find z:

$$4\left(\frac{1}{4}\right) + 8z = 2$$

$$1 + 8z = 2$$

$$8z = 1$$

$$z = \frac{1}{8}$$

Substituting to find y:

$$2\left(\frac{1}{4}\right) + 3y = -\frac{1}{2}$$

$$\frac{1}{2} + 3y = -\frac{1}{2}$$

$$3y = -1$$

$$y = -\frac{1}{3}$$

The solution is $\left(\frac{1}{4}, -\frac{1}{3}, \frac{1}{8}\right)$.

27. To clear each equation of fractions, multiply the first equation by 6, the second equation by 4, and the third equation by 12:

$$2x + 3y - z = 24$$

$$x - 3y + 2z = 6$$

$$6x - 8y - 3z = -64$$

Multiply the first equation by 2 and add it to the second equation:

$$4x + 6y - 2z = 48$$

$$x - 3y + 2z = 6$$

Adding yields the equation $5x + 3y = 54$. Multiply the first equation by –3 and add it to the third equation:

$$-6x - 9y + 3z = -72$$

$$6x - 8y - 3z = -64$$

Adding yields:

$$-17y = -136$$

$$y = 8$$

Substituting to find x:

$$5x + 3(8) = 54$$

$$5x + 24 = 54$$

$$5x = 30$$

$$x = 6$$

Substituting to find z:

$$6 - 3(8) + 2z = 6$$

$$-18 + 2z = 6$$

$$2z = 24$$

$$z = 12$$

The solution is $(6, 8, 12)$.

29. To clear each equation of fractions, multiply the first equation by 6, the second equation by 6, and the third equation by 12:

$$6x - 3y - 2z = -8$$
$$2x - 3z = 30$$
$$-3x + 8y - 12z = -9$$

Multiply the first equation by 8 and the third equation by 3:

$$48x - 24y - 16z = -64$$
$$-9x + 24y - 36z = -27$$

Adding yields the equation:

$$39x - 52z = -91$$
$$3x - 4z = -7$$

So the system becomes:

$$2x - 3z = 30$$
$$3x - 4z = -7$$

Multiply the first equation by 3 and the second equation by -2:

$$6x - 9z = 90$$
$$-6x + 8z = 14$$

Adding yields:

$$-z = 104$$
$$z = -104$$

Substituting to find x:

$$2x - 3(-104) = 30$$
$$2x + 312 = 30$$
$$2x = -282$$
$$x = -141$$

Substituting to find y:

$$6(-141) - 3y - 2(-104) = -8$$
$$-846 - 3y + 208 = -8$$
$$-3y - 638 = -8$$
$$-3y = 630$$
$$y = -210$$

The solution is $(-141, -210, -104)$.

31. Divide the second equation by 5 and the third equation by 10 to produce the system:

$$x - y - z = 0$$
$$x + 4y = 16$$
$$2y - z = 5$$

Multiply the third equation by -1 and add it to the first equation:

$$x - y - z = 0$$
$$-2y + z = -5$$

Adding yields the equation $x - 3y = -5$. So the system becomes:

$$x + 4y = 16$$
$$x - 3y = -5$$

Multiply the second equation by -1:

$$x + 4y = 16$$
$$-x + 3y = 5$$

Adding yields:

$$7y = 21$$
$$y = 3$$

Substituting to find x:
$$x + 12 = 16$$
$$x = 4$$
Substituting to find z:
$$6 - z = 5$$
$$z = 1$$
The currents are 4 amps, 3 amps, and 1 amp.

33. Let x, y, z represent the number of dozens of buns eaten by the three elephants Susie, Minnie, and Bunny. The system of equations is:
$$x + y + z = 40$$
$$y = 2x + 10$$
$$z = y + \frac{1}{3}(15)$$
Rewrite the system as:
$$x + y + z = 40$$
$$y = 2x + 10$$
$$z = y + 5$$
Substituting for y in the third equation: $z = (2x + 10) + 5 = 2x + 15$

Substituting into the first equation:
$$x + y + z = 40$$
$$x + (2x + 10) + (2x + 15) = 40$$
$$5x + 25 = 40$$
$$5x = 15$$
$$x = 3$$
$$y = 2(3) + 10 = 16$$
$$z = 16 + 5 = 21$$
Suzie at 3 dozen buns, Minnie ater 16 dozen buns, and Bunny at 21 dozen buns.

35. Translating into symbols: $3x + 2$

37. Simplifying: $10(0.2x + 0.5y) = 2x + 5y$

39. Solving the equation:
$$x + (3x + 2) = 26$$
$$4x + 2 = 26$$
$$4x = 24$$
$$x = 6$$

41. Adding the two equations results in:
$$-9y = 9$$
$$y = -1$$
Substituting into the second equation:
$$-7(-1) + 4z = 27$$
$$7 + 4z = 27$$
$$4z = 20$$
$$z = 5$$
The solution is $y = -1$ and $z = 5$.

43. Let x represent the smallest number, y represent the middle number, and z represent the larger number. The system of equations is:

$$x+y+z=20$$
$$z=x+y$$
$$y=2x+1$$

Substituting for y in equation 2: $z=x+(2x+1)=3x+1$

Substituting into equation 1:

$$x+(2x+1)+(3x+1)=20$$
$$6x+2=20$$
$$6x=18$$
$$x=3$$
$$y=2(3)+1=7$$
$$z=3+7=10$$

The numbers are 3, 7, and 10.

45. Let x represent the smallest piece, y represent the middle piece, and z represent the larger piece. The system of equations is:

$$x+y+z=20$$
$$z=x+y+2$$
$$y=2x$$

Substituting for y in equation 2: $z=x+(2x)+2=3x+2$

Substituting into equation 1:

$$x+(2x)+(3x+2)=20$$
$$6x+2=20$$
$$6x=18$$
$$x=3$$
$$y=2(3)=6$$
$$z=3+6+2=11$$

The pieces are 3 ft, 6 ft, and 11 ft.

3.3 Matrix Solutions to Linear Systems

1. Form the augmented matrix: $\begin{bmatrix} 1 & 1 & | & 5 \\ 3 & -1 & | & 3 \end{bmatrix}$

Add -3 times row 1 to row 2: $\begin{bmatrix} 1 & 1 & | & 5 \\ 0 & -4 & | & -12 \end{bmatrix}$

Dividing row 2 by -4: $\begin{bmatrix} 1 & 1 & | & 5 \\ 0 & 1 & | & 3 \end{bmatrix}$

So $y=3$. Substituting to find x:

$$x+3=5$$
$$x=2$$

The solution is (2,3).

3. Using the second equation as row 1, form the augmented matrix: $\begin{bmatrix} -1 & 1 & | & -1 \\ 3 & -5 & | & 7 \end{bmatrix}$

Add 3 times row 1 to row 2: $\begin{bmatrix} -1 & 1 & | & -1 \\ 0 & -2 & | & 4 \end{bmatrix}$

Dividing row 2 by –2 and row 1 by –1: $\begin{bmatrix} 1 & -1 & | & 1 \\ 0 & 1 & | & -2 \end{bmatrix}$

So $y = -2$. Substituting to find x:

$$x + 2 = 1$$
$$x = -1$$

The solution is $(-1, -2)$.

5. Form the augmented matrix: $\begin{bmatrix} 2 & -8 & | & 6 \\ 3 & -8 & | & 13 \end{bmatrix}$

Dividing row 1 by 2: $\begin{bmatrix} 1 & -4 & | & 3 \\ 3 & -8 & | & 13 \end{bmatrix}$

Add –3 times row 1 to row 2: $\begin{bmatrix} 1 & -4 & | & 3 \\ 0 & 4 & | & 4 \end{bmatrix}$

Dividing row 2 by 4: $\begin{bmatrix} 1 & -4 & | & 3 \\ 0 & 1 & | & 1 \end{bmatrix}$

So $y = 1$. Substituting to find x:

$$x - 4 = 3$$
$$x = 7$$

The solution is $(7, 1)$.

7. Form the augmented matrix: $\begin{bmatrix} 2 & -1 & | & -10 \\ 4 & 3 & | & 0 \end{bmatrix}$

Dividing row 1 by 2: $\begin{bmatrix} 1 & -\frac{1}{2} & | & -5 \\ 4 & 3 & | & 0 \end{bmatrix}$

Add –4 times row 1 to row 2: $\begin{bmatrix} 1 & -\frac{1}{2} & | & -5 \\ 0 & 5 & | & 20 \end{bmatrix}$

Divide row 2 by 5: $\begin{bmatrix} 1 & -\frac{1}{2} & | & -5 \\ 0 & 1 & | & 4 \end{bmatrix}$

So $y = 4$. Substituting to find x:

$$x - \frac{1}{2}(4) = -5$$
$$x - 2 = -5$$
$$x = -3$$

The solution is $(-3, 4)$.

9. Form the augmented matrix: $\begin{bmatrix} 5 & -3 & | & 27 \\ 6 & 2 & | & -18 \end{bmatrix}$

Dividing row 1 by 5: $\begin{bmatrix} 1 & -\dfrac{3}{5} & | & \dfrac{27}{5} \\ 6 & 2 & | & -18 \end{bmatrix}$

Add –6 times row 1 to row 2: $\begin{bmatrix} 1 & -\dfrac{3}{5} & | & \dfrac{27}{5} \\ 0 & \dfrac{28}{5} & | & -\dfrac{252}{5} \end{bmatrix}$

Multiply row 2 by $\dfrac{5}{28}$: $\begin{bmatrix} 1 & -\dfrac{3}{5} & | & \dfrac{27}{5} \\ 0 & 1 & | & -9 \end{bmatrix}$

So $y = -9$. Substituting to find x:

$$x - \frac{3}{5}(-9) = \frac{27}{5}$$

$$x + \frac{27}{5} = \frac{27}{5}$$

$$x = 0$$

The solution is $(0, -9)$.

11. First rewrite the system as:

$$5x + 2y = -14$$
$$-2x + y = 11$$

Form the augmented matrix: $\begin{bmatrix} 5 & 2 & | & -14 \\ -2 & 1 & | & 11 \end{bmatrix}$

Dividing row 1 by 5: $\begin{bmatrix} 1 & \dfrac{2}{5} & | & -\dfrac{14}{5} \\ -2 & 1 & | & 11 \end{bmatrix}$

Add 2 times row 1 to row 2: $\begin{bmatrix} 1 & \dfrac{2}{5} & | & -\dfrac{14}{5} \\ 0 & \dfrac{9}{5} & | & \dfrac{27}{5} \end{bmatrix}$

Multiply row 2 by $\dfrac{5}{9}$: $\begin{bmatrix} 1 & \dfrac{2}{5} & | & -\dfrac{14}{5} \\ 0 & 1 & | & 3 \end{bmatrix}$

So $y = 3$. Substituting to find x:

$$x + \frac{2}{5}(3) = -\frac{14}{5}$$

$$x + \frac{6}{5} = -\frac{14}{5}$$

$$x = -4$$

The solution is $(-4, 3)$.

13. Form the augmented matrix: $\begin{bmatrix} 2 & 3 & | & 11 \\ -1 & -1 & | & -2 \end{bmatrix}$

Dividing row 1 by 2: $\begin{bmatrix} 1 & \frac{3}{2} & | & \frac{11}{2} \\ -1 & -1 & | & -2 \end{bmatrix}$

Add row 1 to row 2: $\begin{bmatrix} 1 & \frac{3}{2} & | & \frac{11}{2} \\ 0 & \frac{1}{2} & | & \frac{7}{2} \end{bmatrix}$

Multiply row 2 by 2: $\begin{bmatrix} 1 & \frac{3}{2} & | & \frac{11}{2} \\ 0 & 1 & | & 7 \end{bmatrix}$

So $y = 7$. Substituting to find x:

$$x + \frac{3}{2}(7) = \frac{11}{2}$$
$$x + \frac{21}{2} = \frac{11}{2}$$
$$x = -5$$

The solution is $(-5, 7)$.

15. Form the augmented matrix: $\begin{bmatrix} 3 & -2 & | & 16 \\ 4 & 3 & | & -24 \end{bmatrix}$

Dividing row 1 by 3: $\begin{bmatrix} 1 & -\frac{2}{3} & | & \frac{16}{3} \\ 4 & 3 & | & -24 \end{bmatrix}$

Add -4 times row 1 to row 2: $\begin{bmatrix} 1 & -\frac{2}{3} & | & \frac{16}{3} \\ 0 & \frac{17}{3} & | & -\frac{136}{3} \end{bmatrix}$

Multiply row 2 by $\frac{3}{17}$: $\begin{bmatrix} 1 & -\frac{2}{3} & | & \frac{16}{3} \\ 0 & 1 & | & -8 \end{bmatrix}$

So $y = -8$. Substituting to find x:

$$x - \frac{2}{3}(-8) = \frac{16}{3}$$
$$x + \frac{16}{3} = \frac{16}{3}$$
$$x = 0$$

The solution is $(0, -8)$.

17. First rewrite the system as:
$$3x - 2y = 16$$
$$-2x + y = -12$$

Form the augmented matrix: $\begin{bmatrix} 3 & -2 & | & 16 \\ -2 & 1 & | & -12 \end{bmatrix}$

Divide row 1 by 3: $\begin{bmatrix} 1 & -\dfrac{2}{3} & | & \dfrac{16}{3} \\ -2 & 1 & | & -12 \end{bmatrix}$

Add 2 times row 1 to row 2: $\begin{bmatrix} 1 & -\dfrac{2}{3} & | & \dfrac{16}{3} \\ 0 & -\dfrac{1}{3} & | & -\dfrac{4}{3} \end{bmatrix}$

Multiplying row 2 by −3: $\begin{bmatrix} 1 & -\dfrac{2}{3} & | & \dfrac{16}{3} \\ 0 & 1 & | & 4 \end{bmatrix}$

So $y = 4$. Substituting to find x:
$$x - \frac{2}{3}(4) = \frac{16}{3}$$
$$x - \frac{8}{3} = \frac{16}{3}$$
$$x = 8$$
The solution is $(8,4)$.

19. Form the augmented matrix: $\begin{bmatrix} 1 & 1 & 1 & | & 4 \\ 1 & -1 & 2 & | & 1 \\ 1 & -1 & -1 & | & -2 \end{bmatrix}$

Add −1 times row 1 to both row 2 and row 3: $\begin{bmatrix} 1 & 1 & 1 & | & 4 \\ 0 & -2 & 1 & | & -3 \\ 0 & -2 & -2 & | & -6 \end{bmatrix}$

Multiply row 2 by −1 and add it to row 3: $\begin{bmatrix} 1 & 1 & 1 & | & 4 \\ 0 & 2 & -1 & | & 3 \\ 0 & 0 & -3 & | & -3 \end{bmatrix}$

Divide row 3 by −3: $\begin{bmatrix} 1 & 1 & 1 & | & 4 \\ 0 & 2 & -1 & | & 3 \\ 0 & 0 & 1 & | & 1 \end{bmatrix}$

So $z = 1$. Substituting to find y:
$$2y - 1 = 3$$
$$2y = 4$$
$$y = 2$$
Substituting to find x:
$$x + 2 + 1 = 4$$
$$x = 1$$
The solution is $(1,2,1)$.

21. Form the augmented matrix: $\begin{bmatrix} 1 & 2 & 1 & | & 3 \\ 2 & -1 & 2 & | & 6 \\ 3 & 1 & -1 & | & 5 \end{bmatrix}$

Add –2 times row 1 to row 2 and –3 times row 1 to row 3: $\begin{bmatrix} 1 & 2 & 1 & | & 3 \\ 0 & -5 & 0 & | & 0 \\ 0 & -5 & -4 & | & -4 \end{bmatrix}$

Dividing row 2 by –5: $\begin{bmatrix} 1 & 2 & 1 & | & 3 \\ 0 & 1 & 0 & | & 0 \\ 0 & -5 & -4 & | & -4 \end{bmatrix}$

Adding 5 times row 2 to row 3: $\begin{bmatrix} 1 & 2 & 1 & | & 3 \\ 0 & 1 & 0 & | & 0 \\ 0 & 0 & -4 & | & -4 \end{bmatrix}$

Dividing row 3 by –4: $\begin{bmatrix} 1 & 2 & 1 & | & 3 \\ 0 & 1 & 0 & | & 0 \\ 0 & 0 & 1 & | & 1 \end{bmatrix}$

So $y = 0$ and $z = 1$. Substituting to find x:
$$x + 0 + 1 = 3$$
$$x = 2$$
The solution is (2,0,1).

23. Form the augmented matrix: $\begin{bmatrix} 1 & -2 & 1 & | & -4 \\ 2 & 1 & -3 & | & 7 \\ 5 & -3 & 1 & | & -5 \end{bmatrix}$

Add –2 times row 1 to row 2 and –5 times row 1 to row 3: $\begin{bmatrix} 1 & -2 & 1 & | & -4 \\ 0 & 5 & -5 & | & 15 \\ 0 & 7 & -4 & | & 15 \end{bmatrix}$

Dividing row 2 by 5: $\begin{bmatrix} 1 & -2 & 1 & | & -4 \\ 0 & 1 & -1 & | & 3 \\ 0 & 7 & -4 & | & 15 \end{bmatrix}$

Add –7 times row 2 to row 3: $\begin{bmatrix} 1 & -2 & 1 & | & -4 \\ 0 & 1 & -1 & | & 3 \\ 0 & 0 & 3 & | & -6 \end{bmatrix}$

Dividing row 3 by 3: $\begin{bmatrix} 1 & -2 & 1 & | & -4 \\ 0 & 1 & -1 & | & 3 \\ 0 & 0 & 1 & | & -2 \end{bmatrix}$

So $z = -2$. Substituting to find y:
$$y - (-2) = 3$$
$$y + 2 = 3$$
$$y = 1$$
Substituting to find x:
$$x - 2(1) + (-2) = -4$$
$$x - 4 = -4$$
$$x = 0$$

The solution is $(0,1,-2)$.

25. Form the augmented matrix (using the second equation as row 1): $\begin{bmatrix} 1 & -2 & -1 & | & 0 \\ 5 & -3 & 1 & | & 10 \\ 3 & -1 & 2 & | & 10 \end{bmatrix}$

Add -5 times row 1 to row 2 and -3 times row 1 to row 3: $\begin{bmatrix} 1 & -2 & -1 & | & 0 \\ 0 & 7 & 6 & | & 10 \\ 0 & 5 & 5 & | & 10 \end{bmatrix}$

Dividing row 5 by 5, and switching it with row 2: $\begin{bmatrix} 1 & -2 & -1 & | & 0 \\ 0 & 1 & 1 & | & 2 \\ 0 & 7 & 6 & | & 10 \end{bmatrix}$

Add -7 times row 2 to row 3: $\begin{bmatrix} 1 & -2 & -1 & | & 0 \\ 0 & 1 & 1 & | & 2 \\ 0 & 0 & -1 & | & -4 \end{bmatrix}$

Multiplying row 3 by -1: $\begin{bmatrix} 1 & -2 & -1 & | & 0 \\ 0 & 1 & 1 & | & 2 \\ 0 & 0 & 1 & | & 4 \end{bmatrix}$

So $z = 4$. Substituting to find y:
$$y + 4 = 2$$
$$y = -2$$
Substituting to find x:
$$x - 2(-2) - 4 = 0$$
$$x = 0$$
The solution is $(0,-2,4)$.

27. Form the augmented matrix (using the third equation as row 1): $\begin{bmatrix} 1 & 1 & 2 & | & 5 \\ 2 & -5 & 3 & | & 2 \\ 3 & -7 & 1 & | & 0 \end{bmatrix}$

Add -2 times row 1 to row 2 and -3 times row 1 to row 3: $\begin{bmatrix} 1 & 1 & 2 & | & 5 \\ 0 & -7 & -1 & | & -8 \\ 0 & -10 & -5 & | & -15 \end{bmatrix}$

Dividing row 3 by -10 and switching it with row 2: $\begin{bmatrix} 1 & 1 & 2 & | & 5 \\ 0 & 1 & \frac{1}{2} & | & \frac{3}{2} \\ 0 & -7 & -1 & | & -8 \end{bmatrix}$

Add 7 times row 2 to row 3: $\begin{bmatrix} 1 & 1 & 2 & | & 5 \\ 0 & 1 & \frac{1}{2} & | & \frac{3}{2} \\ 0 & 0 & \frac{5}{2} & | & \frac{5}{2} \end{bmatrix}$

Multiplying row 3 by $\frac{2}{5}$: $\begin{bmatrix} 1 & 1 & 2 & | & 5 \\ 0 & 1 & \frac{1}{2} & | & \frac{3}{2} \\ 0 & 0 & 1 & | & 1 \end{bmatrix}$

So $z = 1$. Substituting to find y:

$$y + \frac{1}{2}(1) = \frac{3}{2}$$

$$y + \frac{1}{2} = \frac{3}{2}$$

$$y = 1$$

Substituting to find x:

$$x + 1(1) + 2(1) = 5$$

$$x + 3 = 5$$

$$x = 2$$

The solution is $(2,1,1)$.

29. Form the augmented matrix: $\begin{bmatrix} 1 & 2 & 0 & | & 3 \\ 0 & 1 & 1 & | & 3 \\ 4 & 0 & -1 & | & 2 \end{bmatrix}$

Add -4 times row 1 to row 3: $\begin{bmatrix} 1 & 2 & 0 & | & 3 \\ 0 & 1 & 1 & | & 3 \\ 0 & -8 & -1 & | & -10 \end{bmatrix}$

Add 8 times row 2 to row 3: $\begin{bmatrix} 1 & 2 & 0 & | & 3 \\ 0 & 1 & 1 & | & 3 \\ 0 & 0 & 7 & | & 14 \end{bmatrix}$

Dividing row 3 by 7: $\begin{bmatrix} 1 & 2 & 0 & | & 3 \\ 0 & 1 & 1 & | & 3 \\ 0 & 0 & 1 & | & 2 \end{bmatrix}$

So $z = 2$. Substituting to find y:

$$y + 2 = 3$$

$$y = 1$$

Substituting to find x:

$$x + 2 = 3$$

$$x = 1$$

The solution is $(1,1,2)$.

31. Form the augmented matrix: $\begin{bmatrix} 1 & 3 & 0 & | & 7 \\ 3 & 0 & -4 & | & -8 \\ 0 & 5 & -2 & | & -5 \end{bmatrix}$

Add -3 times row 1 to row 2: $\begin{bmatrix} 1 & 3 & 0 & | & 7 \\ 0 & -9 & -4 & | & -29 \\ 0 & 5 & -2 & | & -5 \end{bmatrix}$

Add 2 times row 3 to row 2: $\begin{bmatrix} 1 & 3 & 0 & | & 7 \\ 0 & 1 & -8 & | & -39 \\ 0 & 5 & -2 & | & -5 \end{bmatrix}$

Add -5 times row 2 to row 3: $\begin{bmatrix} 1 & 3 & 0 & | & 7 \\ 0 & 1 & -8 & | & -39 \\ 0 & 0 & 38 & | & 190 \end{bmatrix}$

Dividing row 3 by 38: $\begin{bmatrix} 1 & 3 & 0 & | & 7 \\ 0 & 1 & -8 & | & -39 \\ 0 & 0 & 1 & | & 5 \end{bmatrix}$

So $z = 5$. Substituting to find y:

$$y - 40 = -39$$
$$y = 1$$

Substituting to find x:

$$x + 3 = 7$$
$$x = 4$$

The solution is $(4, 1, 5)$.

33. Form the augmented matrix: $\begin{bmatrix} 1 & 4 & 0 & | & 13 \\ 2 & 0 & -5 & | & -3 \\ 0 & 4 & -3 & | & 9 \end{bmatrix}$

Add -2 times row 1 to row 2: $\begin{bmatrix} 1 & 4 & 0 & | & 13 \\ 0 & -8 & -5 & | & -29 \\ 0 & 4 & -3 & | & 9 \end{bmatrix}$

Dividing row 2 by -8: $\begin{bmatrix} 1 & 4 & 0 & | & 13 \\ 0 & 1 & \frac{5}{8} & | & \frac{29}{8} \\ 0 & 4 & -3 & | & 9 \end{bmatrix}$

Add -4 times row 2 to row 3: $\begin{bmatrix} 1 & 4 & 0 & | & 13 \\ 0 & 1 & \frac{5}{8} & | & \frac{29}{8} \\ 0 & 0 & -\frac{11}{2} & | & -\frac{11}{2} \end{bmatrix}$

Multiplying row 3 by $-\frac{2}{11}$: $\begin{bmatrix} 1 & 4 & 0 & | & 13 \\ 0 & 1 & \frac{5}{8} & | & \frac{29}{8} \\ 0 & 0 & 1 & | & 1 \end{bmatrix}$

So $z = 1$. Substituting to find y:

$$y + \frac{5}{8}(1) = \frac{29}{8}$$
$$y + \frac{5}{8} = \frac{29}{8}$$
$$y = \frac{24}{8} = 3$$

Substituting to find x:

$$x + 4(3) = 13$$
$$x + 12 = 13$$
$$x = 1$$

The solution is $(1, 3, 1)$.

35. Form the augmented matrix: $\begin{bmatrix} 1 & -2 & 1 & | & -5 \\ 2 & 3 & -2 & | & -9 \\ 2 & -1 & 2 & | & -1 \end{bmatrix}$

Add –2 times row 1 to row 2 and also to row 3: $\begin{bmatrix} 1 & -2 & 1 & | & -5 \\ 0 & 7 & -4 & | & 1 \\ 0 & 3 & 0 & | & 9 \end{bmatrix}$

Switching rows 2 and 3, and dividing the new row 2 by 3: $\begin{bmatrix} 1 & -2 & 1 & | & -5 \\ 0 & 1 & 0 & | & 3 \\ 0 & 7 & -4 & | & 1 \end{bmatrix}$

Add –7 times row 2 to row 3: $\begin{bmatrix} 1 & -2 & 1 & | & -5 \\ 0 & 1 & 0 & | & 3 \\ 0 & 0 & -4 & | & -20 \end{bmatrix}$

Dividing row 3 by –4: $\begin{bmatrix} 1 & -2 & 1 & | & -5 \\ 0 & 1 & 0 & | & 3 \\ 0 & 0 & 1 & | & 5 \end{bmatrix}$

So $z = 5$ and $y = 3$. Substituting to find x:
$$x - 2(3) + 1(5) = -5$$
$$x - 1 = -5$$
$$x = -4$$
The solution is $(-4, 3, 5)$.

37. Form the augmented matrix (using equation 2 as the first row): $\begin{bmatrix} 1 & 3 & -4 & | & 13 \\ 4 & -2 & -1 & | & -5 \\ 3 & -1 & -3 & | & 0 \end{bmatrix}$

Add –4 times row 1 to row 2 and –3 times row 1 to row 3: $\begin{bmatrix} 1 & 3 & -4 & | & 13 \\ 0 & -14 & 15 & | & -57 \\ 0 & -10 & 9 & | & -39 \end{bmatrix}$

Divide row 2 by –14: $\begin{bmatrix} 1 & 3 & -4 & | & 13 \\ 0 & 1 & -\frac{15}{14} & | & \frac{57}{14} \\ 0 & -10 & 9 & | & -39 \end{bmatrix}$

Add 10 times row 2 to row 3: $\begin{bmatrix} 1 & 3 & -4 & | & 13 \\ 0 & 1 & -\frac{15}{14} & | & \frac{57}{14} \\ 0 & 0 & -\frac{12}{7} & | & \frac{12}{7} \end{bmatrix}$

Multiplying row 3 by $-\frac{7}{12}$: $\begin{bmatrix} 1 & 3 & -4 & | & 13 \\ 0 & 1 & -\frac{15}{14} & | & \frac{57}{14} \\ 0 & 0 & 1 & | & -1 \end{bmatrix}$

So $z = -1$. Substituting to find y:

$$y - \frac{15}{14}(-1) = \frac{57}{14}$$

$$y + \frac{15}{14} = \frac{57}{14}$$

$$y = 3$$

Substituting to find x:

$$x + 3(3) - 4(-1) = 13$$

$$x + 13 = 13$$

$$x = 0$$

The solution is $(0, 3, -1)$.

39. Form the augmented matrix (using equation 2 as the first row): $\begin{bmatrix} 7 & -2 & 0 & | & 1 \\ 0 & 5 & 1 & | & 11 \\ 5 & 0 & 2 & | & -3 \end{bmatrix}$

Dividing row 1 by 7: $\begin{bmatrix} 1 & -\frac{2}{7} & 0 & | & \frac{1}{7} \\ 0 & 5 & 1 & | & 11 \\ 5 & 0 & 2 & | & -3 \end{bmatrix}$

Add -5 times row 1 to row 3: $\begin{bmatrix} 1 & -\frac{2}{7} & 0 & | & \frac{1}{7} \\ 0 & 5 & 1 & | & 11 \\ 0 & \frac{10}{7} & 2 & | & -\frac{26}{7} \end{bmatrix}$

Divide row 2 by 5: $\begin{bmatrix} 1 & -\frac{2}{7} & 0 & | & \frac{1}{7} \\ 0 & 1 & \frac{1}{5} & | & \frac{11}{5} \\ 0 & \frac{10}{7} & 2 & | & -\frac{26}{7} \end{bmatrix}$

Add $-\frac{10}{7}$ times row 2 to row 3: $\begin{bmatrix} 1 & -\frac{2}{7} & 0 & | & \frac{1}{7} \\ 0 & 1 & \frac{1}{5} & | & \frac{11}{5} \\ 0 & 0 & \frac{12}{7} & | & -\frac{48}{7} \end{bmatrix}$

Multiplying row 3 by $\frac{7}{12}$: $\begin{bmatrix} 1 & -\frac{2}{7} & 0 & | & \frac{1}{7} \\ 0 & 1 & \frac{1}{5} & | & \frac{11}{5} \\ 0 & 0 & 1 & | & -4 \end{bmatrix}$

So $z = -4$. Substituting to find y:

$$y + \frac{1}{5}(-4) = \frac{11}{5}$$

$$y - \frac{4}{5} = \frac{11}{5}$$

$$y = 3$$

Substituting to find x:

$$x - \frac{2}{7}(3) = \frac{1}{7}$$

$$x - \frac{6}{7} = \frac{1}{7}$$

$$x = 1$$

The solution is $(1, 3, -4)$.

41. Form the augmented matrix: $\begin{bmatrix} \dfrac{1}{3} & \dfrac{1}{5} & \bigg| & 2 \\ \dfrac{1}{3} & -\dfrac{1}{2} & \bigg| & -\dfrac{1}{3} \end{bmatrix}$

Multiplying row 1 by 15 and row 2 by 6: $\begin{bmatrix} 5 & 3 & | & 30 \\ 2 & -3 & | & -2 \end{bmatrix}$

Dividing row 2 by 2: $\begin{bmatrix} 5 & 3 & | & 30 \\ 1 & -\dfrac{3}{2} & \bigg| & -1 \end{bmatrix}$

Add -5 times row 2 to row 1: $\begin{bmatrix} 0 & \dfrac{21}{2} & \bigg| & 35 \\ 1 & -\dfrac{3}{2} & \bigg| & -1 \end{bmatrix}$

Multiplying row 1 by $\dfrac{2}{21}$: $\begin{bmatrix} 0 & 1 & \bigg| & \dfrac{10}{3} \\ 1 & -\dfrac{3}{2} & \bigg| & -1 \end{bmatrix}$

So $y = \dfrac{10}{3}$. Substituting to find x:

$$x - \frac{3}{2}\left(\frac{10}{3}\right) = -1$$

$$x - 5 = -1$$

$$x = 4$$

The solution is $\left(4, \dfrac{10}{3}\right)$.

43. Form the augmented matrix: $\begin{bmatrix} \frac{1}{3} & -\frac{1}{4} & | & 1 \\ \frac{1}{3} & \frac{1}{4} & | & 3 \end{bmatrix}$

Multiplying row 1 by 12 and row 2 by 12: $\begin{bmatrix} 4 & -3 & | & 12 \\ 4 & 3 & | & 36 \end{bmatrix}$

Dividing row 1 by 4: $\begin{bmatrix} 1 & -\frac{3}{4} & | & 3 \\ 4 & 3 & | & 36 \end{bmatrix}$

Add −4 times row 1 to row 2: $\begin{bmatrix} 1 & -\frac{3}{4} & | & 3 \\ 0 & 6 & | & 24 \end{bmatrix}$

Dividing row 2 by 6: $\begin{bmatrix} 1 & -\frac{3}{4} & | & 3 \\ 0 & 1 & | & 4 \end{bmatrix}$

So $y = 4$. Substituting to find x:

$$x - \frac{3}{4}(4) = 3$$
$$x - 3 = 3$$
$$x = 6$$

The solution is (6,4).

45. Form the augmented matrix: $\begin{bmatrix} 2 & -3 & | & 4 \\ 4 & -6 & | & 4 \end{bmatrix}$

Add −2 times row 1 to row 2: $\begin{bmatrix} 2 & -3 & | & 4 \\ 0 & 0 & | & -4 \end{bmatrix}$

The second row states that $0 = -4$, which is false. There is no solution.

47. Form the augmented matrix: $\begin{bmatrix} -6 & 4 & | & 8 \\ -3 & 2 & | & 4 \end{bmatrix}$

Divide row 1 by −2: $\begin{bmatrix} 3 & -2 & | & -4 \\ -3 & 2 & | & 4 \end{bmatrix}$

Adding row 1 to row 2: $\begin{bmatrix} 3 & -2 & | & -4 \\ 0 & 0 & | & 0 \end{bmatrix}$

The second row states that $0 = 0$, which is true. The system is dependent.

49. Graphing the line:

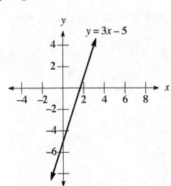

51. Graphing the line:

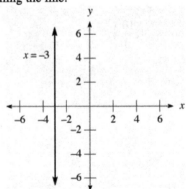

3.4 Determinants and Cramer's Rule

1. Evaluating the determinant: $\begin{vmatrix} 1 & 0 \\ 2 & 3 \end{vmatrix} = 1 \cdot 3 - 0 \cdot 2 = 3 - 0 = 3$

3. Evaluating the determinant: $\begin{vmatrix} 2 & 1 \\ 3 & 4 \end{vmatrix} = 2 \cdot 4 - 1 \cdot 3 = 8 - 3 = 5$

5. Evaluating the determinant: $\begin{vmatrix} 5 & 4 \\ 3 & 2 \end{vmatrix} = 5 \cdot 2 - 3 \cdot 4 = 10 - 12 = -2$

7. Evaluating the determinant: $\begin{vmatrix} 0 & 1 \\ 1 & 0 \end{vmatrix} = 0 \cdot 0 - 1 \cdot 1 = 0 - 1 = -1$

9. Evaluating the determinant: $\begin{vmatrix} -3 & 2 \\ 6 & -4 \end{vmatrix} = (-3) \cdot (-4) - 6 \cdot 2 = 12 - 12 = 0$

11. Evaluating the determinant: $\begin{vmatrix} -3 & -1 \\ 4 & -2 \end{vmatrix} = (-3) \cdot (-2) - (-1) \cdot 4 = 6 + 4 = 10$

13. Solving the equation:
$$\begin{vmatrix} 2x & 1 \\ x & 3 \end{vmatrix} = 10$$
$$6x - x = 10$$
$$5x = 10$$
$$x = 2$$

15. Solving the equation:
$$\begin{vmatrix} 1 & 2x \\ 2 & -3x \end{vmatrix} = 21$$
$$-3x - 4x = 21$$
$$-7x = 21$$
$$x = -3$$

17. Solving the equation:
$$\begin{vmatrix} 2x & -4 \\ x & 2 \end{vmatrix} = -16$$
$$2x(2) + 4x = -16$$
$$4x + 4x = -16$$
$$8x = -16$$
$$x = -2$$

19. Solving the equation:
$$\begin{vmatrix} 11x & -7x \\ 3 & -2 \end{vmatrix} = 3$$
$$11x(-2) + 7x(3) = 3$$
$$-22x + 21x = 3$$
$$-x = 3$$
$$x = -3$$

21. Solving the equation:
$$\begin{vmatrix} 2x & -4 \\ 2 & x \end{vmatrix} = -8x$$
$$2x(x) - 2(-4) = -8x$$
$$2x^2 + 8 = -8x$$
$$2x^2 + 8x + 8 = 0$$
$$x^2 + 4x + 4 = 0$$
$$(x+2)^2 = 0$$
$$x = -2$$

23. Solving the equation:
$$\begin{vmatrix} x^2 & 3 \\ x & 1 \end{vmatrix} = 10$$
$$x^2(1) - 3(x) = 10$$
$$x^2 - 3x = 10$$
$$x^2 - 3x - 10 = 0$$
$$(x+2)(x-5) = 0$$
$$x = -2, 5$$

25. Solving the equation:

$$\begin{vmatrix} x^2 & -4 \\ x & 1 \end{vmatrix} = 32$$

$$x^2(1) - (-4)(x) = 32$$
$$x^2 + 4x = 32$$
$$x^2 + 4x - 32 = 0$$
$$(x+8)(x-4) = 0$$
$$x = -8, 4$$

27. Solving the equation:

$$\begin{vmatrix} x & 5 \\ 1 & x \end{vmatrix} = 4$$

$$x(x) - (1)(5) = 4$$
$$x^2 - 5 = 4$$
$$x^2 - 9 = 0$$
$$(x+3)(x-3) = 0$$
$$x = -3, 3$$

29. First find the determinants:

$$D = \begin{vmatrix} 2 & -3 \\ 4 & -2 \end{vmatrix} = -4 + 12 = 8$$

$$D_x = \begin{vmatrix} 3 & -3 \\ 10 & -2 \end{vmatrix} = -6 + 30 = 24$$

$$D_y = \begin{vmatrix} 2 & 3 \\ 4 & 10 \end{vmatrix} = 20 - 12 = 8$$

Now use Cramer's rule:

$$x = \frac{D_x}{D} = \frac{24}{8} = 3 \qquad y = \frac{D_y}{D} = \frac{8}{8} = 1$$

The solution is (3,1).

31. First find the determinants:

$$D = \begin{vmatrix} 5 & -2 \\ -10 & 4 \end{vmatrix} = 20 - 20 = 0$$

$$D_x = \begin{vmatrix} 4 & -2 \\ 1 & 4 \end{vmatrix} = 16 + 2 = 18$$

$$D_y = \begin{vmatrix} 5 & 4 \\ -10 & 1 \end{vmatrix} = 5 + 40 = 45$$

Since $D = 0$ and other determinants are nonzero, there is no solution, or $\varnothing$.

33. First find the determinants:

$$D = \begin{vmatrix} 4 & -7 \\ 5 & 2 \end{vmatrix} = 8 + 35 = 43$$

$$D_x = \begin{vmatrix} 3 & -7 \\ -3 & 2 \end{vmatrix} = 6 - 21 = -15$$

$$D_y = \begin{vmatrix} 4 & 3 \\ 5 & -3 \end{vmatrix} = -12 - 15 = -27$$

Now use Cramer's rule:

$$x = \frac{D_x}{D} = -\frac{15}{43} \qquad y = \frac{D_y}{D} = -\frac{27}{43}$$

The solution is $\left(-\frac{15}{43}, -\frac{27}{43} \right)$.

35. First find the determinants:

$$D = \begin{vmatrix} 9 & -8 \\ 2 & 3 \end{vmatrix} = 27 + 16 = 43$$

$$D_x = \begin{vmatrix} 4 & -8 \\ 6 & 3 \end{vmatrix} = 12 + 48 = 60$$

$$D_y = \begin{vmatrix} 9 & 4 \\ 2 & 6 \end{vmatrix} = 54 - 8 = 46$$

Now use Cramer's rule:

$$x = \frac{D_x}{D} = \frac{60}{43} \qquad y = \frac{D_y}{D} = \frac{46}{43}$$

The solution is $\left(\frac{60}{43}, \frac{46}{43} \right)$.

37. First find the determinants:

$$D = \begin{vmatrix} 3 & 2 \\ 4 & -5 \end{vmatrix} = -15 - 8 = -23$$

$$D_x = \begin{vmatrix} 6 & 2 \\ 8 & -5 \end{vmatrix} = -30 - 16 = -46$$

$$D_y = \begin{vmatrix} 3 & 6 \\ 4 & 8 \end{vmatrix} = 24 - 24 = 0$$

Now use Cramer's rule:

$$x = \frac{D_x}{D} = \frac{-46}{-23} = 2 \qquad y = \frac{D_y}{D} = \frac{0}{-23} = 0$$

The solution is $(2,0)$.

39. First find the determinants:

$$D = \begin{vmatrix} 12 & -13 \\ 11 & 15 \end{vmatrix} = 180 + 143 = 323$$

$$D_x = \begin{vmatrix} 16 & -13 \\ 18 & 15 \end{vmatrix} = 240 + 234 = 474$$

$$D_y = \begin{vmatrix} 12 & 16 \\ 11 & 18 \end{vmatrix} = 216 - 176 = 40$$

Now use Cramer's rule:

$$x = \frac{D_x}{D} = \frac{474}{323} \qquad y = \frac{D_y}{D} = \frac{40}{323}$$

The solution is $\left(\dfrac{474}{323}, \dfrac{40}{323} \right)$.

41. Duplicating the first two columns:

$$\begin{vmatrix} 1 & 2 & 0 \\ 0 & 2 & 1 \\ 1 & 1 & 1 \end{vmatrix} \begin{matrix} 1 & 2 \\ 0 & 2 \\ 1 & 1 \end{matrix} = 1\cdot2\cdot1 + 2\cdot1\cdot1 + 0\cdot0\cdot1 - 1\cdot2\cdot0 - 1\cdot1\cdot1 - 1\cdot0\cdot2 = 2 + 2 + 0 - 0 - 1 - 0 = 3$$

43. Duplicating the first two columns:

$$\begin{vmatrix} 1 & 2 & 3 \\ 3 & 2 & 1 \\ 1 & 1 & 1 \end{vmatrix} \begin{matrix} 1 & 2 \\ 3 & 2 \\ 1 & 1 \end{matrix} = 1\cdot2\cdot1 + 2\cdot1\cdot1 + 3\cdot3\cdot1 - 1\cdot2\cdot3 - 1\cdot1\cdot1 - 1\cdot3\cdot2 = 2 + 2 + 9 - 6 - 1 - 6 = 0$$

45. Expanding across the first row:

$$\begin{vmatrix} 0 & 1 & 2 \\ 1 & 0 & 1 \\ -1 & 2 & 0 \end{vmatrix} = 0\begin{vmatrix} 0 & 1 \\ 2 & 0 \end{vmatrix} - 1\begin{vmatrix} 1 & 1 \\ -1 & 0 \end{vmatrix} + 2\begin{vmatrix} 1 & 0 \\ -1 & 2 \end{vmatrix} = 0(0-2) - 1(0+1) + 2(2-0) = 0 - 1 + 4 = 3$$

47. Expanding across the first row:

$$\begin{vmatrix} 3 & 0 & 2 \\ 0 & -1 & -1 \\ 4 & 0 & 0 \end{vmatrix} = 3\begin{vmatrix} -1 & -1 \\ 0 & 0 \end{vmatrix} - 0\begin{vmatrix} 0 & -1 \\ 4 & 0 \end{vmatrix} + 2\begin{vmatrix} 0 & -1 \\ 4 & 0 \end{vmatrix} = 3(0-0) - 0(0+4) + 2(0+4) = 0 - 0 + 8 = 8$$

49. Expanding across the first row: $\begin{vmatrix} 2 & -1 & 0 \\ 1 & 0 & -2 \\ 0 & 1 & 2 \end{vmatrix} = 2\begin{vmatrix} 0 & -2 \\ 1 & 2 \end{vmatrix} + 1\begin{vmatrix} 1 & -2 \\ 0 & 2 \end{vmatrix} + 0\begin{vmatrix} 1 & 0 \\ 0 & 1 \end{vmatrix} = 2(0+2) + 1(2-0) + 0 = 4 + 2 = 6$

51. Expanding across the first row:

$$\begin{vmatrix} 1 & 3 & 7 \\ -2 & 6 & 4 \\ 3 & 7 & -1 \end{vmatrix} = 1\begin{vmatrix} 6 & 4 \\ 7 & -1 \end{vmatrix} - 3\begin{vmatrix} -2 & 4 \\ 3 & -1 \end{vmatrix} + 7\begin{vmatrix} -2 & 6 \\ 3 & 7 \end{vmatrix} = 1(-6-28) - 3(2-12) + 7(-14-18) = -34 + 30 - 224 = -228$$

53. Expanding across the first row:

$$\begin{vmatrix} -2 & 0 & 1 \\ 0 & 3 & 2 \\ 1 & 0 & -5 \end{vmatrix} = -2\begin{vmatrix} 3 & 2 \\ 0 & -5 \end{vmatrix} - 0\begin{vmatrix} 0 & 2 \\ 1 & -5 \end{vmatrix} + 1\begin{vmatrix} 0 & 3 \\ 1 & 0 \end{vmatrix} = -2(-15-0) - 0 + 1(0-3) = 30 - 3 = 27$$

55. Expanding across the first row:

$$\begin{vmatrix} -2 & 4 & -1 \\ 0 & 3 & 1 \\ -5 & -2 & 3 \end{vmatrix} = -2\begin{vmatrix} 3 & 1 \\ -2 & 3 \end{vmatrix} - 4\begin{vmatrix} 0 & 1 \\ -5 & 3 \end{vmatrix} - 1\begin{vmatrix} 0 & 3 \\ -5 & -2 \end{vmatrix} = -2(9+2) - 4(0+5) - 1(0+15) = -22 - 20 - 15 = -57$$

57. First find the determinants:

$$D = \begin{vmatrix} 1 & 1 & 1 \\ 1 & -1 & -1 \\ 2 & 2 & -1 \end{vmatrix} = 1\begin{vmatrix} -1 & -1 \\ 2 & -1 \end{vmatrix} - 1\begin{vmatrix} 1 & -1 \\ 2 & -1 \end{vmatrix} + 1\begin{vmatrix} 1 & -1 \\ 2 & 2 \end{vmatrix} = 3 - 1 + 4 = 6$$

$$D_x = \begin{vmatrix} 4 & 1 & 1 \\ 2 & -1 & -1 \\ 2 & 2 & -1 \end{vmatrix} = 4\begin{vmatrix} -1 & -1 \\ 2 & -1 \end{vmatrix} - 1\begin{vmatrix} 2 & -1 \\ 2 & -1 \end{vmatrix} + 1\begin{vmatrix} 2 & -1 \\ 2 & 2 \end{vmatrix} = 12 - 0 + 6 = 18$$

$$D_y = \begin{vmatrix} 1 & 4 & 1 \\ 1 & 2 & -1 \\ 2 & 2 & -1 \end{vmatrix} = 1\begin{vmatrix} 2 & -1 \\ 2 & -1 \end{vmatrix} - 4\begin{vmatrix} 1 & -1 \\ 2 & -1 \end{vmatrix} + 1\begin{vmatrix} 1 & 2 \\ 2 & 2 \end{vmatrix} = 0 - 4 - 2 = -6$$

$$D_z = \begin{vmatrix} 1 & 1 & 4 \\ 1 & -1 & 2 \\ 2 & 2 & 2 \end{vmatrix} = 1\begin{vmatrix} -1 & 2 \\ 2 & 2 \end{vmatrix} - 1\begin{vmatrix} 1 & 2 \\ 2 & 2 \end{vmatrix} + 4\begin{vmatrix} 1 & -1 \\ 2 & 2 \end{vmatrix} = -6 + 2 + 16 = 12$$

Now use Cramer's rule:

$$x = \frac{D_x}{D} = \frac{18}{6} = 3 \qquad y = \frac{D_y}{D} = \frac{-6}{6} = -1 \qquad z = \frac{D_z}{D} = \frac{12}{6} = 2$$

The solution is $(3, -1, 2)$.

59. First find the determinants:

$$D = \begin{vmatrix} 1 & 1 & -1 \\ -1 & 1 & 1 \\ 1 & 1 & 1 \end{vmatrix} = 1\begin{vmatrix} 1 & 1 \\ 1 & 1 \end{vmatrix} - 1\begin{vmatrix} -1 & 1 \\ 1 & 1 \end{vmatrix} - 1\begin{vmatrix} -1 & 1 \\ 1 & 1 \end{vmatrix} = 0 + 2 + 2 = 4$$

$$D_x = \begin{vmatrix} 2 & 1 & -1 \\ 3 & 1 & 1 \\ 4 & 1 & 1 \end{vmatrix} = 2\begin{vmatrix} 1 & 1 \\ 1 & 1 \end{vmatrix} - 1\begin{vmatrix} 3 & 1 \\ 4 & 1 \end{vmatrix} - 1\begin{vmatrix} 3 & 1 \\ 4 & 1 \end{vmatrix} = 0 + 1 + 1 = 2$$

$$D_y = \begin{vmatrix} 1 & 2 & -1 \\ -1 & 3 & 1 \\ 1 & 4 & 1 \end{vmatrix} = 1\begin{vmatrix} 3 & 1 \\ 4 & 1 \end{vmatrix} - 2\begin{vmatrix} -1 & 1 \\ 1 & 1 \end{vmatrix} - 1\begin{vmatrix} -1 & 3 \\ 1 & 4 \end{vmatrix} = -1 + 4 + 7 = 10$$

$$D_z = \begin{vmatrix} 1 & 1 & 2 \\ -1 & 1 & 3 \\ 1 & 1 & 4 \end{vmatrix} = 1\begin{vmatrix} 1 & 3 \\ 1 & 4 \end{vmatrix} - 1\begin{vmatrix} -1 & 3 \\ 1 & 4 \end{vmatrix} + 2\begin{vmatrix} -1 & 1 \\ 1 & 1 \end{vmatrix} = 1 + 7 - 4 = 4$$

Now use Cramer's rule:

$$x = \frac{D_x}{D} = \frac{2}{4} = \frac{1}{2} \qquad y = \frac{D_y}{D} = \frac{10}{4} = \frac{5}{2} \qquad z = \frac{D_z}{D} = \frac{4}{4} = 1$$

The solution is $\left(\frac{1}{2}, \frac{5}{2}, 1 \right)$.

61. First find the determinants:

$$D = \begin{vmatrix} 3 & -1 & 2 \\ 6 & -2 & 4 \\ 1 & -5 & 2 \end{vmatrix} = 3\begin{vmatrix} -2 & 4 \\ -5 & 2 \end{vmatrix} + 1\begin{vmatrix} 6 & 4 \\ 1 & 2 \end{vmatrix} + 2\begin{vmatrix} 6 & -2 \\ 1 & -5 \end{vmatrix} = 48 + 8 - 56 = 0$$

$$D_x = \begin{vmatrix} 4 & -1 & 2 \\ 8 & -2 & 4 \\ 1 & -5 & 2 \end{vmatrix} = 4\begin{vmatrix} -2 & 4 \\ -5 & 2 \end{vmatrix} + 1\begin{vmatrix} 8 & 4 \\ 1 & 2 \end{vmatrix} + 2\begin{vmatrix} 8 & -2 \\ 1 & -5 \end{vmatrix} = 64 + 12 - 76 = 0$$

$$D_y = \begin{vmatrix} 3 & 4 & 2 \\ 6 & 8 & 4 \\ 1 & 1 & 2 \end{vmatrix} = 3\begin{vmatrix} 8 & 4 \\ 1 & 2 \end{vmatrix} - 4\begin{vmatrix} 6 & 4 \\ 1 & 2 \end{vmatrix} + 2\begin{vmatrix} 6 & 8 \\ 1 & 1 \end{vmatrix} = 36 - 32 - 4 = 0$$

$$D_z = \begin{vmatrix} 3 & -1 & 4 \\ 6 & -2 & 8 \\ 1 & -5 & 1 \end{vmatrix} = 3\begin{vmatrix} -2 & 8 \\ -5 & 1 \end{vmatrix} + 1\begin{vmatrix} 6 & 8 \\ 1 & 1 \end{vmatrix} + 4\begin{vmatrix} 6 & -2 \\ 1 & -5 \end{vmatrix} = 114 - 2 - 112 = 0$$

Since $D = 0$ and the other determinants are also 0, there is no unique solution (dependent).

63. First find the determinants:

$$D = \begin{vmatrix} 2 & -1 & 3 \\ 1 & -5 & -2 \\ -4 & -2 & 1 \end{vmatrix} = 2\begin{vmatrix} -5 & -2 \\ -2 & 1 \end{vmatrix} + 1\begin{vmatrix} 1 & -2 \\ -4 & 1 \end{vmatrix} + 3\begin{vmatrix} 1 & -5 \\ -4 & -2 \end{vmatrix} = -18 - 7 - 66 = -91$$

$$D_x = \begin{vmatrix} 4 & -1 & 3 \\ 1 & -5 & -2 \\ 3 & -2 & 1 \end{vmatrix} = 4\begin{vmatrix} -5 & -2 \\ -2 & 1 \end{vmatrix} + 1\begin{vmatrix} 1 & -2 \\ 3 & 1 \end{vmatrix} + 3\begin{vmatrix} 1 & -5 \\ 3 & -2 \end{vmatrix} = -36 + 7 + 39 = 10$$

$$D_y = \begin{vmatrix} 2 & 4 & 3 \\ 1 & 1 & -2 \\ -4 & 3 & 1 \end{vmatrix} = 2\begin{vmatrix} 1 & -2 \\ 3 & 1 \end{vmatrix} - 4\begin{vmatrix} 1 & -2 \\ -4 & 1 \end{vmatrix} + 3\begin{vmatrix} 1 & 1 \\ -4 & 3 \end{vmatrix} = 14 + 28 + 21 = 63$$

$$D_z = \begin{vmatrix} 2 & -1 & 4 \\ 1 & -5 & 1 \\ -4 & -2 & 3 \end{vmatrix} = 2\begin{vmatrix} -5 & 1 \\ -2 & 3 \end{vmatrix} + 1\begin{vmatrix} 1 & 1 \\ -4 & 3 \end{vmatrix} + 4\begin{vmatrix} 1 & -5 \\ -4 & -2 \end{vmatrix} = -26 + 7 - 88 = -107$$

Now use Cramer's rule:

$$x = \frac{D_x}{D} = -\frac{10}{91} \qquad y = \frac{D_y}{D} = -\frac{63}{91} = -\frac{9}{13} \qquad z = \frac{D_z}{D} = \frac{-107}{-91} = \frac{107}{91}$$

The solution is $\left(-\frac{10}{91}, -\frac{9}{13}, \frac{107}{91} \right)$.

65. First find the determinants:

$$D = \begin{vmatrix} 1 & 2 & -1 \\ 2 & 3 & 2 \\ 1 & -3 & 1 \end{vmatrix} = 1\begin{vmatrix} 3 & 2 \\ -3 & 1 \end{vmatrix} - 2\begin{vmatrix} 2 & 2 \\ 1 & 1 \end{vmatrix} - 1\begin{vmatrix} 2 & 3 \\ 1 & -3 \end{vmatrix} = 9 - 0 + 9 = 18$$

$$D_x = \begin{vmatrix} 4 & 2 & -1 \\ 5 & 3 & 2 \\ 6 & -3 & 1 \end{vmatrix} = 4\begin{vmatrix} 3 & 2 \\ -3 & 1 \end{vmatrix} - 2\begin{vmatrix} 5 & 2 \\ 6 & 1 \end{vmatrix} - 1\begin{vmatrix} 5 & 3 \\ 6 & -3 \end{vmatrix} = 36 + 14 + 33 = 83$$

$$D_y = \begin{vmatrix} 1 & 4 & -1 \\ 2 & 5 & 2 \\ 1 & 6 & 1 \end{vmatrix} = 1\begin{vmatrix} 5 & 2 \\ 6 & 1 \end{vmatrix} - 4\begin{vmatrix} 2 & 2 \\ 1 & 1 \end{vmatrix} - 1\begin{vmatrix} 2 & 5 \\ 1 & 6 \end{vmatrix} = -7 - 0 - 7 = -14$$

$$D_z = \begin{vmatrix} 1 & 2 & 4 \\ 2 & 3 & 5 \\ 1 & -3 & 6 \end{vmatrix} = 1\begin{vmatrix} 3 & 5 \\ -3 & 6 \end{vmatrix} - 2\begin{vmatrix} 2 & 5 \\ 1 & 6 \end{vmatrix} + 4\begin{vmatrix} 2 & 3 \\ 1 & -3 \end{vmatrix} = 33 - 14 - 36 = -17$$

Now use Cramer's rule:

$$x = \frac{D_x}{D} = \frac{83}{18} \qquad y = \frac{D_y}{D} = \frac{-14}{18} = -\frac{7}{9} \qquad z = \frac{D_z}{D} = -\frac{17}{18}$$

The solution is $\left(\frac{83}{18}, -\frac{7}{9}, -\frac{17}{18} \right)$.

67. First find the determinants:

$$D = \begin{vmatrix} 3 & -4 & 2 \\ 2 & -3 & 4 \\ 4 & 2 & -3 \end{vmatrix} = 3\begin{vmatrix} -3 & 4 \\ 2 & -3 \end{vmatrix} + 4\begin{vmatrix} 2 & 4 \\ 4 & -3 \end{vmatrix} + 2\begin{vmatrix} 2 & -3 \\ 4 & 2 \end{vmatrix} = 3 - 88 + 32 = -53$$

$$D_x = \begin{vmatrix} 5 & -4 & 2 \\ 7 & -3 & 4 \\ 6 & 2 & -3 \end{vmatrix} = 5\begin{vmatrix} -3 & 4 \\ 2 & -3 \end{vmatrix} + 4\begin{vmatrix} 7 & 4 \\ 6 & -3 \end{vmatrix} + 2\begin{vmatrix} 7 & -3 \\ 6 & 2 \end{vmatrix} = 5 - 180 + 64 = -111$$

$$D_y = \begin{vmatrix} 3 & 5 & 2 \\ 2 & 7 & 4 \\ 4 & 6 & -3 \end{vmatrix} = 3\begin{vmatrix} 7 & 4 \\ 6 & -3 \end{vmatrix} - 5\begin{vmatrix} 2 & 4 \\ 4 & -3 \end{vmatrix} + 2\begin{vmatrix} 2 & 7 \\ 4 & 6 \end{vmatrix} = -135 + 110 - 32 = -57$$

$$D_z = \begin{vmatrix} 3 & -4 & 5 \\ 2 & -3 & 7 \\ 4 & 2 & 6 \end{vmatrix} = 3\begin{vmatrix} -3 & 7 \\ 2 & 6 \end{vmatrix} + 4\begin{vmatrix} 2 & 7 \\ 4 & 6 \end{vmatrix} + 5\begin{vmatrix} 2 & -3 \\ 4 & 2 \end{vmatrix} = -96 - 64 + 80 = -80$$

Now use Cramer's rule:

$$x = \frac{D_x}{D} = \frac{-111}{-53} = \frac{111}{53} \qquad y = \frac{D_y}{D} = \frac{-57}{-53} = \frac{57}{53} \qquad z = \frac{D_z}{D} = \frac{-80}{-53} = \frac{80}{53}$$

The solution is $\left(\frac{111}{53}, \frac{57}{53}, \frac{80}{53} \right)$.

69. First find the determinants:

$$D = \begin{vmatrix} 1 & 0 & -3 \\ 0 & 1 & 2 \\ 1 & 0 & 1 \end{vmatrix} = 1 \begin{vmatrix} 1 & 2 \\ 0 & 1 \end{vmatrix} - 0 \begin{vmatrix} 0 & 2 \\ 1 & 1 \end{vmatrix} - 3 \begin{vmatrix} 0 & 1 \\ 1 & 0 \end{vmatrix} = 1 - 0 + 3 = 4$$

$$D_x = \begin{vmatrix} 1 & 0 & -3 \\ 8 & 1 & 2 \\ 10 & 0 & 1 \end{vmatrix} = 1 \begin{vmatrix} 1 & 2 \\ 0 & 1 \end{vmatrix} - 0 \begin{vmatrix} 8 & 2 \\ 10 & 1 \end{vmatrix} - 3 \begin{vmatrix} 8 & 1 \\ 10 & 0 \end{vmatrix} = 1 - 0 + 30 = 31$$

$$D_y = \begin{vmatrix} 1 & 1 & -3 \\ 0 & 8 & 2 \\ 1 & 10 & 1 \end{vmatrix} = 1 \begin{vmatrix} 8 & 2 \\ 10 & 1 \end{vmatrix} - 1 \begin{vmatrix} 0 & 2 \\ 1 & 1 \end{vmatrix} - 3 \begin{vmatrix} 0 & 8 \\ 1 & 10 \end{vmatrix} = -12 + 2 + 24 = 14$$

$$D_z = \begin{vmatrix} 1 & 0 & 1 \\ 0 & 1 & 8 \\ 1 & 0 & 10 \end{vmatrix} = 1 \begin{vmatrix} 1 & 8 \\ 0 & 10 \end{vmatrix} - 0 \begin{vmatrix} 0 & 8 \\ 1 & 10 \end{vmatrix} + 1 \begin{vmatrix} 0 & 1 \\ 1 & 0 \end{vmatrix} = 10 - 0 - 1 = 9$$

Now use Cramer's rule:

$$x = \frac{D_x}{D} = \frac{31}{4} \qquad y = \frac{D_y}{D} = \frac{14}{4} = \frac{7}{2} \qquad z = \frac{D_z}{D} = \frac{9}{4}$$

The solution is $\left(\frac{31}{4}, \frac{7}{2}, \frac{9}{4} \right)$.

71. First find the determinants:

$$D = \begin{vmatrix} -1 & -7 & 0 \\ 1 & 0 & 3 \\ 0 & 2 & 1 \end{vmatrix} = -1 \begin{vmatrix} 0 & 3 \\ 2 & 1 \end{vmatrix} + 7 \begin{vmatrix} 1 & 3 \\ 0 & 1 \end{vmatrix} + 0 \begin{vmatrix} 1 & 0 \\ 0 & 2 \end{vmatrix} = 6 + 7 + 0 = 13$$

$$D_x = \begin{vmatrix} 1 & -7 & 0 \\ 11 & 0 & 3 \\ 0 & 2 & 1 \end{vmatrix} = 1 \begin{vmatrix} 0 & 3 \\ 2 & 1 \end{vmatrix} + 7 \begin{vmatrix} 11 & 3 \\ 0 & 1 \end{vmatrix} + 0 \begin{vmatrix} 11 & 0 \\ 0 & 2 \end{vmatrix} = -6 + 77 + 0 = 71$$

$$D_y = \begin{vmatrix} -1 & 1 & 0 \\ 1 & 11 & 3 \\ 0 & 0 & 1 \end{vmatrix} = -1 \begin{vmatrix} 11 & 3 \\ 0 & 1 \end{vmatrix} - 1 \begin{vmatrix} 1 & 3 \\ 0 & 1 \end{vmatrix} + 0 \begin{vmatrix} 1 & 11 \\ 0 & 0 \end{vmatrix} = -11 - 1 + 0 = -12$$

$$D_z = \begin{vmatrix} -1 & -7 & 1 \\ 1 & 0 & 11 \\ 0 & 2 & 0 \end{vmatrix} = -1 \begin{vmatrix} 0 & 11 \\ 2 & 0 \end{vmatrix} + 7 \begin{vmatrix} 1 & 11 \\ 0 & 0 \end{vmatrix} + 1 \begin{vmatrix} 1 & 0 \\ 0 & 2 \end{vmatrix} = 22 + 0 + 2 = 24$$

Now use Cramer's rule:

$$x = \frac{D_x}{D} = \frac{71}{13} \qquad y = \frac{D_y}{D} = -\frac{12}{13} \qquad z = \frac{D_z}{D} = \frac{24}{13}$$

The solution is $\left(\frac{71}{13}, -\frac{12}{13}, \frac{24}{13} \right)$.

73. First find the determinants:

$$D = \begin{vmatrix} 1 & -1 & 0 \\ 3 & 0 & 1 \\ 0 & 1 & -2 \end{vmatrix} = 1 \begin{vmatrix} 0 & 1 \\ 1 & -2 \end{vmatrix} + 1 \begin{vmatrix} 3 & 1 \\ 0 & -2 \end{vmatrix} + 0 \begin{vmatrix} 3 & 0 \\ 0 & 1 \end{vmatrix} = -1 - 6 + 0 = -7$$

$$D_x = \begin{vmatrix} 2 & -1 & 0 \\ 11 & 0 & 1 \\ -3 & 1 & -2 \end{vmatrix} = 2 \begin{vmatrix} 0 & 1 \\ 1 & -2 \end{vmatrix} + 1 \begin{vmatrix} 11 & 1 \\ -3 & -2 \end{vmatrix} + 0 \begin{vmatrix} 11 & 0 \\ -3 & 1 \end{vmatrix} = -2 - 19 + 0 = -21$$

$$D_y = \begin{vmatrix} 1 & 2 & 0 \\ 3 & 11 & 1 \\ 0 & -3 & -2 \end{vmatrix} = 1 \begin{vmatrix} 11 & 1 \\ -3 & -2 \end{vmatrix} - 2 \begin{vmatrix} 3 & 1 \\ 0 & -2 \end{vmatrix} + 0 \begin{vmatrix} 3 & 11 \\ 0 & -3 \end{vmatrix} = -19 + 12 + 0 = -7$$

$$D_z = \begin{vmatrix} 1 & -1 & 2 \\ 3 & 0 & 11 \\ 0 & 1 & -3 \end{vmatrix} = 1 \begin{vmatrix} 0 & 11 \\ 1 & -3 \end{vmatrix} + 1 \begin{vmatrix} 3 & 11 \\ 0 & -3 \end{vmatrix} + 2 \begin{vmatrix} 3 & 0 \\ 0 & 1 \end{vmatrix} = -11 - 9 + 6 = -14$$

Now use Cramer's rule:

$$x = \frac{D_x}{D} = \frac{-21}{-7} = 3 \qquad y = \frac{D_y}{D} = \frac{-7}{-7} = 1 \qquad z = \frac{D_z}{D} = \frac{-14}{-7} = 2$$

The solution is (3,1,2).

75. The determinant equation is:

$$\begin{vmatrix} y & x \\ m & 1 \end{vmatrix} = b$$
$$y - mx = b$$
$$y = mx + b$$

77. **a.** Writing the determinant equation:

$$\begin{vmatrix} x & -1.7 \\ 2 & 0.3 \end{vmatrix} = y$$
$$0.3x + 3.4 = y$$
$$y = 0.3x + 3.4$$

b. Substituting $x = 2$: $y = 0.3(2) + 3.4 = 0.6 + 3.4 = 4$ billion dollars

79. **a.** Writing the equation:

$$\begin{vmatrix} x & -3 \\ 7,121 & 767.5 \end{vmatrix} = I$$
$$767.5x + 3(7,121) = I$$
$$I = 767.5x + 21,363$$

b. Substituting $x = 4$: $I = 767.5(4) + 21,363 = \$24,433$

81. Substituting $x = 6$: $y = \begin{vmatrix} 0.1 & 6.9 \\ -2 & 6 \end{vmatrix} = 0.1(6) - (-2)(6.9) = 0.6 + 13.8 = 14.4$ million

83. Find the determinants:

$$D = \begin{vmatrix} -164.2 & 1 \\ 1 & 0 \end{vmatrix} = -164.2(0) - 1 = -1$$

$$D_H = \begin{vmatrix} -164.2 & 719 \\ 1 & 5 \end{vmatrix} = -164.2(5) - 719 = -1540$$

Now using Cramer's rule: $H = \frac{D_H}{D} = \frac{-1540}{-1} = 1,540$ heart transplants

85. First rewrite the system as:
$$-10x + y = 100$$
$$-12x + y = 0$$
Now find the determinants:
$$D = \begin{vmatrix} -10 & 1 \\ -12 & 1 \end{vmatrix} = -10 + 12 = 2$$

$$D_x = \begin{vmatrix} 100 & 1 \\ 0 & 1 \end{vmatrix} = 100 - 0 = 100$$

$$D_y = \begin{vmatrix} -10 & 100 \\ -12 & 0 \end{vmatrix} = 0 + 1200 = 1200$$

Now using Cramer's rule:
$$x = \frac{D_x}{D} = \frac{100}{2} = 50 \qquad\qquad y = \frac{D_y}{D} = \frac{1200}{2} = 600$$

The company must sell 50 items per week to break even.

87. First write the system in the correct form:
$$-0.98x + y = -1,915.8$$
$$y = 30$$
Find the determinants:
$$D = \begin{vmatrix} -0.98 & 1 \\ 0 & 1 \end{vmatrix} = -0.98(1) - 0 = -0.98$$

$$D_x = \begin{vmatrix} -1,915.8 & 1 \\ 30 & 1 \end{vmatrix} = -1,915.8(1) - 30 = -1,945.8$$

Now using Cramer's rule: $x = \dfrac{D_x}{D} = \dfrac{-1,945.8}{-0.98} \approx 1986$

In 1986 approximately 30 million residents were without health insurance.

89. Expanding across row 1:
$$\begin{vmatrix} 2 & 0 & 1 & -3 \\ -1 & 2 & 0 & 1 \\ -3 & 0 & 1 & 0 \\ 1 & 1 & 0 & 0 \end{vmatrix}$$

$$= 2\begin{vmatrix} 2 & 0 & 1 \\ 0 & 1 & 0 \\ 1 & 0 & 0 \end{vmatrix} - 0\begin{vmatrix} -1 & 0 & 1 \\ -3 & 1 & 0 \\ 1 & 0 & 0 \end{vmatrix} + 1\begin{vmatrix} -1 & 2 & 1 \\ -3 & 0 & 0 \\ 1 & 1 & 0 \end{vmatrix} + 3\begin{vmatrix} -1 & 2 & 0 \\ -3 & 0 & 1 \\ 1 & 1 & 0 \end{vmatrix}$$

$$= 2\left(2\begin{vmatrix} 1 & 0 \\ 0 & 0 \end{vmatrix} - 0 + 1\begin{vmatrix} 0 & 1 \\ 1 & 0 \end{vmatrix} \right) - 0 + 1\left(-1\begin{vmatrix} 0 & 0 \\ 1 & 0 \end{vmatrix} - 2\begin{vmatrix} -3 & 0 \\ 1 & 0 \end{vmatrix} + 1\begin{vmatrix} -3 & 0 \\ 1 & 1 \end{vmatrix} \right) + 3\left(-1\begin{vmatrix} 0 & 1 \\ 1 & 0 \end{vmatrix} - 2\begin{vmatrix} -3 & 1 \\ 1 & 0 \end{vmatrix} \right)$$

$$= 2(0 - 0 - 1) + 1(0 - 0 - 3) + 3(1 + 2)$$
$$= -2 - 3 + 9$$
$$= 4$$

91. Expanding down column 3:

$$\begin{vmatrix} 2 & 0 & 1 & -3 \\ -1 & 2 & 0 & 1 \\ -3 & 0 & 1 & 0 \\ 1 & 1 & 0 & 0 \end{vmatrix}$$

$$=1\begin{vmatrix} -1 & 2 & 1 \\ -3 & 0 & 0 \\ 1 & 1 & 0 \end{vmatrix}-0\begin{vmatrix} 2 & 0 & -3 \\ -3 & 0 & 0 \\ 1 & 1 & 0 \end{vmatrix}+1\begin{vmatrix} 2 & 0 & -3 \\ -1 & 2 & 1 \\ 1 & 1 & 0 \end{vmatrix}-0\begin{vmatrix} 2 & 0 & -3 \\ -1 & 2 & 1 \\ -3 & 0 & 0 \end{vmatrix}$$

$$=1\left(-1\begin{vmatrix} 0 & 0 \\ 1 & 0 \end{vmatrix}-2\begin{vmatrix} -3 & 0 \\ 1 & 0 \end{vmatrix}+1\begin{vmatrix} -3 & 0 \\ 1 & 1 \end{vmatrix}\right)-0+1\left(2\begin{vmatrix} 2 & 1 \\ 1 & 0 \end{vmatrix}-0-3\begin{vmatrix} -1 & 2 \\ 1 & 1 \end{vmatrix}\right)-0$$

$$=1(0-0-3)+1(-2-0+9)$$

$$=-3+7$$

$$=4$$

93. Expanding the determinant:

$$\begin{vmatrix} 1 & 3 & 2 & -4 \\ 0 & 4 & 1 & 0 \\ -2 & 1 & 3 & 0 \\ 2 & 3 & 4 & -1 \end{vmatrix}$$

$$=1\begin{vmatrix} 4 & 1 & 0 \\ 1 & 3 & 0 \\ 3 & 4 & -1 \end{vmatrix}-3\begin{vmatrix} 0 & 1 & 0 \\ -2 & 3 & 0 \\ 2 & 4 & -1 \end{vmatrix}+2\begin{vmatrix} 0 & 4 & 0 \\ -2 & 1 & 0 \\ 2 & 3 & -1 \end{vmatrix}+4\begin{vmatrix} 0 & 4 & 1 \\ -2 & 1 & 3 \\ 2 & 3 & 4 \end{vmatrix}$$

$$=4\left(3\begin{vmatrix} 3 & 0 \\ 4 & -1 \end{vmatrix}-1\begin{vmatrix} 1 & 0 \\ 3 & -1 \end{vmatrix}\right)-3\left(-1\begin{vmatrix} -2 & 0 \\ 2 & -1 \end{vmatrix}\right)+2\left(-4\begin{vmatrix} -2 & 0 \\ 2 & -1 \end{vmatrix}\right)+4\left(-4\begin{vmatrix} -2 & 3 \\ 2 & 4 \end{vmatrix}+1\begin{vmatrix} -2 & 1 \\ 2 & 3 \end{vmatrix}\right)$$

$$=4(-3)-1(-1)-3(-2)-8(2)-16(-14)+4(-8)$$

$$=-12+1+6-16+224-32$$

$$=171$$

95. Find the determinants:

$$D=\begin{vmatrix} 1 & 2 & -1 & 3 \\ 2 & 1 & 2 & -2 \\ 1 & -3 & 1 & -1 \\ -2 & 1 & -1 & 3 \end{vmatrix}$$

$$=1\begin{vmatrix} 1 & 2 & -2 \\ -3 & 1 & -1 \\ 1 & -1 & 3 \end{vmatrix}-2\begin{vmatrix} 2 & 2 & -2 \\ 1 & 1 & -1 \\ -2 & -1 & 3 \end{vmatrix}-1\begin{vmatrix} 2 & 1 & -2 \\ 1 & -3 & -1 \\ -2 & 1 & 3 \end{vmatrix}-3\begin{vmatrix} 2 & 1 & 2 \\ 1 & -3 & 1 \\ -2 & 1 & -1 \end{vmatrix}$$

$$=1\left(1\begin{vmatrix} 1 & -1 \\ -1 & 3 \end{vmatrix}-2\begin{vmatrix} -3 & -1 \\ 1 & 3 \end{vmatrix}-2\begin{vmatrix} -3 & 1 \\ 1 & -1 \end{vmatrix}\right)-2\left(2\begin{vmatrix} 1 & -1 \\ -1 & 3 \end{vmatrix}-2\begin{vmatrix} 1 & -1 \\ -2 & 3 \end{vmatrix}-2\begin{vmatrix} 1 & 1 \\ -2 & -1 \end{vmatrix}\right)$$

$$-1\left(2\begin{vmatrix} -3 & -1 \\ 1 & 3 \end{vmatrix}-1\begin{vmatrix} 1 & -1 \\ -2 & 3 \end{vmatrix}-2\begin{vmatrix} 1 & -3 \\ -2 & 1 \end{vmatrix}\right)-3\left(2\begin{vmatrix} -3 & 1 \\ 1 & -1 \end{vmatrix}-1\begin{vmatrix} 1 & 1 \\ -2 & -1 \end{vmatrix}+2\begin{vmatrix} 1 & -3 \\ -2 & 1 \end{vmatrix}\right)$$

$$=1[1(2)-2(-8)-2(2)]-2[2(2)-2(1)-2(1)]-1[2(-8)-1(1)-2(-5)]-3[2(2)-1(1)+2(-5)]$$

$$=1(2+16-4)-2(4-2-2)-1(-16-1+10)-3(4-1-10)$$

$$=1(14)-2(0)-1(-7)-3(-7)$$

$$=14-0+7+21$$

$$=42$$

$$D_x = \begin{vmatrix} 4 & 2 & -1 & 3 \\ 9 & 1 & 2 & -2 \\ 1 & -3 & 1 & -1 \\ -3 & 1 & -1 & 3 \end{vmatrix}$$

$$= 4\begin{vmatrix} 1 & 2 & -2 \\ -3 & 1 & -1 \\ 1 & -1 & 3 \end{vmatrix} - 2\begin{vmatrix} 9 & 2 & -2 \\ 1 & 1 & -1 \\ -3 & -1 & 3 \end{vmatrix} - 1\begin{vmatrix} 9 & 1 & -2 \\ 1 & -3 & -1 \\ -3 & 1 & 3 \end{vmatrix} - 3\begin{vmatrix} 9 & 1 & 2 \\ 1 & -3 & 1 \\ -3 & 1 & -1 \end{vmatrix}$$

$$= 4\left(1\begin{vmatrix} 1 & -1 \\ -1 & 3 \end{vmatrix} - 2\begin{vmatrix} -3 & -1 \\ 1 & 3 \end{vmatrix} - 2\begin{vmatrix} -3 & 1 \\ 1 & -1 \end{vmatrix} \right) - 2\left(9\begin{vmatrix} 1 & -1 \\ -1 & 3 \end{vmatrix} - 2\begin{vmatrix} 1 & -1 \\ -3 & 3 \end{vmatrix} - 2\begin{vmatrix} 1 & 1 \\ -3 & -1 \end{vmatrix} \right)$$

$$- 1\left(9\begin{vmatrix} -3 & -1 \\ 1 & 3 \end{vmatrix} - 1\begin{vmatrix} 1 & -1 \\ -3 & 3 \end{vmatrix} - 2\begin{vmatrix} 1 & -3 \\ -3 & 1 \end{vmatrix} \right) - 3\left(9\begin{vmatrix} -3 & 1 \\ 1 & -1 \end{vmatrix} - 1\begin{vmatrix} 1 & 1 \\ -3 & -1 \end{vmatrix} + 2\begin{vmatrix} 1 & -3 \\ -3 & 1 \end{vmatrix} \right)$$

$$= 4\big[1(2) - 2(-8) - 2(2)\big] - 2\big[9(2) - 2(0) - 2(2)\big] - 1\big[9(-8) - 1(0) - 2(-8)\big] - 3\big[9(2) - 1(2) + 2(-8)\big]$$

$$= 4(2 + 16 - 4) - 2(18 - 0 - 4) - 1(-72 - 0 + 16) - 3(18 - 2 - 16)$$

$$= 4(14) - 2(14) - 1(-56) - 3(0)$$

$$= 56 - 28 + 56 - 0$$

$$= 84$$

$$D_y = \begin{vmatrix} 1 & 4 & -1 & 3 \\ 2 & 9 & 2 & -2 \\ 1 & 1 & 1 & -1 \\ -2 & -3 & -1 & 3 \end{vmatrix}$$

$$= 1\begin{vmatrix} 9 & 2 & -2 \\ 1 & 1 & -1 \\ -3 & -1 & 3 \end{vmatrix} - 4\begin{vmatrix} 2 & 2 & -2 \\ 1 & 1 & -1 \\ -2 & -1 & 3 \end{vmatrix} - 1\begin{vmatrix} 2 & 9 & -2 \\ 1 & 1 & -1 \\ -2 & -3 & 3 \end{vmatrix} - 3\begin{vmatrix} 2 & 9 & 2 \\ 1 & 1 & 1 \\ -2 & -3 & -1 \end{vmatrix}$$

$$= 1\left(9\begin{vmatrix} 1 & -1 \\ -1 & 3 \end{vmatrix} - 2\begin{vmatrix} 1 & -1 \\ -3 & 3 \end{vmatrix} - 2\begin{vmatrix} 1 & 1 \\ -3 & -1 \end{vmatrix} \right) - 4\left(2\begin{vmatrix} 1 & -1 \\ -1 & 3 \end{vmatrix} - 2\begin{vmatrix} 1 & -1 \\ -2 & 3 \end{vmatrix} - 2\begin{vmatrix} 1 & 1 \\ -2 & -1 \end{vmatrix} \right)$$

$$- 1\left(2\begin{vmatrix} 1 & -1 \\ -3 & 3 \end{vmatrix} - 9\begin{vmatrix} 1 & -1 \\ -2 & 3 \end{vmatrix} - 2\begin{vmatrix} 1 & 1 \\ -2 & -3 \end{vmatrix} \right) - 3\left(2\begin{vmatrix} 1 & 1 \\ -3 & -1 \end{vmatrix} - 9\begin{vmatrix} 1 & 1 \\ -2 & -1 \end{vmatrix} + 2\begin{vmatrix} 1 & 1 \\ -2 & -3 \end{vmatrix} \right)$$

$$= 1\big[9(2) - 2(0) - 2(2)\big] - 4\big[2(2) - 2(1) - 2(1)\big] - 1\big[2(0) - 9(1) - 2(-1)\big] - 3\big[2(2) - 9(1) + 2(-1)\big]$$

$$= 1(18 - 0 - 4) - 4(4 - 2 - 2) - 1(0 - 9 + 2) - 3(4 - 9 - 2)$$

$$= 1(14) - 4(0) - 1(-7) - 3(-7)$$

$$= 14 - 0 + 7 + 21$$

$$= 42$$

$$D_z = \begin{vmatrix} 1 & 2 & 4 & 3 \\ 2 & 1 & 9 & -2 \\ 1 & -3 & 1 & -1 \\ -2 & 1 & -3 & 3 \end{vmatrix}$$

$$= 1\begin{vmatrix} 1 & 9 & -2 \\ -3 & 1 & -1 \\ 1 & -3 & 3 \end{vmatrix} - 2\begin{vmatrix} 2 & 9 & -2 \\ 1 & 1 & -1 \\ -2 & -3 & 3 \end{vmatrix} + 4\begin{vmatrix} 2 & 1 & -2 \\ 1 & -3 & -1 \\ -2 & 1 & 3 \end{vmatrix} - 3\begin{vmatrix} 2 & 1 & 9 \\ 1 & -3 & 1 \\ -2 & 1 & -3 \end{vmatrix}$$

$$= 1\left(1\begin{vmatrix} 1 & -1 \\ -3 & 3 \end{vmatrix} - 9\begin{vmatrix} -3 & -1 \\ 1 & 3 \end{vmatrix} - 2\begin{vmatrix} -3 & 1 \\ 1 & -3 \end{vmatrix} \right) - 2\left(2\begin{vmatrix} 1 & -1 \\ -3 & 3 \end{vmatrix} - 9\begin{vmatrix} 1 & -1 \\ -2 & 3 \end{vmatrix} - 2\begin{vmatrix} 1 & 1 \\ -2 & -3 \end{vmatrix} \right)$$

$$+ 4\left(2\begin{vmatrix} -3 & -1 \\ 1 & 3 \end{vmatrix} - 1\begin{vmatrix} 1 & -1 \\ -2 & 3 \end{vmatrix} - 2\begin{vmatrix} 1 & -3 \\ -2 & 1 \end{vmatrix} \right) - 3\left(2\begin{vmatrix} -3 & 1 \\ 1 & -3 \end{vmatrix} - 1\begin{vmatrix} 1 & 1 \\ -2 & -3 \end{vmatrix} + 9\begin{vmatrix} 1 & -3 \\ -2 & 1 \end{vmatrix} \right)$$

$$= 1\big[1(0) - 9(-8) - 2(8)\big] - 2\big[2(0) - 9(1) - 2(-1)\big] + 4\big[2(-8) - 1(1) - 2(-5)\big] - 3\big[2(8) - 1(-1) + 9(-5)\big]$$

$$= 1(0 + 72 - 16) - 2(0 - 9 + 2) + 4(-16 - 1 + 10) - 3(16 + 1 - 45)$$

$$= 1(56) - 2(-7) + 4(-7) - 3(-28)$$

$$= 56 + 14 - 28 + 84$$

$$= 126$$

$$D_w = \begin{vmatrix} 1 & 2 & -1 & 4 \\ 2 & 1 & 2 & 9 \\ 1 & -3 & 1 & 1 \\ -2 & 1 & -1 & -3 \end{vmatrix}$$

$$= 1\begin{vmatrix} 1 & 2 & 9 \\ -3 & 1 & 1 \\ 1 & -1 & -3 \end{vmatrix} - 2\begin{vmatrix} 2 & 2 & 9 \\ 1 & 1 & 1 \\ -2 & -1 & 3 \end{vmatrix} - 1\begin{vmatrix} 2 & 1 & 9 \\ 1 & -3 & 1 \\ -2 & 1 & -3 \end{vmatrix} - 4\begin{vmatrix} 2 & 1 & 2 \\ 1 & -3 & 1 \\ -2 & 1 & -1 \end{vmatrix}$$

$$= 1\left(1\begin{vmatrix} 1 & -1 \\ -1 & -3 \end{vmatrix} - 2\begin{vmatrix} -3 & 1 \\ 1 & -3 \end{vmatrix} + 9\begin{vmatrix} -3 & 1 \\ 1 & -1 \end{vmatrix} \right) - 2\left(2\begin{vmatrix} 1 & 1 \\ -1 & 3 \end{vmatrix} - 2\begin{vmatrix} 1 & 1 \\ -2 & 3 \end{vmatrix} + 9\begin{vmatrix} 1 & 1 \\ -2 & -1 \end{vmatrix} \right)$$

$$- 1\left(2\begin{vmatrix} -3 & 1 \\ 1 & -3 \end{vmatrix} - 1\begin{vmatrix} 1 & 1 \\ -2 & -3 \end{vmatrix} + 9\begin{vmatrix} 1 & -3 \\ -2 & 1 \end{vmatrix} \right) - 4\left(2\begin{vmatrix} -3 & 1 \\ 1 & -1 \end{vmatrix} - 1\begin{vmatrix} 1 & 1 \\ -2 & -1 \end{vmatrix} + 2\begin{vmatrix} 1 & -3 \\ -2 & 1 \end{vmatrix} \right)$$

$$= 1\big[1(-4) - 2(8) + 9(2)\big] - 2\big[2(4) - 2(5) + 9(1)\big] - 1\big[2(8) - 1(-1) + 9(-5)\big] - 4\big[2(2) - 1(1) + 2(-5)\big]$$

$$= 1(-4 - 16 + 18) - 2(8 - 10 + 9) - 1(16 + 1 - 45) - 4(4 - 1 - 10)$$

$$= 1(-2) - 2(7) - 1(-28) - 4(-7)$$

$$= -2 - 14 + 28 + 28$$

$$= 42$$

Now use Cramer's rule:

$$x = \frac{D_x}{D} = \frac{84}{42} = 2 \qquad y = \frac{D_y}{D} = \frac{42}{42} = 1 \qquad z = \frac{D_z}{D} = \frac{126}{42} = 3 \qquad w = \frac{D_w}{D} = \frac{42}{42} = 1$$

The solution is $(2, 1, 3, 1)$.

97. First find the determinants:

$$D = \begin{vmatrix} a & 1 & 1 \\ 1 & a & 1 \\ 1 & 1 & a \end{vmatrix}$$

$$= a \begin{vmatrix} a & 1 \\ 1 & a \end{vmatrix} - 1 \begin{vmatrix} 1 & 1 \\ 1 & a \end{vmatrix} + 1 \begin{vmatrix} 1 & a \\ 1 & 1 \end{vmatrix}$$

$$= a(a^2 - 1) - 1(a-1) + 1(1-a)$$

$$= a(a+1)(a-1) - 1(a-1) - 1(a-1)$$

$$= (a-1)(a^2 + a - 2)$$

$$= (a-1)(a-1)(a+2)$$

$$D_y = \begin{vmatrix} a & 1 & 1 \\ 1 & 1 & 1 \\ 1 & 1 & a \end{vmatrix}$$

$$= a \begin{vmatrix} 1 & 1 \\ 1 & a \end{vmatrix} - 1 \begin{vmatrix} 1 & 1 \\ 1 & a \end{vmatrix} + 1 \begin{vmatrix} 1 & 1 \\ 1 & 1 \end{vmatrix}$$

$$= a(a-1) - 1(a-1) + 1(0)$$

$$= a(a-1) - 1(a-1)$$

$$= (a-1)(a-1)$$

$$D_x = \begin{vmatrix} 1 & 1 & 1 \\ 1 & a & 1 \\ 1 & 1 & a \end{vmatrix}$$

$$= 1 \begin{vmatrix} a & 1 \\ 1 & a \end{vmatrix} - 1 \begin{vmatrix} 1 & 1 \\ 1 & a \end{vmatrix} + 1 \begin{vmatrix} 1 & a \\ 1 & 1 \end{vmatrix}$$

$$= 1(a^2 - 1) - 1(a-1) + 1(1-a)$$

$$= (a+1)(a-1) - 1(a-1) - 1(a-1)$$

$$= (a-1)(a+1-2)$$

$$= (a-1)(a-1)$$

$$D_z = \begin{vmatrix} a & 1 & 1 \\ 1 & a & 1 \\ 1 & 1 & 1 \end{vmatrix}$$

$$= a \begin{vmatrix} a & 1 \\ 1 & 1 \end{vmatrix} - 1 \begin{vmatrix} 1 & 1 \\ 1 & 1 \end{vmatrix} + 1 \begin{vmatrix} 1 & a \\ 1 & 1 \end{vmatrix}$$

$$= a(a-1) - 1(0) + 1(1-a)$$

$$= a(a-1) - 1(a-1)$$

$$= (a-1)(a-1)$$

Now use Cramer's rule:

$$x = \frac{D_x}{D} = \frac{(a-1)(a-1)}{(a-1)(a-1)(a+2)} = \frac{1}{a+2}$$

$$y = \frac{D_y}{D} = \frac{(a-1)(a-1)}{(a-1)(a-1)(a+2)} = \frac{1}{a+2}$$

$$z = \frac{D_z}{D} = \frac{(a-1)(a-1)}{(a-1)(a-1)(a+2)} = \frac{1}{a+2}$$

The solution is $\left(\dfrac{1}{a+2}, \dfrac{1}{a+2}, \dfrac{1}{a+2} \right)$.

99. Translating into symbols: $3x + 2$

101. Simplifying: $25 - \dfrac{385}{9} = \dfrac{225}{9} - \dfrac{385}{9} = -\dfrac{160}{9}$

103. Simplifying: $0.08(4,000) = 320$

105. Simplifying: $10(0.2x + 0.5y) = 2x + 5y$

107. Solving the equation:

$$x + (3x + 2) = 26$$
$$4x + 2 = 26$$
$$4x = 24$$
$$x = 6$$

109. Multiply the first equation by –20:

$$-60y - 20z = -340$$
$$5y + 20z = 65$$

Adding yields:

$$-55y = -275$$
$$y = 5$$

Substituting into the first equation:

$$3(5) + z = 17$$
$$15 + z = 17$$
$$z = 2$$

The solution is $y = 5, z = 2$.

Landmark Review

1. The intersection point is (1,2).

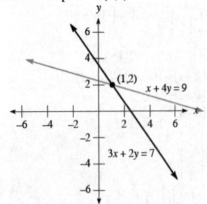

2. The intersection point is (0,–4).

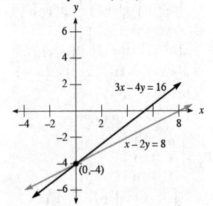

3. The intersection point is (2,3).

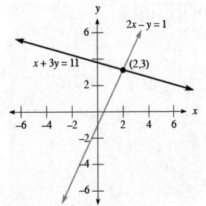

4. There is no solution (inconsistent).

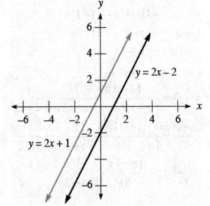

5. Substituting into the first equation:
$$2x - 3(x+1) = -6$$
$$2x - 3x - 3 = -6$$
$$-x - 3 = -6$$
$$-x = -3$$
$$x = 3$$
$$y = 3 + 1 = 4$$

The solution is (3,4).

6. Substituting into the first equation:
$$x - 4(3x - 14) = 1$$
$$x - 12x + 56 = 1$$
$$-11x + 56 = 1$$
$$-11x = -55$$
$$x = 5$$
$$y = 3(5) - 14 = 1$$

The solution is (5,1).

7. Substituting into the first equation:
$$(2y - 1) - 5y = -4$$
$$-3y - 1 = -4$$
$$-3y = -3$$
$$y = 1$$
$$x = 2(1) - 1 = 1$$

The solution is (1,1).

8. Substituting into the first equation:
$$(4y - 5) - y = 1$$
$$3y - 5 = 1$$
$$3y = 6$$
$$y = 2$$
$$x = 4(2) - 5 = 3$$

The solution is (3,2).

9. Adding the two equations yields:
$$2x = 2$$
$$x = 1$$
Substituting into the second equation:
$$1 + y = 2$$
$$y = 1$$
The solution is $(1,1)$.

10. Adding the two equations yields: $0 = 0$
Since this statement is true, the system is dependent (the lines coincide).

11. Multiplying the first equation by -2:
$$-8x - 4y = -12$$
$$6x + 4y = 2$$
Adding the two equations yields:
$$-2x = -10$$
$$x = 5$$
Substituting into the first equation:
$$4(5) + 2y = 6$$
$$20 + 2y = 6$$
$$2y = -14$$
$$y = -7$$
The solution is $(5,-7)$.

12. Multiplying the second equation by -2:
$$10x - 4y = -2$$
$$-10x + 6y = -2$$
Adding the two equations yields:
$$2y = -4$$
$$y = -2$$
Substituting into the first equation:
$$10x - 4(-2) = -2$$
$$10x + 8 = -2$$
$$10x = -10$$
$$x = -1$$
The solution is $(-1,-2)$.

13. Form the augmented matrix: $\begin{bmatrix} 1 & 1 & 1 & | & 2 \\ 1 & -1 & 2 & | & 0 \\ 1 & -1 & 3 & | & 2 \end{bmatrix}$

Add -1 times row 1 to row 2 and -1 times row 1 to row 3: $\begin{bmatrix} 1 & 1 & 1 & | & 2 \\ 0 & -2 & 1 & | & -2 \\ 0 & -2 & 2 & | & 0 \end{bmatrix}$

Divide row 2 by -2: $\begin{bmatrix} 1 & 1 & 1 & | & 2 \\ 0 & 1 & -\frac{1}{2} & | & 1 \\ 0 & -2 & 2 & | & 0 \end{bmatrix}$

Add 2 times row 2 to row 3: $\begin{bmatrix} 1 & 1 & 1 & | & 2 \\ 0 & 1 & -\frac{1}{2} & | & 1 \\ 0 & 0 & 1 & | & 2 \end{bmatrix}$

So $z = 2$. Substituting to find y:
$$y - \frac{1}{2}(2) = 1$$
$$y - 1 = 1$$
$$y = 2$$
Substituting to find x:
$$x + 2 + 2 = 2$$
$$x + 4 = 2$$
$$x = -2$$
The solution is $(-2,2,2)$.

14. Form the augmented matrix: $\begin{bmatrix} 1 & 1 & 1 & | & 0 \\ 1 & -1 & 2 & | & -5 \\ 1 & -1 & 3 & | & -6 \end{bmatrix}$

Add -1 times row 1 to row 2 and -1 times row 1 to row 3: $\begin{bmatrix} 1 & 1 & 1 & | & 0 \\ 0 & -2 & 1 & | & -5 \\ 0 & -2 & 2 & | & -6 \end{bmatrix}$

Divide row 2 by -2: $\begin{bmatrix} 1 & 1 & 1 & | & 0 \\ 0 & 1 & -\frac{1}{2} & | & \frac{5}{2} \\ 0 & -2 & 2 & | & -6 \end{bmatrix}$

Add 2 times row 2 to row 3: $\begin{bmatrix} 1 & 1 & 1 & | & 0 \\ 0 & 1 & -\frac{1}{2} & | & \frac{5}{2} \\ 0 & 0 & 1 & | & -1 \end{bmatrix}$

So $z = -1$. Substituting to find y:

$$y - \frac{1}{2}(-1) = \frac{5}{2}$$
$$y + \frac{1}{2} = \frac{5}{2}$$
$$y = 2$$

Substituting to find x:

$$x + 2 - 1 = 0$$
$$x + 1 = 0$$
$$x = -1$$

The solution is $(-1, 2, -1)$.

15. First clear the system of fractions by multiplying the first two equations by 4 and the third equation by 2:

$$x - y - z = 9$$
$$-2x - y - 4z = 3$$
$$x - 2y + z = -4$$

Form the augmented matrix: $\begin{bmatrix} 1 & -1 & -1 & | & 9 \\ -2 & -1 & -4 & | & 3 \\ 1 & -2 & 1 & | & -4 \end{bmatrix}$

Add 2 times row 1 to row 2 and -1 times row 1 to row 3: $\begin{bmatrix} 1 & -1 & -1 & | & 9 \\ 0 & -3 & -6 & | & 21 \\ 0 & -1 & 2 & | & -13 \end{bmatrix}$

Divide row 2 by -3: $\begin{bmatrix} 1 & -1 & -1 & | & 9 \\ 0 & 1 & 2 & | & -7 \\ 0 & -1 & 2 & | & -13 \end{bmatrix}$

Add row 2 to row 3: $\begin{bmatrix} 1 & -1 & -1 & | & 9 \\ 0 & 1 & 2 & | & -7 \\ 0 & 0 & 4 & | & -20 \end{bmatrix}$

Divide row 3 by 4: $\begin{bmatrix} 1 & -1 & -1 & | & 9 \\ 0 & 1 & 2 & | & -7 \\ 0 & 0 & 1 & | & -5 \end{bmatrix}$

So $z = -5$. Substituting to find y:

$$y + 2(-5) = -7$$
$$y - 10 = -7$$
$$y = 3$$

Substituting to find x:

$$x - 3 + 5 = 9$$
$$x + 2 = 9$$
$$x = 7$$

The solution is $(7, 3, -5)$.

16. Form the augmented matrix:
$$\left[\begin{array}{ccc|c} 8 & -4 & 0 & 0 \\ 0 & -2 & 4 & 1 \\ 12 & 0 & -2 & 2 \end{array}\right]$$

Divide row 1 by 8:
$$\left[\begin{array}{ccc|c} 1 & -\dfrac{1}{2} & 0 & 0 \\ 0 & -2 & 4 & 1 \\ 12 & 0 & -2 & 2 \end{array}\right]$$

Add -12 times row 1 to row 3:
$$\left[\begin{array}{ccc|c} 1 & -\dfrac{1}{2} & 0 & 0 \\ 0 & -2 & 4 & 1 \\ 0 & 6 & -2 & 2 \end{array}\right]$$

Divide row 2 by -2:
$$\left[\begin{array}{ccc|c} 1 & -\dfrac{1}{2} & 0 & 0 \\ 0 & 1 & -2 & -\dfrac{1}{2} \\ 0 & 6 & -2 & 2 \end{array}\right]$$

Add -6 times row 2 to row 3:
$$\left[\begin{array}{ccc|c} 1 & -\dfrac{1}{2} & 0 & 0 \\ 0 & 1 & -2 & -\dfrac{1}{2} \\ 0 & 0 & 10 & 5 \end{array}\right]$$

Divide row 3 by 10:
$$\left[\begin{array}{ccc|c} 1 & -\dfrac{1}{2} & 0 & 0 \\ 0 & 1 & -2 & -\dfrac{1}{2} \\ 0 & 0 & 1 & \dfrac{1}{2} \end{array}\right]$$

So $z = \dfrac{1}{2}$. Substituting to find y:

$$y - 2\left(\dfrac{1}{2}\right) = -\dfrac{1}{2}$$
$$y - 1 = -\dfrac{1}{2}$$
$$y = \dfrac{1}{2}$$

Substituting to find x:

$$x - \frac{1}{2}\left(\frac{1}{2}\right) = 0$$

$$x - \frac{1}{4} = 0$$

$$x = \frac{1}{4}$$

The solution is $\left(\frac{1}{4}, \frac{1}{2}, \frac{1}{2}\right)$.

3.5 Applications of Systems of Equations

1. Let x and y represent the two numbers. The system of equations is:
$$y = 2x + 3$$
$$x + y = 18$$
Substituting into the second equation:
$$x + 2x + 3 = 18$$
$$3x = 15$$
$$x = 5$$
$$y = 2(5) + 3 = 13$$
The two numbers are 5 and 13.

3. Let x and y represent the two numbers. The system of equations is:
$$y - x = 6$$
$$2x = 4 + y$$
The second equation is $y = 2x - 4$. Substituting into the first equation:
$$2x - 4 - x = 6$$
$$x = 10$$
$$y = 2(10) - 4 = 16$$
The two numbers are 10 and 16.

5. Let x, y, and z represent the three numbers. The system of equations is:
$$x + y + z = 8$$
$$2x = z - 2$$
$$x + z = 5$$
The third equation is $z = 5 - x$. Substituting into the second equation:
$$2x = 5 - x - 2$$
$$3x = 3$$
$$x = 1$$
$$z = 5 - 1 = 4$$
Substituting into the first equation:
$$1 + y + 4 = 8$$
$$y = 3$$
The three numbers are 1, 3, and 4.

7. Let x and y represent the two numbers. The system of equations is:

$$y = 5x + 8$$
$$x + y = 26$$

Substituting into the second equation:

$$x + 5x + 8 = 26$$
$$6x + 8 = 26$$
$$6x = 18$$
$$x = 3$$
$$y = 5(3) + 8 = 23$$

The two numbers are 3 and 23.

9. Let x and y represent the two numbers. The system of equations is:

$$y - x = 9$$
$$y = 2x - 6$$

Substituting into the first equation:

$$2x - 6 - x = 9$$
$$x - 6 = 9$$
$$x = 15$$
$$y = 2(15) - 6 = 24$$

The two numbers are 15 and 24.

11. Let a represent the number of adult tickets and c represent the number of children's tickets. The system of equations is:

$$a + c = 925$$
$$2a + c = 1150$$

Multiply the first equation by -1:

$$-a - c = -925$$
$$2a + c = 1150$$

Adding yields:

$$a = 225$$
$$c = 700$$

Linda sold 225 adult tickets and 700 children's tickets sold.

13. Let x represent the amount charged at 6% and y represent the amount charged at 7%. The system of equations is:

$$x + y = 20,000$$
$$0.06x + 0.07y = 1,280$$

Multiplying the first equation by -0.06:

$$-0.06x - 0.06y = -1,200$$
$$0.06x + 0.07y = 1,280$$

Adding yields:

$$0.01y = 80$$
$$y = 8,000$$
$$x = 12,000$$

Mr. Jones charged \$12,000 at 6% and \$8,000 at 7%.

15. Let x represent the amount charged at 6% and $2x$ represent the amount charged at 7.5%. The equation is:

$$0.075(2x) + 0.06(x) = 840$$
$$0.21x = 840$$
$$x = 4,000$$
$$2x = 8,000$$

Susan charged \$4,000 at 6% and \$8,000 at 7.5%.

17. Let x, y and z represent the amounts withdrawn in the three accounts. The system of equations is:
$$x + y + z = 2,200$$
$$z = 3x$$
$$0.06x + 0.08y + 0.09z = 178$$
Substituting into the first equation:
$$x + y + 3x = 2,200$$
$$4x + y = 2,200$$
Substituting into the third equation:
$$0.06x + 0.08y + 0.09(3x) = 178$$
$$0.33x + 0.08y = 178$$
The system of equations becomes:
$$4x + y = 2,200$$
$$0.33x + 0.08y = 178$$
Multiply the first equation by -0.08:
$$-0.32x - 0.08y = -176$$
$$0.33x + 0.08y = 178$$
Adding yields:
$$0.01x = 2$$
$$x = 200$$
$$z = 3(200) = 600$$
$$y = 2,200 - 4(200) = 1,400$$
William withdrew $200 at 6%, $1,400 at 8%, and $600 at 9%.

19. Let x represent the amount of 20% alcohol and y represent the amount of 50% alcohol. The system of equations is:
$$x + y = 9$$
$$0.20x + 0.50y = 0.30(9)$$
Multiplying the first equation by -0.2:
$$-0.20x - 0.20y = -1.8$$
$$0.20x + 0.50y = 2.7$$
Adding yields:
$$0.30y = 0.9$$
$$y = 3$$
$$x = 6$$
The mixture contains 3 gallons of 50% alcohol and 6 gallons of 20% alcohol.

21. Let x represent the amount of 20% disinfectant and y represent the amount of 14% disinfectant.
The system of equations is:
$$x + y = 15$$
$$0.20x + 0.14y = 0.16(15)$$
Multiplying the first equation by -0.14:
$$-0.14x - 0.14y = -2.1$$
$$0.20x + 0.14y = 2.4$$
Adding yields:
$$0.06x = 0.3$$
$$x = 5$$
$$y = 10$$
The mixture contains 5 gallons of 20% disinfectant and 10 gallons of 14% disinfectant.

23. Let x represent the amount of nuts and y represent the amount of oats. The system of equations is:
$$x + y = 25$$
$$1.55x + 1.35y = 1.45(25)$$
Multiplying the first equation by -1.35:
$$-1.35x - 1.35y = -33.75$$
$$1.55x + 1.35y = 36.25$$
Adding yields:
$$0.20x = 2.5$$
$$x = 12.5$$
$$y = 12.5$$
The mixture contains 12.5 pounds of oats and 12.5 pounds of nuts.

25. Let b represent the rate of the boat and c represent the rate of the current. The system of equations is:
$$2(b + c) = 24$$
$$3(b - c) = 18$$
The system of equations simplifies to:
$$b + c = 12$$
$$b - c = 6$$
Adding yields:
$$2b = 18$$
$$b = 9$$
$$c = 3$$
The rate of the boat is 9 mph and the rate of the current is 3 mph.

27. Let a represent the rate of the airplane and w represent the rate of the wind. The system of equations is:
$$2(a + w) = 600$$
$$\frac{5}{2}(a - w) = 600$$
The system of equations simplifies to:
$$a + w = 300$$
$$a - w = 240$$
Adding yields:
$$2a = 540$$
$$a = 270$$
$$w = 30$$
The rate of the airplane is 270 mph and the rate of the wind is 30 mph.

29. Let n represent the number of nickels and d represent the number of dimes. The system of equations is:
$$n + d = 20$$
$$0.05n + 0.10d = 1.40$$
Multiplying the first equation by -0.05:
$$-0.05n - 0.05d = -1$$
$$0.05n + 0.10d = 1.40$$
Adding yields:
$$0.05d = 0.40$$
$$d = 8$$
$$n = 12$$
Bob has 12 nickels and 8 dimes.

31. Let n, d, and q represent the number of nickels, dimes, and quarters. The system of equations is:
$$n + d + q = 9$$
$$0.05n + 0.10d + 0.25q = 1.20$$
$$d = n$$

Substituting into the first equation:
$$n + n + q = 9$$
$$2n + q = 9$$

Substituting into the second equation:
$$0.05n + 0.10n + 0.25q = 1.20$$
$$0.15n + 0.25q = 1.20$$

The system of equations becomes:
$$2n + q = 9$$
$$0.15n + 0.25q = 1.20$$

Multiplying the first equation by -0.25:
$$-0.50n - 0.25q = -2.25$$
$$0.15n + 0.25q = 1.20$$

Adding yields:
$$-0.35n = -1.05$$
$$n = 3$$
$$d = 3$$
$$q = 9 - 2(3) = 3$$

The collection contains 3 nickels, 3 dimes, and 3 quarters.

33. Let n, d, and q represent the number of nickels, dimes, and quarters. The system of equations is:
$$n + d + q = 140$$
$$0.05n + 0.10d + 0.25q = 10.00$$
$$d = 2q$$

Substituting into the first equation:
$$n + 2q + q = 140$$
$$n + 3q = 140$$

Substituting into the second equation:
$$0.05n + 0.10(2q) + 0.25q = 10.00$$
$$0.05n + 0.45q = 10.00$$

The system of equations becomes:
$$n + 3q = 140$$
$$0.05n + 0.45q = 10.00$$

Multiplying the first equation by -0.05:
$$-0.05n - 0.15q = -7$$
$$0.05n + 0.45q = 10$$

Adding yields:
$$0.30q = 3$$
$$q = 10$$
$$d = 2(10) = 20$$
$$n = 140 - 3(10) = 110$$

Kaela has 110 nickels in the collection.

35. Let n represent the number of nickels and d represent the number of dimes. The system of equations is:

$$0.05n + 0.10d = 1.70$$
$$n = d + 4$$

Substituting into the first equation:

$$0.05(d+4) + 0.10d = 1.70$$
$$0.05d + 0.2 + 0.10d = 1.70$$
$$0.15d + 0.2 = 1.7$$
$$0.15d = 1.5$$
$$d = 10$$
$$n = 10 + 4 = 14$$

John has 14 nickels and 10 dimes.

37. Let $x = mp + b$ represent the relationship. Using the points $(2,300)$ and $(1.5,400)$ results in the system:

$$300 = 2m + b$$
$$400 = 1.5m + b$$

Multiplying the second equation by -1:

$$300 = 2m + b$$
$$-400 = -1.5m - b$$

Adding yields:

$$-100 = 0.5m$$
$$m = -200$$
$$b = 300 - 2(-200) = 700$$

The equation is $x = -200p + 700$. Substituting $p = 3$: $x = -200(3) + 700 = 100$ items

39. Let w represent the width and l represent the length. The system of equations is:

$$l = 3w + 5$$
$$2w + 2l = 58$$

Substituting into the second equation:

$$2w + 2(3w + 5) = 58$$
$$2w + 6w + 10 = 58$$
$$8w + 10 = 58$$
$$8w = 48$$
$$w = 6$$
$$l = 3(6) + 5 = 23$$

The width is 6 inches and the length is 23 inches.

41. The system of equations is:

$$a + b + c = 128$$
$$9a + 3b + c = 128$$
$$25a + 5b + c = 0$$

Multiply the first equation by -1 and add it to the second equation:

$$-a - b - c = -128$$
$$9a + 3b + c = 128$$

Adding yields:

$$8a + 2b = 0$$
$$4a + b = 0$$

Multiply the first equation by -1 and add it to the third equation:

$$-a - b - c = -128$$
$$25a + 5b + c = 0$$

Adding yields:

$$24a + 4b = -128$$
$$6a + b = -32$$

The system simplifies to:

$$4a + b = 0$$
$$6a + b = -32$$

Multiplying the first equation by –1:
$$-4a - b = 0$$
$$6a + b = -32$$
Adding yields:
$$2a = -32$$
$$a = -16$$
Substituting to find b:
$$4(-16) + b = 0$$
$$b = 64$$
Substituting to find c:
$$-16 + 64 + c = 128$$
$$c = 80$$
The equation for the height is $h = -16t^2 + 64t + 80$.

43. Let p represent the pre-registration tickets sold and o represent the on-site registration tickets sold. The system of equations is:
$$p + o = 29$$
$$28p + 38o = 922$$
Multiply the first equation by –28:
$$-28p - 28o = -812$$
$$28p + 38o = 922$$
Adding yields:
$$10o = 110$$
$$o = 11$$
Substituting into the first equation:
$$p + 11 = 29$$
$$p = 18$$
There were 18 pre-registration tickets sold and 11 on-site registration tickets sold.

45. No, the graph does not include the boundary line.

47. Substituting $x = 4 - y$ into the second equation:
$$(4 - y) - 2y = 4$$
$$4 - 3y = 4$$
$$-3y = 0$$
$$y = 0$$
The solution is (4,0).

49. Solving the inequality:
$$20x + 9,300 > 18,000$$
$$20x > 8,700$$
$$x > 435$$

3.6 Systems of Linear Inequalities and Applications

1. Graphing the solution set:

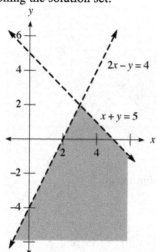

3. Graphing the solution set:

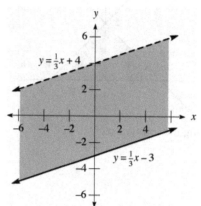

5. Graphing the solution set:

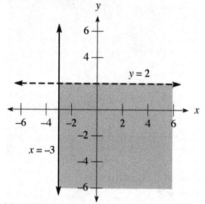

7. Graphing the solution set:

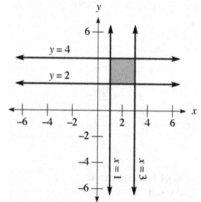

9. Graphing the solution set:

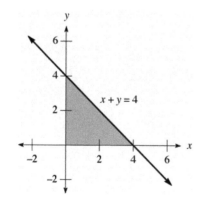

11. Graphing the solution set:

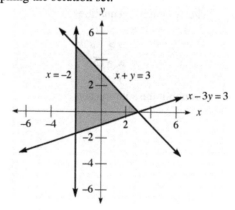

13. Graphing the solution set:

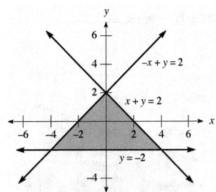

15. Graphing the solution set:

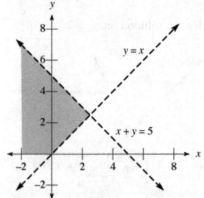

17. Graphing the solution set:

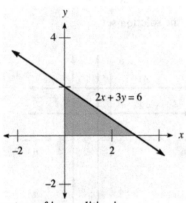

19. Graphing the solution set:

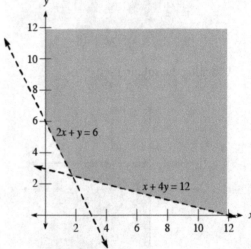

21. The system of inequalities is:
$$x + y \le 4$$
$$-x + y < 4$$

23. The system of inequalities is:
$$x + y \ge 4$$
$$-x + y < 4$$

25. **a.** The system of inequalities is:
$$0.55x + 0.65y \le 40$$
$$x \ge 2y$$
$$x > 15$$
$$y \ge 0$$

Graphing the solution set:

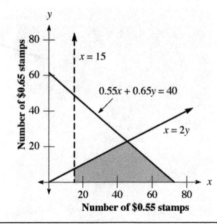

b. Substitute $x = 20$:

$$2y \le 20$$
$$y \le 10$$

The most he can purchase is ten 65-cent stamps.

27. The revenue is given by: $R(x) = 22x$

The cost is given by: $C(x) = 14x + 24{,}000$

Finding the break-even point:

$$R(x) = C(x)$$
$$22x = 14x + 24{,}000$$
$$8x = 24{,}000$$
$$x = 3{,}000 \text{ items}$$

Sketching the graph:

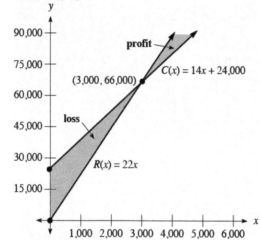

29. The revenue is given by: $R(x) = 225x$

The cost is given by: $C(x) = 175x + 120{,}000$

Finding the break-even point:

$$R(x) = C(x)$$
$$225x = 175x + 120{,}000$$
$$50x = 120{,}000$$
$$x = 2{,}400 \text{ items}$$

Sketching the graph:

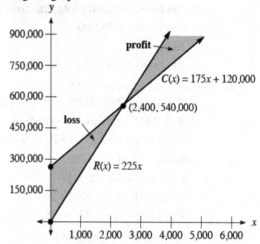

31. The revenue is given by: $R(x) = 9.50x$

The cost is given by: $C(x) = 6.50x + 19{,}500$

Finding the break-even point:

$$R(x) = C(x)$$
$$9.5x = 6.5x + 19{,}500$$
$$3x = 19{,}500$$
$$x = 6{,}500 \text{ items}$$

Sketching the graph:

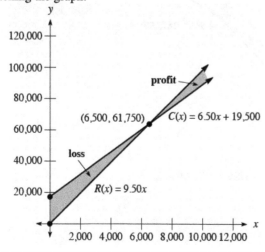

33. The revenue is given by: $R(x) = 9.75x$

The cost is given by: $C(x) = 8.25x + 1{,}200$

Finding the break-even point:

$$R(x) = C(x)$$
$$9.75x = 8.25x + 1{,}200$$
$$1.5x = 1{,}200$$
$$x = 800 \text{ items}$$

Sketching the graph:

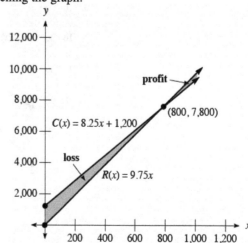

35. Finding the equilibrium price and quantity:
$$s(p) = d(p)$$
$$4p = 4{,}200 - 6p$$
$$10p = 4{,}200$$
$$p = \$420$$
$$s = 4(420) = 1{,}680 \text{ units}$$

37. Finding the equilibrium price and quantity:
$$s(p) = d(p)$$
$$2{,}000 + 5p = 10{,}000 - 11p$$
$$16p = 8{,}000$$
$$p = \$500$$
$$s = 2{,}000 + 5(500) = 4{,}500 \text{ units}$$

39. Finding the equilibrium price and quantity:
$$s(p) = d(p)$$
$$6{,}000 + 6p = 24{,}000 - 24p$$
$$30p = 18{,}000$$
$$p = \$600$$
$$s = 6{,}000 + 6(600) = 9{,}600 \text{ units}$$

41. **a.** The revenue, cost, and profit functions are given by:
$$C(x) = 24x + 75{,}000$$
$$R(x) = 40x$$
$$P(x) = R(x) - C(x) = 40x - (24x + 75{,}000) = 16x - 75{,}000$$

b. Evaluating when $x = 2{,}000$:
$$C(2{,}000) = 24(2{,}000) + 75{,}000 = \$123{,}000$$
$$R(2{,}000) = 40(2{,}000) = \$80{,}000$$
$$P(2{,}000) = 16(2{,}000) - 75{,}000 = -\$43{,}000$$

c. Evaluating when $x = 8{,}000$:
$$C(8{,}000) = 24(8{,}000) + 75{,}000 = \$267{,}000$$
$$R(8{,}000) = 40(8{,}000) = \$320{,}000$$
$$P(8{,}000) = 16(8{,}000) - 75{,}000 = \$53{,}000$$

d. Finding the break-even point:
$$R(x) = C(x)$$
$$40x = 24x + 75{,}000$$
$$16x = 75{,}000$$
$$x = 4{,}688 \text{ websites}$$

Sketching the graph:

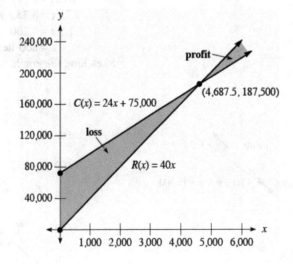

43. The *x*-intercept is 3, the *y*-intercept is 6, and the slope is –2.

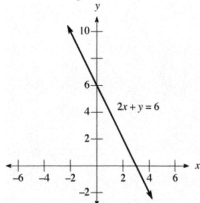

45. The *x*-intercept is –2, there is no *y*-intercept, and there is no slope.

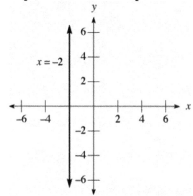

47. First find the slope: $m = \dfrac{-1-2}{4-(-3)} = \dfrac{-3}{4+3} = -\dfrac{3}{7}$. Using the point-slope formula:

$$y - 2 = -\frac{3}{7}(x+3)$$
$$y - 2 = -\frac{3}{7}x - \frac{9}{7}$$
$$y = -\frac{3}{7}x + \frac{5}{7}$$

49. Since the line is vertical, its equation is $x = 4$.

51. The domain is all real numbers and the range is $\{y \mid y \geq -9\}$. This is a function.

53. Evaluating the function: $h(0) + g(0) = \left[3 \cdot 0^2 - 2 \cdot 0 - 8\right] + \left[3 \cdot 0 + 4\right] = -8 + 4 = -4$

55. Evaluating the function: $g(f(2)) = g(2-2) = g(0) = 3 \cdot 0 + 4 = 4$

57. Finding the composition: $f(g(x)) = f(3x+4) = (3x+4) - 2 = 3x+2$

59. Finding the quotient: $\dfrac{g(x)}{h(x)} = \dfrac{3x+4}{3x^2 - 2x - 8} = \dfrac{3x+4}{(x-2)(3x+4)} = \dfrac{1}{x-2}$

Chapter 3 Review

1. Solving the second equation for y:
    $$-2x + y = 11$$
    $$y = 2x + 11$$
    Substituting into the first equation:
    $$4x + 2(2x + 11) = -2$$
    $$4x + 4x + 22 = -2$$
    $$8x + 22 = -2$$
    $$8x = -24$$
    $$x = -3$$
    $$y = 2(-3) + 11 = 5$$
    The solution is $(-3, 5)$.

2. Solving the first equation for x:
    $$x - 5y = 10$$
    $$x = 5y + 10$$
    Substituting into the second equation:
    $$5(5y + 10) + 3y = -6$$
    $$25y + 50 + 3y = -6$$
    $$28y + 50 = -6$$
    $$28y = -56$$
    $$y = -2$$
    $$x = 5(-2) + 10 = 0$$
    The solution is $(0, -2)$.

3. Multiply the first equation by 2:
    $$12x - 2y = 14$$
    $$3x + 2y = 16$$
    Adding the two equations:
    $$15x = 30$$
    $$x = 2$$
    Substituting into the second equation:
    $$3(2) + 2y = 16$$
    $$6 + 2y = 16$$
    $$2y = 10$$
    $$y = 5$$
    The solution is $(2, 5)$.

4. To clear each equation of fractions, multiply the first equation by 5 and the second equation by 4:
    $$x + 3y = 10$$
    $$x + 2y = 8$$
    Subtracting the two equations yields $y = 2$. Substituting into the second equation:
    $$x + 2(2) = 8$$
    $$x + 4 = 8$$
    $$x = 4$$
    The solution is $(4, 8)$.

5. Multiplying the second equation by –1 and adding it to the first equation:
$$-2x+4y+4z=7$$
$$2x-3y+z=-1$$
Adding yields $y+5z=6$. Multiplying the first equation by –2 and adding it to the third equation:
$$4x-8y-8z=-14$$
$$-4x+2y-4z=-4$$
Adding yields $-6y-12z=-18$. So the system of equations becomes:
$$y+5z=6$$
$$-6y-12z=-18$$
Dividing the second equation by –6:
$$y+5z=6$$
$$y+2z=3$$
Subtracting yields:
$$3z=3$$
$$z=1$$
Substituting into the second equation:
$$y+2(1)=3$$
$$y+2=3$$
$$y=1$$
Substituting into the original first equation:
$$-2x+4(1)+4(1)=7$$
$$-2x+8=7$$
$$-2x=-1$$
$$x=\frac{1}{2}$$
The solution is $\left(\frac{1}{2},1,1\right)$.

6. Form the augmented matrix using equation 3 as row 1: $\begin{bmatrix} 1 & 3 & 2 & | & 1 \\ 5 & -2 & -2 & | & 3 \\ 3 & -1 & -4 & | & -7 \end{bmatrix}$

Add –5 times row 1 to row 2 and –3 times row 1 to row 3: $\begin{bmatrix} 1 & 3 & 2 & | & 1 \\ 0 & -17 & -12 & | & -2 \\ 0 & -10 & -10 & | & -10 \end{bmatrix}$

Divide row 3 by –10 and switch with row 2: $\begin{bmatrix} 1 & 3 & 2 & | & 1 \\ 0 & 1 & 1 & | & 1 \\ 0 & -17 & -12 & | & -2 \end{bmatrix}$

Add 17 times row 2 to row 3: $\begin{bmatrix} 1 & 3 & 2 & | & 1 \\ 0 & 1 & 1 & | & 1 \\ 0 & 0 & 5 & | & 15 \end{bmatrix}$

Divide row 3 by 5: $\begin{bmatrix} 1 & 3 & 2 & | & 1 \\ 0 & 1 & 1 & | & 1 \\ 0 & 0 & 1 & | & 3 \end{bmatrix}$

So $z = 3$. Substituting to find y:
$$y+3=1$$
$$y=-2$$

Substituting to find x:
$$x + 3(-2) + 2(3) = 1$$
$$x = 1$$
The solution is $(1, -2, 3)$.

7. Evaluating the determinant: $\begin{vmatrix} 4 & 7 \\ -2 & -3 \end{vmatrix} = 4 \cdot (-3) - 7 \cdot (-2) = -12 + 14 = 2$

8. Expanding across the first row:
$$\begin{vmatrix} 1 & -2 & -3 \\ 2 & 1 & 3 \\ 1 & -3 & 2 \end{vmatrix} = 1\begin{vmatrix} 1 & 3 \\ -3 & 2 \end{vmatrix} + 2\begin{vmatrix} 2 & 3 \\ 1 & 2 \end{vmatrix} - 3\begin{vmatrix} 2 & 1 \\ 1 & -3 \end{vmatrix} = 1(2+9) + 2(4-3) - 3(-6-1) = 11 + 2 + 21 = 34$$

9. First find the determinants:
$$D = \begin{vmatrix} 2 & 3 \\ 4 & -5 \end{vmatrix} = -10 - 12 = -22$$
$$D_x = \begin{vmatrix} 7 & 3 \\ 11 & -5 \end{vmatrix} = -35 - 33 = -68$$
$$D_y = \begin{vmatrix} 2 & 7 \\ 4 & 11 \end{vmatrix} = 22 - 28 = -6$$

Now use Cramer's rule:
$$x = \frac{D_x}{D} = \frac{-68}{-22} = \frac{34}{11} \qquad y = \frac{D_y}{D} = \frac{-6}{-22} = \frac{3}{11}$$
The solution is $\left(\dfrac{34}{11}, \dfrac{3}{11}\right)$.

10. Let x and y represent the two numbers. The system of equations is:
$$y = 3x + 4$$
$$x + y = 16$$
Substituting into the second equation:
$$x + 3x + 4 = 16$$
$$4x + 4 = 16$$
$$4x = 12$$
$$x = 3$$
$$y = 3(3) + 4 = 13$$
The numbers are 3 and 13.

11. Let x represent the amount Ralph owes at 12% and $2x$ represent the amount he owes at 10%. The equation is:
$$0.12(x) + 0.10(2x) = 560$$
$$0.32x = 560$$
$$x = 1,750$$
$$2x = 3,500$$
Ralph owes $1,750 at 12% and $3,500 at 10%.

12. Let a represent the adult tickets and c represent the children's tickets. The system of equations is:
$$a + c = 905$$
$$12a + 7c = 9{,}050$$
Multiply the first equation by –7:
$$-7a - 7c = -6{,}335$$
$$12a + 7c = 9{,}050$$
Adding yields:
$$5a = 2{,}715$$
$$a = 543$$
$$c = 905 - 543 = 362$$
There were 543 adult tickets and 362 children's tickets sold.

13. Let b and c represent the rates of the boat and current. The system of equations is:
$$8(b + c) = 80$$
$$5(b - c) = 20$$
Simplifying the system by dividing the first equation by 8 and the second equation by 5:
$$b + c = 10$$
$$b - c = 4$$
Adding yields:
$$2b = 14$$
$$b = 7$$
$$c = 10 - 7 = 3$$
The boat's speed is 7 mph and the current's speed is 3 mph.

14. Let n, d, and q represent the number of nickels, dimes, and quarters. The system of equations is:
$$n + d + q = 22$$
$$0.05n + 0.10d + 0.25q = 1.75$$
$$n = 3d$$
Substituting into the first equation:
$$3d + d + q = 22$$
$$4d + q = 22$$
Substituting into the second equation:
$$0.05(3d) + 0.10d + 0.25q = 1.75$$
$$0.25d + 0.25q = 1.75$$
$$d + q = 7$$
The system of equations becomes:
$$4d + q = 22$$
$$d + q = 7$$
Subtracting:
$$3d = 15$$
$$d = 5$$
$$q = 7 - 5 = 2$$
$$n = 3(5) = 15$$
The collection consists of 15 nickels, 5 dimes, and 2 quarters.

15. Graphing the solution set:

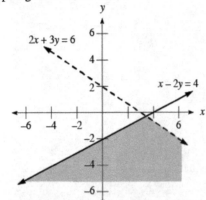

16. Graphing the solution set:

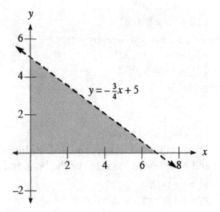

17. A system of inequalities that describes the shaded region is:

$$y \le \frac{1}{3}x + 2$$

$$y < -\frac{3}{2}x + 3$$

18. A system of inequalities that describes the shaded region is:

$$y > x + 2$$

$$y \le -\frac{3}{2}x - 3$$

Chapter 3 Cumulative Review

1. Simplifying: $3^2 - 7^2 = 9 - 49 = -40$

2. Simplifying: $(3-7)^2 = (-4)^2 = 16$

3. Simplifying: $16 - 9 \div 3 - 6 \cdot 2 = 16 - 3 - 12 = 1$

4. Simplifying: $3(8-11)^3 + 2(2-6)^2 = 3(-3)^3 + 2(-4)^2 = 3(-27) + 2(16) = -81 + 32 = -49$

5. Simplifying: $6\left(\frac{2}{3}\right) - 18\left(\frac{2}{3}\right)^2 = 6\left(\frac{2}{3}\right) - 18\left(\frac{4}{9}\right) = 4 - 8 = -4$

6. Simplifying: $18\left(\frac{5}{6}\right) - 72\left(\frac{5}{6}\right)^2 = 18\left(\frac{5}{6}\right) - 72\left(\frac{25}{36}\right) = 15 - 50 = -35$

7. Evaluating when $x = -3$: $x^2 + 10x - 25 = (-3)^2 + 10(-3) - 25 = 9 - 30 - 25 = -46$

8. Evaluating when $x = -3$: $(x+5)(x-5) = (-3+5)(-3-5) = (2)(-8) = -16$

9. Simplifying: $3(2x-4) + 5(3x-1) = 6x - 12 + 15x - 5 = 21x - 17$

10. Simplifying: $7 - 2[4x - 5(x+3)] = 7 - 2(4x - 5x - 15) = 7 - 2(-x - 15) = 7 + 2x + 30 = 2x + 37$

11. Simplifying: $-6\left(\frac{2}{3}x + \frac{5}{2}y\right) = -6\left(\frac{2}{3}x\right) - 6\left(\frac{5}{2}y\right) = -4x - 15y$

12. Simplifying: $8\left(\frac{1}{4}x - \frac{3}{8}y\right) = 8\left(\frac{1}{4}x\right) - 8\left(\frac{3}{8}y\right) = 2x - 3y$

13. Solving the equation:

$$-3y + 6 = 7y - 4$$
$$-10y = -10$$
$$y = 1$$

14. Solving the equation:

$$-30 + 6(7x+5) = 0$$
$$-30 + 42x + 30 = 0$$
$$42x = 0$$
$$x = 0$$

15. Solving the equation:
$$|7x+2|+4=3$$
$$|7x+2|=-1$$
Since this statement is false, there is no solution, or $\varnothing$.

16. Solving the equation:
$$\left|\frac{3}{2}x-1\right|+2=1$$
$$\left|\frac{3}{2}x-1\right|=-1$$
Since this statement is false, there is no solution, or $\varnothing$.

17. Solving for y:
$$y-4=-2(x+1)$$
$$y-4=-2x-2$$
$$y=-2x+2$$

18. Solving for y:
$$y+2=\frac{3}{4}(x+8)$$
$$y+2=\frac{3}{4}x+6$$
$$y=\frac{3}{4}x+4$$

19. Solving for x:
$$ax+1=bx-3$$
$$ax-bx=-4$$
$$x(a-b)=-4$$
$$x=\frac{-4}{a-b}$$

20. Solving for x:
$$ax-3=cx-4$$
$$ax-cx=-1$$
$$x(a-c)=-1$$
$$x=\frac{-1}{a-c}=\frac{1}{c-a}$$

21. Solving the inequality:
$$-4t\le 12$$
$$t\ge -3$$

The solution is $[-3,\infty)$.

22. Solving the inequality:
$$|3x-1|\ge 5$$

$$3x-1\le -5 \qquad \text{or} \qquad 3x-1\ge 5$$
$$3x\le -4 \qquad\qquad\qquad 3x\ge 6$$
$$x\le -\frac{4}{3} \qquad\qquad\qquad x\ge 2$$

The solution is $\left(-\infty,-\frac{4}{3}\right]\cup[2,\infty)$.

23. The set is: $A\cup B=\{0,1,3,5,7,10,15\}$

24. The set is: $A\cap B=\{5\}$

25. Multiply the second equation by –2:
$$-2x+7y=-27$$
$$2x-6y=22$$
Adding yields $y=-5$. Substituting into the second equation:
$$-x+3(-5)=-11$$
$$-x-15=-11$$
$$-x=4$$
$$x=-4$$
The solution is $(-4,-5)$.

26. Multiply the first equation by –5 and the second equation by 3:
$$-30x-15y=-65$$
$$30x+15y=21$$
Adding yields $0=-44$, which is false. There is no solution, or $\varnothing$. The system is inconsistent (lines are parallel).

27. Substituting into the first equation:
$$3x+(-3x+1)=1$$
$$1=1$$
Since the result is true, the two lines coincide. The solution set can be written as $\{(x,y)\,|\,y=-3x+1\}$.

28. Solving the first equation for z:
$$5x+2y=-z$$
$$z=-5x-2y$$
Substituting into the second equation:
$$3y-4(-5x-2y)=-22$$
$$3y+20x+8y=-22$$
$$20x+11y=-22$$
Substituting into the third equation:
$$7x+2(-5x-2y)=8$$
$$7x-10x-4y=8$$
$$-3x-4y=8$$
This results in the system:
$$20x+11y=-22$$
$$-3x-4y=8$$
Multiplying the first equation by 4 and the second equation by 11:
$$80x+44y=-88$$
$$-33x-44y=88$$
Adding yields:
$$47x=0$$
$$x=0$$
Substituting into the first equation:
$$20(0)+11y=-22$$
$$11y=-22$$
$$y=-2$$
Substituting into the original first equation:
$$5(0)+2(-2)=-z$$
$$-4=-z$$
$$z=4$$
The solution is $(0,-2,4)$.

29. Graphing the linear inequality:

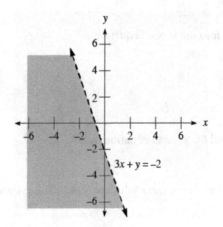

$$3x+y=-2$$

30. Expanding across the first row:

$$\begin{vmatrix} -2 & 0 & 1 \\ 1 & 2 & 1 \\ 3 & -1 & 0 \end{vmatrix} = -2\begin{vmatrix} 2 & 1 \\ -1 & 0 \end{vmatrix} - 0\begin{vmatrix} 1 & 1 \\ 3 & 0 \end{vmatrix} + 1\begin{vmatrix} 1 & 2 \\ 3 & -1 \end{vmatrix} = -2(0+1)-0+1(-1-6) = -2-0-7 = -9$$

31. Graphing the solution set:

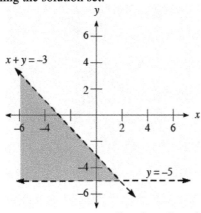

32. Graphing the solution set:

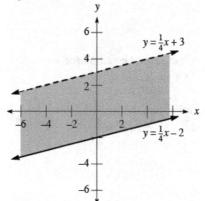

33. Computing the slope: $m = \dfrac{\dfrac{7}{10}+\dfrac{1}{5}}{\dfrac{3}{5}-\dfrac{3}{2}} = \dfrac{\dfrac{7}{10}+\dfrac{2}{10}}{\dfrac{6}{10}-\dfrac{15}{10}} = \dfrac{\dfrac{9}{10}}{-\dfrac{9}{10}} = -1$

34. Solving for y:

$$2x - 7y = 14$$
$$-7y = -2x + 14$$
$$y = \frac{2}{7}x - 2$$

So $m = \dfrac{2}{7}$, $b = -2$.

35. Using the slope-intercept formula: $y = -\dfrac{1}{2}x + 13$

36. First solve for y to find the slope:

$$4x - 3y = 17$$
$$-3y = -4x + 17$$
$$y = \frac{4}{3}x - \frac{17}{3}$$

So the perpendicular slope is $-\dfrac{3}{4}$. Since the y-intercept is -3, the equation is $y = -\dfrac{3}{4}x - 3$.

37. First find the slope: $m = \dfrac{2-(-6)}{9-5} = \dfrac{8}{4} = 2$. Using the point-slope formula:

$$y - 2 = 2(x - 9)$$
$$y - 2 = 2x - 18$$
$$y = 2x - 16$$

38. Evaluating: $f(-3) = -3 - 1 = -4$

39. Evaluating: $g(-2) + 5 = \left[3 - (-2)^2\right] + 5 = 3 - 4 + 5 = 4$

40. Simplifying: $(f - g)(x) = f(x) - g(x) = (x-1) - (3 - x^2) = x - 1 - 3 + x^2 = x^2 + x - 4$

41. Simplifying: $(g \circ f)(x) = g(x-1) = 3 - (x-1)^2 = 3 - x^2 + 2x - 1 = -x^2 + 2x + 2$

42. Evaluating: $f(2) = 1$

43. Evaluating: $(f + g)(-3) = f(-3) + g(-3) = 3 + (-1) = 2$

44. Evaluating: $(g \circ f)(-8) = g\big[f(-8)\big] = g(-3) = -1$

45. $g(x) = 1$ when $x = 8$.

Chapter 3 Test

1. Solving the second equation for y:
$$6x + y = 8$$
$$y = -6x + 8$$
Substituting into the first equation:
$$4x - 2(-6x + 8) = 9$$
$$4x + 12x - 16 = 9$$
$$16x - 16 = 9$$
$$16x = 25$$
$$x = \frac{25}{16}$$
Substituting to find y: $y = -6\left(\dfrac{25}{16}\right) + 8 = -\dfrac{75}{8} + \dfrac{64}{8} = -\dfrac{11}{8}$. The solution is $\left(\dfrac{25}{16}, -\dfrac{11}{8}\right)$.

2. Solving the first equation for x:
$$x - 6y = -50$$
$$x = 6y - 50$$
Substituting into the second equation:
$$-2(6y - 50) + 8y = 64$$
$$-12y + 100 + 8y = 64$$
$$-4y + 100 = 64$$
$$-4y = -36$$
$$y = 9$$
Substituting to find x: $x = 6(9) - 50 = 54 - 50 = 4$. The solution is $(4, 9)$.

3. Multiply the first equation by -2:
$$-2x + 2y = 2$$
$$14x - 2y = 70$$
Adding yields:
$$12x = 72$$
$$x = 6$$
Substituting into the first equation:
$$6 - y = -1$$
$$-y = -7$$
$$y = 7$$
The solution is $(6, 7)$.

4. To clear each equation of fractions, multiply the first equation by 7 and the second equation by 15:
$$x + 3y = 14$$
$$3x - 5y = 0$$
Multiply the first equation by –3:
$$-3x - 9y = -42$$
$$3x - 5y = 0$$
Adding yields:
$$-14y = -42$$
$$y = 3$$
Substituting into the first equation:
$$x + 3(3) = 14$$
$$x + 9 = 14$$
$$x = 5$$
The solution is $(4,2)$.

5. Adding the first and third equations:
$$5x + 3y = 7$$
Multiplying the first equation by 2 and adding to the second equation:
$$2x + 8y + 4z = 10$$
$$x - 2y - 4z = -3$$
Adding yields:
$$3x + 6y = 7$$
So we have the system:
$$5x + 3y = 7$$
$$3x + 6y = 7$$
Multiplying the first equation by –2:
$$-10x - 6y = -14$$
$$3x + 6y = 7$$
Adding the two equations:
$$-7x = -7$$
$$x = 1$$
Substituting to find y:
$$5(1) + 3y = 7$$
$$5 + 3y = 7$$
$$3y = 2$$
$$y = \frac{2}{3}$$
Substituting into the original first equation:
$$1 + 4\left(\frac{2}{3}\right) + 2z = 5$$
$$\frac{11}{3} + 2z = 5$$
$$2z = \frac{4}{3}$$
$$z = \frac{2}{3}$$
The solution is $\left(1, \frac{2}{3}, \frac{2}{3}\right)$.

6. Form the augmented matrix using the third equation as row 1: $\begin{bmatrix} -1 & 5 & 1 & | & 13 \\ 4 & -1 & -2 & | & -12 \\ -3 & -6 & 1 & | & -5 \end{bmatrix}$

Multiply row 1 by -1: $\begin{bmatrix} 1 & -5 & -1 & | & -13 \\ 4 & -1 & -2 & | & -12 \\ -3 & -6 & 1 & | & -5 \end{bmatrix}$

Add -4 times row 1 to row 2 and 3 times row 1 to row 3: $\begin{bmatrix} 1 & -5 & -1 & | & -13 \\ 0 & 19 & 2 & | & 40 \\ 0 & -21 & -2 & | & -44 \end{bmatrix}$

Add row 2 to row 3: $\begin{bmatrix} 1 & -5 & -1 & | & -13 \\ 0 & 19 & 2 & | & 40 \\ 0 & -2 & 0 & | & -4 \end{bmatrix}$

Divide row 3 by -2 and switch with row 2: $\begin{bmatrix} 1 & -5 & -1 & | & -13 \\ 0 & 1 & 0 & | & 2 \\ 0 & 19 & 2 & | & 40 \end{bmatrix}$

Add -19 times row 2 to row 3: $\begin{bmatrix} 1 & -5 & -1 & | & -13 \\ 0 & 1 & 0 & | & 2 \\ 0 & 0 & 2 & | & 2 \end{bmatrix}$

Divide row 3 by 2: $\begin{bmatrix} 1 & -5 & -1 & | & -13 \\ 0 & 1 & 0 & | & 2 \\ 0 & 0 & 1 & | & 1 \end{bmatrix}$

So $z = 1$ and $y = 2$. Substituting to find x:
$$x - 5(2) - 1(1) = -13$$
$$x - 11 = -13$$
$$x = -2$$
The solution is $(-2, 2, 1)$.

7. Evaluating the determinant: $\begin{vmatrix} 3 & -5 \\ -2 & 4 \end{vmatrix} = 3 \cdot 4 - (-5) \cdot (-2) = 12 - 10 = 2$

8. Expanding across the first row:

$\begin{vmatrix} 1 & 2 & 3 \\ 4 & 5 & 6 \\ 7 & 8 & 9 \end{vmatrix} = 1 \begin{vmatrix} 5 & 6 \\ 8 & 9 \end{vmatrix} - 2 \begin{vmatrix} 4 & 6 \\ 7 & 9 \end{vmatrix} + 3 \begin{vmatrix} 4 & 5 \\ 7 & 8 \end{vmatrix} = 1(45-48) - 2(36-42) + 3(32-35) = -3 + 12 - 9 = 0$

9. First find the determinants:

$$D = \begin{vmatrix} 4 & -2 \\ 3 & 5 \end{vmatrix} = 20 + 6 = 26$$

$$D_x = \begin{vmatrix} 5 & -2 \\ 11 & 5 \end{vmatrix} = 25 + 22 = 47$$

$$D_y = \begin{vmatrix} 4 & 5 \\ 3 & 11 \end{vmatrix} = 44 - 15 = 29$$

Now use Cramer's rule:

$$x = \frac{D_x}{D} = \frac{47}{26} \qquad\qquad y = \frac{D_y}{D} = \frac{29}{26}$$

The solution is $\left(\dfrac{47}{26}, \dfrac{29}{26}\right)$.

10. Let x and y represent the two numbers. The system of equations is:

$$y = \frac{1}{2}x + 2$$
$$x + y = 8$$

Substituting into the second equation:

$$x + \frac{1}{2}x + 2 = 8$$
$$\frac{3}{2}x + 2 = 8$$
$$\frac{3}{2}x = 6$$
$$x = 4$$
$$y = \frac{1}{2}(4) + 2 = 4$$

The numbers are 4 and 4.

11. Let x represent the amount Ralph owes at 13% and $3x$ represent the amount he owes at 17%. The equation is:

$$0.13(x) + 0.17(3x) = 768$$
$$0.64x = 768$$
$$x = 1,200$$
$$3x = 3,600$$

Ralph owes \$1,200 at 13% and \$3,600 at 17%.

12. Let a represent the adult tickets and c represent the children's tickets. The system of equations is:

$$a + c = 890$$
$$15a + 5c = 11,750$$

Multiply the first equation by –5:

$$-5a - 5c = -4,450$$
$$15a + 5c = 11,750$$

Adding yields:

$$10a = 7,300$$
$$a = 730$$
$$c = 890 - 730 = 160$$

There were 730 adult tickets and 160 children's tickets sold.

13. Let b and c represent the rates of the boat and current. The system of equations is:

$$4(b + c) = 36$$
$$11(b - c) = 33$$

Simplifying the system by dividing the first equation by 4 and the second equation by 11:

$$b + c = 9$$
$$b - c = 3$$

Adding yields:

$$2b = 12$$
$$b = 6$$
$$c = 9 - 6 = 3$$

The boat's speed is 6 mph and the current's speed is 3 mph.

14. Let $n, d,$ and q represent the number of nickels, dimes, and quarters. The system of equations is:
$$n + d + q = 8$$
$$0.05n + 0.10d + 0.25q = 1.05$$
$$n = d + q$$
Substituting into the first equation:
$$d + q + d + q = 8$$
$$2d + 2q = 8$$
$$d + q = 4$$
Substituting into the second equation:
$$0.05(d + q) + 0.10d + 0.25q = 1.05$$
$$0.15d + 0.30q = 1.05$$
$$d + 2q = 7$$
The system of equations becomes:
$$d + 2q = 7$$
$$d + q = 4$$
Subtracting:
$$q = 3$$
$$d = 4 - 3 = 1$$
$$n = 1 + 3 = 4$$
The collection consists of 4 nickels, 1 dime, and 3 quarters.

15. Graphing the solution set:

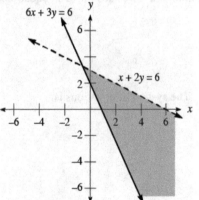

16. Graphing the solution set:

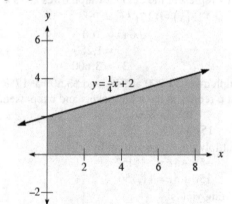

17. A system of inequalities that describes the shaded region is:
$$y < \frac{4}{3}x + 1$$
$$y \le -\frac{4}{3}x + 1$$

18. A system of inequalities that describes the shaded region is:
$$y < \frac{4}{3}x + 1$$
$$y \ge -\frac{4}{3}x + 1$$

Chapter 4
Exponents and Polynomials

4.1 Sums and Differences of Polynomials

1. This is a trinomial. The degree is 2 and the leading coefficient is 5.
3. This is a binomial. The degree is 1 and the leading coefficient is 3.
5. This is a trinomial. The degree is 2 and the leading coefficient is 8.
7. This is a polynomial. The degree is 3 and the leading coefficient is 4.

9. This is a monomial. The degree is 0 and the leading coefficient is $-\dfrac{3}{4}$.

11. This is a trinomial. The degree is 3 and the leading coefficient is 6.

13. Simplifying: $(4x+2)+(3x-1) = 7x+1$

15. Simplifying: $2x^2 - 3x + 10x - 15 = 2x^2 + 7x - 15$

17. Simplifying: $12a^2 + 8ab - 15ab - 10b^2 = 12a^2 - 7ab - 10b^2$

19. Simplifying: $\left(5x^2 - 6x + 1\right) - \left(4x^2 + 7x - 2\right) = 5x^2 - 6x + 1 - 4x^2 - 7x + 2 = x^2 - 13x + 3$

21. Simplifying:
$$\left(\frac{1}{2}x^2 - \frac{1}{3}x - \frac{1}{6}\right) - \left(\frac{1}{4}x^2 + \frac{7}{12}x\right) + \left(\frac{1}{3}x - \frac{1}{12}\right) = \frac{1}{2}x^2 - \frac{1}{3}x - \frac{1}{6} - \frac{1}{4}x^2 - \frac{7}{12}x + \frac{1}{3}x - \frac{1}{12} = \frac{1}{4}x^2 - \frac{7}{12}x - \frac{1}{4}$$

23. Simplifying: $\left(y^3 - 2y^2 - 3y + 4\right) - \left(2y^3 - y^2 + y - 3\right) = y^3 - 2y^2 - 3y + 4 - 2y^3 + y^2 - y + 3 = -y^3 - y^2 - 4y + 7$

25. Simplifying:
$$\left(5x^3 - 4x^2\right) - \left(3x + 4\right) + \left(5x^2 - 7\right) - \left(3x^3 + 6\right) = 5x^3 - 4x^2 - 3x - 4 + 5x^2 - 7 - 3x^3 - 6 = 2x^3 + x^2 - 3x - 17$$

27. Simplifying:
$$\left(\frac{4}{7}x^2 - \frac{1}{7}xy + \frac{1}{14}y^2\right) - \left(\frac{1}{2}x^2 - \frac{2}{7}xy - \frac{9}{14}y^2\right) = \frac{4}{7}x^2 - \frac{1}{7}xy + \frac{1}{14}y^2 - \frac{1}{2}x^2 + \frac{2}{7}xy + \frac{9}{14}y^2$$
$$= \frac{8}{14}x^2 - \frac{7}{14}x^2 - \frac{1}{7}xy + \frac{2}{7}xy + \frac{1}{14}y^2 + \frac{9}{14}y^2$$
$$= \frac{1}{14}x^2 + \frac{1}{7}xy + \frac{5}{7}y^2$$

29. Simplifying:
$$\left(3a^3 + 2a^2b + ab^2 - b^3\right) - \left(6a^3 - 4a^2b + 6ab^2 - b^3\right) = 3a^3 + 2a^2b + ab^2 - b^3 - 6a^3 + 4a^2b - 6ab^2 + b^3$$
$$= -3a^3 + 6a^2b - 5ab^2$$

31. Subtracting: $p(x) - q(x) = \left(2x^2 - 7x\right) - \left(2x^2 - 4x\right) = 2x^2 - 7x - 2x^2 + 4x = -3x$

33. Adding: $\left(x^2 - 6xy + y^2\right) + \left(2x^2 - 6xy - y^2\right) = x^2 - 6xy + y^2 + 2x^2 - 6xy - y^2 = 3x^2 - 12xy$

35. Subtracting: $q(x) - p(x) = \left(9x^5 - 4x^3 - 6\right) - \left(-8x^5 - 4x^3 + 6\right) = 9x^5 - 4x^3 - 6 + 8x^5 + 4x^3 - 6 = 17x^5 - 12$

37. Adding:

$$\left(11a^2 + 3ab + 2b^2\right) + \left(9a^2 - 2ab + b^2\right) + \left(-6a^2 - 3ab + 5b^2\right)$$
$$= 11a^2 + 3ab + 2b^2 + 9a^2 - 2ab + b^2 - 6a^2 - 3ab + 5b^2$$
$$= 14a^2 - 2ab + 8b^2$$

39. Simplifying: $-\left[2 - (4 - x)\right] = -(2 - 4 + x) = -(-2 + x) = 2 - x$

41. Simplifying: $-5\left[-(x - 3) - (x + 2)\right] = -5(-x + 3 - x - 2) = -5(-2x + 1) = 10x - 5$

43. Simplifying: $4x - 5\left[3 - (x - 4)\right] = 4x - 5(3 - x + 4) = 4x - 5(7 - x) = 4x - 35 + 5x = 9x - 35$

45. Simplifying:

$$-(3x - 4y) - \left[(4x + 2y) - (3x + 7y)\right] = -(3x - 4y) - (4x + 2y - 3x - 7y)$$
$$= -(3x - 4y) - (x - 5y)$$
$$= -3x + 4y - x + 5y$$
$$= 9y - 4x$$

47. Simplifying:

$$4a - \left\{3a + 2\left[a - 5(a + 1) + 4\right]\right\} = 4a - \left[3a + 2(a - 5a - 5 + 4)\right]$$
$$= 4a - \left[3a + 2(-4a - 1)\right]$$
$$= 4a - (3a - 8a - 2)$$
$$= 4a - (-5a - 2)$$
$$= 4a + 5a + 2$$
$$= 9a + 2$$

49. Evaluating when $x = 2$: $2(2)^2 - 3(2) - 4 = 2(4) - 3(2) - 4 = 8 - 6 - 4 = -2$

51. **a.** Evaluating when $x = 12$: $P(12) = \frac{3}{2}(12)^2 - \frac{3}{4}(12) + 1 = \frac{3}{2}(144) - \frac{3}{4}(12) + 1 = 216 - 9 + 1 = 208$

  b. Evaluating when $x = -8$: $P(-8) = \frac{3}{2}(-8)^2 - \frac{3}{4}(-8) + 1 = \frac{3}{2}(64) - \frac{3}{4}(-8) + 1 = 96 + 6 + 1 = 103$

53. **a.** Evaluating when $x = 4$: $Q(4) = (4)^3 - (4)^2 + (4) - 1 = 64 - 16 + 4 - 1 = 51$

  b. Evaluating when $x = -2$: $Q(-2) = (-2)^3 - (-2)^2 + (-2) - 1 = -8 - 4 - 2 - 1 = -15$

55. **a.** Evaluating when $x = 10$: $R(10) = 11.5(10) - 0.05(10)^2 = 115 - 5 = 110$

  b. Evaluating when $x = -10$: $R(-10) = 11.5(-10) - 0.05(-10)^2 = -115 - 5 = -120$

57. **a.** Evaluating when $x = -4$: $P(-4) = 600 + 1{,}000(-4) - 100(-4)^2 = 600 - 4{,}000 - 1{,}600 = -5{,}000$

  b. Evaluating when $x = 4$: $P(4) = 600 + 1{,}000(4) - 100(4)^2 = 600 + 4{,}000 - 1{,}600 = 3{,}000$

59. The amount of caffeine Mary drinks is: $3(43) + 54 + 2(23) = 229$ milligrams

61. Substituting $t = 3$: $h = -16(3)^2 + 128(3) = 240$ feet   Substituting $t = 5$: $h = -16(5)^2 + 128(5) = 240$ feet

63. The weekly profit is given by:

$$P(x) = R(x) - C(x) = \left(100x - 0.5x^2\right) - (60x + 300) = 100x - 0.5x^2 - 60x - 300 = -0.5x^2 + 40x - 300$$

Substituting $x = 60$: $P(60) = -0.5(60)^2 + 40(60) - 300 = \$300$

65. The weekly profit is given by:

$$P(x) = R(x) - C(x) = \left(10x - 0.002x^2\right) - (800 + 6.5x) = 10x - 0.002x^2 - 800 - 6.5x = -0.002x^2 + 3.5x - 800$$

Substituting $x = 1{,}000$: $P(1{,}000) = -0.002(1{,}000)^2 + 3.5(1{,}000) - 800 = \$700$

67. An expression for the area of the pathway is: $(10+2x)(40+2x)-400$

Substituting $x=5$: $(10+2\cdot 5)(40+2\cdot 5)-400=20\cdot 50-400=600$ ft^2

Substituting $x=8$: $(10+2\cdot 8)(40+2\cdot 8)-400=26\cdot 56-400=1{,}056$ ft^2

69. The volume of the box is given by: $V=(9-2x)(12-2x)(x)$ in^2

Substituting $x=2$: $V=(9-2\cdot 2)(12-2\cdot 2)(2)=(5)(8)(2)=80$ in^2

71. Simplifying: $2x^2-3x+10x-15=2x^2+7x-15$

73. Simplifying: $\left(6x^3-2x^2y+8xy^2\right)+\left(-9x^2y+3xy^2-12y^3\right)=6x^3-11x^2y+11xy^2-12y^3$

75. Simplifying: $4x^3(-3x)=-12x^{3+1}=-12x^4$ 77. Simplifying: $4x^3\left(5x^2\right)=20x^{3+2}=20x^5$

79. Simplifying: $\left(a^3\right)^2=a^{3\cdot 2}=a^6$

81. Simplifying: $11.5(130)-0.05(130)^2=1{,}495-845=650$

83. Simplifying: $-1(5-x)=-5+x=x-5$ 85. Simplifying: $-1(7-x)=-7+x=x-7$

87. Simplifying: $5\left(x-\dfrac{1}{5}\right)=5\cdot x-5\cdot\dfrac{1}{5}=5x-1$ 89. Simplifying: $x\left(1-\dfrac{1}{x}\right)=x\cdot 1-x\cdot\dfrac{1}{x}=x-1$

91. Simplifying: $12\left(\dfrac{1}{4}x+\dfrac{2}{3}y\right)=12\cdot\dfrac{1}{4}x+12\cdot\dfrac{2}{3}y=3x+8y$

93. Simplifying: $x^2\left(1-\dfrac{4}{x^2}\right)=x^2\cdot 1-x^2\cdot\dfrac{4}{x^2}=x^2-4$

95.
a. From the graph: $f(-3)=5$ b. From the graph: $f(0)=-4$

c. From the graph: $f(1)=-3$ d. From the graph: $g(-1)=3$

e. From the graph: $g(0)=4$ f. From the graph: $g(2)=0$

g. From the graph: $f(g(2))=f(0)=-4$ h. From the graph: $g(f(2))=g(0)=4$

i. From the graph: $(f(2))^2=(0)^2=0$ j. From the graph: $f(f(2))=f(0)=-4$

k. From the graph: $f(f(1))=f(-3)=5$ l. From the graph: $g(g(1))=g(3)=-5$

m. $f(x)=0$ when $x=\pm 2$.   n. $g(x)=-5$ when $x=\pm 3$.

o. $f(x)=g(x)$ when $x=\pm 2$.

4.2 Multiplication of Polynomials

1. Multiplying: $2x\left(6x^2 - 5x + 4\right) = 2x \cdot 6x^2 - 2x \cdot 5x + 2x \cdot 4 = 12x^3 - 10x^2 + 8x$

3. Multiplying: $-3a^2\left(a^3 - 6a^2 + 7\right) = -3a^2 \cdot a^3 - \left(-3a^2\right) \cdot 6a^2 + \left(-3a^2\right) \cdot 7 = -3a^5 + 18a^4 - 21a^2$

5. Multiplying: $2a^2b\left(a^3 - ab + b^3\right) = 2a^2b \cdot a^3 - 2a^2b \cdot ab + 2a^2b \cdot b^3 = 2a^5b - 2a^3b^2 + 2a^2b^4$

7. Multiplying using the vertical format:

$$
\begin{array}{rr}
x & -5 \\
x & +3 \\
\hline
x^2 & -5x \\
& +3x \quad -15 \\
\hline
x^2 & -2x \quad -15
\end{array}
$$

The product is $x^2 - 2x - 15$.

9. Multiplying using the vertical format:

$$
\begin{array}{rr}
2x^2 & -3 \\
3x^2 & -5 \\
\hline
6x^4 & -9x^2 \\
& -10x^2 \quad +15 \\
\hline
6x^4 & -19x^2 \quad +15
\end{array}
$$

The product is $6x^4 - 19x^2 + 15$.

11. Multiplying using the vertical format:

$$
\begin{array}{rrr}
x^2 & +6x & +5 \\
& x & +3 \\
\hline
x^3 & +6x^2 & +5x \\
& +3x^2 & +18x \quad +15 \\
\hline
x^3 & +9x^2 & +23x \quad +15
\end{array}
$$

The product is $x^3 + 9x^2 + 23x + 15$.

13. Multiplying using the vertical format:

$$
\begin{array}{rrr}
a^2 & +ab & +b^2 \\
& a & -b \\
\hline
a^3 & +a^2b & +ab^2 \\
& -a^2b & -ab^2 \quad -b^3 \\
\hline
a^3 & & -b^3
\end{array}
$$

The product is $a^3 - b^3$.

15. Multiplying using the vertical format:

$$
\begin{array}{rrr}
4x^2 & -2xy & +y^2 \\
& 2x & +y \\
\hline
8x^3 & -4x^2y & +2xy^2 \\
& +4x^2y & -2xy^2 \quad +y^3 \\
\hline
8x^3 & & +y^3
\end{array}
$$

The product is $8x^3 + y^3$.

17. Multiplying using the vertical format:

$$
\begin{array}{rrr}
a^2 & +ab & +b^2 \\
& 2a & -3b \\
\hline
2a^3 & +2a^2b & +2ab^2 \\
& -3a^2b & -3ab^2 \quad -3b^3 \\
\hline
2a^3 & -a^2b & -ab^2 \quad -3b^3
\end{array}
$$

The product is $2a^3 - a^2b - ab^2 - 3b^3$.

19. Multiplying using FOIL: $(x-2)(x+3) = x^2 + 3x - 2x - 6 = x^2 + x - 6$

21. Multiplying using FOIL: $(2a+3)(3a+2) = 6a^2 + 4a + 9a + 6 = 6a^2 + 13a + 6$

23. Multiplying using FOIL: $(5-3t)(4+2t) = 20 + 10t - 12t - 6t^2 = 20 - 2t - 6t^2$

25. Multiplying using FOIL: $\left(x^3 + 3\right)\left(x^3 - 5\right) = x^6 - 5x^3 + 3x^3 - 15 = x^6 - 2x^3 - 15$

27. Multiplying using FOIL: $(5x - 6y)(4x + 3y) = 20x^2 + 15xy - 24xy - 18y^2 = 20x^2 - 9xy - 18y^2$

29. Multiplying using FOIL: $\left(3t + \dfrac{1}{3}\right)\left(6t - \dfrac{2}{3}\right) = 18t^2 - 2t + 2t - \dfrac{2}{9} = 18t^2 - \dfrac{2}{9}$

31. a. Simplifying: $p(x) - q(x) = (4x-3) - (2x+1) = 4x - 3 - 2x - 1 = 2x - 4$

    b. Simplifying: $p(x) + q(x) = (4x-3) + (2x+1) = 6x - 2$

    c. Simplifying: $p(x) \cdot q(x) = (4x-3)(2x+1) = 8x^2 - 2x - 3$

33. Finding the product: $(5x + 2y)^2 = (5x)^2 + 2(5x)(2y) + (2y)^2 = 25x^2 + 20xy + 4y^2$

35. Finding the product: $\left(5-3t^3\right)^2 = (5)^2 - 2(5)\left(3t^3\right) + \left(3t^3\right)^2 = 25 - 30t^3 + 9t^6$

37. Finding the product: $(2a+3b)(2a-3b) = (2a)^2 - (3b)^2 = 4a^2 - 9b^2$

39. Finding the product: $\left(3r^2+7s\right)\left(3r^2-7s\right) = \left(3r^2\right)^2 - (7s)^2 = 9r^4 - 49s^2$

41. Finding the product: $\left(y+\dfrac{3}{2}\right)^2 = (y)^2 + 2(y)\left(\dfrac{3}{2}\right) + \left(\dfrac{3}{2}\right)^2 = y^2 + 3y + \dfrac{9}{4}$

43. Finding the product: $\left(a-\dfrac{1}{2}\right)^2 = (a)^2 - 2(a)\left(\dfrac{1}{2}\right) + \left(\dfrac{1}{2}\right)^2 = a^2 - a + \dfrac{1}{4}$

45. Finding the product: $\left(x+\dfrac{1}{4}\right)^2 = (x)^2 + 2(x)\left(\dfrac{1}{4}\right) + \left(\dfrac{1}{4}\right)^2 = x^2 + \dfrac{1}{2}x + \dfrac{1}{16}$

47. Finding the product: $\left(t+\dfrac{1}{3}\right)^2 = (t)^2 + 2(t)\left(\dfrac{1}{3}\right) + \left(\dfrac{1}{3}\right)^2 = t^2 + \dfrac{2}{3}t + \dfrac{1}{9}$

49. Finding the product: $\left(\dfrac{1}{3}x-\dfrac{2}{5}\right)\left(\dfrac{1}{3}x+\dfrac{2}{5}\right) = \left(\dfrac{1}{3}x\right)^2 - \left(\dfrac{2}{5}\right)^2 = \dfrac{1}{9}x^2 - \dfrac{4}{25}$

51. Expanding and simplifying:

$$
\begin{aligned}
(x-2)^3 &= (x-2)(x-2)^2 \\
&= (x-2)\left(x^2-4x+4\right) \\
&= x^3 - 4x^2 + 4x - 2x^2 + 8x - 8 \\
&= x^3 - 6x^2 + 12x - 8
\end{aligned}
$$

53. Expanding and simplifying:

$$
\begin{aligned}
\left(x-\dfrac{1}{2}\right)^3 &= \left(x-\dfrac{1}{2}\right)\left(x-\dfrac{1}{2}\right)^2 \\
&= \left(x-\dfrac{1}{2}\right)\left(x^2-x+\dfrac{1}{4}\right) \\
&= x^3 - x^2 + \dfrac{1}{4}x - \dfrac{1}{2}x^2 + \dfrac{1}{2}x - \dfrac{1}{8} \\
&= x^3 - \dfrac{3}{2}x^2 + \dfrac{3}{4}x - \dfrac{1}{8}
\end{aligned}
$$

55. Expanding and simplifying:

$$
\begin{aligned}
3(x-1)(x-2)(x-3) &= 3(x-1)\left(x^2-5x+6\right) \\
&= 3\left(x^3 - 5x^2 + 6x - x^2 + 5x - 6\right) \\
&= 3\left(x^3 - 6x^2 + 11x - 6\right) \\
&= 3x^3 - 18x^2 + 33x - 18
\end{aligned}
$$

57. Expanding and simplifying: $\left(b^2+8\right)\left(a^2+1\right) = a^2b^2 + b^2 + 8a^2 + 8$

59. Expanding and simplifying:

$$(x+1)^2 + (x+2)^2 + (x+3)^2 = x^2 + 2x + 1 + x^2 + 4x + 4 + x^2 + 6x + 9 = 3x^2 + 12x + 14$$

61. Expanding and simplifying:

$$(2x+3)^2 - (2x-3)^2 = \left(4x^2+12x+9\right) - \left(4x^2-12x+9\right) = 4x^2 + 12x + 9 - 4x^2 + 12x - 9 = 24x$$

63. Simplifying: $(x+3)^2 - 2(x+3) - 8 = x^2 + 6x + 9 - 2x - 6 - 8 = x^2 + 4x - 5$

65. Simplifying: $(2a-3)^2 - 9(2a-3) + 20 = 4a^2 - 12a + 9 - 18a + 27 + 20 = 4a^2 - 30a + 56$

67. Simplifying:

$$
\begin{aligned}
2(4a+2)^2 - 3(4a+2) - 20 &= 2\left(16a^2+16a+4\right) - 3(4a+2) - 20 \\
&= 32a^2 + 32a + 8 - 12a - 6 - 20 \\
&= 32a^2 + 20a - 18
\end{aligned}
$$

69. Evaluating when $a = 2$ and $b = 3$:

    a. $a^4 - b^4 = 2^4 - 3^4 = 16 - 81 = -65$

    b. $(a-b)^4 = (2-3)^4 = (-1)^4 = 1$

    c. $\left(a^2 + b^2\right)(a+b)(a-b) = \left(2^2 + 3^2\right)(2+3)(2-3) = (13)(5)(-1) = -65$

71. The expression is: $6 + 0.05(x - 400) = 6 + 0.05x - 20 = 0.05x - 14$

    Substituting $x = 592$: $0.05(592) - 14 = \$15.60$

73. Since $R = xp$, substitute $x = 900 - 300p$ to obtain: $R(p) = (900 - 300p)p = 900p - 300p^2$

    To find $R(x)$, we first solve for p:

$$x = 900 - 300p$$
$$300p = 900 - x$$
$$p = 3 - \frac{x}{300}$$

    Now substitute to obtain: $R(x) = x\left(3 - \dfrac{x}{300}\right) = 3x - \dfrac{x^2}{300}$

    Substituting $p = \$1.60$: $R(1.60) = 900(1.60) - 300(1.60)^2 = \$672$. The revenue is \$672.

75. Since $R = xp$, substitute $x = 350 - 10p$ to obtain: $R(p) = (350 - 10p)p = 350p - 10p^2$

    To find $R(x)$, we first solve for p:

$$x = 350 - 10p$$
$$10p = 350 - x$$
$$p = 35 - \frac{x}{10}$$

    Now substitute to obtain: $R(x) = x\left(35 - \dfrac{x}{10}\right) = 35x - \dfrac{x^2}{10}$

    Substituting $x = 65$: $R(65) = 35(65) - \dfrac{(65)^2}{10} = \$1{,}852.50$. The revenue is \$1,852.50.

77. Since $R(x) = 35x - \dfrac{x^2}{10}$ and $C(x) = 5x + 500$, then:

$$P(x) = R(x) - C(x) = 35x - \frac{x^2}{10} - (5x + 500) = -\frac{x^2}{10} + 30x - 500$$

$$P(60) = -\frac{(60)^2}{10} + 30(60) - 500 = \$940$$

79. Expanding the formula:

$$A = 100(1+r)^4$$
$$= 100(1+r)^2 (1+r)^2$$
$$= 100\left(1 + 2r + r^2\right)\left(1 + 2r + r^2\right)$$
$$= 100\left(1 + 2r + r^2 + 2r + 4r^2 + 2r^3 + r^2 + 2r^3 + r^4\right)$$
$$= 100\left(1 + 4r + 6r^2 + 4r^3 + r^4\right)$$
$$= 100 + 400r + 600r^2 + 400r^3 + 100r^4$$

81. Finding the cost in 10 years: $F = 4.00(1 + 0.08)^{10} = 4(1.08)^{10} \approx \$8.64$

83. Finding the tuition 20 years ago: $F = 5{,}131(1+0.08)^{-20} = 5{,}131(1.08)^{-20} \approx \$1{,}100.85$

Finding the tuition 30 years ago: $F = 5{,}131(1+0.08)^{-30} = 5{,}131(1.08)^{-30} \approx \$509.91$

85. Simplifying: $\dfrac{8a^3}{a} = 8a^{3-1} = 8a^2$

87. Simplifying: $\dfrac{-48a}{a} = -48$

89. Simplifying: $\dfrac{16a^5b^4}{8a^2b^3} = 2a^{5-2}b^{4-3} = 2a^3b$

91. Simplifying: $\dfrac{-24a^5b^5}{8a^5b^3} = -3a^{5-5}b^{5-3} = -3b^2$

93. Simplifying: $\dfrac{x^3y^4}{-x^3} = -x^{3-3}y^4 = -y^4$

95. Multiply the first equation by -1 and add it to the second equation:
$$-x-y-z=-6$$
$$2x-y+z=3$$
Adding yields the equation $x-2y=-3$. Multiply the first equation by 3 and add it to the third equation:
$$3x+3y+3z=18$$
$$x+2y-3z=-4$$
Adding yields the equation $4x+5y=14$. So the system becomes:
$$x-2y=-3$$
$$4x+5y=14$$
Multiply the first equation by -4 and add it to the second equation:
$$-4x+8y=12$$
$$4x+5y=14$$
Adding yields:
$$13y=26$$
$$y=2$$
Substituting to find x:
$$4x+5(2)=14$$
$$4x+10=14$$
$$4x=4$$
$$x=1$$
Substituting into the original first equation:
$$1+2+z=6$$
$$z+3=6$$
$$z=3$$
The solution is $(1,2,3)$.

97. Multiply the third equation by -1 and add it to the first equation:
$$3x+4y=15$$
$$-4y+3z=-9$$
Adding yields the equation $3x+3z=6$, or $x+z=2$. So the system becomes:
$$2x-5z=-3$$
$$x+z=2$$
Multiply the second equation by -2:
$$2x-5z=-3$$
$$-2x-2z=-4$$
Adding yields:
$$-7z=-7$$
$$z=1$$

Substituting to find x:
$$2x - 5(1) = -3$$
$$2x - 5 = -3$$
$$2x = 2$$
$$x = 1$$

Substituting into the original first equation:
$$3(1) + 4y = 15$$
$$4y + 3 = 15$$
$$4y = 12$$
$$y = 3$$

The solution is $(1, 3, 1)$.

99. Multiplying using FOIL: $\left[(x+y)-4\right]\left[(x+y)+5\right] = (x+y)^2 + (x+y) - 20 = x^2 + 2xy + y^2 + x + y - 20$

101. Multiplying: $(x^n - 2)(x^n - 3) = x^{2n} - 3x^n - 2x^n + 6 = x^{2n} - 5x^n + 6$

103. Multiplying: $(2x^n + 3)(5x^n - 1) = 10x^{2n} - 2x^n + 15x^n - 3 = 10x^{2n} + 13x^n - 3$

105. Multiplying: $(x^n + 5)^2 = (x^n)^2 + 2(x^n)(5) + (5)^2 = x^{2n} + 10x^n + 25$

107. Multiplying: $(x^n + 1)(x^{2n} - x^n + 1) = x^{3n} - x^{2n} + x^n + x^{2n} - x^n + 1 = x^{3n} + 1$

4.3 Greatest Common Factor and Factoring by Grouping

1. Factoring the expression: $10x^3 - 15x^2 = 5x^2(2x - 3)$

3. Factoring the expression: $9y^6 + 18y^3 = 9y^3(y^3 + 2)$

5. Factoring the expression: $9a^2b - 6ab^2 = 3ab(3a - 2b)$

7. Factoring the expression: $21xy^4 + 7x^2y^2 = 7xy^2(3y^2 + x)$

9. Factoring the expression: $3a^2 - 21a + 33 = 3(a^2 - 7a + 11)$

11. Factoring the expression: $4x^3 - 16x^2 + 20x = 4x(x^2 - 4x + 5)$

13. Factoring the expression: $10x^4y^2 + 20x^3y^3 + 30x^2y^4 = 10x^2y^2(x^2 + 2xy + 3y^2)$

15. Factoring the expression: $-x^2y + xy^2 - x^2y^2 = xy(-x + y - xy)$

17. Factoring the expression: $4x^3y^2z - 8x^2y^2z^2 + 6xy^2z^3 = 2xy^2z(2x^2 - 4xz + 3z^2)$

19. Factoring the expression: $20a^2b^2c^2 - 30ab^2c + 25a^2bc^2 = 5abc(4abc - 6b + 5ac)$

21. Factoring the expression: $5x(a - 2b) - 3y(a - 2b) = (a - 2b)(5x - 3y)$

23. Factoring the expression: $3x^2(x+y)^2 - 6y^2(x+y)^2 = 3(x+y)^2(x^2 - 2y^2)$

25. Factoring the expression: $2x^2(x+5) + 7x(x+5) + 8(x+5) = (x+5)(2x^2 + 7x + 8)$

27. Factoring by grouping: $3xy + 3y + 2ax + 2a = 3y(x+1) + 2a(x+1) = (x+1)(3y + 2a)$

29. Factoring by grouping: $x^2y + x + 3xy + 3 = x(xy+1) + 3(xy+1) = (xy+1)(x+3)$

31. Factoring by grouping: $3xy^2 - 6y^2 + 4x - 8 = 3y^2(x-2) + 4(x-2) = (x-2)(3y^2 + 4)$

33. Factoring by grouping: $x^2 - ax - bx + ab = x(x-a) - b(x-a) = (x-a)(x-b)$

35. Factoring by grouping: $ab + 5a - b - 5 = a(b+5) - 1(b+5) = (b+5)(a-1)$

37. Factoring by grouping: $a^4b^2 + a^4 - 5b^2 - 5 = a^4\left(b^2 + 1\right) - 5\left(b^2 + 1\right) = \left(b^2 + 1\right)\left(a^4 - 5\right)$

39. Factoring by grouping: $x^3 + 3x^2 + 4x + 12 = x^2\left(x + 3\right) + 4\left(x + 3\right) = \left(x + 3\right)\left(x^2 + 4\right)$

41. Factoring by grouping: $x^3 + 2x^2 + 25x + 50 = x^2\left(x + 2\right) + 25\left(x + 2\right) = \left(x + 2\right)\left(x^2 + 25\right)$

43. Factoring by grouping: $2x^3 + 3x^2 + 8x + 12 = x^2\left(2x + 3\right) + 4\left(2x + 3\right) = \left(2x + 3\right)\left(x^2 + 4\right)$

45. Factoring by grouping: $4x^3 + 12x^2 + 9x + 27 = 4x^2\left(x + 3\right) + 9\left(x + 3\right) = \left(x + 3\right)\left(4x^2 + 9\right)$

47. It will be $3 \cdot 2 = 6$.

49. Using factoring by grouping:
$$P + Pr + \left(P + Pr\right)r = \left(P + Pr\right) + \left(P + Pr\right)r = \left(P + Pr\right)\left(1 + r\right) = P\left(1 + r\right)\left(1 + r\right) = P\left(1 + r\right)^2$$

51. Factoring the revenue: $R(x) = 35x - 0.1x^2 = x\left(35 - 0.1x\right)$. So the price is $p = 35 - 0.1x$.

Substituting $x = 65$: $p = 35 - 0.1\left(65\right) = \$28.50$. The price is $28.50.

53. First find the slope: $m = \dfrac{73 - 80}{2009 - 2007} = -\dfrac{7}{2} = -3.5$

Using the point-slope formula:
$$\begin{aligned}
y - 80 &= -3.5\left(x - 2007\right) \\
y - 80 &= -3.5x + 7{,}024.5 \\
y &= -3.5x + 7{,}104.5
\end{aligned}$$

Evaluating when $x = 2010$: $y = -3.5\left(2010\right) + 7{,}104.5 = 69.5$ million

55. Factoring out the greatest common factor: $3x^4 - 9x^3y - 18x^2y^2 = 3x^2\left(x^2 - 3xy - 6y^2\right)$

57. Factoring out the greatest common factor: $2x^2\left(x - 3\right) - 4x\left(x - 3\right) - 3\left(x - 3\right) = \left(x - 3\right)\left(2x^2 - 4x - 3\right)$

59. Multiplying using FOIL: $\left(x + 2\right)\left(3x - 1\right) = 3x^2 - x + 6x - 2 = 3x^2 + 5x - 2$

61. Multiplying using FOIL: $\left(x - 1\right)\left(3x - 2\right) = 3x^2 - 2x - 3x + 2 = 3x^2 - 5x + 2$

63. Multiplying using FOIL: $\left(x + 2\right)\left(x + 3\right) = x^2 + 3x + 2x + 6 = x^2 + 5x + 6$

65. Multiplying using FOIL: $\left(2y + 5\right)\left(3y - 7\right) = 6y^2 - 14y + 15y - 35 = 6y^2 + y - 35$

67. Multiplying using FOIL: $\left(4 - 3a\right)\left(5 - a\right) = 20 - 4a - 15a + 3a^2 = 20 - 19a + 3a^2$

69. Multiplying using FOIL: $\left(5 + 2x\right)\left(5 - 2x\right) = 25 - 10x + 10x - 4x^2 = 25 - 4x^2$

71. Completing the table:

Two Numbers a and b	Their Product ab	Their Sum $a + b$
1,−24	−24	−23
−1,24	−24	23
2,−12	−24	−10
−2,12	−24	10
3,−8	−24	−5
−3,8	−24	5
4,−6	−24	−2
−4,6	−24	2

73. The two numbers are 9 and 4.

75. The two numbers are 8 and −5.

77. The two numbers are −12 and 4.

Landmark Review

1. This is a binomial with degree 1 and leading coefficient 5.
2. This is a monomial with degree 0 and leading coefficient 14.
3. This is a trinomial with degree 2 and leading coefficient 9.
4. This is a trinomial with degree 2 and leading coefficient 14.
5. Simplifying: $(3x-4)-(5x+3) = 3x-4-5x-3 = -2x-7$
6. Simplifying: $5x^2 - 3 + 14x - 3x + 4 = 5x^2 + 11x + 1$
7. Simplifying: $4x + 13y^2 - 3x^2 - 5y^2 + 4x^2 - 3 = 8y^2 + x^2 + 4x - 3$
8. Simplifying: $11x^3 + 10y - 3x^2 - 3y + 6x^2 + 4x^3 - 13 = 15x^3 + 3x^2 + 7y - 13$
9. Multiplying: $2a(2a^2 + 4a - 5) = 4a^3 + 8a^2 - 10a$
10. Multiplying: $8xy(5x + 3y + 2xy) = 40x^2y + 24xy^2 + 16x^2y^2$
11. Multiplying: $(x-1)(x-8) = x^2 - 8x - x + 8 = x^2 - 9x + 8$
12. Multiplying: $(x-2)(y+6) = xy + 6x - 2y - 12$
13. Multiplying: $(x^2 - 4)(x-7) = x^3 - 7x^2 - 4x + 28$
14. Multiplying: $(x^2 + 6)(x-8) = x^3 - 8x^2 + 6x - 48$
15. Multiplying: $(3a+5)(a+2) = 3a^2 + 6a + 5a + 10 = 3a^2 + 11a + 10$
16. Multiplying: $(2y-1)(3y-2) = 6y^2 - 4y - 3y + 2 = 6y^2 - 7y + 2$
17. Factoring: $15x^3 + 5x = 5x(3x^2 + 1)$
18. Factoring: $24x^2y^2 + 18xy = 6xy(4xy + 3)$
19. Factoring: $14x^3y^2 + 21x^2y^2 + 35xy = 7xy(2x^2y + 3xy + 5)$
20. Factoring: $9x^5y^3 + 6x^2y^3 + 18x^3y^2 = 3x^2y^2(3x^3y + 2y + 6x)$
21. Factoring: $4xy^2 + 12y^2 + 5ax + 15a = 4y^2(x+3) + 5a(x+3) = (x+3)(4y^2 + 5a)$
22. Factoring: $6ab + 18a - 2b - 6 = 6a(b+3) - 2(b+3) = 2(b+3)(3a-1)$
23. Factoring: $4a^2 - 2a^2b - 4bc^2 + 8c^2 = 2a^2(2-b) + 4c^2(2-b) = 2(2-b)(a^2 + 2c^2) = -2(b-2)(a^2 + 2c^2)$
24. Factoring: $6x^3 + 18x^2 + 6x + 18 = 6x^2(x+3) + 6(x+3) = 6(x+3)(x^2 + 1)$

4.4 Factoring Trinomials

1. Factoring the trinomial: $x^2 + 7x + 12 = (x+3)(x+4)$

3. Factoring the trinomial: $x^2 - x - 12 = (x+3)(x-4)$

5. Factoring the trinomial: $y^2 + y - 6 = (y+3)(y-2)$

7. Factoring the trinomial: $16 - 6x - x^2 = (2-x)(8+x)$

9. Factoring the trinomial: $12 + 8x + x^2 = (2+x)(6+x)$

11. Factoring the trinomial: $16 - x^2 = (4+x)(4-x)$

13. Factoring the trinomial: $x^2 + 3xy + 2y^2 = (x+2y)(x+y)$

15. Factoring the trinomial: $a^2 + 3ab - 18b^2 = (a+6b)(a-3b)$

17. Factoring the trinomial: $x^2 - 2xa - 48a^2 = (x-8a)(x+6a)$

19. Factoring the trinomial: $x^2 - 12xb + 36b^2 = (x-6b)^2$

21. Factoring the trinomial: $3a^2 - 21a + 30 = 3(a^2 - 7a + 10) = 3(a-5)(a-2)$

23. Factoring the trinomial: $4x^3 - 16x^2 - 20x = 4x(x^2 - 4x - 5) = 4x(x-5)(x+1)$

25. Factoring the trinomial: $3x^2 - 6xy - 9y^2 = 3(x^2 - 2xy - 3y^2) = 3(x-3y)(x+y)$

27. Factoring the trinomial: $2a^5 + 4a^4 b + 4a^3 b^2 = 2a^3(a^2 + 2ab + 2b^2)$

29. Factoring the trinomial: $10x^4 y^2 + 20x^3 y^3 - 30x^2 y^4 = 10x^2 y^2(x^2 + 2xy - 3y^2) = 10x^2 y^2(x+3y)(x-y)$

31. Factoring completely: $2x^2 + 7x - 15 = (2x-3)(x+5)$

33. Factoring completely: $2x^2 + x - 15 = (2x-5)(x+3)$

35. Factoring completely: $2x^2 - 13x + 15 = (2x-3)(x-5)$

37. Factoring completely: $2x^2 - 11x + 15 = (2x-5)(x-3)$

39. The trinomial $2x^2 + 7x + 15$ does not factor (prime).

41. Factoring completely: $2 + 7a + 6a^2 = (2+3a)(1+2a)$

43. Factoring completely: $60y^2 - 15y - 45 = 15(4y^2 - y - 3) = 15(4y+3)(y-1)$

45. Factoring completely: $6x^4 - x^3 - 2x^2 = x^2(6x^2 - x - 2) = x^2(3x-2)(2x+1)$

47. Factoring completely: $40r^3 - 120r^2 + 90r = 10r(4r^2 - 12r + 9) = 10r(2r-3)^2$

49. Factoring completely: $4x^2 - 11xy - 3y^2 = (4x+y)(x-3y)$

51. Factoring completely: $10x^2 - 3xa - 18a^2 = (2x-3a)(5x+6a)$

53. Factoring completely: $18a^2 + 3ab - 28b^2 = (3a+4b)(6a-7b)$

55. Factoring completely: $600 + 800t - 800t^2 = 200(3 + 4t - 4t^2) = 200(1+2t)(3-2t)$

57. Factoring completely: $9y^4 + 9y^3 - 10y^2 = y^2(9y^2 + 9y - 10) = y^2(3y-2)(3y+5)$

59. Factoring completely: $24a^2 - 2a^3 - 12a^4 = 2a^2(12 - a - 6a^2) = 2a^2(3+2a)(4-3a)$

61. Factoring completely: $8x^4 y^2 - 2x^3 y^3 - 6x^2 y^4 = 2x^2 y^2(4x^2 - xy - 3y^2) = 2x^2 y^2(4x+3y)(x-y)$

63. Factoring completely: $300x^4 + 1000x^2 + 300 = 100(3x^4 + 10x^2 + 3) = 100(3x^2 + 1)(x^2 + 3)$

65. Factoring completely: $20a^4 + 37a^2 + 15 = (5a^2 + 3)(4a^2 + 5)$

67. Factoring completely: $9 + 3r^2 + 12r^4 = 3(3 + r^2 + 4r^4) = 3(3 + 4r^2)(1 + r^2)$

69. Factoring completely: $2x^2(x+5) + 7x(x+5) + 6(x+5) = (x+5)(2x^2 + 7x + 6) = (x+5)(2x+3)(x+2)$

71. Factoring completely: $x^2(2x+3) + 7x(2x+3) + 10(2x+3) = (2x+3)(x^2 + 7x + 10) = (2x+3)(x+5)(x+2)$

73. Factoring completely: $3x^2(x-3) + 7x(x-3) - 20(x-3) = (x-3)(3x^2 + 7x - 20) = (x-3)(3x-5)(x+4)$

75. Factoring completely: $6x^2(x-2) - 17x(x-2) + 12(x-2) = (x-2)(6x^2 - 17x + 12) = (x-2)(3x-4)(2x-3)$

77. Factoring completely: $12x^2(x+3) + 7x(x+3) - 45(x+3) = (x+3)(12x^2 + 7x - 45) = (x+3)(4x+9)(3x-5)$

79. Factoring completely:
$$6x^2(5x-2) - 11x(5x-2) - 10(5x-2) = (5x-2)(6x^2 - 11x - 10) = (5x-2)(3x+2)(2x-5)$$

81. Factoring completely:
$$20x^2(2x+3) + 47x(2x+3) + 21(2x+3) = (2x+3)(20x^2 + 47x + 21) = (2x+3)(5x+3)(4x+7)$$

83. Multiplying out, the polynomial is: $(3x + 5y)(3x - 5y) = 9x^2 - 25y^2$

85. The polynomial factors as $a^2 + 260a + 2500 = (a+10)(a+250)$, so the other factor is $a + 250$.

87. The polynomial factors as $12x^2 - 107x + 210 = (x-6)(12x - 35)$, so the other factor is $12x - 35$.

89. The polynomial factors as $54x^2 + 111x + 56 = (6x+7)(9x+8)$, so the other factor is $9x + 8$.

91. The polynomial factors as $35x^2 + 19x - 24 = (5x-3)(7x+8)$, so the other factor is $7x + 8$.

93. Factoring the right side: $y = 4x^2 + 18x - 10 = 2(2x^2 + 9x - 5) = 2(2x-1)(x+5)$

Evaluating when $x = \dfrac{1}{2}$: $y = 2\left(2 \cdot \dfrac{1}{2} - 1\right)\left(\dfrac{1}{2} + 5\right) = 2(0)\left(\dfrac{11}{2}\right) = 0$

Evaluating when $x = -5$: $y = 2(2 \cdot (-5) - 1)(-5 + 5) = 2(-11)(0) = 0$

Evaluating when $x = 2$: $y = 2(2 \cdot 2 - 1)(2 + 5) = 2(3)(7) = 42$

95. Multiplying: $(2x - 3)(2x + 3) = (2x)^2 - (3)^2 = 4x^2 - 9$

97. Multiplying: $(2x - 3)^2 = (2x - 3)(2x - 3) = 4x^2 - 12x + 9$

99. Multiplying: $(2x - 3)(4x^2 + 6x + 9) = 8x^3 + 12x^2 + 18x - 12x^2 - 18x - 27 = 8x^3 - 27$

101. Writing as a square: $\dfrac{25}{64} = \left(\dfrac{5}{8}\right)^2$

103. Writing as a square: $x^6 = \left(x^3\right)^2$

105. Writing as a square: $16x^4 = \left(4x^2\right)^2$

107. Writing as a cube: $\dfrac{1}{8} = \left(\dfrac{1}{2}\right)^3$

109. Writing as a cube: $x^6 = \left(x^2\right)^3$

111. Writing as a cube: $27x^3 = (3x)^3$

113. Writing as a cube: $8y^3 = (2y)^3$

115. Factoring completely: $8x^6 + 26x^3y^2 + 15y^4 = (2x^3 + 5y^2)(4x^3 + 3y^2)$

117. Factoring completely: $3x^2 + 295x - 500 = (3x - 5)(x + 100)$

119. Factoring completely: $\dfrac{1}{8}x^2 + x + 2 = \left(\dfrac{1}{4}x + 1\right)\left(\dfrac{1}{2}x + 2\right)$

121. Factoring completely: $2x^2 + 1.5x + 0.25 = (2x + 0.5)(x + 0.5)$

4.5 Factoring Special Products

1. Factoring the trinomial: $x^2 - 6x + 9 = (x-3)^2$

3. Factoring the trinomial: $a^2 - 12a + 36 = (a-6)^2$

5. Factoring the trinomial: $25 - 10t + t^2 = (5-t)^2$

7. Factoring the trinomial: $\frac{1}{9}x^2 + 2x + 9 = \left(\frac{1}{3}x+3\right)^2$

9. Factoring the trinomial: $4y^4 - 12y^2 + 9 = \left(2y^2 - 3\right)^2$

11. Factoring the trinomial: $16a^2 + 40ab + 25b^2 = (4a+5b)^2$

13. Factoring the trinomial: $\frac{1}{25} + \frac{1}{10}t^2 + \frac{1}{16}t^4 = \left(\frac{1}{5} + \frac{1}{4}t^2\right)^2$

15. Factoring the trinomial: $y^2 + 3y + \frac{9}{4} = \left(y + \frac{3}{2}\right)^2$

17. Factoring the trinomial: $a^2 - a + \frac{1}{4} = \left(a - \frac{1}{2}\right)^2$

19. Factoring the trinomial: $x^2 - \frac{1}{2}x + \frac{1}{16} = \left(x - \frac{1}{4}\right)^2$

21. Factoring the trinomial: $t^2 + \frac{2}{3}t + \frac{1}{9} = \left(t + \frac{1}{3}\right)^2$

23. Factoring the trinomial: $16x^2 - 48x + 36 = 4\left(4x^2 - 12x + 9\right) = 4(2x-3)^2$

25. Factoring the trinomial: $75a^3 + 30a^2 + 3a = 3a\left(25a^2 + 10a + 1\right) = 3a(5a+1)^2$

27. Factoring the trinomial: $(x+2)^2 + 6(x+2) + 9 = (x+2+3)^2 = (x+5)^2$

29. Factoring: $x^2 - 9 = (x+3)(x-3)$

31. Factoring: $49x^2 - 64y^2 = (7x+8y)(7x-8y)$

33. Factoring: $4a^2 - \frac{1}{4} = \left(2a + \frac{1}{2}\right)\left(2a - \frac{1}{2}\right)$

35. Factoring: $x^2 - \frac{9}{25} = \left(x + \frac{3}{5}\right)\left(x - \frac{3}{5}\right)$

37. Factoring: $9x^2 - 16y^2 = (3x+4y)(3x-4y)$

39. Factoring: $250 - 10t^2 = 10\left(25 - t^2\right) = 10(5+t)(5-t)$

41. Factoring: $x^4 - 81 = \left(x^2 + 9\right)\left(x^2 - 9\right) = \left(x^2 + 9\right)(x+3)(x-3)$

43. Factoring: $9x^6 - 1 = \left(3x^3 + 1\right)\left(3x^3 - 1\right)$

45. Factoring: $16a^4 - 81 = \left(4a^2 + 9\right)\left(4a^2 - 9\right) = \left(4a^2 + 9\right)(2a+3)(2a-3)$

47. Factoring: $\frac{1}{81} - \frac{y^4}{16} = \left(\frac{1}{9} + \frac{y^2}{4}\right)\left(\frac{1}{9} - \frac{y^2}{4}\right) = \left(\frac{1}{9} + \frac{y^2}{4}\right)\left(\frac{1}{3} + \frac{y}{2}\right)\left(\frac{1}{3} - \frac{y}{2}\right)$

49. Factoring: $\frac{x^4}{16} - \frac{16}{81} = \left(\frac{x^2}{4} + \frac{4}{9}\right)\left(\frac{x^2}{4} - \frac{4}{9}\right) = \left(\frac{x^2}{4} + \frac{4}{9}\right)\left(\frac{x}{2} + \frac{2}{3}\right)\left(\frac{x}{2} - \frac{2}{3}\right)$

51. Factoring: $a^4 - \frac{81}{256} = \left(a^2 + \frac{9}{16}\right)\left(a^2 - \frac{9}{16}\right) = \left(a^2 + \frac{9}{16}\right)\left(a + \frac{3}{4}\right)\left(a - \frac{3}{4}\right)$

53. Factoring: $x^6 - y^6 = \left(x^3 + y^3\right)\left(x^3 - y^3\right) = (x+y)(x-y)\left(x^2 - xy + y^2\right)\left(x^2 + xy + y^2\right)$

55. Factoring: $2a^7 - 128a = 2a\left(a^6 - 64\right) = 2a\left(a^3 + 8\right)\left(a^3 - 8\right) = 2a(a+2)(a-2)\left(a^2 - 2a + 4\right)\left(a^2 + 2a + 4\right)$

57. Factoring: $(x-2)^2 - 9 = (x-2+3)(x-2-3) = (x+1)(x-5)$

59. Factoring: $(y+4)^2 - 16 = (y+4+4)(y+4-4) = y(y+8)$

61. Factoring: $x^2 - 10x + 25 - y^2 = (x-5)^2 - y^2 = (x-5+y)(x-5-y)$

63. Factoring: $a^2 + 8a + 16 - b^2 = (a+4)^2 - b^2 = (a+4+b)(a+4-b)$

65. Factoring: $x^2 + 2xy + y^2 - a^2 = (x+y)^2 - a^2 = (x+y+a)(x+y-a)$

67. Factoring: $x^3 + 3x^2 - 4x - 12 = x^2(x+3) - 4(x+3) = (x+3)(x^2-4) = (x+3)(x+2)(x-2)$

69. Factoring: $x^3 + 2x^2 - 25x - 50 = x^2(x+2) - 25(x+2) = (x+2)(x^2-25) = (x+2)(x+5)(x-5)$

71. Factoring: $2x^3 + 3x^2 - 8x - 12 = x^2(2x+3) - 4(2x+3) = (2x+3)(x^2-4) = (2x+3)(x+2)(x-2)$

73. Factoring: $4x^3 + 12x^2 - 9x - 27 = 4x^2(x+3) - 9(x+3) = (x+3)(4x^2-9) = (x+3)(2x+3)(2x-3)$

75. Factoring: $(2x-5)^2 - 100 = (2x-5-10)(2x-5+10) = (2x-15)(2x+5)$

77. Factoring: $(a-3)^2 - (4b)^2 = (a-3-4b)(a-3+4b)$

79. Factoring: $a^2 - 6a + 9 - 16b^2 = (a-3)^2 - (4b)^2 = (a-3-4b)(a-3+4b)$

81. Factoring: $x^2(x+4) - 6x(x+4) + 9(x+4) = (x+4)(x^2-6x+9) = (x+4)(x-3)^2$

83. Factoring: $x^3 - y^3 = (x-y)(x^2+xy+y^2)$ **85.** Factoring: $a^3 + 8 = (a+2)(a^2-2a+4)$

87. Factoring: $27 + x^3 = (3+x)(9-3x+x^2)$ **89.** Factoring: $y^3 - 1 = (y-1)(y^2+y+1)$

91. Factoring: $10r^3 - 1{,}250 = 10(r^3-125) = 10(r-5)(r^2+5r+25)$

93. Factoring: $64 + 27a^3 = (4+3a)(16-12a+9a^2)$ **95.** Factoring: $8x^3 - 27y^3 = (2x-3y)(4x^2+6xy+9y^2)$

97. Factoring: $t^3 + \dfrac{1}{27} = \left(t+\dfrac{1}{3}\right)\left(t^2-\dfrac{1}{3}t+\dfrac{1}{9}\right)$ **99.** Factoring: $27x^3 - \dfrac{1}{27} = \left(3x-\dfrac{1}{3}\right)\left(9x^2+x+\dfrac{1}{9}\right)$

101. Factoring: $64a^3 + 125b^3 = (4a+5b)(16a^2-20ab+25b^2)$

103. Since $9x^2 + 30x + 25 = (3x+5)^2$ and $9x^2 - 30x + 25 = (3x-5)^2$, two values of b are $b = 30$ and $b = -30$.

105. Since $25x^2 - 90x + 81 = (5x-9)^2$, a value of c is $c = 81$.

107. Factoring the greatest common factor: $y^3 + 25y = y(y^2+25)$

109. Factoring the greatest common factor: $2ab^5 + 8ab^4 + 2ab^3 = 2ab^3(b^2+4b+1)$

111. Factoring by grouping: $4x^2 - 6x + 2ax - 3a = 2x(2x-3) + a(2x-3) = (2x-3)(2x+a)$

113. Factoring by grouping: $15ax - 10a + 12x - 8 = 5a(3x-2) + 4(3x-2) = (3x-2)(5a+4)$

115. Factoring the difference of squares: $x^2 - 4 = (x+2)(x-2)$

117. Factoring the difference of squares: $A^2 - 25 = (A+5)(A-5)$

119. Factoring the perfect square trinomial: $x^2 - 6x + 9 = (x-3)^2$

121. Factoring the perfect square trinomial: $x^2 + 8xy + 16y^2 = (x+4y)^2$

123. Factoring: $6a^2 - 11a + 4 = (3a-4)(2a-1)$

125. Factoring: $12x^2 - 32x - 35 = (6x+5)(2x-7)$

127. Factoring the sum of cubes: $x^3 + 8 = (x+2)(x^2-2x+4)$

129. Factoring the difference of cubes: $8x^3 - 27 = (2x - 3)(4x^2 + 6x + 9)$

131. Multiply the first equation by 2 and the second equation by 7:
$$8x - 14y = 6$$
$$35x + 14y = -21$$

Adding yields:
$$43x = -15$$
$$x = -\frac{15}{43}$$

Substituting into the original second equation:
$$5\left(-\frac{15}{43}\right) + 2y = -3$$
$$-\frac{75}{43} + 2y = -3$$
$$2y = -\frac{54}{43}$$
$$y = -\frac{27}{43}$$

The solution is $\left(-\frac{15}{43}, -\frac{27}{43}\right)$.

133. For practice we'll solve this using augmented matrices. Form the augmented matrix: $\begin{bmatrix} 3 & 4 & 0 & | & 15 \\ 2 & 0 & -5 & | & -3 \\ 0 & 4 & -3 & | & 9 \end{bmatrix}$

Divide row 1 by 3: $\begin{bmatrix} 1 & \frac{4}{3} & 0 & | & 5 \\ 2 & 0 & -5 & | & -3 \\ 0 & 4 & -3 & | & 9 \end{bmatrix}$

Add -2 times row 1 to row 2: $\begin{bmatrix} 1 & \frac{4}{3} & 0 & | & 5 \\ 0 & -\frac{8}{3} & -5 & | & -13 \\ 0 & 4 & -3 & | & 9 \end{bmatrix}$

Multiply row 2 by $-\frac{3}{8}$: $\begin{bmatrix} 1 & \frac{4}{3} & 0 & | & 5 \\ 0 & 1 & \frac{15}{8} & | & \frac{39}{8} \\ 0 & 4 & -3 & | & 9 \end{bmatrix}$

Multiply row 2 by -4 and add it to row 3: $\begin{bmatrix} 1 & \frac{4}{3} & 0 & | & 5 \\ 0 & 1 & \frac{15}{8} & | & \frac{39}{8} \\ 0 & 0 & -\frac{21}{2} & | & -\frac{21}{2} \end{bmatrix}$

Multiply row 3 by $-\dfrac{2}{21}$: $\begin{bmatrix} 1 & \dfrac{4}{3} & 0 & \Big| & 5 \\ 0 & 1 & \dfrac{15}{8} & \Big| & \dfrac{39}{8} \\ 0 & 0 & 1 & \Big| & 1 \end{bmatrix}$

So $z = 1$. Substituting to find y:

$$y + \frac{15}{8}(1) = \frac{39}{8}$$
$$y + \frac{15}{8} = \frac{39}{8}$$
$$y = 3$$

Substituting to find x:

$$x + \frac{4}{3}(3) = 5$$
$$x + 4 = 5$$
$$x = 1$$

The solution is $(1,3,1)$.

135. Factoring completely: $a^2 - b^2 + 6b - 9 = a^2 - \left(b^2 - 6b + 9\right) = a^2 - (b-3)^2 = (a-b+3)(a+b-3)$

137. Factoring completely: $(x-3)^2 - (y+5)^2 = \big((x-3)-(y+5)\big)\big((x-3)+(y+5)\big) = (x-y-8)(x+y+2)$

139. Since $144x^2 - 168xy + 49y^2 = (12x - 7y)^2$, a value of k is $k = 144$.

141. Since $49x^2 + 126x + 81 = (7x+9)^2$ and $49x^2 - 126x + 81 = (7x-9)^2$, two values of k are $k = \pm 126$.

4.6 Factoring: A General Review

1. Factoring: $x^2 - 81 = (x+9)(x-9)$ **3.** Factoring: $x^2 + 2x - 15 = (x-3)(x+5)$

5. Factoring: $x^2(x+2) + 6x(x+2) + 9(x+2) = (x+2)\left(x^2 + 6x + 9\right) = (x+2)(x+3)^2$

7. Factoring: $x^2 y^2 + 2y^2 + x^2 + 2 = y^2\left(x^2 + 2\right) + 1\left(x^2 + 2\right) = \left(x^2 + 2\right)\left(y^2 + 1\right)$

9. Factoring: $2a^3b + 6a^2b + 2ab = 2ab\left(a^2 + 3a + 1\right)$ **11.** The polynomial $x^2 + x + 1$ does not factor (prime).

13. Factoring: $12a^2 - 75 = 3\left(4a^2 - 25\right) = 3(2a+5)(2a-5)$

15. Factoring: $9x^2 - 12xy + 4y^2 = (3x - 2y)^2$ **17.** Factoring: $25 - 10t + t^2 = (5-t)^2$

19. Factoring: $4x^3 + 16xy^2 = 4x\left(x^2 + 4y^2\right)$

21. Factoring: $2y^3 + 20y^2 + 50y = 2y\left(y^2 + 10y + 25\right) = 2y(y+5)^2$

23. Factoring: $a^7 + 8a^4b^3 = a^4\left(a^3 + 8b^3\right) = a^4(a+2b)\left(a^2 - 2ab + 4b^2\right)$

25. Factoring: $t^2 + 6t + 9 - x^2 = (t+3)^2 - x^2 = (t+3+x)(t+3-x)$

27. Factoring: $x^3 + 5x^2 - 9x - 45 = x^2(x+5) - 9(x+5) = (x+5)\left(x^2 - 9\right) = (x+5)(x+3)(x-3)$

29. Factoring: $5a^2 + 10ab + 5b^2 = 5\left(a^2 + 2ab + b^2\right) = 5(a+b)^2$

31. The polynomial $x^2 + 49$ does not factor (prime).

33. Factoring: $3x^2 + 15xy + 18y^2 = 3(x^2 + 5xy + 6y^2) = 3(x+2y)(x+3y)$

35. Factoring: $9a^2 + 2a + \dfrac{1}{9} = \left(3a + \dfrac{1}{3}\right)^2$

37. Factoring: $x^2(x-3) - 14x(x-3) + 49(x-3) = (x-3)(x^2 - 14x + 49) = (x-3)(x-7)^2$

39. Factoring: $x^2 - 64 = (x+8)(x-8)$ 41. Factoring: $8 - 14x - 15x^2 = (2-5x)(4+3x)$

43. Factoring: $49a^7 - 9a^5 = a^5(49a^2 - 9) = a^5(7a+3)(7a-3)$

45. Factoring: $r^2 - \dfrac{1}{25} = \left(r + \dfrac{1}{5}\right)\left(r - \dfrac{1}{5}\right)$ 47. The polynomial $49x^2 + 9y^2$ does not factor (prime).

49. Factoring: $100x^2 - 100x - 600 = 100(x^2 - x - 6) = 100(x-3)(x+2)$

51. Factoring: $25a^3 + 20a^2 + 3a = a(25a^2 + 20a + 3) = a(5a+3)(5a+1)$

53. Factoring: $3x^4 - 14x^2 - 5 = (3x^2 + 1)(x^2 - 5)$

55. Factoring: $24a^5b - 3a^2b = 3a^2b(8a^3 - 1) = 3a^2b(2a-1)(4a^2 + 2a + 1)$

57. Factoring: $64 - r^3 = (4-r)(16 + 4r + r^2)$

59. Factoring: $20x^4 - 45x^2 = 5x^2(4x^2 - 9) = 5x^2(2x+3)(2x-3)$

61. Factoring: $400t^2 - 900 = 100(4t^2 - 9) = 100(2t+3)(2t-3)$

63. Factoring: $16x^5 - 44x^4 + 30x^3 = 2x^3(8x^2 - 22x + 15) = 2x^3(4x-5)(2x-3)$

65. Factoring: $y^6 - 1 = (y^3 + 1)(y^3 - 1) = (y+1)(y-1)(y^2 - y + 1)(y^2 + y + 1)$

67. Factoring: $50 - 2a^2 = 2(25 - a^2) = 2(5+a)(5-a)$

69. Factoring: $12x^4y^2 + 36x^3y^3 + 27x^2y^4 = 3x^2y^2(4x^2 + 12xy + 9y^2) = 3x^2y^2(2x+3y)^2$

71. Factoring: $x^2 - 4x + 4 - y^2 = (x-2)^2 - y^2 = (x-2+y)(x-2-y)$

73. Factoring: $a^2 - \dfrac{4}{3}ab + \dfrac{4}{9}b^2 = \left(a - \dfrac{2}{3}b\right)^2$ 75. Factoring: $x^2 - \dfrac{4}{5}xy + \dfrac{4}{25}y^2 = \left(x - \dfrac{2}{5}y\right)^2$

77. Factoring: $a^2 - \dfrac{5}{3}ab + \dfrac{25}{36}b^2 = \left(a - \dfrac{5}{6}b\right)^2$ 79. Factoring: $x^2 - \dfrac{8}{5}xy + \dfrac{16}{25}y^2 = \left(x - \dfrac{4}{5}y\right)^2$

81. Factoring: $2x^2(x+2) - 13x(x+2) + 15(x+2) = (x+2)(2x^2 - 13x + 15) = (x+2)(2x-3)(x-5)$

83. Factoring: $(x-4)^3 + (x-4)^4 = (x-4)^3(1 + x - 4) = (x-4)^3(x-3)$

85. Factoring: $2y^3 - 54 = 2(y^3 - 27) = 2(y-3)(y^2 + 3y + 9)$

87. Factoring: $2a^3 - 128b^3 = 2(a^3 - 64b^3) = 2(a-4b)(a^2 + 4ab + 16b^2)$

89. Factoring: $2x^3 + 432y^3 = 2(x^3 + 216y^3) = 2(x+6y)(x^2 - 6xy + 36y^2)$

91. Let g and d represent the number of geese and ducks. The system of equations is:
$$g + d = 108$$
$$1.4g + 0.6d = 112.80$$
Substituting $d = 108 - g$ into the second equation:
$$1.4g + 0.6(108 - g) = 112.80$$
$$1.4g + 64.8 - 0.6g = 112.80$$
$$0.8g = 48$$
$$g = 60$$
$$d = 48$$
He bought 60 geese and 48 ducks.

93. Let o represent the number of oranges and a represent the number of apples. The system of equations is:
$$\frac{o}{3}(0.10) + \frac{a}{12}(0.15) = 6.80$$
$$\frac{5o}{3}(0.10) + \frac{a}{48}(0.15) = 25.45$$
Clearing each equation of fractions:
$$12 \cdot \frac{o}{3}(0.10) + 12 \cdot \frac{a}{12}(0.15) = 12 \cdot 6.80 \qquad 48 \cdot \frac{5o}{3}(0.10) + 48 \cdot \frac{a}{48}(0.15) = 48 \cdot 25.45$$
$$0.4o + 0.15a = 81.6 \qquad\qquad 8o + 0.15a = 1221.6$$
So the system becomes:
$$0.4o + 0.15a = 81.6$$
$$8o + 0.15a = 1221.6$$
Multiply the first equation by -20:
$$-8o - 3a = -1632$$
$$8o + 0.15a = 1221.6$$
Adding yields:
$$-2.85a = -410.4$$
$$a = 144$$
Substituting to find o:
$$8o + 0.15(144) = 1221.6$$
$$8o + 21.6 = 1221.6$$
$$8o = 1200$$
$$o = 150$$
So 150 oranges and 144 apples were bought.

95. Simplifying: $x^2 + (x+1)^2 = x^2 + x^2 + 2x + 1 = 2x^2 + 2x + 1$

97. Simplifying: $\dfrac{16t^2 - 64t + 48}{16} = \dfrac{16(t^2 - 4t + 3)}{16} = t^2 - 4t + 3$

99. Factoring: $x^2 - 2x - 24 = (x - 6)(x + 4)$

101. Factoring: $2x^3 - 5x^2 - 3x = x(2x^2 - 5x - 3) = x(2x + 1)(x - 3)$

103. Factoring: $x^3 + 2x^2 - 9x - 18 = x^2(x + 2) - 9(x + 2) = (x + 2)(x^2 - 9) = (x + 2)(x + 3)(x - 3)$

105. Factoring: $x^3 + 2x^2 - 5x - 10 = x^2(x + 2) - 5(x + 2) = (x + 2)(x^2 - 5)$

107. Solving the equation:
$$x - 6 = 0$$
$$x = 6$$

109. Solving the equation:
$$2x + 1 = 0$$
$$2x = -1$$
$$x = -\frac{1}{2}$$

4.7 Solving Equations by Factoring

1. Solving the equation:

$$x^2 - 5x - 6 = 0$$
$$(x+1)(x-6) = 0$$
$$x = -1, 6$$

3. Solving the equation:

$$x^3 - 5x^2 + 6x = 0$$
$$x\left(x^2 - 5x + 6\right) = 0$$
$$x(x-2)(x-3) = 0$$
$$x = 0, 2, 3$$

5. Solving the equation:

$$3y^2 + 11y - 4 = 0$$
$$(3y-1)(y+4) = 0$$
$$y = -4, \frac{1}{3}$$

7. Solving the equation:

$$60x^2 - 130x + 60 = 0$$
$$10\left(6x^2 - 13x + 6\right) = 0$$
$$10(3x-2)(2x-3) = 0$$
$$x = \frac{2}{3}, \frac{3}{2}$$

9. Solving the equation:

$$\frac{1}{10}t^2 - \frac{5}{2} = 0$$
$$10\left(\frac{1}{10}t^2 - \frac{5}{2}\right) = 10(0)$$
$$t^2 - 25 = 0$$
$$(t+5)(t-5) = 0$$
$$t = -5, 5$$

11. Solving the equation:

$$100x^4 = 400x^3 + 2100x^2$$
$$100x^4 - 400x^3 - 2100x^2 = 0$$
$$100x^2\left(x^2 - 4x - 21\right) = 0$$
$$100x^2(x-7)(x+3) = 0$$
$$x = -3, 0, 7$$

13. Solving the equation:

$$\frac{1}{5}y^2 - 2 = -\frac{3}{10}y$$
$$10\left(\frac{1}{5}y^2 - 2\right) = 10\left(-\frac{3}{10}y\right)$$
$$2y^2 - 20 = -3y$$
$$2y^2 + 3y - 20 = 0$$
$$(y+4)(2y-5) = 0$$
$$y = -4, \frac{5}{2}$$

15. Solving the equation:

$$9x^2 - 12x = 0$$
$$3x(3x-4) = 0$$
$$x = 0, \frac{4}{3}$$

17. Solving the equation:

$$0.02r + 0.01 = 0.15r^2$$
$$2r + 1 = 15r^2$$
$$15r^2 - 2r - 1 = 0$$
$$(5r+1)(3r-1) = 0$$
$$r = -\frac{1}{5}, \frac{1}{3}$$

19. Solving the equation:

$$-100x = 10x^2$$
$$0 = 10x^2 + 100x$$
$$0 = 10x(x+10)$$
$$x = -10, 0$$

21. Solving the equation:

$$(x+6)(x-2) = -7$$
$$x^2 + 4x - 12 = -7$$
$$x^2 + 4x - 5 = 0$$
$$(x+5)(x-1) = 0$$
$$x = -5, 1$$

23. Solving the equation:

$$(y-4)(y+1) = -6$$
$$y^2 - 3y - 4 = -6$$
$$y^2 - 3y + 2 = 0$$
$$(y-2)(y-1) = 0$$
$$y = 1, 2$$

25. Solving the equation:

$$(x+1)^2 = 3x+7$$
$$x^2 + 2x + 1 = 3x + 7$$
$$x^2 - x - 6 = 0$$
$$(x+2)(x-3) = 0$$
$$x = -2, 3$$

27. Solving the equation:

$$(2r+3)(2r-1) = -(3r+1)$$
$$4r^2 + 4r - 3 = -3r - 1$$
$$4r^2 + 7r - 2 = 0$$
$$(r+2)(4r-1) = 0$$
$$r = -2, \frac{1}{4}$$

29. Solving the equation:

$$3x^2 + x = 10$$
$$3x^2 + x - 10 = 0$$
$$(3x-5)(x+2) = 0$$
$$x = -2, \frac{5}{3}$$

31. Solving the equation:

$$12(x+3) + 12(x-3) = 3(x^2 - 9)$$
$$12x + 36 + 12x - 36 = 3x^2 - 27$$
$$24x = 3x^2 - 27$$
$$3x^2 - 24x - 27 = 0$$
$$3(x^2 - 8x - 9) = 0$$
$$3(x-9)(x+1) = 0$$
$$x = -1, 9$$

33. Solving the equation:

$$(y+3)^2 + y^2 = 9$$
$$y^2 + 6y + 9 + y^2 = 9$$
$$2y^2 + 6y = 0$$
$$2y(y+3) = 0$$
$$y = -3, 0$$

35. Solving the equation:

$$(x+3)^2 + 1^2 = 2$$
$$x^2 + 6x + 9 + 1 = 2$$
$$x^2 + 6x + 8 = 0$$
$$(x+4)(x+2) = 0$$
$$x = -4, -2$$

37. Solving the equation:

$$(3x+1)(x-4) = (x-3)(x+3)$$
$$3x^2 - 11x - 4 = x^2 - 9$$
$$2x^2 - 11x + 5 = 0$$
$$(2x-1)(x-5) = 0$$
$$x = \frac{1}{2}, 5$$

39. Solving the equation:

$$(3x-2)(x+1) = (x-4)^2$$
$$3x^2 + x - 2 = x^2 - 8x + 16$$
$$2x^2 + 9x - 18 = 0$$
$$(2x-3)(x+6) = 0$$
$$x = -6, \frac{3}{2}$$

41. Solving the equation:

$$(2x-3)(x-5) = (x+1)(x-3)$$
$$2x^2 - 13x + 15 = x^2 - 2x - 3$$
$$x^2 - 11x + 18 = 0$$
$$(x-2)(x-9) = 0$$
$$x = 2, 9$$

43. Solving the equation:

$$x^3 + 3x^2 - 4x - 12 = 0$$
$$x^2(x+3) - 4(x+3) = 0$$
$$(x+3)(x^2 - 4) = 0$$
$$(x+3)(x+2)(x-2) = 0$$
$$x = -3, -2, 2$$

45. Solving the equation:

$$x^3 + 2x^2 - 25x - 50 = 0$$
$$x^2(x+2) - 25(x+2) = 0$$
$$(x+2)(x^2 - 25) = 0$$
$$(x+2)(x+5)(x-5) = 0$$
$$x = -5, -2, 5$$

47. Solving the equation:

$$9a^3 = 16a$$
$$9a^3 - 16a = 0$$
$$a(9a^2 - 16) = 0$$
$$a(3a+4)(3a-4) = 0$$
$$a = -\frac{4}{3}, 0, \frac{4}{3}$$

49. Solving the equation:

$$2x^3 + 3x^2 - 8x - 12 = 0$$
$$x^2(2x+3) - 4(2x+3) = 0$$
$$(2x+3)(x^2-4) = 0$$
$$(2x+3)(x+2)(x-2) = 0$$
$$x = -2, -\frac{3}{2}, 2$$

51. Solving the equation:

$$4x^3 + 12x^2 - 9x - 27 = 0$$
$$4x^2(x+3) - 9(x+3) = 0$$
$$(x+3)(4x^2-9) = 0$$
$$(x+3)(2x+3)(2x-3) = 0$$
$$x = -3, -\frac{3}{2}, \frac{3}{2}$$

53. Solving $f(x) = 0$:

$$\left(x+\frac{3}{2}\right)^2 = 0$$
$$x + \frac{3}{2} = 0$$
$$x = -\frac{3}{2}$$

55. Solving $f(x) = 0$:

$$(x-3)^2 - 25 = 0$$
$$x^2 - 6x + 9 - 25 = 0$$
$$x^2 - 6x - 16 = 0$$
$$(x+2)(x-8) = 0$$
$$x = -2, 8$$

57. Solving $f(x) = g(x)$:

$$x^2 + 6x + 3 = -6$$
$$x^2 + 6x + 9 = 0$$
$$(x+3)^2 = 0$$
$$x + 3 = 0$$
$$x = -3$$

59. Solving $f(x) = g(x)$:

$$x^2 + 6x + 3 = 10$$
$$x^2 + 6x - 7 = 0$$
$$(x+7)(x-1) = 0$$
$$x = -7, 1$$

61. Solving $h(x) = f(x)$:

$$x^2 - 5x = 0$$
$$x(x-5) = 0$$
$$x = 0, 5$$

63. Solving $h(x) = f(x)$:

$$x^2 - 5x = 2x + 8$$
$$x^2 - 7x - 8 = 0$$
$$(x-8)(x+1) = 0$$
$$x = -1, 8$$

65. Solving $f(x) = x$:

$$x^2 = x$$
$$x^2 - x = 0$$
$$x(x-1) = 0$$
$$x = 0, 1$$

67. Solving $f(x) = x$:

$$\frac{1}{3}x + 1 = x$$
$$x + 3 = 3x$$
$$2x = 3$$
$$x = \frac{3}{2}$$

69. Let x and $x + 2$ represent the two integers. The equation is:

$$x(x+2) = 99$$
$$x^2 + 2x = 99$$
$$x^2 + 2x - 99 = 0$$
$$(x+11)(x-9) = 0$$
$$x = -11, 9$$
$$x + 2 = -9, 11$$

The two integers are either –11 and –9, or 9 and 11.

71. Let x and $14 - x$ represent the two numbers. The equation is:
$$x(14 - x) = 48$$
$$14x - x^2 = 48$$
$$0 = x^2 - 14x + 48$$
$$0 = (x - 8)(x - 6)$$
$$x = 8, 6$$
$$14 - x = 6, 8$$
The two numbers are 6 and 8.

73. Let x and $x + 2$ represent the two integers. The equation is:
$$x(x + 2) = 5(x + x + 2) - 10$$
$$x(x + 2) = 5(2x + 2) - 10$$
$$x^2 + 2x = 10x + 10 - 10$$
$$x^2 - 8x = 0$$
$$x(x - 8) = 0$$
$$x = 8 \quad (x = 0 \text{ is impossible})$$
$$x + 2 = 10$$
The dimensions are 8 and 10.

75. Let x and $x + 2$ represent the two integers. The equation is:
$$x(x + 2) = 4(x + x + 2) - 1$$
$$x(x + 2) = 4(2x + 2) - 1$$
$$x^2 + 2x = 8x + 8 - 1$$
$$x^2 + 2x = 8x + 7$$
$$x^2 - 6x - 7 = 0$$
$$(x + 1)(x - 7) = 0$$
$$x = 7 \quad (x = -1 \text{ is impossible})$$
$$x + 2 = 9$$
The two integers are 7 and 9.

77. Solving the equation:
$$(2x + 1)(4x - 2) = 126$$
$$8x^2 - 2 = 126$$
$$8x^2 - 128 = 0$$
$$x^2 - 16 = 0$$
$$(x + 4)(x - 4) = 0$$
$$x = 4 \quad (x = -4 \text{ is impossible})$$
$$l = 4(4) - 2 = 14$$
$$w = 2(4) + 1 = 9$$
The length is 14 cm and the width is 9 cm.

79. Solving the equation:
$$\frac{1}{2}(2x)(3x + 1) = 80$$
$$3x^2 + x = 80$$
$$3x^2 + x - 80 = 0$$
$$(3x + 16)(x - 5) = 0$$
$$x = 5 \quad \left(x = -\frac{16}{3} \text{ is impossible} \right)$$
$$b = 3(5) + 1 = 16$$
$$h = 2(5) = 10$$
The base is 16 m and the height is 10 m.

81. Solving the equation:

$$\frac{1}{2}(2x+4)(x+4)=63$$
$$x^2+6x+8=63$$
$$x^2+6x-55=0$$
$$(x+11)(x-5)=0$$
$$x=5 \quad (x=-11 \text{ is impossible})$$
$$b=5+4=9$$
$$h=2(5)+4=14$$

The base is 9 in. and the height is 14 in.

83. Using the Pythagorean theorem:

$$(2x+2)^2+x^2=(3x-2)^2$$
$$4x^2+8x+4+x^2=9x^2-12x+4$$
$$5x^2+8x+4=9x^2-12x+4$$
$$4x^2-20x=0$$
$$4x(x-5)=0$$
$$x=5 \quad (x=0 \text{ is impossible})$$

85. Let x, $x + 2$, and $x + 4$ represent the three sides. Using the Pythagorean theorem:

$$x^2+(x+2)^2=(x+4)^2$$
$$x^2+x^2+4x+4=x^2+8x+16$$
$$2x^2+4x+4=x^2+8x+16$$
$$x^2-4x-12=0$$
$$(x-6)(x+2)=0$$
$$x=6 \quad (x=-2 \text{ is impossible})$$

The lengths of the three sides are 6, 8, and 10.

87. Let w represent the width and $3w + 2$ represent the length. Using the area formula:

$$w(3w+2)=16$$
$$3w^2+2w=16$$
$$3w^2+2w-16=0$$
$$(3w+8)(w-2)=0$$
$$w=2 \quad (w=-\frac{8}{3} \text{ is impossible})$$
$$3w+2=8$$

The dimensions are 2 meters by 8 meters.

89. Let h represent the height and $4h + 2$ represent the base. Using the area formula:

$$\frac{1}{2}(4h+2)(h)=36$$
$$4h^2+2h=72$$
$$4h^2+2h-72=0$$
$$2(2h^2+h-36)=0$$
$$2(2h+9)(h-4)=0$$
$$h=4 \quad (h=-\frac{9}{2} \text{ is impossible})$$
$$4h+2=18$$

The base is 18 cm and the height is 4 cm.

91. Setting $h = 0$ in the equation:

$$32t - 16t^2 = 0$$
$$16t(2 - t) = 0$$
$$t = 0, 2$$

The object is on the ground at 0 and 2 seconds.

93. Let w represent the width of the lawn. The dimensions of the large rectangle (garden plus lawn) are $40 + 2w$ by $35 + 2w$. Solving the equation:

$$(40 + 2w)(35 + 2w) - (40)(35) = 316$$
$$1,400 + 150w + 4w^2 - 1,400 = 316$$
$$4w^2 + 150w - 316 = 0$$
$$2w^2 + 75w - 158 = 0$$
$$(2w + 79)(w - 2) = 0$$
$$w = 2 \quad \left(w = -\frac{79}{2} \text{ is impossible} \right)$$

The width of the lawn is 2 yards.

95. The area of the path is the difference in the two areas: $2,975 - (75)(35) = 2,975 - 2,625 = 350 \text{ ft}^2$

97. Let x and $2x$ represent the widths of the path. The dimensions of the large rectangle (tennis court plus path) are $78 + 4x$ by $36 + 2x$. Solving the equation:

$$(78 + 4x)(36 + 2x) = 7,560$$
$$2,808 + 300x + 8x^2 = 7,560$$
$$8x^2 + 300x - 4,752 = 0$$
$$2x^2 + 75x - 1,188 = 0$$
$$(2x + 99)(x - 12) = 0$$
$$x = 12 \quad \left(x = -\frac{99}{2} \text{ is impossible} \right)$$

The width of the path is 12 feet.

99. Let x and $2x$ represent the widths of the margin. The dimensions of the small rectangle (page minus margins) are $10 - 3x$ by $7 - 3x$. Solving the equation:

$$70 - (10 - 3x)(7 - 3x) = 23.25$$
$$70 - (70 - 51x + 9x^2) = 23.25$$
$$51x - 9x^2 = 23.25$$
$$9x^2 - 51x + 23.25 = 0$$
$$900x^2 - 5,100x + 2,325 = 0$$
$$12x^2 - 68x + 31 = 0$$
$$(6x - 31)(2x - 1) = 0$$
$$x = \frac{1}{2} \quad \left(x = \frac{31}{6} \approx 5.2 \text{ is too large} \right)$$

The width of the left margin is 0.5 inches.

101. Substituting $v = 48$ and $h = 32$:

$$h = vt - 16t^2$$
$$32 = 48t - 16t^2$$
$$0 = -16t^2 + 48t - 32$$
$$0 = -16(t^2 - 3t + 2)$$
$$0 = -16(t - 1)(t - 2)$$
$$t = 1, 2$$

It will reach a height of 32 feet after 1 sec and 2 sec.

103. Substituting $v = 24$ and $h = 0$:

$$h = vt - 16t^2$$
$$0 = 24t - 16t^2$$
$$0 = -16t^2 + 24t$$
$$0 = -8t(2t - 3)$$
$$t = 0, \frac{3}{2}$$

It will be on the ground after 0 sec and $\frac{3}{2}$ sec.

105. Substituting $h = 192$:

$$192 = 96 + 80t - 16t^2$$
$$0 = -16t^2 + 80t - 96$$
$$0 = -16\left(t^2 - 5t + 6\right)$$
$$0 = -16(t-2)(t-3)$$
$$t = 2, 3$$

The bullet will be 192 feet in the air after 2 sec and 3 sec.

107. Multiply the second equation by 5:

$$2x - 5y = -8$$
$$15x + 5y = 25$$

Adding yields:

$$17x = 17$$
$$x = 1$$

Substituting to find y:

$$3 + y = 5$$
$$y = 2$$

The solution is $(1, 2)$.

109. To clear each equation of fractions, multiply the first equation by 6 and the second equation by 20:

$$2x - y = 18$$
$$-4x + 5y = 0$$

Multiply the first equation by 2:

$$4x - 2y = 36$$
$$-4x + 5y = 0$$

Adding yields:

$$3y = 36$$
$$y = 12$$

Substituting to find x:

$$2x - 12 = 18$$
$$2x = 30$$
$$x = 15$$

The solution is $(15, 12)$.

111. Graphing the solution set:

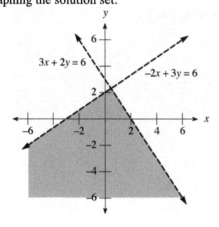

113. Graphing the solution set:

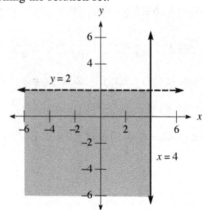

Chapter 4 Review

1. Simplifying: $\left(\dfrac{2}{3}x^3 - 3x - \dfrac{4}{3}\right) - \left(\dfrac{1}{3}x^2 - \dfrac{2}{3}x + \dfrac{4}{3}\right) = \dfrac{2}{3}x^3 - 3x - \dfrac{4}{3} - \dfrac{1}{3}x^2 + \dfrac{2}{3}x - \dfrac{4}{3} = \dfrac{2}{3}x^3 - \dfrac{1}{3}x^2 - \dfrac{7}{3}x - \dfrac{8}{3}$

2. Simplifying: $6 - 3\left[4(5x+2) - 13x\right] = 6 - 3(20x + 8 - 13x) = 6 - 3(7x + 8) = 6 - 21x - 24 = -21x - 18$

3. The revenue is given by: $R(x) = xp = x(24 - 0.2x) = 24x - 0.2x^2$

4. The profit is given by:
$$P(x) = R(x) - C(x) = \left(24x - 0.2x^2\right) - (3x + 25) = 24x - 0.2x^2 - 3x - 25 = -0.2x^2 + 21x - 25$$

5. Substituting $x = 100$ into the revenue equation: $R(100) = 24(100) - 0.2(100)^2 = 2{,}400 - 2{,}000 = \$400$.
   The revenue is $400.

6. Substituting $x = 100$ into the cost equation: $C(100) = 3(100) + 25 = 300 + 25 = \$325$. The cost is $325.

7. Substituting $x = 100$ into the profit equation: $P(100) = -0.2(100)^2 + 21(100) - 25 = -2{,}000 + 2{,}100 - 25 = \$75$
   The profit is $75. Note that this also could have been found by subtracting the answers from problems 5 and 6.

8. Multiplying: $(x+3)(-3x+5) = -3x^2 + 5x - 9x + 15 = -3x^2 - 4x + 15$

9. Multiplying: $(2x+3)\left(2x^2 - 4x - 1\right) = 4x^3 - 8x^2 - 2x + 6x^2 - 12x - 3 = 4x^3 - 2x^2 - 14x - 3$

10. Multiplying: $(4a-3)^2 = (4a)^2 - 2(4a)(3) + (3)^2 = 16a^2 - 24a + 9$

11. Multiplying: $(2x-5)(2x+5) = (2x)^2 - (5)^2 = 4x^2 - 25$

12. Multiplying: $x(x+4)(2x-5) = x\left(2x^2 + 3x - 20\right) = 2x^3 + 3x^2 - 20x$

13. Multiplying: $\left(3x - \dfrac{1}{5}\right)\left(5x + \dfrac{1}{3}\right) = 15x^2 + x - x - \dfrac{1}{15} = 15x^2 - \dfrac{1}{15}$

14. Factoring: $x^2 - 3x - 10 = (x-5)(x+2)$

15. Factoring: $6x^4 + 14x^2 - 40 = 2\left(3x^4 + 7x^2 - 20\right) = 2\left(3x^2 - 5\right)\left(x^2 + 4\right)$

16. Factoring: $16x^4 - 81y^4 = \left(4x^2 + 9y^2\right)\left(4x^2 - 9y^2\right) = \left(4x^2 + 9y^2\right)(2x + 3y)(2x - 3y)$

17. Factoring: $6ab + 3ay - 8bx - 4xy = 3a(2b+y) - 4x(2b+y) = (2b+y)(3a-4x)$

18. Factoring: $y^3 - \dfrac{1}{64} = y^3 - \left(\dfrac{1}{4}\right)^3 = \left(y - \dfrac{1}{4}\right)\left(y^2 + \dfrac{1}{4}y + \dfrac{1}{16}\right)$

19. Factoring: $2x^4y^3 + 6x^3y^4 - 20x^2y^5 = 2x^2y^3\left(x^2 + 3xy - 10y^2\right) = 2x^2y^3(x + 5y)(x - 2y)$

20. Factoring: $4a^2 - 4ab + b^2 - 16 = (2a - b)^2 - 4^2 = (2a - b + 4)(2a - b - 4)$

21. Factoring: $81 - x^4 = \left(9 + x^2\right)\left(9 - x^2\right) = \left(9 + x^2\right)(3 + x)(3 - x)$

22. Solving the equation:

$$\frac{1}{2}x^2 = \frac{23}{6}x - \frac{7}{3}$$

$$6\left(\frac{1}{2}x^2\right) = 6\left(\frac{23}{6}x - \frac{7}{3}\right)$$

$$3x^2 = 23x - 14$$

$$3x^2 - 23x + 14 = 0$$

$$(3x-2)(x-7) = 0$$

$$x = \frac{2}{3}, 7$$

23. Solving the equation:

$$36x^4 = 9x^3$$

$$36x^4 - 9x^3 = 0$$

$$9x^3(4x-1) = 0$$

$$x = 0, \frac{1}{4}$$

24. Solving the equation:

$$(x-3)(x+4) = 8$$

$$x^2 + x - 12 = 8$$

$$x^2 + x - 20 = 0$$

$$(x+5)(x-4) = 0$$

$$x = -5, 4$$

25. Solving the equation:

$$x^3 + 3x^2 - 16x - 48 = 0$$

$$x^2(x+3) - 16(x+3) = 0$$

$$(x+3)(x^2 - 16) = 0$$

$$(x+3)(x+4)(x-4) = 0$$

$$x = -4, -3, 4$$

26. Setting $f(x) = g(x)$:

$$x^2 + 4x - 28 = -7$$

$$x^2 + 4x - 21 = 0$$

$$(x+7)(x-3) = 0$$

$$x = -7, 3$$

27. Setting $f(x) = g(x)$:

$$x^2 + 4x - 28 = -2x - 12$$

$$x^2 + 6x - 16 = 0$$

$$(x+8)(x-2) = 0$$

$$x = -8, 2$$

28. Using the Pythagorean theorem:

$$(3x+3)^2 + 7^2 = (4x-3)^2$$

$$9x^2 + 18x + 9 + 49 = 16x^2 - 24x + 9$$

$$9x^2 + 18x + 58 = 16x^2 - 24x + 9$$

$$7x^2 - 42x - 49 = 0$$

$$x^2 - 6x - 7 = 0$$

$$(x-7)(x+1) = 0$$

$$x = 7 \quad (x = -1 \text{ is impossible})$$

29. Using the area formula:

$$\frac{1}{2}(4x+2)\left(\frac{x}{3}+4\right) = 35$$

$$(2x+1)\left(\frac{x}{3}+4\right) = 35$$

$$\frac{2}{3}x^2 + \frac{25}{3}x + 4 = 35$$

$$\frac{2}{3}x^2 + \frac{25}{3}x - 31 = 0$$

$$2x^2 + 25x - 93 = 0$$

$$(2x+31)(x-3) = 0$$

$$x = 3 \text{ in.} \qquad (x = -\frac{31}{2} \text{ is impossible})$$

30. Using the area formula:

$$x(x-3)=18$$
$$x^2-3x=18$$
$$x^2-3x-18=0$$
$$(x-6)(x+3)=0$$
$$x=6 \text{ cm} \qquad (x=-3 \text{ is impossible})$$

Chapter 4 Cumulative Review

1. Simplifying: $(-3)^3=(-3)(-3)(-3)=-27$

2. Simplifying: $(-3)^{-3}=\dfrac{1}{(-3)^3}=-\dfrac{1}{27}$

3. Simplifying: $\left|-14-61\right|-17=\left|-75\right|-17=75-17=58$

4. Simplifying: $5^3+3\left(4^2-2^2\right)=5^3+3(16-4)=125+3(12)=125+36=161$

5. Simplifying: $84\div7\cdot4=12\cdot4=48$

6. Simplifying: $77\div7\cdot11=11\cdot11=121$

7. Simplifying: $\dfrac{7-2^3}{-4\left(6^2-5^2\right)}=\dfrac{7-8}{-4(36-25)}=\dfrac{-1}{-4(11)}=\dfrac{-1}{-44}=\dfrac{1}{44}$

8. Simplifying: $\dfrac{8^2-32}{2^3(14-3\cdot6)}=\dfrac{64-32}{8(14-18)}=\dfrac{32}{8(-4)}=\dfrac{32}{-32}=-1$

9. Evaluating: $P(1)=12.25(1)-0.01(1)^2=12.25-0.01(1)=12.25-0.01=12.24$

10. Evaluating: $P(-1)=12.25(-1)-0.01(-1)^2=-12.25-0.01(1)=-12.25-0.01=-12.26$

11. Evaluating: $Q(3)=\dfrac{5}{3}(3)^2+\dfrac{2}{3}(3)-7=\dfrac{5}{3}(9)+\dfrac{2}{3}(3)-7=15+2-7=10$

12. Evaluating: $Q(-3)=\dfrac{5}{3}(-3)^2+\dfrac{2}{3}(-3)-7=\dfrac{5}{3}(9)+\dfrac{2}{3}(-3)-7=15-2-7=6$

13. Simplifying: $17\left(x-\dfrac{1}{17}\right)=17\cdot x-17\cdot\dfrac{1}{17}=17x-1$

14. Simplifying: $6\left(\dfrac{5}{3}x-\dfrac{7}{2}y\right)=6\cdot\dfrac{5}{3}x-6\cdot\dfrac{7}{2}y=10x-21y$

15. Simplifying: $(4x+1)-(5x-2)=4x+1-5x+2=-x+3$

16. Simplifying: $5a-3\left[4+(a-2)\right]=5a-3(a+2)=5a-3a-6=2a-6$

17. Simplifying:
$$\left(4x^3+8\right)-\left(5x^2-8\right)+\left(3x^3-2\right)+\left(6x^2+1\right)=\left(4x^3+3x^3\right)+\left(-5x^2+6x^2\right)+(8+8-2+1)=7x^3+x^2+15$$

18. Simplifying:
$$\left(\dfrac{4}{5}x^2-\dfrac{1}{3}\right)-\left(\dfrac{2}{15}x^2+\dfrac{8}{5}x\right)+\left(\dfrac{5}{3}x^2-\dfrac{1}{15}\right)+\left(\dfrac{2}{5}x^2+\dfrac{2}{5}\right)$$
$$=\left(\dfrac{4}{5}x^2-\dfrac{2}{15}x^2+\dfrac{5}{3}x^2+\dfrac{2}{5}x^2\right)+\left(-\dfrac{8}{5}x\right)+\left(-\dfrac{1}{3}-\dfrac{1}{15}+\dfrac{2}{5}\right)$$
$$=\dfrac{41}{15}x^2-\dfrac{8}{5}x$$

19. Multiplying: $\left(2x^2y\right)^5=2^5\left(x^2\right)^5y^5=32x^{10}y^5$

20. Multiplying: $\left(-5ab^3\right)\left(4a^2b^2\right)=-20a^3b^5$

21. Dividing: $\dfrac{48x^2 y}{16xy^9} = 3x^{2-1}y^{1-9} = 3xy^{-8} = \dfrac{3x}{y^8}$

22. Dividing: $\dfrac{\left(5a^2 b\right)^3}{\left(a^4 b\right)^2} = \dfrac{125a^6 b^3}{a^8 b^2} = 125a^{6-8}b^{3-2} = 125a^{-2}b = \dfrac{125b}{a^2}$

23. Multiplying: $(4x+5)(2x-1) = 8x^2 - 4x + 10x - 5 = 8x^2 + 6x - 5$

24. Multiplying: $2x\left(9x^2 + 4x + 7\right) = 18x^3 + 8x^2 + 14x$

25. Multiplying: $\left(x - \dfrac{3}{4}\right)^2 = \left(x - \dfrac{3}{4}\right)\left(x - \dfrac{3}{4}\right) = x^2 - \dfrac{3}{2}x + \dfrac{9}{16}$

26. Multiplying:

$$\left(x + \dfrac{3}{4}\right)^3 = \left(x + \dfrac{3}{4}\right)\left(x + \dfrac{3}{4}\right)^2$$
$$= \left(x + \dfrac{3}{4}\right)\left(x^2 + \dfrac{3}{2}x + \dfrac{9}{16}\right)$$
$$= x^3 + \dfrac{3}{2}x^2 + \dfrac{9}{16}x + \dfrac{3}{4}x^2 + \dfrac{9}{8}x + \dfrac{27}{64}$$
$$= x^3 + \dfrac{9}{4}x^2 + \dfrac{27}{16}x + \dfrac{27}{64}$$

27. Multiplying: $\left(8 \times 10^4\right)\left(2 \times 10^3\right) = 16 \times 10^7 = 1.6 \times 10^8$

28. Dividing: $\dfrac{9 \times 10^8}{3 \times 10^2} = \dfrac{9}{3} \times 10^{8-2} = 3 \times 10^6$

29. Factoring: $x^2 + ax - bx - ab = x(x+a) - b(x+a) = (x+a)(x-b)$

30. Factoring: $8a^2 + 10a - 7 = (4a+7)(2a-1)$

31. Factoring: $(x-1)^2 - 16 = (x-1-4)(x-1+4) = (x-5)(x+3)$

32. Factoring: $\dfrac{1}{27} + t^3 = t^3 + \dfrac{1}{27} = \left(t + \dfrac{1}{3}\right)\left(t^2 - \dfrac{1}{3}t + \dfrac{1}{9}\right)$

33. Solving the equation:

$$5x - 3 = 12$$
$$5x = 15$$
$$x = 3$$

34. Solving the equation:

$$|x+7| - 4 = -2$$
$$|x+7| = 2$$
$$x + 7 = -2, 2$$
$$x = -9, -5$$

35. Solving the equation:

$$\dfrac{2}{3}x + 8 = -12$$
$$\dfrac{2}{3}x = -20$$
$$2x = -60$$
$$x = -30$$

36. Solving the equation:

$$\dfrac{2}{3}x = 2 - \dfrac{4}{3}x$$
$$3\left(\dfrac{2}{3}x\right) = 3\left(2 - \dfrac{4}{3}x\right)$$
$$2x = 6 - 4x$$
$$6x = 6$$
$$x = 1$$

37. Solving the equation:
$$16a^4 = 49a^2$$
$$16a^4 - 49a^2 = 0$$
$$a^2\left(16a^2 - 49\right) = 0$$
$$a^2\left(4a + 7\right)\left(4a - 7\right) = 0$$
$$a = -\frac{7}{4}, 0, \frac{7}{4}$$

38. Solving the equation:
$$\left(x + 5\right)^2 = 2x + 9$$
$$x^2 + 10x + 25 = 2x + 9$$
$$x^2 + 8x + 16 = 0$$
$$\left(x + 4\right)^2 = 0$$
$$x = -4$$

39. Multiply the first equation by -1:
$$7x + 7y = 28$$
$$-7x + y = -4$$
Adding yields:
$$8y = 24$$
$$y = 3$$
Substituting into the second equation:
$$-7x + 3 = -4$$
$$-7x = -7$$
$$x = 1$$
The solution is $(1,3)$.

40. Setting the two equations equal:
$$-\frac{1}{5}x - 2 = -3x - 2$$
$$5\left(-\frac{1}{5}x - 2\right) = 5\left(-3x - 2\right)$$
$$-x - 10 = -15x - 10$$
$$14x = 0$$
$$x = 0$$
Substituting into the second equation: $y = -3(0) - 2 = -2$. The solution is $(0,-2)$.

41. Finding the slope: $m = \dfrac{1 - 2}{4 - (-3)} = -\dfrac{1}{7}$

42. Finding the slope: $m = \dfrac{4 - 2}{3 - (-16)} = \dfrac{2}{19}$

43. Evaluating: $f(-4) = \dfrac{4(-4) - 2}{3} = \dfrac{-16 - 2}{3} = \dfrac{-18}{3} = -6$

44. Evaluating: $g(8) = \dfrac{3(8) + 2}{4} = \dfrac{24 + 2}{4} = \dfrac{26}{4} = \dfrac{13}{2}$

45. Evaluating: $(g \circ f)(11) = g\big[f(11)\big] = g\left[\dfrac{4(11) - 2}{3}\right] = g(14) = \dfrac{3(14) + 2}{4} = \dfrac{44}{4} = 11$

46. Evaluating: $(f \circ g)(2) = f\big[g(2)\big] = f\left[\dfrac{3(2) + 2}{4}\right] = f(2) = \dfrac{4(2) - 2}{3} = \dfrac{6}{3} = 2$

47. Let b represent the base and $4b - 4$ represent the height. Using the area formula:

$$\frac{1}{2}b(4b-4)=12$$
$$2b^2 - 2b = 12$$
$$2b^2 - 2b - 12 = 0$$
$$b^2 - b - 6 = 0$$
$$(b-3)(b+2)=0$$
$$b = 3 \qquad (b=-2 \text{ is impossible})$$
$$4b - 4 = 4(3) - 4 = 8$$

The base is 3 feet and the height is 8 feet.

48. Let x represent the largest angle, $\frac{1}{3}x$ represent the smallest angle, and $\frac{1}{3}x + 30$ represent the remaining angle. Since the sum of the angles is $180°$, the equation is:

$$\frac{1}{3}x + \frac{1}{3}x + 30 + x = 180$$
$$\frac{5}{3}x + 30 = 180$$
$$\frac{5}{3}x = 150$$
$$x = \frac{3}{5} \cdot 150 = 90$$
$$\frac{1}{3}x = \frac{1}{3}(90) = 30$$
$$\frac{1}{3}x + 30 = 30 + 30 = 60$$

The angles are $30°$, $60°$, and $90°$.

49. The sum is: $31 + 16 + 27 = 74$ users

50. Since there were 80 total users, there were $80 - 74 = 6$ users using neither Yahoo nor Google.

Chapter 4 Test

1. Simplifying: $\left(\frac{6}{5}x^3 - 2x - \frac{3}{5}\right) - \left(\frac{6}{5}x^2 - \frac{2}{5}x + \frac{3}{5}\right) = \frac{6}{5}x^3 - 2x - \frac{3}{5} - \frac{6}{5}x^2 + \frac{2}{5}x - \frac{3}{5} = \frac{6}{5}x^3 - \frac{6}{5}x^2 - \frac{8}{5}x - \frac{6}{5}$

2. Simplifying: $5 - 7[9(2x+1) - 16x] = 5 - 7(18x + 9 - 16x) = 5 - 7(2x+9) = 5 - 14x - 63 = -14x - 58$

3. The revenue is given by: $R(x) = xp = x(36 - 0.3x) = 36x - 0.3x^2$

4. The profit is given by:
$$P(x) = R(x) - C(x) = \left(36x - 0.3x^2\right) - \left(4x + 50\right) = 36x - 0.3x^2 - 4x - 50 = -0.3x^2 + 32x - 50$$

5. Substituting $x = 100$ into the revenue equation: $R(100) = 36(100) - 0.3(100)^2 = 3{,}600 - 3{,}000 = \$600$.
The revenue is $600.

6. Substituting $x = 100$ into the cost equation: $C(100) = 4(100) + 50 = 400 + 50 = \$450$. The cost is $450.

7. Substituting $x = 100$ into the profit equation: $P(100) = -0.3(100)^2 + 32(100) - 50 = -3{,}000 + 3{,}200 - 50 = \$150$
The profit is $150. Note that this also could have been found by subtracting the answers from problems 5 and 6.

8. Multiplying: $(x+7)(-5x+4) = -5x^2 + 4x - 35x + 28 = -5x^2 - 31x + 28$

9. Multiplying: $(3x-2)(2x^2 + 6x - 5) = 6x^3 + 18x^2 - 15x - 4x^2 - 12x + 10 = 6x^3 + 14x^2 - 27x + 10$

10. Multiplying: $\left(3a^4 - 7\right)^2 = \left(3a^4\right)^2 - 2\left(3a^4\right)(7) + (7)^2 = 9a^8 - 42a^4 + 49$

11. Multiplying: $(2x+3)(2x-3)=(2x)^2-(3)^2=4x^2-9$

12. Multiplying: $x(x-7)(3x+4)=x(3x^2-17x-28)=3x^3-17x^2-28x$

13. Multiplying: $\left(2x-\dfrac{1}{7}\right)\left(7x+\dfrac{1}{2}\right)=14x^2+x-x-\dfrac{1}{14}=14x^2-\dfrac{1}{14}$

14. Factoring: $x^2-6x+5=(x-5)(x-1)$

15. Factoring: $15x^4+33x^2-36=3(5x^4+11x^2-12)=3(5x^2-4)(x^2+3)$

16. Factoring: $81x^4-16y^4=(9x^2+4y^2)(9x^2-4y^2)=(9x^2+4y^2)(3x+2y)(3x-2y)$

17. Factoring: $6ax-ay+18b^2x-3b^2y=a(6x-y)+3b^2(6x-y)=(6x-y)(a+3b^2)$

18. Factoring: $y^3-\dfrac{1}{27}=y^3-\left(\dfrac{1}{3}\right)^3=\left(y-\dfrac{1}{3}\right)\left(y^2+\dfrac{1}{3}y+\dfrac{1}{9}\right)$

19. Factoring: $3x^4y^4+15x^3y^5-72x^2y^6=3x^2y^4(x^2+5xy-24y^2)=3x^2y^4(x+8y)(x-3y)$

20. Factoring: $a^2-2ab-36+b^2=a^2-2ab+b^2-36=(a-b)^2-6^2=(a-b+6)(a-b-6)$

21. Factoring: $16-x^4=(4+x^2)(4-x^2)=(4+x^2)(2+x)(2-x)$

22. Solving the equation:

$$\frac{1}{4}x^2=-\frac{21}{8}x-\frac{5}{4}$$
$$8\left(\frac{1}{4}x^2\right)=8\left(-\frac{21}{8}x-\frac{5}{4}\right)$$
$$2x^2=-21x-10$$
$$2x^2+21x+10=0$$
$$(2x+1)(x+10)=0$$
$$x=-10,-\frac{1}{2}$$

23. Solving the equation:

$$243x^3=81x^4$$
$$243x^3-81x^4=0$$
$$81x^3(3-x)=0$$
$$x=0,3$$

24. Solving the equation:

$$(x+5)(x-2)=8$$
$$x^2+3x-10=8$$
$$x^2+3x-18=0$$
$$(x+6)(x-3)=0$$
$$x=-6,3$$

25. Solving the equation:

$$x^3+5x^2-9x-45=0$$
$$x^2(x+5)-9(x+5)=0$$
$$(x+5)(x^2-9)=0$$
$$(x+5)(x+3)(x-3)=0$$
$$x=-5,-3,3$$

26. Setting $f(x)=g(x)$:

$$x^2-2x-15=0$$
$$(x-5)(x+3)=0$$
$$x=-3,5$$

27. Setting $f(x)=g(x)$:

$$x^2-2x-15=5-3x$$
$$x^2+x-20=0$$
$$(x+5)(x-4)=0$$
$$x=-5,4$$

28. Using the Pythagorean theorem:

$$(2x)^2 + 8^2 = (3x+1)^2$$
$$4x^2 + 64 = 9x^2 + 6x + 1$$
$$5x^2 + 6x - 63 = 0$$
$$(5x+21)(x-3) = 0$$
$$x = 3 \quad \left(x = -\frac{21}{5} \text{ is impossible} \right)$$

29. Using the area formula:

$$\frac{1}{2}(2x+6)\left(\frac{x}{2}-1\right) = 12$$
$$(x+3)\left(\frac{x}{2}-1\right) = 12$$
$$\frac{1}{2}x^2 + \frac{1}{2}x - 3 = 12$$
$$\frac{1}{2}x^2 + \frac{1}{2}x - 15 = 0$$
$$x^2 + x - 30 = 0$$
$$(x+6)(x-5) = 0$$
$$x = 5 \text{ in.} \quad (x = -6 \text{ is impossible})$$

30. Using the area formula:

$$x(x-4) = 12$$
$$x^2 - 4x = 12$$
$$x^2 - 4x - 12 = 0$$
$$(x-6)(x+2) = 0$$
$$x = 6 \text{ cm} \quad (x = -2 \text{ is impossible})$$

Chapter 5
Rational Expressions, Equations, and Functions

5.1 Basic Properties and Reducing to Lowest Terms

1. Reducing to lowest terms: $\dfrac{x^2-16}{6x+24}=\dfrac{(x+4)(x-4)}{6(x+4)}=\dfrac{x-4}{6}$

3. Reducing to lowest terms: $\dfrac{a^4-81}{a-3}=\dfrac{\left(a^2+9\right)\left(a^2-9\right)}{a-3}=\dfrac{\left(a^2+9\right)(a+3)(a-3)}{a-3}=\left(a^2+9\right)(a+3)$

5. Reducing to lowest terms: $\dfrac{20y^2-45}{10y^2-5y-15}=\dfrac{5\left(4y^2-9\right)}{5\left(2y^2-y-3\right)}=\dfrac{5(2y+3)(2y-3)}{5(2y-3)(y+1)}=\dfrac{2y+3}{y+1}$

7. Reducing to lowest terms: $\dfrac{12y-2xy-2x^2y}{6y-4xy-2x^2y}=\dfrac{2y\left(6-x-x^2\right)}{2y\left(3-2x-x^2\right)}=\dfrac{2y(3+x)(2-x)}{2y(3+x)(1-x)}=\dfrac{2-x}{1-x}=\dfrac{x-2}{x-1}$

9. Reducing to lowest terms: $\dfrac{(x-3)^2(x+2)}{(x+2)^2(x-3)}=\dfrac{x-3}{x+2}$

11. Reducing to lowest terms: $\dfrac{x^3+1}{x^2-1}=\dfrac{(x+1)\left(x^2-x+1\right)}{(x+1)(x-1)}=\dfrac{x^2-x+1}{x-1}$

13. Reducing to lowest terms: $\dfrac{4am-4an}{3n-3m}=\dfrac{4a(m-n)}{3(n-m)}=\dfrac{-4a}{3}$

15. Reducing to lowest terms: $\dfrac{ab-a+b-1}{ab+a+b+1}=\dfrac{a(b-1)+1(b-1)}{a(b+1)+1(b+1)}=\dfrac{(b-1)(a+1)}{(b+1)(a+1)}=\dfrac{b-1}{b+1}$

17. Reducing to lowest terms: $\dfrac{21x^2-23x+6}{21x^2+x-10}=\dfrac{(7x-3)(3x-2)}{(7x+5)(3x-2)}=\dfrac{7x-3}{7x+5}$

19. Reducing to lowest terms: $\dfrac{8x^2-6x-9}{8x^2-18x+9}=\dfrac{(4x+3)(2x-3)}{(4x-3)(2x-3)}=\dfrac{4x+3}{4x-3}$

21. Reducing to lowest terms: $\dfrac{4x^2+29x+45}{8x^2-10x-63}=\dfrac{(x+5)(4x+9)}{(2x-7)(4x+9)}=\dfrac{x+5}{2x-7}$

23. Reducing to lowest terms: $\dfrac{3a^2+10ax-25x^2}{25x^2-9a^2}=\dfrac{(a+5x)(3a-5x)}{(5x+3a)(5x-3a)}=-\dfrac{5x+a}{5x+3a}$

25. Reducing to lowest terms: $\dfrac{a^3+b^3}{a^2-b^2}=\dfrac{(a+b)\left(a^2-ab+b^2\right)}{(a+b)(a-b)}=\dfrac{a^2-ab+b^2}{a-b}$

27. Reducing to lowest terms: $\dfrac{8x^4-8x}{4x^4+4x^3+4x^2}=\dfrac{8x\left(x^3-1\right)}{4x^2\left(x^2+x+1\right)}=\dfrac{8x(x-1)\left(x^2+x+1\right)}{4x^2\left(x^2+x+1\right)}=\dfrac{2(x-1)}{x}=\dfrac{2x-2}{x}$

29. Reducing to lowest terms: $\dfrac{ax+2x+3a+6}{ay+2y-4a-8}=\dfrac{x(a+2)+3(a+2)}{y(a+2)-4(a+2)}=\dfrac{(a+2)(x+3)}{(a+2)(y-4)}=\dfrac{x+3}{y-4}$

31. Reducing to lowest terms:

$$\dfrac{x^3+3x^2-4x-12}{x^2+x-6}=\dfrac{x^2(x+3)-4(x+3)}{(x+3)(x-2)}=\dfrac{(x+3)\left(x^2-4\right)}{(x+3)(x-2)}=\dfrac{(x+3)(x+2)(x-2)}{(x+3)(x-2)}=x+2$$

33. Reducing to lowest terms: $\dfrac{9x^2-4y^2}{2y^2+3xy-9x^2}=\dfrac{(3x+2y)(3x-2y)}{(2y-3x)(y+3x)}=-\dfrac{3x+2y}{3x+y}$

35. Reducing to lowest terms: $\dfrac{x^3-8}{x^2-4}=\dfrac{(x-2)\left(x^2+2x+4\right)}{(x-2)(x+2)}=\dfrac{x^2+2x+4}{x+2}$

37. Reducing to lowest terms: $\dfrac{8x^3-27}{4x^2-9}=\dfrac{(2x-3)\left(4x^2+6x+9\right)}{(2x-3)(2x+3)}=\dfrac{4x^2+6x+9}{2x+3}$

39. Reducing to lowest terms: $\dfrac{x+2}{x^3+8}=\dfrac{x+2}{(x+2)\left(x^2-2x+4\right)}=\dfrac{1}{x^2-2x+4}$

41. Reducing to lowest terms: $\dfrac{x-4}{4-x}=\dfrac{x-4}{-1(x-4)}=-1$

43. Reducing to lowest terms: $\dfrac{y^2-36}{6-y}=\dfrac{(y+6)(y-6)}{-1(y-6)}=-(y+6)=-y-6$

45. Reducing to lowest terms: $\dfrac{1-9a^2}{9a^2-6a+1}=\dfrac{-1\left(9a^2-1\right)}{(3a-1)^2}=\dfrac{-1(3a+1)(3a-1)}{(3a-1)^2}=-\dfrac{3a+1}{3a-1}$

47. Reducing to lowest terms: $\dfrac{(3x-5)-(3a-5)}{x-a}=\dfrac{3x-3a}{x-a}=\dfrac{3(x-a)}{x-a}=3$

49. Reducing to lowest terms: $\dfrac{\left(x^2-4\right)-\left(a^2-4\right)}{x-a}=\dfrac{x^2-a^2}{x-a}=\dfrac{(x+a)(x-a)}{x-a}=x+a$

51. Reducing to lowest terms:

$$\dfrac{\left(x^2+3x\right)-\left(a^2+3a\right)}{x-a}=\dfrac{\left(x^2-a^2\right)+(3x-3a)}{x-a}=\dfrac{(x+a)(x-a)+3(x-a)}{x-a}=\dfrac{(x-a)(x+a+3)}{x-a}=x+a+3$$

53. The domain is $\{x \mid x \neq 1\}$.

55. The domain is $\{x \mid x \neq 2\}$.

57. Setting the denominator equal to 0:

$$t^2-16=0$$
$$(t+4)(t-4)=0$$
$$t=-4,4$$

The domain is $\{t \mid t \neq -4, t \neq 4\}$.

59. Finding each function value:

$$g(0) = \frac{0+3}{0-1} = \frac{3}{-1} = -3 \qquad\qquad g(-3) = \frac{-3+3}{-3-1} = \frac{0}{-4} = 0$$

$$g(3) = \frac{3+3}{3-1} = \frac{6}{2} = 3 \qquad\qquad g(-1) = \frac{-1+3}{-1-1} = \frac{2}{-2} = -1$$

$$g(1) = \frac{1+3}{1-1} = \frac{4}{0}, \text{ which is undefined}$$

61. Finding each function value:

$$h(0) = \frac{0-3}{0+1} = \frac{-3}{1} = -3 \qquad\qquad h(-3) = \frac{-3-3}{-3+1} = \frac{-6}{-2} = 3$$

$$h(3) = \frac{3-3}{3+1} = \frac{0}{4} = 0 \qquad\qquad h(-1) = \frac{-1-3}{-1+1} = \frac{-4}{0}, \text{ which is undefined}$$

$$h(1) = \frac{1-3}{1+1} = \frac{-2}{2} = -1$$

63. a. Evaluating the difference quotient: $\dfrac{f(x)-f(a)}{x-a} = \dfrac{4x-4a}{x-a} = \dfrac{4(x-a)}{x-a} = 4$

b. Evaluating the difference quotient: $\dfrac{f(x+h)-f(x)}{h} = \dfrac{4x+4h-4x}{h} = \dfrac{4h}{h} = 4$

65. a. Evaluating the difference quotient: $\dfrac{f(x)-f(a)}{x-a} = \dfrac{(5x+3)-(5a+3)}{x-a} = \dfrac{5x-5a}{x-a} = \dfrac{5(x-a)}{x-a} = 5$

b. Evaluating the difference quotient: $\dfrac{f(x+h)-f(x)}{h} = \dfrac{5(x+h)+3-(5x+3)}{h} = \dfrac{5x+5h+3-5x-3}{h} = \dfrac{5h}{h} = 5$

67. a. Evaluating the difference quotient: $\dfrac{f(x)-f(a)}{x-a} = \dfrac{x^2-a^2}{x-a} = \dfrac{(x+a)(x-a)}{x-a} = x+a$

b. Evaluating the difference quotient:

$$\frac{f(x+h)-f(x)}{h} = \frac{(x+h)^2-x^2}{h} = \frac{x^2+2xh+h^2-x^2}{h} = \frac{2xh+h^2}{h} = \frac{h(2x+h)}{h} = 2x+h$$

69. a. Evaluating the difference quotient: $\dfrac{f(x)-f(a)}{x-a} = \dfrac{\left(x^2+1\right)-\left(a^2+1\right)}{x-a} = \dfrac{x^2-a^2}{x-a} = \dfrac{(x+a)(x-a)}{x-a} = x+a$

b. Evaluating the difference quotient:

$$\frac{f(x+h)-f(x)}{h} = \frac{(x+h)^2+1-\left(x^2+1\right)}{h} = \frac{x^2+2xh+h^2+1-x^2-1}{h} = \frac{2xh+h^2}{h} = \frac{h(2x+h)}{h} = 2x+h$$

71. a. Evaluating the difference quotient:

$$\begin{aligned}
\frac{f(x)-f(a)}{x-a} &= \frac{\left(x^2-3x+4\right)-\left(a^2-3a+4\right)}{x-a} \\
&= \frac{x^2-a^2-3x+3a}{x-a} \\
&= \frac{(x+a)(x-a)-3(x-a)}{x-a} \\
&= \frac{(x-a)(x+a-3)}{x-a} \\
&= x+a-3
\end{aligned}$$

b. Evaluating the difference quotient:

$$\frac{f(x+h)-f(x)}{h} = \frac{(x+h)^2 - 3(x+h)+4-\left(x^2-3x+4\right)}{h}$$

$$= \frac{x^2+2xh+h^2-3x-3h+4-x^2+3x-4}{h}$$

$$= \frac{2xh+h^2-3h}{h}$$

$$= \frac{h(2x+h-3)}{h}$$

$$= 2x+h-3$$

73. **a.** Evaluating the difference quotient:

$$\frac{f(x)-f(a)}{x-a} = \frac{\left(2x^2+3x-4\right)-\left(2a^2+3a-4\right)}{x-a}$$

$$= \frac{2x^2-2a^2+3x-3a}{x-a}$$

$$= \frac{2(x+a)(x-a)+3(x-a)}{x-a}$$

$$= \frac{(x-a)(2x+2a+3)}{x-a}$$

$$= 2x+2a+3$$

b. Evaluating the difference quotient:

$$\frac{f(x+h)-f(x)}{h} = \frac{2(x+h)^2+3(x+h)-4-\left(2x^2+3x-4\right)}{h}$$

$$= \frac{2x^2+4xh+2h^2+3x+3h-4-2x^2-3x+4}{h}$$

$$= \frac{4xh+2h^2+3h}{h}$$

$$= \frac{h(4x+2h+3)}{h}$$

$$= 4x+2h+3$$

75. Completing the table:

Weeks x	Weight (lb) $W(x)$
0	200
1	194
4	184
12	173
24	168

77. **a.** The total cost function is: $C(n)=1,200+540n$

b. The average yearly cost function is: $\bar{C}(n)=\dfrac{1,200+540n}{n}$

c. Evaluating when $n = 10$: $\bar{C}(10)=\dfrac{1,200+540(10)}{10}=\dfrac{6,600}{10}=\$660$ per year

d. Evaluating when $n = 15$: $\bar{C}(15)=\dfrac{1,200+540(15)}{15}=\dfrac{9,300}{15}=\$620$ per year

e. The average yearly cost is decreasing as n increases.

79. Multiplying: $\dfrac{6}{7} \cdot \dfrac{14}{18} = \dfrac{6}{7} \cdot \dfrac{2 \cdot 7}{3 \cdot 6} = \dfrac{2}{3}$

81. Multiplying: $5y^2 \cdot 4x^2 = 20x^2y^2$

83. Factoring: $x^2 - 4 = (x+2)(x-2)$

85. Factoring: $x^3 - x^2y = x^2(x-y)$

87. **a.** From the graph: $f(2) = 2$

    b. From the graph: $f(-1) = -4$

    c. From the graph: $f(0)$ is undefined

    d. From the graph: $g(3) = 2$

    e. From the graph: $g(6) = 1$

    f. From the graph: $g(-1) = -6$

    g. From the graph: $f(g(6)) = f(1) = 4$

5.2 Multiplication and Division of Rational Expressions

1. Performing the operations: $\dfrac{2}{9} \cdot \dfrac{3}{4} = \dfrac{2}{3 \cdot 3} \cdot \dfrac{3}{2 \cdot 2} = \dfrac{1}{2 \cdot 3} = \dfrac{1}{6}$

3. Performing the operations: $\dfrac{3}{4} \div \dfrac{1}{3} = \dfrac{3}{4} \cdot \dfrac{3}{1} = \dfrac{9}{4}$

5. Performing the operations: $\dfrac{3}{7} \cdot \dfrac{14}{24} \div \dfrac{1}{2} = \dfrac{1}{4} \div \dfrac{1}{2} = \dfrac{1}{4} \cdot \dfrac{2}{1} = \dfrac{2}{4} = \dfrac{1}{2}$

7. Performing the operations: $\dfrac{10x^2}{5y^2} \cdot \dfrac{15y^3}{2x^4} = \dfrac{150x^2y^3}{10x^4y^2} = \dfrac{15y}{x^2}$

9. Performing the operations: $\dfrac{11a^2b}{5ab^2} \div \dfrac{22a^3b^2}{10ab^4} = \dfrac{11a^2b}{5ab^2} \cdot \dfrac{10ab^4}{22a^3b^2} = \dfrac{110a^3b^5}{110a^4b^4} = \dfrac{b}{a}$

11. Performing the operations: $\dfrac{6x^2}{5y^3} \cdot \dfrac{11z^2}{2x^2} \div \dfrac{33z^5}{10y^8} = \dfrac{33z^2}{5y^3} \cdot \dfrac{10y^8}{33z^5} = \dfrac{2y^8z^2}{y^3z^5} = \dfrac{2y^5}{z^3}$

13. Performing the operations: $\dfrac{x^2-9}{x^2-4} \cdot \dfrac{x-2}{x-3} = \dfrac{(x+3)(x-3)}{(x+2)(x-2)} \cdot \dfrac{x-2}{x-3} = \dfrac{x+3}{x+2}$

15. Performing the operations: $\dfrac{y^2-1}{y+2} \cdot \dfrac{y^2+5y+6}{y^2+2y-3} = \dfrac{(y+1)(y-1)}{y+2} \cdot \dfrac{(y+2)(y+3)}{(y+3)(y-1)} = y+1$

17. Performing the operations: $\dfrac{3x-12}{x^2-4} \cdot \dfrac{x^2+6x+8}{x-4} = \dfrac{3(x-4)}{(x+2)(x-2)} \cdot \dfrac{(x+4)(x+2)}{x-4} = \dfrac{3(x+4)}{x-2}$

19. Performing the operations: $\dfrac{xy}{xy+1} \div \dfrac{x}{y} = \dfrac{xy}{xy+1} \cdot \dfrac{y}{x} = \dfrac{y^2}{xy+1}$

21. Performing the operations: $\dfrac{1}{x^2-9} \div \dfrac{1}{x^2+9} = \dfrac{1}{x^2-9} \cdot \dfrac{x^2+9}{1} = \dfrac{x^2+9}{x^2-9}$

23. Performing the operations: $\dfrac{5x-10}{6x-9} \div \dfrac{6-3x}{8x-12} = \dfrac{5x-10}{6x-9} \cdot \dfrac{8x-12}{6-3x} = \dfrac{5(x-2)}{3(2x-3)} \cdot \dfrac{4(2x-3)}{-3(x-2)} = -\dfrac{20}{9}$

25. Performing the operations: $\dfrac{5x+2y}{25x^2-5xy-6y^2} \cdot \dfrac{20x^2-7xy-3y^2}{4x+y} = \dfrac{5x+2y}{(5x+2y)(5x-3y)} \cdot \dfrac{(5x-3y)(4x+y)}{4x+y} = 1$

27. Performing the operations:

$\dfrac{a^2-5a+6}{a^2-2a-3} \div \dfrac{a-5}{a^2+3a+2} = \dfrac{a^2-5a+6}{a^2-2a-3} \cdot \dfrac{a^2+3a+2}{a-5} = \dfrac{(a-3)(a-2)}{(a-3)(a+1)} \cdot \dfrac{(a+2)(a+1)}{a-5} = \dfrac{(a-2)(a+2)}{a-5}$

29. Performing the operations:

$$\frac{4t^2-1}{6t^2+t-2} \div \frac{8t^3+1}{27t^3+8} = \frac{4t^2-1}{6t^2+t-2} \cdot \frac{27t^3+8}{8t^3+1} = \frac{(2t+1)(2t-1)}{(3t+2)(2t-1)} \cdot \frac{(3t+2)(9t^2-6t+4)}{(2t+1)(4t^2-2t+1)} = \frac{9t^2-6t+4}{4t^2-2t+1}$$

31. Performing the operations:

$$\frac{2x^2-5x-12}{4x^2+8x+3} \div \frac{x^2-16}{2x^2+7x+3} = \frac{2x^2-5x-12}{4x^2+8x+3} \cdot \frac{2x^2+7x+3}{x^2-16} = \frac{(2x+3)(x-4)}{(2x+1)(2x+3)} \cdot \frac{(2x+1)(x+3)}{(x+4)(x-4)} = \frac{x+3}{x+4}$$

33. Performing the operations:

$$\frac{2a^2-21ab-36b^2}{a^2-11ab-12b^2} \div \frac{10a+15b}{a^2-b^2} = \frac{2a^2-21ab-36b^2}{a^2-11ab-12b^2} \cdot \frac{a^2-b^2}{10a+15b} = \frac{(2a+3b)(a-12b)}{(a-12b)(a+b)} \cdot \frac{(a+b)(a-b)}{5(2a+3b)} = \frac{a-b}{5}$$

35. Performing the operations: $\dfrac{6c^2-c-15}{9c^2-25} \cdot \dfrac{15c^2+22c-5}{6c^2+5c-6} = \dfrac{(3c-5)(2c+3)}{(3c+5)(3c-5)} \cdot \dfrac{(3c+5)(5c-1)}{(3c-2)(2c+3)} = \dfrac{5c-1}{3c-2}$

37. Performing the operations: $\dfrac{6x^2-11xy+3y^2}{2x^2-7xy+6y^2} \cdot \dfrac{3x^2+8xy+4y^2}{2y^2-3xy-9x^2} = \dfrac{(3x-y)(2x-3y)}{(2x-3y)(x-2y)} \cdot \dfrac{(3x+2y)(x+2y)}{(2y+3x)(y-3x)} = -\dfrac{x+2y}{x-2y}$

39. Performing the operations:

$$\frac{360x^3-490x}{36x^2+84x+49} \cdot \frac{30x^2+83x+56}{150x^3+65x^2-280x} = \frac{10x\left(36x^2-49\right)}{(6x+7)^2} \cdot \frac{(6x+7)(5x+8)}{5x\left(30x^2+13x-56\right)}$$

$$= \frac{10x(6x+7)(6x-7)}{(6x+7)^2} \cdot \frac{(6x+7)(5x+8)}{5x(6x-7)(5x+8)}$$

$$= 2$$

41. Performing the operations:

$$\frac{x^5-x^2}{5x^2-5x} \cdot \frac{10x^4-10x^2}{2x^4+2x^3+2x^2} = \frac{x^2\left(x^3-1\right)}{5x(x-1)} \cdot \frac{10x^2\left(x^2-1\right)}{2x^2\left(x^2+x+1\right)}$$

$$= \frac{x^2(x-1)\left(x^2+x+1\right)}{5x(x-1)} \cdot \frac{10x^2(x+1)(x-1)}{2x^2\left(x^2+x+1\right)}$$

$$= x(x+1)(x-1)$$

43. Performing the operations:

$$\frac{a^2-16b^2}{a^2-8ab+16b^2} \cdot \frac{a^2-9ab+20b^2}{a^2-7ab+12b^2} \div \frac{a^2-25b^2}{a^2-6ab+9b^2}$$

$$= \frac{a^2-16b^2}{a^2-8ab+16b^2} \cdot \frac{a^2-9ab+20b^2}{a^2-7ab+12b^2} \cdot \frac{a^2-6ab+9b^2}{a^2-25b^2}$$

$$= \frac{(a+4b)(a-4b)}{(a-4b)^2} \cdot \frac{(a-5b)(a-4b)}{(a-3b)(a-4b)} \cdot \frac{(a-3b)^2}{(a+5b)(a-5b)}$$

$$= \frac{(a+4b)(a-3b)}{(a-4b)(a+5b)}$$

45. Performing the operations:

$$\frac{2y^2-7y-15}{42y^2-29y-5} \cdot \frac{12y^2-16y+5}{7y^2-36y+5} \div \frac{4y^2-9}{49y^2-1} = \frac{2y^2-7y-15}{42y^2-29y-5} \cdot \frac{12y^2-16y+5}{7y^2-36y+5} \cdot \frac{49y^2-1}{4y^2-9}$$

$$= \frac{(2y+3)(y-5)}{(6y-5)(7y+1)} \cdot \frac{(6y-5)(2y-1)}{(7y-1)(y-5)} \cdot \frac{(7y+1)(7y-1)}{(2y+3)(2y-3)}$$

$$= \frac{2y-1}{2y-3}$$

47. Performing the operations:

$$\frac{xy-2x+3y-6}{xy+2x-4y-8}\cdot\frac{xy+x-4y-4}{xy-x+3y-3}=\frac{x(y-2)+3(y-2)}{x(y+2)-4(y+2)}\cdot\frac{x(y+1)-4(y+1)}{x(y-1)+3(y-1)}$$

$$=\frac{(y-2)(x+3)}{(y+2)(x-4)}\cdot\frac{(y+1)(x-4)}{(y-1)(x+3)}$$

$$=\frac{(y-2)(y+1)}{(y+2)(y-1)}$$

49. Performing the operations:

$$\frac{xy^2-y^2+4xy-4y}{xy-3y+4x-12}\div\frac{xy^3+2xy^2+y^3+2y^2}{xy^2-3y^2+2xy-6y}=\frac{xy^2-y^2+4xy-4y}{xy-3y+4x-12}\cdot\frac{xy^2-3y^2+2xy-6y}{xy^3+2xy^2+y^3+2y^2}$$

$$=\frac{y^2(x-1)+4y(x-1)}{y(x-3)+4(x-3)}\cdot\frac{y^2(x-3)+2y(x-3)}{xy^2(y+2)+y^2(y+2)}$$

$$=\frac{y(x-1)(y+4)}{(x-3)(y+4)}\cdot\frac{y(x-3)(y+2)}{y^2(y+2)(x+1)}$$

$$=\frac{x-1}{x+1}$$

51. Performing the operations:

$$\frac{2x^3+10x^2-8x-40}{x^3+4x^2-9x-36}\cdot\frac{x^2+x-12}{2x^2+14x+20}=\frac{2x^2(x+5)-8(x+5)}{x^2(x+4)-9(x+4)}\cdot\frac{(x+4)(x-3)}{2(x^2+7x+10)}$$

$$=\frac{2(x+5)(x^2-4)}{(x+4)(x^2-9)}\cdot\frac{(x+4)(x-3)}{2(x+5)(x+2)}$$

$$=\frac{2(x+5)(x+2)(x-2)}{(x+4)(x+3)(x-3)}\cdot\frac{(x+4)(x-3)}{2(x+5)(x+2)}$$

$$=\frac{x-2}{x+3}$$

53. Performing the operations: $\dfrac{w^3-w^2x}{wy-w}\div\left(\dfrac{w-x}{y-1}\right)^2=\dfrac{w^3-w^2x}{wy-w}\cdot\left(\dfrac{y-1}{w-x}\right)^2=\dfrac{w^2(w-x)}{w(y-1)}\cdot\dfrac{(y-1)^2}{(w-x)^2}=\dfrac{w(y-1)}{w-x}$

55. Performing the operations:

$$\frac{mx+my+2x+2y}{6x^2-5xy-4y^2}\div\frac{2mx-4x+my-2y}{3mx-6x-4my+8y}=\frac{mx+my+2x+2y}{6x^2-5xy-4y^2}\cdot\frac{3mx-6x-4my+8y}{2mx-4x+my-2y}$$

$$=\frac{m(x+y)+2(x+y)}{(3x-4y)(2x+y)}\cdot\frac{3x(m-2)-4y(m-2)}{2x(m-2)+y(m-2)}$$

$$=\frac{(x+y)(m+2)}{(3x-4y)(2x+y)}\cdot\frac{(m-2)(3x-4y)}{(m-2)(2x+y)}$$

$$=\frac{(x+y)(m+2)}{(2x+y)^2}$$

57. Performing the operations: $\dfrac{1-4d^2}{(d-c)^2}\cdot\dfrac{d^2-c^2}{1+2d}=\dfrac{(1+2d)(1-2d)}{(d-c)^2}\cdot\dfrac{(d+c)(d-c)}{1+2d}=\dfrac{(1-2d)(d+c)}{d-c}$

59. Performing the operations:

$$\frac{r^2-s^2}{r^2+rs+s^2}\cdot\frac{r^3-s^3}{r^2+s^2}\div\frac{r^4-s^4}{r^2-s^2}=\frac{r^2-s^2}{r^2+rs+s^2}\cdot\frac{r^3-s^3}{r^2+s^2}\cdot\frac{r^2-s^2}{r^4-s^4}$$

$$=\frac{(r+s)(r-s)}{r^2+rs+s^2}\cdot\frac{(r-s)(r^2+rs+s^2)}{r^2+s^2}\cdot\frac{(r-s)(r+s)}{(r-s)(r+s)(r^2+s^2)}$$

$$=\frac{(r+s)(r-s)^2}{(r^2+s^2)^2}$$

61. Finding the product: $(3x-6)\cdot\dfrac{x}{x-2}=\dfrac{3(x-2)}{1}\cdot\dfrac{x}{x-2}=3x$

63. Finding the product: $(x^2-25)\cdot\dfrac{2}{x-5}=\dfrac{(x+5)(x-5)}{1}\cdot\dfrac{2}{x-5}=2(x+5)$

65. Finding the product: $(x^2-3x+2)\cdot\dfrac{3}{3x-3}=\dfrac{(x-2)(x-1)}{1}\cdot\dfrac{3}{3(x-1)}=x-2$

67. Finding the product: $(y-3)(y-4)(y+3)\cdot\dfrac{-1}{y^2-9}=\dfrac{(y-3)(y-4)(y+3)}{1}\cdot\dfrac{-1}{(y+3)(y-3)}=-(y-4)=4-y$

69. Finding the product: $a(a+5)(a-5)\cdot\dfrac{a+1}{a^2+5a}=\dfrac{a(a+5)(a-5)}{1}\cdot\dfrac{a+1}{a(a+5)}=(a-5)(a+1)$

71. **a.** Simplifying: $\dfrac{16-1}{64-1}=\dfrac{15}{63}=\dfrac{5}{21}$

b. Reducing: $\dfrac{25x^2-9}{125x^3-27}=\dfrac{(5x-3)(5x+3)}{(5x-3)(25x^2+15x+9)}=\dfrac{5x+3}{25x^2+15x+9}$

c. Multiplying: $\dfrac{25x^2-9}{125x^3-27}\cdot\dfrac{5x-3}{5x+3}=\dfrac{(5x-3)(5x+3)}{(5x-3)(25x^2+15x+9)}\cdot\dfrac{5x-3}{5x+3}=\dfrac{5x-3}{25x^2+15x+9}$

d. Dividing: $\dfrac{25x^2-9}{125x^3-27}\div\dfrac{5x-3}{25x^2+15x+9}=\dfrac{(5x-3)(5x+3)}{(5x-3)(25x^2+15x+9)}\cdot\dfrac{25x^2+15x+9}{5x-3}=\dfrac{5x+3}{5x-3}$

73. **a.** Multiplying: $f(x)\cdot g(x)=\dfrac{x^2-x-6}{x-1}\cdot\dfrac{x+2}{x^2-4x+3}=\dfrac{(x-3)(x+2)}{x-1}\cdot\dfrac{x+2}{(x-3)(x-1)}=\dfrac{(x+2)^2}{(x-1)^2}$

b. Dividing: $f(x)\div g(x)=\dfrac{x^2-x-6}{x-1}\div\dfrac{x+2}{x^2-4x+3}=\dfrac{(x-3)(x+2)}{x-1}\cdot\dfrac{(x-3)(x-1)}{x+2}=(x-3)^2$

c. Dividing: $g(x)\div f(x)=\dfrac{x+2}{x^2-4x+3}\div\dfrac{x^2-x-6}{x-1}=\dfrac{x+2}{(x-3)(x-1)}\cdot\dfrac{x-1}{(x-3)(x+2)}=\dfrac{1}{(x-3)^2}$

Number of Copies x	Price per Copy ($) $p(x)$
1	20.33
10	9.33
20	6.40
50	4.00
100	3.05

75. **a.** Completing the table:

b. Finding the revenue: $R = 50 \cdot \dfrac{2(50+60)}{50+5} = 50 \cdot \dfrac{220}{55} = \$200$

c. Finding the revenue: $R = 100 \cdot \dfrac{2(100+60)}{100+5} = 100 \cdot \dfrac{320}{105} \approx \$305$

d. The revenue equation is given by: $R(x) = \dfrac{2x(x+60)}{x+5}$

77. Finding the diameters:

Venus: $0.9(7{,}900) = 7{,}110$ miles $\qquad$ Saturn: $9.5(7{,}900) = 75{,}050$ miles

79. Combining: $\dfrac{4}{9} + \dfrac{2}{9} = \dfrac{6}{9} = \dfrac{2 \cdot 3}{3 \cdot 3} = \dfrac{2}{3}$

81. Combining: $\dfrac{3}{14} + \dfrac{7}{30} = \dfrac{3}{14} \cdot \dfrac{15}{15} + \dfrac{7}{30} \cdot \dfrac{7}{7} = \dfrac{45}{210} + \dfrac{49}{210} = \dfrac{94}{210} = \dfrac{47}{105}$

83. Multiplying: $-1(7-x) = -7 + x = x - 7$ $\qquad$ **85.** Multiplying: $-2(2x-5) = -4x + 10$

87. Factoring: $x^2 - 1 = (x+1)(x-1)$ $\qquad$ **89.** Factoring: $2x + 10 = 2(x+5)$

91. Factoring: $a^3 - b^3 = (a-b)\left(a^2 + ab + b^2\right)$ $\qquad$ **93.** Factoring: $4x^2 - 9 = (2x+3)(2x-3)$

95. Performing the operations:

$$\frac{x^6 + y^6}{x^4 + 4x^2y^2 + 3y^4} \div \frac{x^4 + 3x^2y^2 + 2y^4}{x^4 + 5x^2y^2 + 6y^4} = \frac{x^6 + y^6}{x^4 + 4x^2y^2 + 3y^4} \cdot \frac{x^4 + 5x^2y^2 + 6y^4}{x^4 + 3x^2y^2 + 2y^4}$$

$$= \frac{\left(x^2 + y^2\right)\left(x^4 - x^2y^2 + y^4\right)}{\left(x^2 + 3y^2\right)\left(x^2 + y^2\right)} \cdot \frac{\left(x^2 + 3y^2\right)\left(x^2 + 2y^2\right)}{\left(x^2 + 2y^2\right)\left(x^2 + y^2\right)}$$

$$= \frac{x^4 - x^2y^2 + y^4}{x^2 + y^2}$$

97. Performing the operations:

$$\frac{a^2(2a+b) + 6a(2a+b) + 5(2a+b)}{3a^2(2a+b) - 2a(2a+b) + (2a+b)} \div \frac{a+1}{a-1} = \frac{a^2(2a+b) + 6a(2a+b) + 5(2a+b)}{3a^2(2a+b) - 2a(2a+b) + (2a+b)} \cdot \frac{a-1}{a+1}$$

$$= \frac{(2a+b)\left(a^2 + 6a + 5\right)}{(2a+b)\left(3a^2 - 2a + 1\right)} \cdot \frac{a-1}{a+1}$$

$$= \frac{(2a+b)(a+5)(a+1)}{(2a+b)\left(3a^2 - 2a + 1\right)} \cdot \frac{a-1}{a+1}$$

$$= \frac{(a+5)(a-1)}{3a^2 - 2a + 1}$$

99. Performing the operations:

$$\frac{p^3 + q^3}{q - p} \div \frac{(p+q)^2}{p^2 - q^2} = \frac{p^3 + q^3}{q - p} \cdot \frac{p^2 - q^2}{(p+q)^2} = \frac{(p+q)\left(p^2 - pq + q^2\right)}{-1(p-q)} \cdot \frac{(p+q)(p-q)}{(p+q)^2} = -\left(p^2 - pq + q^2\right)$$

5.3 Addition and Subtraction of Rational Expressions

1. Combining the rational expressions: $\dfrac{x}{x+3} + \dfrac{3}{x+3} = \dfrac{x+3}{x+3} = 1$

3. Combining the rational expressions: $\dfrac{4}{y-4} - \dfrac{y}{y-4} = \dfrac{4-y}{y-4} = \dfrac{-1(y-4)}{y-4} = -1$

5. Combining the rational expressions: $\dfrac{x}{x^2-y^2} - \dfrac{y}{x^2-y^2} = \dfrac{x-y}{x^2-y^2} = \dfrac{x-y}{(x+y)(x-y)} = \dfrac{1}{x+y}$

7. Combining the rational expressions: $\dfrac{2x-3}{x-2} - \dfrac{x-1}{x-2} = \dfrac{2x-3-x+1}{x-2} = \dfrac{x-2}{x-2} = 1$

9. Combining the rational expressions: $\dfrac{1}{a} + \dfrac{2}{a^2} - \dfrac{3}{a^3} = \dfrac{1}{a} \cdot \dfrac{a^2}{a^2} + \dfrac{2}{a^2} \cdot \dfrac{a}{a} - \dfrac{3}{a^3} = \dfrac{a^2+2a-3}{a^3}$

11. Combining the rational expressions: $\dfrac{7x-2}{2x+1} - \dfrac{5x-3}{2x+1} = \dfrac{7x-2-5x+3}{2x+1} = \dfrac{2x+1}{2x+1} = 1$

13. Combining the fractions: $\dfrac{3}{4} + \dfrac{1}{2} = \dfrac{3}{4} + \dfrac{1}{2} \cdot \dfrac{2}{2} = \dfrac{3}{4} + \dfrac{2}{4} = \dfrac{5}{4}$

15. Combining the fractions: $\dfrac{2}{5} - \dfrac{1}{15} = \dfrac{2}{5} \cdot \dfrac{3}{3} - \dfrac{1}{15} = \dfrac{6}{15} - \dfrac{1}{15} = \dfrac{5}{15} = \dfrac{1}{3}$

17. Combining the fractions: $\dfrac{5}{6} + \dfrac{7}{8} = \dfrac{5}{6} \cdot \dfrac{4}{4} + \dfrac{7}{8} \cdot \dfrac{3}{3} = \dfrac{20}{24} + \dfrac{21}{24} = \dfrac{41}{24}$

19. Combining the fractions: $\dfrac{9}{48} - \dfrac{3}{54} = \dfrac{9}{48} \cdot \dfrac{9}{9} - \dfrac{3}{54} \cdot \dfrac{8}{8} = \dfrac{81}{432} - \dfrac{24}{432} = \dfrac{57}{432} = \dfrac{19}{144}$

21. Combining the fractions: $\dfrac{3}{4} - \dfrac{1}{8} + \dfrac{2}{3} = \dfrac{3}{4} \cdot \dfrac{6}{6} - \dfrac{1}{8} \cdot \dfrac{3}{3} + \dfrac{2}{3} \cdot \dfrac{8}{8} = \dfrac{18}{24} - \dfrac{3}{24} + \dfrac{16}{24} = \dfrac{31}{24}$

23. Combining the fractions: $\dfrac{1}{3} - \dfrac{1}{2} + \dfrac{5}{6} = \dfrac{1}{3} \cdot \dfrac{2}{2} - \dfrac{1}{2} \cdot \dfrac{3}{3} + \dfrac{5}{6} = \dfrac{2}{6} - \dfrac{3}{6} + \dfrac{5}{6} = \dfrac{4}{6} = \dfrac{2}{3}$

25. **a.** Multiplying: $\dfrac{3}{8} \cdot \dfrac{1}{6} = \dfrac{3}{8} \cdot \dfrac{1}{2 \cdot 3} = \dfrac{1}{16}$

    b. Dividing: $\dfrac{3}{8} \div \dfrac{1}{6} = \dfrac{3}{8} \cdot \dfrac{6}{1} = \dfrac{3}{2 \cdot 4} \cdot \dfrac{2 \cdot 3}{1} = \dfrac{9}{4}$

    c. Adding: $\dfrac{3}{8} + \dfrac{1}{6} = \dfrac{3}{8} \cdot \dfrac{3}{3} + \dfrac{1}{6} \cdot \dfrac{4}{4} = \dfrac{9}{24} + \dfrac{4}{24} = \dfrac{13}{24}$

    d. Multiplying: $\dfrac{x+3}{x-3} \cdot \dfrac{5x+15}{x^2-9} = \dfrac{x+3}{x-3} \cdot \dfrac{5(x+3)}{(x+3)(x-3)} = \dfrac{5(x+3)}{(x-3)^2}$

    e. Dividing: $\dfrac{x+3}{x-3} \div \dfrac{5x+15}{x^2-9} = \dfrac{x+3}{x-3} \cdot \dfrac{(x+3)(x-3)}{5(x+3)} = \dfrac{x+3}{5}$

f. Subtracting:

$$\frac{x+3}{x-3}-\frac{5x+15}{x^2-9}=\frac{x+3}{x-3}\cdot\frac{x+3}{x+3}-\frac{5x+15}{(x+3)(x-3)}$$

$$=\frac{x^2+6x+9}{(x+3)(x-3)}-\frac{5x+15}{(x+3)(x-3)}$$

$$=\frac{x^2+x-6}{(x+3)(x-3)}$$

$$=\frac{(x+3)(x-2)}{(x+3)(x-3)}$$

$$=\frac{x-2}{x-3}$$

27. Subtracting the functions:

$$f(x)-g(x)=\frac{3x+1}{2x-6}-\frac{x+2}{x-3}=\frac{3x+1}{2(x-3)}-\frac{x+2}{x-3}\cdot\frac{2}{2}=\frac{3x+1}{2(x-3)}-\frac{2x+4}{2(x-3)}=\frac{3x+1-2x-4}{2(x-3)}=\frac{x-3}{2(x-3)}=\frac{1}{2}$$

29. Subtracting the functions:

$$f(x)-g(x)=\frac{6x+5}{5x-25}-\frac{x+2}{x-5}=\frac{6x+5}{5(x-5)}-\frac{x+2}{x-5}\cdot\frac{5}{5}=\frac{6x+5}{5(x-5)}-\frac{5x+10}{5(x-5)}=\frac{6x+5-5x-10}{5(x-5)}=\frac{x-5}{5(x-5)}=\frac{1}{5}$$

31. Combining the rational expressions:

$$\frac{x+1}{2x-2}-\frac{2}{x^2-1}=\frac{x+1}{2(x-1)}\cdot\frac{x+1}{x+1}-\frac{2}{(x+1)(x-1)}\cdot\frac{2}{2}$$

$$=\frac{x^2+2x+1}{2(x+1)(x-1)}-\frac{4}{2(x+1)(x-1)}$$

$$=\frac{x^2+2x-3}{2(x+1)(x-1)}$$

$$=\frac{(x+3)(x-1)}{2(x+1)(x-1)}$$

$$=\frac{x+3}{2(x+1)}$$

33. Combining the rational expressions:

$$\frac{1}{a-b}-\frac{3ab}{a^3-b^3}=\frac{1}{a-b}\cdot\frac{a^2+ab+b^2}{a^2+ab+b^2}-\frac{3ab}{a^3-b^3}$$

$$=\frac{a^2+ab+b^2}{a^3-b^3}-\frac{3ab}{a^3-b^3}$$

$$=\frac{a^2-2ab+b^2}{a^3-b^3}$$

$$=\frac{(a-b)^2}{(a-b)\left(a^2+ab+b^2\right)}$$

$$=\frac{a-b}{a^2+ab+b^2}$$

35. Combining the rational expressions:

$$\frac{x-2}{2x+3} - \frac{2x-11}{3-4x-4x^2} = \frac{x-2}{2x+3} + \frac{2x-11}{4x^2+4x-3}$$

$$= \frac{x-2}{2x+3} \cdot \frac{2x-1}{2x-1} + \frac{2x-11}{(2x+3)(2x-1)}$$

$$= \frac{2x^2-5x+2}{(2x+3)(2x-1)} + \frac{2x-11}{(2x+3)(2x-1)}$$

$$= \frac{2x^2-3x-9}{(2x+3)(2x-1)}$$

$$= \frac{(2x+3)(x-3)}{(2x+3)(2x-1)}$$

$$= \frac{x-3}{2x-1}$$

37. Combining the rational expressions:

$$\frac{1}{2y-3} - \frac{18y}{8y^3-27} = \frac{1}{2y-3} \cdot \frac{4y^2+6y+9}{4y^2+6y+9} - \frac{18y}{8y^3-27}$$

$$= \frac{4y^2+6y+9}{8y^3-27} - \frac{18y}{8y^3-27}$$

$$= \frac{4y^2-12y+9}{8y^3-27}$$

$$= \frac{(2y-3)^2}{(2y-3)(4y^2+6y+9)}$$

$$= \frac{2y-3}{4y^2+6y+9}$$

39. Combining the rational expressions:

$$\frac{x}{x^2-5x+6} - \frac{3}{3-x} = \frac{x}{(x-2)(x-3)} + \frac{3}{x-3} \cdot \frac{x-2}{x-2}$$

$$= \frac{x}{(x-2)(x-3)} + \frac{3x-6}{(x-2)(x-3)}$$

$$= \frac{4x-6}{(x-2)(x-3)}$$

$$= \frac{2(2x-3)}{(x-3)(x-2)}$$

41. Combining the rational expressions:

$$\frac{2}{4t-5} + \frac{9}{8t^2-38t+35} = \frac{2}{4t-5} \cdot \frac{2t-7}{2t-7} + \frac{9}{(4t-5)(2t-7)}$$

$$= \frac{4t-14}{(4t-5)(2t-7)} + \frac{9}{(4t-5)(2t-7)}$$

$$= \frac{4t-5}{(4t-5)(2t-7)}$$

$$= \frac{1}{2t-7}$$

43. Combining the rational expressions:

$$\frac{1}{a^2-5a+6}+\frac{3}{a^2-a-2}=\frac{1}{(a-2)(a-3)}\cdot\frac{a+1}{a+1}+\frac{3}{(a-2)(a+1)}\cdot\frac{a-3}{a-3}$$

$$=\frac{a+1}{(a-2)(a-3)(a+1)}+\frac{3a-9}{(a-2)(a-3)(a+1)}$$

$$=\frac{4a-8}{(a-2)(a-3)(a+1)}$$

$$=\frac{4(a-2)}{(a-2)(a-3)(a+1)}$$

$$=\frac{4}{(a-3)(a+1)}$$

45. Combining the rational expressions:

$$\frac{1}{8x^3-1}-\frac{1}{4x^2-1}=\frac{1}{(2x-1)(4x^2+2x+1)}\cdot\frac{2x+1}{2x+1}-\frac{1}{(2x+1)(2x-1)}\cdot\frac{4x^2+2x+1}{4x^2+2x+1}$$

$$=\frac{2x+1}{(2x+1)(2x-1)(4x^2+2x+1)}-\frac{4x^2+2x+1}{(2x+1)(2x-1)(4x^2+2x+1)}$$

$$=\frac{2x+1-4x^2-2x-1}{(2x+1)(2x-1)(4x^2+2x+1)}$$

$$=\frac{-4x^2}{(2x+1)(2x-1)(4x^2+2x+1)}$$

47. Combining the rational expressions:

$$\frac{4}{4x^2-9}-\frac{6}{8x^2-6x-9}=\frac{4}{(2x+3)(2x-3)}\cdot\frac{4x+3}{4x+3}-\frac{6}{(2x-3)(4x+3)}\cdot\frac{2x+3}{2x+3}$$

$$=\frac{16x+12}{(2x+3)(2x-3)(4x+3)}-\frac{12x+18}{(2x+3)(2x-3)(4x+3)}$$

$$=\frac{16x+12-12x-18}{(2x+3)(2x-3)(4x+3)}$$

$$=\frac{4x-6}{(2x+3)(2x-3)(4x+3)}$$

$$=\frac{2(2x-3)}{(2x+3)(2x-3)(4x+3)}$$

$$=\frac{2}{(2x+3)(4x+3)}$$

49. Combining the rational expressions:

$$\frac{4a}{a^2+6a+5} - \frac{3a}{a^2+5a+4} = \frac{4a}{(a+5)(a+1)} \cdot \frac{a+4}{a+4} - \frac{3a}{(a+4)(a+1)} \cdot \frac{a+5}{a+5}$$

$$= \frac{4a^2+16a}{(a+4)(a+5)(a+1)} - \frac{3a^2+15a}{(a+4)(a+5)(a+1)}$$

$$= \frac{4a^2+16a-3a^2-15a}{(a+4)(a+5)(a+1)}$$

$$= \frac{a^2+a}{(a+4)(a+5)(a+1)}$$

$$= \frac{a(a+1)}{(a+4)(a+5)(a+1)}$$

$$= \frac{a}{(a+4)(a+5)}$$

51. Combining the rational expressions:

$$\frac{2x-1}{x^2+x-6} - \frac{x+2}{x^2+5x+6} = \frac{2x-1}{(x+3)(x-2)} \cdot \frac{x+2}{x+2} - \frac{x+2}{(x+3)(x+2)} \cdot \frac{x-2}{x-2}$$

$$= \frac{2x^2+3x-2}{(x+3)(x+2)(x-2)} - \frac{x^2-4}{(x+3)(x+2)(x-2)}$$

$$= \frac{2x^2+3x-2-x^2+4}{(x+3)(x+2)(x-2)}$$

$$= \frac{x^2+3x+2}{(x+3)(x+2)(x-2)}$$

$$= \frac{(x+2)(x+1)}{(x+3)(x+2)(x-2)}$$

$$= \frac{x+1}{(x-2)(x+3)}$$

53. Combining the rational expressions:

$$\frac{2x-8}{3x^2+8x+4} + \frac{x+3}{3x^2+5x+2} = \frac{2x-8}{(3x+2)(x+2)} + \frac{x+3}{(3x+2)(x+1)}$$

$$= \frac{2x-8}{(3x+2)(x+2)} \cdot \frac{x+1}{x+1} + \frac{x+3}{(3x+2)(x+1)} \cdot \frac{x+2}{x+2}$$

$$= \frac{2x^2-6x-8}{(3x+2)(x+2)(x+1)} + \frac{x^2+5x+6}{(3x+2)(x+2)(x+1)}$$

$$= \frac{3x^2-x-2}{(3x+2)(x+2)(x+1)}$$

$$= \frac{(3x+2)(x-1)}{(3x+2)(x+2)(x+1)}$$

$$= \frac{x-1}{(x+1)(x+2)}$$

55. Combining the rational expressions:

$$\frac{2}{x^2+5x+6} - \frac{4}{x^2+4x+3} + \frac{3}{x^2+3x+2} = \frac{2}{(x+3)(x+2)} - \frac{4}{(x+3)(x+1)} + \frac{3}{(x+2)(x+1)}$$

$$= \frac{2}{(x+3)(x+2)} \cdot \frac{x+1}{x+1} - \frac{4}{(x+3)(x+1)} \cdot \frac{x+2}{x+2} + \frac{3}{(x+2)(x+1)} \cdot \frac{x+3}{x+3}$$

$$= \frac{2x+2}{(x+3)(x+2)(x+1)} - \frac{4x+8}{(x+3)(x+2)(x+1)} + \frac{3x+9}{(x+3)(x+2)(x+1)}$$

$$= \frac{2x+2-4x-8+3x+9}{(x+3)(x+2)(x+1)}$$

$$= \frac{x+3}{(x+3)(x+2)(x+1)}$$

$$= \frac{1}{(x+2)(x+1)}$$

57. Combining the rational expressions:

$$\frac{2x+8}{x^2+5x+6} - \frac{x+5}{x^2+4x+3} - \frac{x-1}{x^2+3x+2} = \frac{2x+8}{(x+3)(x+2)} - \frac{x+5}{(x+3)(x+1)} - \frac{x-1}{(x+2)(x+1)}$$

$$= \frac{2x+8}{(x+3)(x+2)} \cdot \frac{x+1}{x+1} - \frac{x+5}{(x+3)(x+1)} \cdot \frac{x+2}{x+2} - \frac{x-1}{(x+2)(x+1)} \cdot \frac{x+3}{x+3}$$

$$= \frac{2x^2+10x+8}{(x+3)(x+2)(x+1)} - \frac{x^2+7x+10}{(x+3)(x+2)(x+1)} - \frac{x^2+2x-3}{(x+3)(x+2)(x+1)}$$

$$= \frac{2x^2+10x+8-x^2-7x-10-x^2-2x+3}{(x+3)(x+2)(x+1)}$$

$$= \frac{x+1}{(x+3)(x+2)(x+1)}$$

$$= \frac{1}{(x+2)(x+3)}$$

59. Combining the rational expressions: $2 + \dfrac{3}{2x+1} = \dfrac{2}{1} \cdot \dfrac{2x+1}{2x+1} + \dfrac{3}{2x+1} = \dfrac{4x+2}{2x+1} + \dfrac{3}{2x+1} = \dfrac{4x+5}{2x+1}$

61. Combining the rational expressions: $5 + \dfrac{2}{4-t} = \dfrac{5}{1} \cdot \dfrac{4-t}{4-t} + \dfrac{2}{4-t} = \dfrac{20-5t}{4-t} + \dfrac{2}{4-t} = \dfrac{22-5t}{4-t}$

63. Combining the rational expressions: $x - \dfrac{4}{2x+3} = \dfrac{x}{1} \cdot \dfrac{2x+3}{2x+3} - \dfrac{4}{2x+3} = \dfrac{2x^2+3x}{2x+3} - \dfrac{4}{2x+3} = \dfrac{2x^2+3x-4}{2x+3}$

65. Combining the rational expressions:

$$\frac{x}{x+2} + \frac{1}{2x+4} - \frac{3}{x^2+2x} = \frac{x}{x+2} \cdot \frac{2x}{2x} + \frac{1}{2(x+2)} \cdot \frac{x}{x} - \frac{3}{x(x+2)} \cdot \frac{2}{2}$$

$$= \frac{2x^2}{2x(x+2)} + \frac{x}{2x(x+2)} - \frac{6}{2x(x+2)}$$

$$= \frac{2x^2+x-6}{2x(x+2)}$$

$$= \frac{(2x-3)(x+2)}{2x(x+2)}$$

$$= \frac{2x-3}{2x}$$

67. Combining the rational expressions:

$$\frac{1}{x} + \frac{x}{2x+4} - \frac{2}{x^2+2x} = \frac{1}{x} \cdot \frac{2(x+2)}{2(x+2)} + \frac{x}{2(x+2)} \cdot \frac{x}{x} - \frac{2}{x(x+2)} \cdot \frac{2}{2}$$

$$= \frac{2x+4}{2x(x+2)} + \frac{x^2}{2x(x+2)} - \frac{4}{2x(x+2)}$$

$$= \frac{x^2+2x}{2x(x+2)}$$

$$= \frac{x(x+2)}{2x(x+2)}$$

$$= \frac{1}{2}$$

69. Finding the sum:

$$f(x) + g(x) = \frac{2}{x+4} + \frac{x-1}{x^2+3x-4}$$

$$= \frac{2}{x+4} \cdot \frac{x-1}{x-1} + \frac{x-1}{(x+4)(x-1)}$$

$$= \frac{2x-2}{(x+4)(x-1)} + \frac{x-1}{(x+4)(x-1)}$$

$$= \frac{3x-3}{(x+4)(x-1)}$$

$$= \frac{3(x-1)}{(x+4)(x-1)}$$

$$= \frac{3}{x+4}$$

71. Finding the sum:

$$f(x) + g(x) = \frac{2x}{x^2-x-2} + \frac{5}{x^2+x-6}$$

$$= \frac{2x}{(x-2)(x+1)} \cdot \frac{x+3}{x+3} + \frac{5}{(x+3)(x-2)} \cdot \frac{x+1}{x+1}$$

$$= \frac{2x^2+6x}{(x-2)(x+1)(x+3)} + \frac{5x+5}{(x-2)(x+1)(x+3)}$$

$$= \frac{2x^2+11x+5}{(x-2)(x+1)(x+3)}$$

$$= \frac{(2x+1)(x+5)}{(x-2)(x+1)(x+3)}$$

73. Substituting the values: $P = \dfrac{1}{10} + \dfrac{1}{0.2} = 0.1 + 5 = 5.1 = \dfrac{51}{10}$

75. Substituting $a = 2$ and $b = 4$: $T = \dfrac{(2)(4)}{2+4} = \dfrac{8}{6} = 1\dfrac{1}{3}$ hours = 1 hour 20 minutes

77. Writing the expression and simplifying: $x + \dfrac{4}{x} = \dfrac{x^2+4}{x}$

79. Writing the expression and simplifying: $\dfrac{1}{x} + \dfrac{1}{x+1} = \dfrac{1}{x} \cdot \dfrac{x+1}{x+1} + \dfrac{1}{x+1} \cdot \dfrac{x}{x} = \dfrac{x+1}{x(x+1)} + \dfrac{x}{x(x+1)} = \dfrac{2x+1}{x(x+1)}$

81. Dividing: $\dfrac{3}{4} \div \dfrac{5}{8} = \dfrac{3}{4} \cdot \dfrac{8}{5} = \dfrac{24}{20} = \dfrac{4 \cdot 6}{4 \cdot 5} = \dfrac{6}{5}$

83. Dividing: $\dfrac{1}{15} \div \dfrac{3}{5} = \dfrac{1}{15} \cdot \dfrac{5}{3} = \dfrac{5}{45} = \dfrac{5 \cdot 1}{5 \cdot 9} = \dfrac{1}{9}$

85. Multiplying: $x\left(1+\dfrac{2}{x}\right) = x \cdot 1 + x \cdot \dfrac{2}{x} = x+2$

87. Multiplying: $3x\left(\dfrac{1}{x}-\dfrac{1}{3}\right) = 3x \cdot \dfrac{1}{x} - 3x \cdot \dfrac{1}{3} = 3-x$

89. Factoring: $x^2 - 4 = (x+2)(x-2)$

91. Factoring: $x^3 - 27 = (x-3)\left(x^2+3x+9\right)$

93. Simplifying the expression:

$$\left(1-\frac{1}{x}\right)\left(1-\frac{1}{x+1}\right)\left(1-\frac{1}{x+2}\right)\left(1-\frac{1}{x+3}\right) = \left(\frac{x}{x}-\frac{1}{x}\right)\left(\frac{x+1}{x+1}-\frac{1}{x+1}\right)\left(\frac{x+2}{x+2}-\frac{1}{x+2}\right)\left(\frac{x+3}{x+3}-\frac{1}{x+3}\right)$$

$$= \left(\frac{x-1}{x}\right)\left(\frac{x}{x+1}\right)\left(\frac{x+1}{x+2}\right)\left(\frac{x+2}{x+3}\right)$$

$$= \frac{x-1}{x+3}$$

95. Simplifying the expression:

$$\left(\frac{a^2-b^2}{u^2-v^2}\right)\left(\frac{av-au}{b-a}\right)+\left(\frac{a^2-av}{u+v}\right)\left(\frac{1}{a}\right) = \frac{(a+b)(a-b)}{(u+v)(u-v)} \cdot \frac{a(v-u)}{b-a} + \frac{a(a-v)}{u+v} \cdot \frac{1}{a}$$

$$= \frac{a(a+b)}{u+v}+\frac{a-v}{u+v}$$

$$= \frac{a^2+ab+a-v}{u+v}$$

97. Simplifying the expression:

$$\frac{18x-19}{4x^2+27x-7}-\frac{12x-41}{3x^2+17x-28} = \frac{18x-19}{(4x-1)(x+7)} \cdot \frac{3x-4}{3x-4} - \frac{12x-41}{(3x-4)(x+7)} \cdot \frac{4x-1}{4x-1}$$

$$= \frac{54x^2-129x+76}{(4x-1)(x+7)(3x-4)}-\frac{48x^2-176x+41}{(4x-1)(x+7)(3x-4)}$$

$$= \frac{54x^2-129x+76-48x^2+176x-41}{(4x-1)(x+7)(3x-4)}$$

$$= \frac{6x^2+47x+35}{(4x-1)(x+7)(3x-4)}$$

$$= \frac{(6x+5)(x+7)}{(4x-1)(x+7)(3x-4)}$$

$$= \frac{6x+5}{(4x-1)(3x-4)}$$

99. Simplifying the expression:

$$\left(\frac{1}{y^2-1} \div \frac{1}{y^2+1}\right)\left(\frac{y^3+1}{y^4-1}\right) + \frac{1}{(y+1)^2(y-1)} = \frac{y^2+1}{y^2-1} \cdot \frac{y^3+1}{y^4-1} + \frac{1}{(y+1)^2(y-1)}$$

$$= \frac{y^2+1}{(y+1)(y-1)} \cdot \frac{(y+1)(y^2-y+1)}{(y^2+1)(y+1)(y-1)} + \frac{1}{(y+1)^2(y-1)}$$

$$= \frac{y^2-y+1}{(y+1)(y-1)^2} \cdot \frac{y+1}{y+1} + \frac{1}{(y+1)^2(y-1)} \cdot \frac{y-1}{y-1}$$

$$= \frac{y^3+1+y-1}{(y+1)^2(y-1)^2}$$

$$= \frac{y^3+y}{(y+1)^2(y-1)^2}$$

$$= \frac{y(y^2+1)}{(y+1)^2(y-1)^2}$$

5.4 Complex Rational Expressions

1. Simplifying the complex fraction: $\dfrac{\frac{3}{4}}{\frac{2}{3}} = \dfrac{\frac{3}{4} \cdot 12}{\frac{2}{3} \cdot 12} = \dfrac{9}{8}$

3. Simplifying the complex fraction: $\dfrac{\frac{1}{3}-\frac{1}{4}}{\frac{1}{2}+\frac{1}{8}} = \dfrac{\left(\frac{1}{3}-\frac{1}{4}\right) \cdot 24}{\left(\frac{1}{2}+\frac{1}{8}\right) \cdot 24} = \dfrac{8-6}{12+3} = \dfrac{2}{15}$

5. Simplifying the complex fraction: $\dfrac{3+\frac{2}{5}}{1-\frac{3}{7}} = \dfrac{\left(3+\frac{2}{5}\right) \cdot 35}{\left(1-\frac{3}{7}\right) \cdot 35} = \dfrac{105+14}{35-15} = \dfrac{119}{20}$

7. Simplifying the complex fraction: $\dfrac{\frac{1}{x}}{1+\frac{1}{x}} = \dfrac{\left(\frac{1}{x}\right) \cdot x}{\left(1+\frac{1}{x}\right) \cdot x} = \dfrac{1}{x+1}$

9. Simplifying the complex fraction: $\dfrac{1+\frac{1}{a}}{1-\frac{1}{a}} = \dfrac{\left(1+\frac{1}{a}\right) \cdot a}{\left(1-\frac{1}{a}\right) \cdot a} = \dfrac{a+1}{a-1}$

11. Simplifying the complex fraction: $\dfrac{\frac{1}{x}-\frac{1}{y}}{\frac{1}{x}+\frac{1}{y}} = \dfrac{\left(\frac{1}{x}-\frac{1}{y}\right) \cdot xy}{\left(\frac{1}{x}+\frac{1}{y}\right) \cdot xy} = \dfrac{y-x}{y+x}$

13. Simplifying the complex fraction:

$$\frac{\dfrac{x-5}{x^2-4}}{\dfrac{x^2-25}{x+2}}=\frac{\dfrac{x-5}{(x+2)(x-2)}\cdot(x+2)(x-2)}{\dfrac{(x+5)(x-5)}{x+2}\cdot(x+2)(x-2)}=\frac{x-5}{(x+5)(x-5)(x-2)}=\frac{1}{(x+5)(x-2)}$$

15. Simplifying the complex fraction:

$$\frac{\dfrac{4a}{2a^3+2}}{\dfrac{8a}{4a+4}}=\frac{\dfrac{4a}{2(a+1)(a^2-a+1)}\cdot2(a+1)(a^2-a+1)}{\dfrac{8a}{4(a+1)}\cdot2(a+1)(a^2-a+1)}=\frac{4a}{4a(a^2-a+1)}=\frac{1}{a^2-a+1}$$

17. Simplifying the complex fraction: $\dfrac{1-\dfrac{9}{x^2}}{1-\dfrac{1}{x}-\dfrac{6}{x^2}}=\dfrac{\left(1-\dfrac{9}{x^2}\right)\cdot x^2}{\left(1-\dfrac{1}{x}-\dfrac{6}{x^2}\right)\cdot x^2}=\dfrac{x^2-9}{x^2-x-6}=\dfrac{(x+3)(x-3)}{(x+2)(x-3)}=\dfrac{x+3}{x+2}$

19. Simplifying the complex fraction: $\dfrac{2+\dfrac{5}{a}-\dfrac{3}{a^2}}{2-\dfrac{5}{a}+\dfrac{2}{a^2}}=\dfrac{\left(2+\dfrac{5}{a}-\dfrac{3}{a^2}\right)\cdot a^2}{\left(2-\dfrac{5}{a}+\dfrac{2}{a^2}\right)\cdot a^2}=\dfrac{2a^2+5a-3}{2a^2-5a+2}=\dfrac{(2a-1)(a+3)}{(2a-1)(a-2)}=\dfrac{a+3}{a-2}$

21. Simplifying the complex fraction:

$$\frac{1+\dfrac{1}{x+3}}{1+\dfrac{7}{x-3}}=\frac{\left(1+\dfrac{1}{x+3}\right)\cdot(x+3)(x-3)}{\left(1+\dfrac{7}{x-3}\right)\cdot(x+3)(x-3)}$$

$$=\frac{(x+3)(x-3)+x-3}{(x+3)(x-3)+7(x+3)}$$

$$=\frac{x^2-9+x-3}{x^2-9+7x+21}$$

$$=\frac{x^2+x-12}{x^2+7x+12}$$

$$=\frac{(x+4)(x-3)}{(x+4)(x+3)}$$

$$=\frac{x-3}{x+3}$$

23. Simplifying the complex fraction:

$$\frac{1-(a+1)^{-1}}{1+(a-1)^{-1}}=\frac{1-\dfrac{1}{a+1}}{1+\dfrac{1}{a-1}}$$

$$=\frac{\left(1-\dfrac{1}{a+1}\right)\cdot(a+1)(a-1)}{\left(1+\dfrac{1}{a-1}\right)\cdot(a+1)(a-1)}$$

$$=\frac{(a+1)(a-1)-(a-1)}{(a+1)(a-1)+(a+1)}$$

$$=\frac{(a-1)(a+1-1)}{(a+1)(a-1+1)}$$

$$=\frac{a(a-1)}{a(a+1)}$$

$$=\frac{a-1}{a+1}$$

25. Simplifying the complex fraction:

$$\frac{(x+3)^{-1}+(x-3)^{-1}}{(x+3)^{-1}-(x-3)^{-1}} = \frac{\dfrac{1}{x+3}+\dfrac{1}{x-3}}{\dfrac{1}{x+3}-\dfrac{1}{x-3}}$$

$$= \frac{\left(\dfrac{1}{x+3}+\dfrac{1}{x-3}\right)\cdot(x+3)(x-3)}{\left(\dfrac{1}{x+3}-\dfrac{1}{x-3}\right)\cdot(x+3)(x-3)}$$

$$= \frac{(x-3)+(x+3)}{(x-3)-(x+3)}$$

$$= \frac{2x}{-6}$$

$$= -\frac{x}{3}$$

27. Simplifying the complex fraction:

$$\frac{\dfrac{y+1}{y-1}+\dfrac{y-1}{y+1}}{\dfrac{y+1}{y-1}-\dfrac{y-1}{y+1}} = \frac{\left(\dfrac{y+1}{y-1}+\dfrac{y-1}{y+1}\right)\cdot(y+1)(y-1)}{\left(\dfrac{y+1}{y-1}-\dfrac{y-1}{y+1}\right)\cdot(y+1)(y-1)}$$

$$= \frac{(y+1)^2+(y-1)^2}{(y+1)^2-(y-1)^2}$$

$$= \frac{y^2+2y+1+y^2-2y+1}{y^2+2y+1-y^2+2y-1}$$

$$= \frac{2y^2+2}{4y}$$

$$= \frac{2\left(y^2+1\right)}{4y}$$

$$= \frac{y^2+1}{2y}$$

29. Simplifying the complex fraction: $1-\dfrac{x}{1-\dfrac{1}{x}} = 1-\dfrac{x\bullet x}{\left(1-\dfrac{1}{x}\right)\bullet x} = 1-\dfrac{x^2}{x-1} = \dfrac{x-1-x^2}{x-1} = \dfrac{-x^2+x-1}{x-1}$

31. Simplifying the complex fraction: $1+\dfrac{1}{1+\dfrac{1}{1+1}} = 1+\dfrac{1}{1+\dfrac{1}{2}} = 1+\dfrac{1}{\dfrac{3}{2}} = 1+\dfrac{2}{3} = \dfrac{5}{3}$

33. Simplifying the complex fraction:

$$\frac{1-\dfrac{1}{x+\dfrac{1}{2}}}{1+\dfrac{1}{x+\dfrac{1}{2}}} = \frac{1-\dfrac{1\bullet 2}{\left(x+\dfrac{1}{2}\right)\bullet 2}}{1+\dfrac{1\bullet 2}{\left(x+\dfrac{1}{2}\right)\bullet 2}} = \frac{1-\dfrac{2}{2x+1}}{1+\dfrac{2}{2x+1}} = \frac{\left(1-\dfrac{2}{2x+1}\right)(2x+1)}{\left(1+\dfrac{2}{2x+1}\right)(2x+1)} = \frac{2x+1-2}{2x+1+2} = \frac{2x-1}{2x+3}$$

35. Simplifying the complex fraction:

$$\frac{\dfrac{1}{x+h}-\dfrac{1}{x}}{h}=\frac{\left(\dfrac{1}{x+h}-\dfrac{1}{x}\right)\cdot x(x+h)}{h\cdot x(x+h)}=\frac{x-(x+h)}{hx(x+h)}=\frac{x-x-h}{hx(x+h)}=\frac{-h}{hx(x+h)}=-\frac{1}{x(x+h)}$$

37. Simplifying the complex fraction:

$$\frac{\dfrac{1}{x+8}-\dfrac{1}{x}}{8}=\frac{\left(\dfrac{1}{x+8}-\dfrac{1}{x}\right)\cdot x(x+8)}{8x(x+8)}=\frac{x-(x+8)}{8x(x+8)}=\frac{x-x-8}{8x(x+8)}=\frac{-8}{8x(x+8)}=-\frac{1}{x(x+8)}$$

39. Simplifying the expression:

$$\frac{1}{(x+6)^2}-\frac{1}{x^2}=\frac{1}{(x+6)^2}\cdot\frac{x^2}{x^2}-\frac{1}{x^2}\cdot\frac{(x+6)^2}{(x+6)^2}$$

$$=\frac{x^2-x^2-12x-36}{x^2(x+6)^2}$$

$$=\frac{-12x-36}{x^2(x+6)^2}$$

$$=-\frac{12(x+3)}{x^2(x+6)^2}$$

41. Simplifying the complex fraction: $\dfrac{\dfrac{3}{ab}+\dfrac{4}{bc}-\dfrac{2}{ac}}{\dfrac{5}{abc}}=\dfrac{\left(\dfrac{3}{ab}+\dfrac{4}{bc}-\dfrac{2}{ac}\right)\cdot abc}{\left(\dfrac{5}{abc}\right)\cdot abc}=\dfrac{3c+4a-2b}{5}$

43. Simplifying the complex fraction:

$$\frac{\dfrac{t^2-2t-8}{t^2+7t+6}}{\dfrac{t^2-t-6}{t^2+2t+1}}=\frac{\dfrac{(t-4)(t+2)}{(t+6)(t+1)}\cdot(t+6)(t+1)^2}{\dfrac{(t-3)(t+2)}{(t+1)^2}\cdot(t+6)(t+1)^2}=\frac{(t-4)(t+2)(t+1)}{(t-3)(t+2)(t+6)}=\frac{(t-4)(t+1)}{(t+6)(t-3)}$$

45. Simplifying the complex fraction:

$$\frac{5+\left(\dfrac{b-1}{4}\right)^{-1}}{\left(\dfrac{b+5}{7}\right)^{-1}-\left(\dfrac{b-1}{3}\right)^{-1}}=\frac{5+\dfrac{4}{b-1}}{\dfrac{7}{b+5}-\dfrac{3}{b-1}}$$

$$=\frac{\left(5+\dfrac{4}{b-1}\right)\cdot(b+5)(b-1)}{\left(\dfrac{7}{b+5}-\dfrac{3}{b-1}\right)\cdot(b+5)(b-1)}$$

$$=\frac{5(b+5)(b-1)+4(b+5)}{7(b-1)-3(b+5)}$$

$$=\frac{(b+5)(5b-5+4)}{7b-7-3b-15}$$

$$=\frac{(b+5)(5b-1)}{4b-22}$$

$$=\frac{(5b-1)(b+5)}{2(2b-11)}$$

47. Simplifying the complex fraction:

$$\cfrac{\cfrac{3}{x^2-x-6}}{\cfrac{2}{x+2}-\cfrac{4}{x-3}} = \cfrac{\cfrac{3}{(x-3)(x+2)}\cdot(x-3)(x+2)}{\left(\cfrac{2}{x+2}-\cfrac{4}{x-3}\right)\cdot(x-3)(x+2)}$$

$$= \frac{3}{2(x-3)-4(x+2)}$$

$$= \frac{3}{2x-6-4x-8}$$

$$= \frac{3}{-2x-14}$$

$$= -\frac{3}{2x+14}$$

49. Simplifying the complex fraction: $\cfrac{\cfrac{1}{m-4}+\cfrac{1}{m-5}}{\cfrac{1}{m^2-9m+20}} = \cfrac{\left(\cfrac{1}{m-4}+\cfrac{1}{m-5}\right)\cdot(m-4)(m-5)}{\cfrac{1}{(m-4)(m-5)}\cdot(m-4)(m-5)} = \frac{(m-5)+(m-4)}{1} = 2m-9$

51. Simplifying the complex fraction: $\cfrac{\cfrac{1}{x+2}-\cfrac{1}{x-2}}{\cfrac{1}{x+2}+\cfrac{1}{x-2}} = \cfrac{\left(\cfrac{1}{x+2}-\cfrac{1}{x-2}\right)\cdot(x+2)(x-2)}{\left(\cfrac{1}{x+2}+\cfrac{1}{x-2}\right)\cdot(x+2)(x-2)} = \frac{(x-2)-(x+2)}{(x-2)+(x+2)} = -\frac{4}{2x} = -\frac{2}{x}$

53. Simplifying the quotient:

$$\frac{f(x)}{g(x)} = \cfrac{2+\cfrac{3}{x}-\cfrac{18}{x^2}-\cfrac{27}{x^3}}{2+\cfrac{9}{x}+\cfrac{9}{x^2}}$$

$$= \cfrac{\left(2+\cfrac{3}{x}-\cfrac{18}{x^2}-\cfrac{27}{x^3}\right)\cdot x^3}{\left(2+\cfrac{9}{x}+\cfrac{9}{x^2}\right)\cdot x^3}$$

$$= \frac{2x^3+3x^2-18x-27}{2x^3+9x^2+9x}$$

$$= \frac{x^2(2x+3)-9(2x+3)}{x(2x^2+9x+9)}$$

$$= \frac{(2x+3)(x^2-9)}{x(2x+3)(x+3)}$$

$$= \frac{(2x+3)(x+3)(x-3)}{x(2x+3)(x+3)}$$

$$= \frac{x-3}{x}$$

55. Simplifying the quotient: $\cfrac{f(x)}{g(x)} = \cfrac{1+\cfrac{1}{x+3}}{1-\cfrac{1}{x+3}} = \cfrac{\left(1+\cfrac{1}{x+3}\right)\cdot(x+3)}{\left(1-\cfrac{1}{x+3}\right)\cdot(x+3)} = \frac{x+3+1}{x+3-1} = \frac{x+4}{x+2}$

57. **a.** Simplifying the difference quotient: $\dfrac{f(x)-f(a)}{x-a}=\dfrac{\dfrac{4}{x}-\dfrac{4}{a}}{x-a}=\dfrac{\left(\dfrac{4}{x}-\dfrac{4}{a}\right)ax}{(x-a)ax}=\dfrac{4a-4x}{ax(x-a)}=\dfrac{-4(x-a)}{ax(x-a)}=-\dfrac{4}{ax}$

b. Simplifying the difference quotient:

$$\dfrac{f(x)-f(a)}{x-a}=\dfrac{\dfrac{1}{x+1}-\dfrac{1}{a+1}}{x-a}$$

$$=\dfrac{\left(\dfrac{1}{x+1}-\dfrac{1}{a+1}\right)(x+1)(a+1)}{(x-a)(x+1)(a+1)}$$

$$=\dfrac{a+1-x-1}{(x-a)(x+1)(a+1)}$$

$$=\dfrac{a-x}{(x-a)(x+1)(a+1)}$$

$$=-\dfrac{1}{(x+1)(a+1)}$$

c. Simplifying the difference quotient:

$$\dfrac{f(x)-f(a)}{x-a}=\dfrac{\dfrac{1}{x^2}-\dfrac{1}{a^2}}{x-a}=\dfrac{\left(\dfrac{1}{x^2}-\dfrac{1}{a^2}\right)a^2x^2}{a^2x^2(x-a)}=\dfrac{a^2-x^2}{a^2x^2(x-a)}=\dfrac{(a+x)(a-x)}{a^2x^2(x-a)}=-\dfrac{a+x}{a^2x^2}$$

59. **a.** As v approaches 0, the denominator approaches 1.

b. Solving for v:

$$h=\dfrac{f}{1+\dfrac{v}{s}}$$

$$h=\dfrac{f\cdot s}{\left(1+\dfrac{v}{s}\right)s}$$

$$h=\dfrac{fs}{s+v}$$

$$h(s+v)=fs$$

$$s+v=\dfrac{fs}{h}$$

$$v=\dfrac{fs}{h}-s$$

$$v=\dfrac{fs-sh}{h}=\dfrac{fs}{h}-s$$

61. Multiplying: $x(y-2)=xy-2x$

63. Multiplying: $6\left(\dfrac{x}{2}-3\right)=6\cdot\dfrac{x}{2}-6\cdot3=3x-18$

65. Multiplying: $xab\cdot\dfrac{1}{x}=ab$

67. Multiplying: $st^2\left(\dfrac{2}{s}-\dfrac{3}{t^2}\right)=st^2\cdot\dfrac{2}{s}-st^2\cdot\dfrac{3}{t^2}=2t^2-3s$

69. Factoring: $y^2-25=(y+5)(y-5)$

71. Factoring: $xa+xb=x(a+b)$

73. Solving the equation:

$$5x - 4 = 6$$
$$5x = 10$$
$$x = 2$$

75. Solving the equation:

$$x^2 - 2x - 12 = 2x$$
$$x^2 - 4x - 12 = 0$$
$$(x-6)(x+2) = 0$$
$$x = -2, 6$$

Landmark Review

1. Simplifying: $\dfrac{3a^2 - 27}{6a - 18} = \dfrac{3(a^2 - 9)}{6(a-3)} = \dfrac{3(a+3)(a-3)}{6(a-3)} = \dfrac{a+3}{2}$

2. Simplifying: $\dfrac{y-3}{y^2 - 6y + 9} = \dfrac{y-3}{(y-3)^2} = \dfrac{1}{y-3}$

3. Simplifying: $\dfrac{3x^3 - 6x^2 - 45x}{x^2 + 5x + 6} = \dfrac{3x(x^2 - 2x - 15)}{x^2 + 5x + 6} = \dfrac{3x(x+3)(x-5)}{(x+3)(x+2)} = \dfrac{3x(x-5)}{x+2}$

4. Simplifying: $\dfrac{5x^2 + 22x + 8}{25x^2 - 4} = \dfrac{(5x+2)(x+4)}{(5x+2)(5x-2)} = \dfrac{x+4}{5x-2}$

5. Performing the operations: $\dfrac{3a^4}{6a + 18} \cdot \dfrac{a+3}{a^3} = \dfrac{3a^4(a+3)}{6a^3(a+3)} = \dfrac{a}{2}$

6. Performing the operations: $\dfrac{4x^2 - 12x}{x^2 - 1} \cdot \dfrac{x^2 + x}{4x} = \dfrac{4x(x-3)}{(x+1)(x-1)} \cdot \dfrac{x(x+1)}{4x} = \dfrac{x(x-3)}{x-1}$

7. Performing the operations:

$$\frac{y^2 - 3y}{2y^2 - 8} \div \frac{y^2 - 25}{y^2 + 3y - 10} = \frac{y^2 - 3y}{2y^2 - 8} \cdot \frac{y^2 + 3y - 10}{y^2 - 25} = \frac{y(y-3)}{2(y+2)(y-2)} \cdot \frac{(y+5)(y-2)}{(y+5)(y-5)} = \frac{y(y-3)}{2(y+2)(y-5)}$$

8. Performing the operations: $(x^2 + 8x + 15) \cdot \dfrac{2x}{x+5} = (x+5)(x+3) \cdot \dfrac{2x}{x+5} = 2x(x+3)$

9. Performing the operations: $\dfrac{8}{4x + 16} \div \dfrac{2}{x+4} = \dfrac{8}{4x+16} \cdot \dfrac{x+4}{2} = \dfrac{8}{4(x+4)} \cdot \dfrac{x+4}{2} = \dfrac{8(x+4)}{8(x+4)} = 1$

10. Performing the operations:

$$\frac{4}{y+3} + \frac{24}{y^2 - 9} = \frac{4}{y+3} \cdot \frac{y-3}{y-3} + \frac{24}{(y+3)(y-3)}$$

$$= \frac{4y - 12}{(y+3)(y-3)} + \frac{24}{(y+3)(y-3)}$$

$$= \frac{4y + 12}{(y+3)(y-3)}$$

$$= \frac{4(y+3)}{(y+3)(y-3)}$$

$$= \frac{4}{y-3}$$

11. Performing the operations:
$$\frac{a+5}{a+4}+\frac{8}{a^2-16}=\frac{a+5}{a+4}\cdot\frac{a-4}{a-4}+\frac{8}{(a+4)(a-4)}$$
$$=\frac{a^2+a-20}{(a+4)(a-4)}+\frac{8}{(a+4)(a-4)}$$
$$=\frac{a^2+a-12}{(a+4)(a-4)}$$
$$=\frac{(a+4)(a-3)}{(a+4)(a-4)}$$
$$=\frac{a-3}{a-4}$$

12. Performing the operations: $\dfrac{x^2}{x+4}-\dfrac{16}{x+4}=\dfrac{x^2-16}{x+4}=\dfrac{(x+4)(x-4)}{x+4}=x-4$

13. Performing the operations:
$$\frac{x+2}{x-1}-\frac{6}{x^2-1}=\frac{x+2}{x-1}\cdot\frac{x+1}{x+1}-\frac{6}{(x+1)(x-1)}$$
$$=\frac{x^2+3x+2}{(x+1)(x-1)}-\frac{6}{(x+1)(x-1)}$$
$$=\frac{x^2+3x-4}{(x+1)(x-1)}$$
$$=\frac{(x+4)(x-1)}{(x+1)(x-1)}$$
$$=\frac{x+4}{x+1}$$

14. Performing the operations: $\dfrac{x}{(x+2)(x+3)}-\dfrac{2}{(x+2)(x+3)}=\dfrac{x-2}{(x+2)(x+3)}$

15. Simplifying the complex fraction: $\dfrac{1-\dfrac{3}{a}}{1-\dfrac{4}{a}}=\dfrac{\left(1-\dfrac{3}{a}\right)\cdot a}{\left(1-\dfrac{4}{a}\right)\cdot a}=\dfrac{a-3}{a-4}$

16. Simplifying the complex fraction: $\dfrac{\dfrac{2}{x}+\dfrac{1}{y}}{\dfrac{3}{x}+\dfrac{1}{y}}=\dfrac{\left(\dfrac{2}{x}+\dfrac{1}{y}\right)\cdot xy}{\left(\dfrac{3}{x}+\dfrac{1}{y}\right)\cdot xy}=\dfrac{2y+x}{3y+x}=\dfrac{x+2y}{x+3y}$

17. Simplifying the complex fraction:
$$\frac{\dfrac{4x+1}{x^2-9}}{\dfrac{16x^2-1}{x-3}}=\frac{\dfrac{4x+1}{(x+3)(x-3)}\cdot(x+3)(x-3)}{\dfrac{(4x+1)(4x-1)}{x-3}\cdot(x+3)(x-3)}=\frac{4x+1}{(4x+1)(4x-1)(x+3)}=\frac{1}{(4x-1)(x+3)}$$

18. Simplifying the complex fraction:

$$\frac{\dfrac{y-1}{y+1}-\dfrac{y+1}{y-1}}{\dfrac{y-1}{y+1}+\dfrac{y+1}{y-1}} = \frac{\left(\dfrac{y-1}{y+1}-\dfrac{y+1}{y-1}\right)\cdot(y+1)(y-1)}{\left(\dfrac{y-1}{y+1}+\dfrac{y+1}{y-1}\right)\cdot(y+1)(y-1)}$$

$$=\frac{(y-1)^2-(y+1)^2}{(y-1)^2+(y+1)^2}$$

$$=\frac{y^2-2y+1-y^2-2y-1}{y^2-2y+1+y^2+2y+1}$$

$$=\frac{-4y}{2y^2+2}$$

$$=\frac{-4y}{2(y^2+1)}$$

$$=-\frac{2y}{y^2+1}$$

5.5 Rational Equations

1. Solving the equation:

$$\frac{x}{5}+4=\frac{5}{3}$$

$$15\left(\frac{x}{5}+4\right)=15\left(\frac{5}{3}\right)$$

$$3x+60=25$$

$$3x=-35$$

$$x=-\frac{35}{3}$$

3. Solving the equation:

$$\frac{a}{3}+2=\frac{4}{5}$$

$$15\left(\frac{a}{3}+2\right)=15\left(\frac{4}{5}\right)$$

$$5a+30=12$$

$$5a=-18$$

$$a=-\frac{18}{5}$$

5. Solving the equation:

$$\frac{y}{2}+\frac{y}{4}+\frac{y}{6}=3$$

$$12\left(\frac{y}{2}+\frac{y}{4}+\frac{y}{6}\right)=12(3)$$

$$6y+3y+2y=36$$

$$11y=36$$

$$y=\frac{36}{11}$$

7. Solving the equation:

$$\frac{5}{2x}=\frac{1}{x}+\frac{3}{4}$$

$$4x\left(\frac{5}{2x}\right)=4x\left(\frac{1}{x}+\frac{3}{4}\right)$$

$$10=4+3x$$

$$3x=6$$

$$x=2$$

9. Solving the equation:

$$\frac{1}{x}=\frac{1}{3}-\frac{2}{3x}$$

$$3x\left(\frac{1}{x}\right)=3x\left(\frac{1}{3}-\frac{2}{3x}\right)$$

$$3=x-2$$

$$x=5$$

11. Solving the equation:

$$\frac{2x}{x-3}+2=\frac{2}{x-3}$$

$$(x-3)\left(\frac{2x}{x-3}+2\right)=(x-3)\left(\frac{2}{x-3}\right)$$

$$2x+2(x-3)=2$$

$$2x+2x-6=2$$

$$4x=8$$

$$x=2$$

13. Solving the equation:

$$1 - \frac{1}{x} = \frac{12}{x^2}$$
$$x^2\left(1 - \frac{1}{x}\right) = x^2\left(\frac{12}{x^2}\right)$$
$$x^2 - x = 12$$
$$x^2 - x - 12 = 0$$
$$(x + 3)(x - 4) = 0$$
$$x = -3, 4$$

15. Solving the equation:

$$y - \frac{4}{3y} = -\frac{1}{3}$$
$$3y\left(y - \frac{4}{3y}\right) = 3y\left(-\frac{1}{3}\right)$$
$$3y^2 - 4 = -y$$
$$3y^2 + y - 4 = 0$$
$$(3y + 4)(y - 1) = 0$$
$$x = -\frac{4}{3}, 1$$

17. Solving the equation:

$$\frac{x+2}{x+1} = \frac{1}{x+1} + 2$$
$$(x+1)\left(\frac{x+2}{x+1}\right) = (x+1)\left(\frac{1}{x+1} + 2\right)$$
$$x + 2 = 1 + 2(x + 1)$$
$$x + 2 = 1 + 2x + 2$$
$$x + 2 = 2x + 3$$
$$x = -1 \quad \text{(does not check)}$$

There is no solution (–1 does not check).

19. Solving the equation:

$$\frac{x+2}{3x-1} = \frac{x-12}{4-9x-9x^2}$$
$$\frac{x+2}{3x-1} = -\frac{x-12}{9x^2+9x-4}$$
$$\frac{x+2}{3x-1} = -\frac{x-12}{(3x-1)(3x+4)}$$
$$(3x-1)(3x+4)\left(\frac{x+2}{3x-1}\right) = (3x-1)(3x+4)\left(-\frac{x-12}{(3x-1)(3x+4)}\right)$$
$$(3x+4)(x+2) = -(x-12)$$
$$3x^2 + 10x + 8 = -x + 12$$
$$3x^2 + 11x - 4 = 0$$
$$(3x-1)(x+4) = 0$$
$$x = -4 \quad \left(x = \frac{1}{3} \text{ does not check}\right)$$

21. Solving the equation:

$$6 - \frac{5}{x^2} = \frac{7}{x}$$
$$x^2\left(6 - \frac{5}{x^2}\right) = x^2\left(\frac{7}{x}\right)$$
$$6x^2 - 5 = 7x$$
$$6x^2 - 7x - 5 = 0$$
$$(2x+1)(3x-5) = 0$$
$$x = -\frac{1}{2}, \frac{5}{3}$$

23. Solving the equation:

$$\frac{1}{x-1} - \frac{1}{x+1} = \frac{3x}{x^2 - 1}$$

$$(x+1)(x-1)\left(\frac{1}{x-1} - \frac{1}{x+1}\right) = (x+1)(x-1)\left(\frac{3x}{(x+1)(x-1)}\right)$$

$$(x+1) - (x-1) = 3x$$

$$x + 1 - x + 1 = 3x$$

$$3x = 2$$

$$x = \frac{2}{3}$$

25. Solving the equation:

$$\frac{t-4}{t^2 - 3t} = \frac{-2}{t^2 - 9}$$

$$t(t+3)(t-3) \cdot \frac{t-4}{t(t-3)} = t(t+3)(t-3) \cdot \frac{-2}{(t+3)(t-3)}$$

$$(t+3)(t-4) = -2t$$

$$t^2 - t - 12 = -2t$$

$$t^2 + t - 12 = 0$$

$$(t+4)(t-3) = 0$$

$$t = -4 \quad (t = 3 \text{ does not check})$$

27. Solving the equation:

$$\frac{3}{y-4} - \frac{2}{y+1} = \frac{5}{y^2 - 3y - 4}$$

$$(y-4)(y+1)\left(\frac{3}{y-4} - \frac{2}{y+1}\right) = (y-4)(y+1)\left(\frac{5}{(y-4)(y+1)}\right)$$

$$3(y+1) - 2(y-4) = 5$$

$$3y + 3 - 2y + 8 = 5$$

$$y + 11 = 5$$

$$y = -6$$

29. Solving the equation:

$$\frac{2}{1+a} = \frac{3}{1-a} + \frac{5}{a}$$

$$a(1+a)(1-a)\left(\frac{2}{1+a}\right) = a(1+a)(1-a)\left(\frac{3}{1-a} + \frac{5}{a}\right)$$

$$2a(1-a) = 3a(1+a) + 5(1+a)(1-a)$$

$$2a - 2a^2 = 3a + 3a^2 + 5 - 5a^2$$

$$-2a^2 + 2a = -2a^2 + 3a + 5$$

$$2a = 3a + 5$$

$$-a = 5$$

$$a = -5$$

31. Solving the equation:

$$\frac{3}{2x-6} - \frac{x+1}{4x-12} = 4$$

$$4(x-3)\left(\frac{3}{2(x-3)} - \frac{x+1}{4(x-3)}\right) = 4(x-3)(4)$$

$$6 - (x+1) = 16x - 48$$

$$5 - x = 16x - 48$$

$$-17x = -53$$

$$x = \frac{53}{17}$$

33. Solving the equation:

$$\frac{y+2}{y^2-y} - \frac{6}{y^2-1} = 0$$

$$y(y+1)(y-1)\left(\frac{y+2}{y(y-1)} - \frac{6}{(y+1)(y-1)}\right) = y(y+1)(y-1)(0)$$

$$(y+1)(y+2) - 6y = 0$$

$$y^2 + 3y + 2 - 6y = 0$$

$$y^2 - 3y + 2 = 0$$

$$(y-1)(y-2) = 0$$

$$y = 2 \quad (y = 1 \text{ does not check})$$

35. Solving the equation:

$$\frac{4}{2x-6} - \frac{12}{4x+12} = \frac{12}{x^2-9}$$

$$4(x+3)(x-3)\left(\frac{4}{2(x-3)} - \frac{12}{4(x+3)}\right) = 4(x+3)(x-3)\left(\frac{12}{(x+3)(x-3)}\right)$$

$$8(x+3) - 12(x-3) = 48$$

$$8x + 24 - 12x + 36 = 48$$

$$-4x + 60 = 48$$

$$-4x = -12$$

$$x = 3 \quad (x = 3 \text{ does not check})$$

There is no solution (3 does not check).

37. Solving the equation:

$$\frac{2}{y^2-7y+12} - \frac{1}{y^2-9} = \frac{4}{y^2-y-12}$$

$$(y+3)(y-3)(y-4)\left(\frac{2}{(y-3)(y-4)} - \frac{1}{(y+3)(y-3)}\right) = (y+3)(y-3)(y-4)\left(\frac{4}{(y-4)(y+3)}\right)$$

$$2(y+3) - (y-4) = 4(y-3)$$

$$2y + 6 - y + 4 = 4y - 12$$

$$y + 10 = 4y - 12$$

$$-3y = -22$$

$$y = \frac{22}{3}$$

39. Solving the equation:

$$f(x) = g(x)$$

$$\frac{2}{x-3} + \frac{x}{x^2-9} = \frac{4}{x+3}$$

$$(x+3)(x-3)\left(\frac{2}{x-3} + \frac{x}{(x+3)(x-3)}\right) = (x+3)(x-3)\left(\frac{4}{x+3}\right)$$

$$2(x+3) + x = 4(x-3)$$

$$2x + 6 + x = 4x - 12$$

$$3x + 6 = 4x - 12$$

$$-x = -18$$

$$x = 18$$

41. Solving the equation:

$$f(x) = g(x)$$

$$\frac{3}{2} - \frac{1}{x-4} = \frac{-2}{2x-8}$$

$$2(x-4)\left(\frac{3}{2} - \frac{1}{x-4}\right) = 2(x-4)\left(\frac{-2}{2(x-4)}\right)$$

$$3(x-4) - 2 = -2$$

$$3x - 12 - 2 = -2$$

$$3x - 14 = -2$$

$$3x = 12$$

$$x = 4 \quad \text{(does not check)}$$

There is no solution (4 does not check).

43. a. Solving the equation:

$$f(x) + g(x) = \frac{5}{8}$$

$$\frac{1}{x-3} + \frac{1}{x+3} = \frac{5}{8}$$

$$8(x-3)(x+3)\left(\frac{1}{x-3} + \frac{1}{x+3}\right) = 8(x-3)(x+3)\left(\frac{5}{8}\right)$$

$$8(x+3) + 8(x-3) = 5(x-3)(x+3)$$

$$8x + 24 + 8x - 24 = 5x^2 - 45$$

$$16x = 5x^2 - 45$$

$$0 = 5x^2 - 16x - 45$$

$$0 = (5x+9)(x-5)$$

$$x = -\frac{9}{5}, 5$$

b. Solving the equation:

$$\frac{f(x)}{g(x)} = 5$$

$$\frac{\dfrac{1}{x-3}}{\dfrac{1}{x+3}} = 5$$

$$\frac{x+3}{x-3} = 5$$

$$x+3 = 5(x-3)$$

$$x+3 = 5x-15$$

$$18 = 4x$$

$$x = \frac{9}{2}$$

c. Solving the equation:

$$f(x) = g(x)$$

$$\frac{1}{x-3} = \frac{1}{x+3}$$

$$x+3 = x-3$$

$$3 = -3 \quad \text{(false)}$$

There is no solution $(\varnothing)$.

45. a. Solving the equation:

$$6x - 2 = 0$$

$$6x = 2$$

$$x = \frac{1}{3}$$

b. Solving the equation:

$$\frac{6}{x} - 2 = 0$$

$$x\left(\frac{6}{x} - 2\right) = x(0)$$

$$6 - 2x = 0$$

$$6 = 2x$$

$$x = 3$$

c. Solving the equation:

$$\frac{x}{6} - 2 = -\frac{1}{2}$$

$$6\left(\frac{x}{6} - 2\right) = 6\left(-\frac{1}{2}\right)$$

$$x - 12 = -3$$

$$x = 9$$

d. Solving the equation:

$$\frac{6}{x} - 2 = -\frac{1}{2}$$

$$2x\left(\frac{6}{x} - 2\right) = 2x\left(-\frac{1}{2}\right)$$

$$12 - 4x = -x$$

$$12 = 3x$$

$$x = 4$$

e. Solving the equation:

$$\frac{6}{x^2} + 6 = \frac{20}{x}$$

$$x^2\left(\frac{6}{x^2} + 6\right) = x^2\left(\frac{20}{x}\right)$$

$$6 + 6x^2 = 20x$$

$$6x^2 - 20x + 6 = 0$$

$$3x^2 - 10x + 3 = 0$$

$$(3x-1)(x-3) = 0$$

$$x = \frac{1}{3}, 3$$

47. **a.** Dividing: $\dfrac{6}{x^2-2x-8} \div \dfrac{x+3}{x+2} = \dfrac{6}{(x-4)(x+2)} \cdot \dfrac{x+2}{x+3} = \dfrac{6}{(x-4)(x+3)}$

b. Adding:

$$\dfrac{6}{x^2-2x-8} + \dfrac{x+3}{x+2} = \dfrac{6}{(x-4)(x+2)} + \dfrac{x+3}{x+2} \cdot \dfrac{x-4}{x-4}$$

$$= \dfrac{6}{(x-4)(x+2)} + \dfrac{x^2-x-12}{(x-4)(x+2)}$$

$$= \dfrac{x^2-x-6}{(x-4)(x+2)}$$

$$= \dfrac{(x-3)(x+2)}{(x-4)(x+2)}$$

$$= \dfrac{x-3}{x-4}$$

c. Solving the equation:

$$\dfrac{6}{x^2-2x-8} + \dfrac{x+3}{x+2} = 2$$

$$(x-4)(x+2)\left(\dfrac{6}{(x-4)(x+2)} + \dfrac{x+3}{x+2}\right) = (x-4)(x+2)(2)$$

$$6 + (x-4)(x+3) = 2(x-4)(x+2)$$

$$6 + x^2 - x - 12 = 2x^2 - 4x - 16$$

$$0 = x^2 - 3x - 10$$

$$0 = (x-5)(x+2)$$

$$x = -5 \qquad (x = -2 \text{ does not check})$$

49. Solving for x:

$$\dfrac{1}{x} = \dfrac{1}{b} - \dfrac{1}{a}$$

$$abx\left(\dfrac{1}{x}\right) = abx\left(\dfrac{1}{b} - \dfrac{1}{a}\right)$$

$$ab = ax - bx$$

$$ab = x(a-b)$$

$$x = \dfrac{ab}{a-b}$$

51. Solving for y:

$$x = \dfrac{y-3}{y-1}$$

$$x(y-1) = y-3$$

$$xy - x = y - 3$$

$$xy - y = x - 3$$

$$y(x-1) = x - 3$$

$$y = \dfrac{x-3}{x-1}$$

53. Solving for y:

$$x = \dfrac{2y+1}{3y+1}$$

$$x(3y+1) = 2y+1$$

$$3xy + x = 2y + 1$$

$$3xy - 2y = -x + 1$$

$$y(3x-2) = -x + 1$$

$$y = \dfrac{1-x}{3x-2}$$

55. Graphing the function:

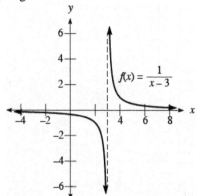

$$f(x) = \frac{1}{x-3}$$

57. Graphing the function:

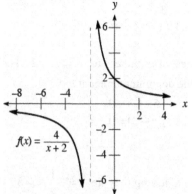

$$f(x) = \frac{4}{x+2}$$

59. Graphing the function:

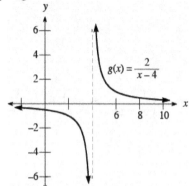

$$g(x) = \frac{2}{x-4}$$

61. Graphing the function:

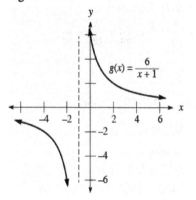

$$g(x) = \frac{6}{x+1}$$

63. Setting the denominator equal to 0:
$$3x - 5 = 0$$
$$3x = 5$$
$$x = \frac{5}{3}$$

The vertical asymptote is $x = \frac{5}{3}$. The domain is $\left\{ x \mid x \neq \frac{5}{3} \right\}$.

65. Setting the denominator equal to 0:
$$2x - 3 = 0$$
$$2x = 3$$
$$x = \frac{3}{2}$$

The vertical asymptote is $x = \frac{3}{2}$. The domain is $\left\{ x \mid x \neq \frac{3}{2} \right\}$.

67. Setting the denominator equal to 0:
$$x^2 - 9 = 0$$
$$(x+3)(x-3) = 0$$
$$x = -3, 3$$

The vertical asymptotes are $x = -3, x = 3$. The domain is $\left\{ x \mid x \neq \pm 3 \right\}$.

69. Setting the denominator equal to 0:
$$2x^2 + 6x = 0$$
$$2x(x+3) = 0$$
$$x = 0, -3$$

The vertical asymptotes are $x = 0, x = -3$. The domain is $\left\{ x \mid x \neq 0, -3 \right\}$.

71. Setting the denominator equal to 0:
$$x^2 - 3x + 2 = 0$$
$$(x-1)(x-2) = 0$$
$$x = 1, 2$$

The vertical asymptotes are $x = 1, x = 2$. The domain is $\{x \mid x \neq 1, 2\}$.

73. Setting the denominator equal to 0:
$$2x^2 - 5x - 3 = 0$$
$$(2x+1)(x-3) = 0$$
$$x = -\frac{1}{2}, 3$$

The vertical asymptotes are $x = -\frac{1}{2}, x = 3$. The domain is $\left\{x \mid x \neq -\frac{1}{2}, 3\right\}$.

75. Substituting $y_1 = 12$ and $y_2 = 8$:
$$\frac{1}{h} = \frac{1}{12} + \frac{1}{8} = \frac{2}{24} + \frac{3}{24} = \frac{5}{24}$$
$$h = \frac{24}{5} \text{ feet}$$

77. Multiplying: $39.3 \cdot 60 = 2{,}358$

79. Multiplying: $2x\left(\frac{1}{x} + \frac{1}{2x}\right) = 2x \cdot \frac{1}{x} + 2x \cdot \frac{1}{2x} = 2 + 1 = 3$

81. Dividing: $65{,}000 \div 5{,}280 \approx 12.3$

83. Solving the equation:
$$12(x+3) + 12(x-3) = 3(x^2 - 9)$$
$$12x + 36 + 12x - 36 = 3x^2 - 27$$
$$24x = 3x^2 - 27$$
$$3x^2 - 24x - 27 = 0$$
$$3(x^2 - 8x - 9) = 0$$
$$3(x-9)(x+1) = 0$$
$$x = -1, 9$$

85. Solving the equation:
$$\frac{1}{10} - \frac{1}{12} = \frac{1}{x}$$
$$60x\left(\frac{1}{10} - \frac{1}{12}\right) = 60x\left(\frac{1}{x}\right)$$
$$6x - 5x = 60$$
$$x = 60$$

87. Solving the equation:
$$\frac{12}{x} + \frac{8}{x^2} - \frac{75}{x^3} - \frac{50}{x^4} = 0$$
$$x^4\left(\frac{12}{x} + \frac{8}{x^2} - \frac{75}{x^3} - \frac{50}{x^4}\right) = x^4(0)$$
$$12x^3 + 8x^2 - 75x - 50 = 0$$
$$4x^2(3x+2) - 25(3x+2) = 0$$
$$(3x+2)(4x^2 - 25) = 0$$
$$(3x+2)(2x+5)(2x-5) = 0$$
$$x = -\frac{5}{2}, -\frac{2}{3}, \frac{5}{2}$$

89. Solving the equation:
$$\frac{1}{x^3} - \frac{1}{3x^2} - \frac{1}{4x} + \frac{1}{12} = 0$$
$$12x^3\left(\frac{1}{x^3} - \frac{1}{3x^2} - \frac{1}{4x} + \frac{1}{12}\right) = 12x^3(0)$$
$$12 - 4x - 3x^2 + x^3 = 0$$
$$x^2(x-3) - 4(x-3) = 0$$
$$(x-3)(x^2 - 4) = 0$$
$$(x-3)(x+2)(x-2) = 0$$
$$x = -2, 2, 3$$

91. Solving for x:

$$\frac{2}{x} + \frac{4}{x+a} = \frac{-6}{a-x}$$

$$x(x+a)(a-x)\left(\frac{2}{x} + \frac{4}{x+a}\right) = x(x+a)(a-x)\left(\frac{-6}{a-x}\right)$$

$$2(x+a)(a-x) + 4x(a-x) = -6x(x+a)$$

$$2a^2 - 2x^2 + 4ax - 4x^2 = -6x^2 - 6ax$$

$$2a^2 = -10ax$$

$$x = -\frac{a}{5}$$

93. Solving for v:

$$\frac{s-vt}{t^2} = -16$$

$$s - vt = -16t^2$$

$$s + 16t^2 = vt$$

$$v = \frac{16t^2 + s}{t}$$

95. Solving for f:

$$\frac{1}{p} = \frac{1}{f} + \frac{1}{g}$$

$$pfg\left(\frac{1}{p}\right) = pfg\left(\frac{1}{f} + \frac{1}{g}\right)$$

$$fg = pg + pf$$

$$fg - pf = pg$$

$$f(g-p) = pg$$

$$f = \frac{pg}{g-p}$$

5.6 Applications

1. Let x and $3x$ represent the two numbers. The equation is:

$$\frac{1}{x} + \frac{1}{3x} = \frac{20}{3}$$

$$3x\left(\frac{1}{x} + \frac{1}{3x}\right) = 3x\left(\frac{20}{3}\right)$$

$$3 + 1 = 20x$$

$$20x = 4$$

$$x = \frac{1}{5}$$

$$3x = \frac{3}{5}$$

The numbers are $\frac{1}{5}$ and $\frac{3}{5}$.

3. Let x represent the number. The equation is:

$$x + \frac{1}{x} = \frac{10}{3}$$

$$3x\left(x + \frac{1}{x}\right) = 3x\left(\frac{10}{3}\right)$$

$$3x^2 + 3 = 10x$$

$$3x^2 - 10x + 3 = 0$$

$$(3x-1)(x-3) = 0$$

$$x = \frac{1}{3}, 3$$

The number is either 3 or $\frac{1}{3}$.

5. Let x and $x + 1$ represent the two integers. The equation is:

$$\frac{1}{x} + \frac{1}{x+1} = \frac{7}{12}$$

$$12x(x+1)\left(\frac{1}{x} + \frac{1}{x+1}\right) = 12x(x+1)\left(\frac{7}{12}\right)$$

$$12(x+1) + 12x = 7x(x+1)$$

$$12x + 12 + 12x = 7x^2 + 7x$$

$$0 = 7x^2 - 17x - 12$$

$$0 = (7x+4)(x-3)$$

$$x = 3 \qquad \left(x = -\frac{4}{7} \text{ is not an integer}\right)$$

The two integers are 3 and 4.

7. Let x represent the number. The equation is:

$$\frac{7+x}{9+x} = \frac{5}{6}$$

$$6(9+x)\left(\frac{7+x}{9+x}\right) = 6(9+x)\left(\frac{5}{6}\right)$$

$$6(7+x) = 5(9+x)$$

$$42 + 6x = 45 + 5x$$

$$x = 3$$

The number is 3.

9. **a-b.** Completing the table.

	d (miles)	r (mph)	t (hours)
Upstream	1.5	$5-x$	$\dfrac{1.5}{5-x}$
Downstream	3	$5+x$	$\dfrac{3}{5+x}$

c. The times are the same, so the equation is $\dfrac{3}{5+x} = \dfrac{1.5}{5-x}$.

d. Setting the times equal:

$$\frac{3}{5+x} = \frac{1.5}{5-x}$$

$$3(5-x) = 1.5(5+x)$$

$$15 - 3x = 7.5 + 1.5x$$

$$7.5 = 4.5x$$

$$x = \frac{75}{45} = \frac{5}{3}$$

The speed of the current is $\dfrac{5}{3}$ mph.

11. Let x represent the speed of the boat. Since the total time is 3 hours:

$$\frac{8}{x-2}+\frac{8}{x+2}=3$$

$$(x+2)(x-2)\left(\frac{8}{x-2}+\frac{8}{x+2}\right)=3(x+2)(x-2)$$

$$8(x+2)+8(x-2)=3x^2-12$$

$$16x=3x^2-12$$

$$0=3x^2-16x-12$$

$$0=(3x+2)(x-6)$$

$$x=6 \quad \left(x=-\frac{2}{3} \text{ is impossible}\right)$$

The speed of the boat is 6 mph.

13. **a-b.** Completing the table.

	d (miles)	r (mph)	t (hours)
Train A	150	$x+15$	$\dfrac{150}{x+15}$
Train B	120	x	$\dfrac{120}{x}$

c. The times are the same, so the equation is $\dfrac{150}{x+15}=\dfrac{120}{x}$.

d. Setting the times equal:

$$\frac{150}{x+15}=\frac{120}{x}$$

$$150x=120(x+15)$$

$$150x=120x+1800$$

$$30x=1800$$

$$x=60$$

The speed of train A is 75 mph and the speed of train B is 60 mph.

15. The smaller plane makes the trip in 3 hours, so the 747 must take $1\frac{1}{2}$ hours to complete the trip. Thus the average

speed is given by: $\dfrac{810 \text{ miles}}{1\frac{1}{2} \text{ hours}}=540$ miles per hour

17. Let r represent the bus's usual speed. The difference of the two times is $\frac{1}{2}$ hour, therefore:

$$\frac{270}{r}-\frac{270}{r+6}=\frac{1}{2}$$

$$2r(r+6)\left(\frac{270}{r}-\frac{270}{r+6}\right)=2r(r+6)\left(\frac{1}{2}\right)$$

$$540(r+6)-540(r)=r(r+6)$$

$$540r+3240-540r=r^2+6r$$

$$0=r^2+6r-3240$$

$$0=(r-54)(r+60)$$

$$r=54 \quad (r=-60 \text{ is impossible})$$

The usual speed is 54 mph.

19. Let x represent the time to fill the tank if both pipes are open. The rate equation is:

$$\frac{1}{8} - \frac{1}{16} = \frac{1}{x}$$

$$16x\left(\frac{1}{8} - \frac{1}{16}\right) = 16x\left(\frac{1}{x}\right)$$

$$2x - x = 16$$

$$x = 16$$

It will take 16 hours to fill the tank if both pipes are open.

21. Let x represent the time to fill the pool with both pipes open. The rate equation is:

$$\frac{1}{10} - \frac{1}{15} = \frac{1}{2} \cdot \frac{1}{x}$$

$$30x\left(\frac{1}{10} - \frac{1}{15}\right) = 30x\left(\frac{1}{2x}\right)$$

$$3x - 2x = 15$$

$$x = 15$$

It will take 15 hours to fill the pool with both pipes open.

23. Let x represent the time to fill the sink with the hot water faucet. The rate equation is:

$$\frac{1}{3.5} + \frac{1}{x} = \frac{1}{2.1}$$

$$7.35x\left(\frac{1}{3.5} + \frac{1}{x}\right) = 7.35x\left(\frac{1}{2.1}\right)$$

$$2.1x + 7.35 = 3.5x$$

$$7.35 = 1.4x$$

$$x = 5.25$$

It will take $5\frac{1}{4}$ minutes to fill the sink with the hot water faucet.

25. Let x represent the time to fill the sink with both pipes open. The rate equation is:

$$\frac{1}{3.5} + \frac{1}{2.7} = \frac{1}{x}$$

$$(3.5)(2.7)(x)\left(\frac{1}{3.5} + \frac{1}{2.7}\right) = (3.5)(2.7)(x)\left(\frac{1}{x}\right)$$

$$2.7x + 3.5x = 9.45$$

$$6.2x = 9.45$$

$$x = \frac{9.45}{6.2} \approx 1.52$$

It will take approximately 1.52 minutes to fill the sink with both pipes open.

27. Solving the equation:

$$\frac{1}{3}\left[\left(x + \frac{2}{3}x\right) + \frac{1}{3}\left(x + \frac{2}{3}x\right)\right] = 10$$

$$\left(x + \frac{2}{3}x\right) + \frac{1}{3}\left(x + \frac{2}{3}x\right) = 30$$

$$x + \frac{2}{3}x + \frac{1}{3}x + \frac{2}{9}x = 30$$

$$\frac{20}{9}x = 30$$

$$20x = 270$$

$$x = \frac{27}{2}$$

29. **a.** Finding the grams of carbon: $(2.5 \text{ moles})\left(\dfrac{12.01 \text{ grams}}{1 \text{ mole}}\right) \approx 30 \text{ grams}$

b. Finding the moles of carbon: $(39 \text{ grams})\left(\dfrac{1 \text{ mole}}{12.01 \text{ grams}}\right) \approx 3.25 \text{ moles}$

31. Sketching the graph:

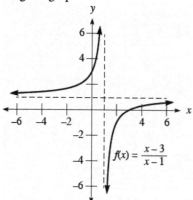

33. Sketching the graph:

$f(x) = \dfrac{x+3}{x-1}$

35. Sketching the graph:

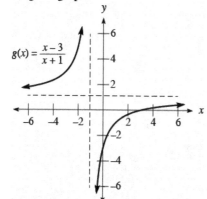

37. Sketching the graph:

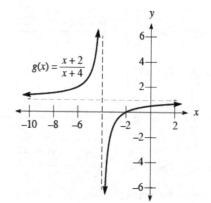

39. Finding the difference: $2{,}230{,}644 - 2{,}109{,}429 = 121{,}215$ fans

41. Dividing: $\dfrac{10x^5}{5x^2} = 2x^{5-2} = 2x^3$

43. Dividing: $\dfrac{4x^4 y^3}{-2x^2 y} = -2x^{4-2} y^{3-1} = -2x^2 y^2$

45. Dividing: $4{,}628 \div 25 = 185.12$

47. Dividing: $\dfrac{(x-3)^2}{x-3} = x-3$

49. Multiplying: $2x^2(2x-4) = 4x^3 - 8x^2$

51. Multiplying:
$$(2x-4)(2x^2+4x+5) = 2x(2x^2+4x+5) - 4(2x^2+4x+5)$$
$$= 4x^3 + 8x^2 + 10x - 8x^2 - 16x - 20$$
$$= 4x^3 - 6x - 20$$

53. Subtracting: $(2x^2 - 7x + 9) - (2x^2 - 4x) = 2x^2 - 7x + 9 - 2x^2 + 4x = -3x + 9$

55. Factoring: $x^2 - a^2 = (x+a)(x-a)$

57. Factoring: $x^2 - 6xy - 7y^2 = (x - 7y)(x + y)$

5.7 Division of Polynomials

1. Dividing: $\dfrac{4x^3 - 8x^2 + 6x}{2x} = \dfrac{4x^3}{2x} - \dfrac{8x^2}{2x} + \dfrac{6x}{2x} = 2x^2 - 4x + 3$

3. Dividing: $\dfrac{10x^4 + 15x^3 - 20x^2}{-5x^2} = \dfrac{10x^4}{-5x^2} + \dfrac{15x^3}{-5x^2} - \dfrac{20x^2}{-5x^2} = -2x^2 - 3x + 4$

5. Dividing: $\dfrac{8y^5 + 10y^3 - 6y}{4y^3} = \dfrac{8y^5}{4y^3} + \dfrac{10y^3}{4y^3} - \dfrac{6y}{4y^3} = 2y^2 + \dfrac{5}{2} - \dfrac{3}{2y^2}$

7. Dividing: $\dfrac{5x^3 - 8x^2 - 6x}{-2x^2} = \dfrac{5x^3}{-2x^2} - \dfrac{8x^2}{-2x^2} - \dfrac{6x}{-2x^2} = -\dfrac{5}{2}x + 4 + \dfrac{3}{x}$

9. Dividing: $\dfrac{28a^3b^5 + 42a^4b^3}{7a^2b^2} = \dfrac{28a^3b^5}{7a^2b^2} + \dfrac{42a^4b^3}{7a^2b^2} = 4ab^3 + 6a^2b$

11. Dividing: $\dfrac{10x^3y^2 - 20x^2y^3 - 30x^3y^3}{-10x^2y} = \dfrac{10x^3y^2}{-10x^2y} - \dfrac{20x^2y^3}{-10x^2y} - \dfrac{30x^3y^3}{-10x^2y} = -xy + 2y^2 + 3xy^2$

13. Dividing by factoring: $\dfrac{x^2 - x - 6}{x - 3} = \dfrac{(x - 3)(x + 2)}{x - 3} = x + 2$

15. Dividing by factoring: $\dfrac{2a^2 - 3a - 9}{2a + 3} = \dfrac{(2a + 3)(a - 3)}{2a + 3} = a - 3$

17. Dividing by factoring: $\dfrac{5x^2 - 14xy - 24y^2}{x - 4y} = \dfrac{(5x + 6y)(x - 4y)}{x - 4y} = 5x + 6y$

19. Dividing by factoring: $\dfrac{x^3 - y^3}{x - y} = \dfrac{(x - y)(x^2 + xy + y^2)}{x - y} = x^2 + xy + y^2$

21. Dividing by factoring: $\dfrac{y^4 - 16}{y - 2} = \dfrac{(y^2 + 4)(y^2 - 4)}{y - 2} = \dfrac{(y^2 + 4)(y + 2)(y - 2)}{y - 2} = (y^2 + 4)(y + 2)$

23. Dividing by factoring:

$$\dfrac{x^3 + 2x^2 - 25x - 50}{x - 5} = \dfrac{x^2(x + 2) - 25(x + 2)}{x - 5} = \dfrac{(x + 2)(x^2 - 25)}{x - 5} = \dfrac{(x + 2)(x + 5)(x - 5)}{x - 5} = (x + 2)(x + 5)$$

25. Dividing by factoring:

$$\dfrac{4x^3 + 12x^2 - 9x - 27}{x + 3} = \dfrac{4x^2(x + 3) - 9(x + 3)}{x + 3} = \dfrac{(x + 3)(4x^2 - 9)}{x + 3} = \dfrac{(x + 3)(2x + 3)(2x - 3)}{x + 3} = (2x + 3)(2x - 3)$$

27. Dividing using long division:

$$\require{enclose}
\begin{array}{r}
x - 7 \\
x + 2 \enclose{longdiv}{x^2 - 5x - 7} \\
\underline{x^2 + 2x} \\
-7x - 7 \\
\underline{-7x - 14} \\
7
\end{array}$$

The quotient is $x - 7 + \dfrac{7}{x + 2}$.

29. Dividing using long division:

$$\require{enclose}
\begin{array}{r}
2x + 5 \\
3x - 4 \enclose{longdiv}{6x^2 + 7x - 18} \\
\underline{6x^2 - 8x} \\
15x - 18 \\
\underline{15x - 20} \\
2
\end{array}$$

The quotient is $2x + 5 + \dfrac{2}{3x - 4}$.

31. Dividing using long division:

$$\begin{array}{r}
y^2 - 3y - 13 \\
2y-3\overline{\smash{\big)}\,2y^3 - 9y^2 - 17y + 39} \\
\underline{2y^3 - 3y^2} \\
-6y^2 - 17y \\
\underline{-6y^2 + 9y} \\
-26y + 39 \\
\underline{-26y + 39} \\
0
\end{array}$$

The quotient is $y^2 - 3y - 13$.

35. Dividing using long division:

$$\begin{array}{r}
3y^2 + 6y + 8 \\
2y-4\overline{\smash{\big)}\,6y^3 + 0y^2 - 8y + 5} \\
\underline{6y^3 - 12y^2} \\
12y^2 - 8y \\
\underline{12y^2 - 24y} \\
16y + 5 \\
\underline{16y - 32} \\
37
\end{array}$$

The quotient is $3y^2 + 6y + 8 + \dfrac{37}{2y-4}$.

39. Dividing using long division:

$$\begin{array}{r}
y^3 + 2y^2 + 4y + 8 \\
y-2\overline{\smash{\big)}\,y^4 + 0y^3 + 0y^2 + 0y - 16} \\
\underline{y^4 - 2y^3} \\
2y^3 + 0y^2 \\
\underline{2y^3 - 4y^2} \\
4y^2 + 0y \\
\underline{4y^2 - 8y} \\
8y - 16 \\
\underline{8y - 16} \\
0
\end{array}$$

The quotient is $y^3 + 2y^2 + 4y + 8$.

33. Dividing using long division:

$$\begin{array}{r}
x - 3 \\
2x^2 - 3x + 2\overline{\smash{\big)}\,2x^3 - 9x^2 + 11x - 6} \\
\underline{2x^3 - 3x^2 + 2x} \\
-6x^2 + 9x - 6 \\
\underline{-6x^2 + 9x - 6} \\
0
\end{array}$$

The quotient is $x - 3$.

37. Dividing using long division:

$$\begin{array}{r}
a^3 + 2a^2 + 4a + 6 \\
a-2\overline{\smash{\big)}\,a^4 + 0a^3 + 0a^2 - 2a + 5} \\
\underline{a^4 - 2a^3} \\
2a^3 + 0a^2 \\
\underline{2a^3 - 4a^2} \\
4a^2 - 2a \\
\underline{4a^2 - 8a} \\
6a + 5 \\
\underline{6a - 12} \\
17
\end{array}$$

The quotient is $a^3 + 2a^2 + 4a + 6 + \dfrac{17}{a-2}$.

41. Finding the quotient using long division:

$$\begin{array}{r}
2x^2 - 5x + 1 \\
x+1\overline{\smash{\big)}\,2x^3 - 3x^2 - 4x + 5} \\
\underline{2x^3 + 2x^2} \\
-5x^2 - 4x \\
\underline{-5x^2 - 5x} \\
x + 5 \\
\underline{x + 1} \\
4
\end{array}$$

The quotient is $\dfrac{p(x)}{q(x)} = 2x^2 - 5x + 1 + \dfrac{4}{x+1}$.

43. Finding the quotient using long division:

$$
\begin{array}{r}
x^2 - 2x + 1 \\
x^2 + 3x + 2 \overline{)\,x^4 +\ x^3 - 3x^2 -\ x + 2} \\
\underline{x^4 + 3x^3 + 2x^2} \\
-2x^3 - 5x^2 -\ x \\
\underline{-2x^3 - 6x^2 - 4x} \\
x^2 + 3x + 2 \\
\underline{x^2 + 3x + 2} \\
0
\end{array}
$$

The quotient is $\dfrac{p(x)}{q(x)} = x^2 - 2x + 1$.

45. Using long division:

$$
\begin{array}{r}
x^2 + 3x + 2 \\
x + 3 \overline{)\,x^3 + 6x^2 + 11x + 6} \\
\underline{x^3 + 3x^2} \\
3x^2 + 11x \\
\underline{3x^2 +\ 9x} \\
2x + 6 \\
\underline{2x + 6} \\
0
\end{array}
$$

So $x^3 + 6x^2 + 11x + 6 = (x+3)\left(x^2 + 3x + 2\right) = (x+3)(x+2)(x+1)$.

47. Using long division:

$$
\begin{array}{r}
x^2 + 2x - 8 \\
x + 3 \overline{)\,x^3 + 5x^2 - 2x - 24} \\
\underline{x^3 + 3x^2} \\
2x^2 - 2x \\
\underline{2x^2 + 6x} \\
-8x - 24 \\
\underline{-8x - 24} \\
0
\end{array}
$$

So $x^3 + 5x^2 - 2x - 24 = (x+3)\left(x^2 + 2x - 8\right) = (x+3)(x+4)(x-2)$.

49. Yes, the two answers are equivalent.

51. Evaluating the function: $P(-2) = (-2)^2 - 5(-2) - 7 = 4 + 10 - 7 = 7$

The remainder is the same (7).

53. **a.** Using long division:

$$
\begin{array}{r}
x^2 - x + 3 \\
x - 2 \overline{\smash{\big)}\ x^3 - 3x^2 + 5x - 6} \\
\underline{x^3 - 2x^2} \\
-x^2 + 5x \\
\underline{-x^2 + 2x} \\
3x - 6 \\
\underline{3x - 6} \\
0
\end{array}
$$

Since the remainder is 0, $x - 2$ is a factor of $x^3 - 3x^2 + 5x - 6$.

Also note that: $P(2) = (2)^3 - 3(2)^2 + 5(2) - 6 = 8 - 12 + 10 - 6 = 0$

b. Using long division:

$$
\begin{array}{r}
x^3 - x + 1 \\
x - 5 \overline{\smash{\big)}\ x^4 - 5x^3 - x^2 + 6x - 5} \\
\underline{x^4 - 5x^3} \\
-x^2 + 6x \\
\underline{-x^2 + 5x} \\
x - 5 \\
\underline{x - 5} \\
0
\end{array}
$$

Since the remainder is 0, $x - 5$ is a factor of $x^4 - 5x^3 - x^2 + 6x - 5$.

Also note that: $P(5) = (5)^4 - 5(5)^3 - (5)^2 + 6(5) - 5 = 625 - 625 - 25 + 30 - 5 = 0$

55. **a.** Evaluating: $p(4) = (4)^3 + (4)^2 - 14(4) - 24 = 64 + 16 - 56 - 24 = 0$

b. Using long division:

$$
\begin{array}{r}
x^2 + 5x + 6 \\
x - 4 \overline{\smash{\big)}\ x^3 + \ x^2 - 14x - 24} \\
\underline{x^3 - 4x^2} \\
5x^2 - 14x \\
\underline{5x^2 - 20x} \\
6x - 24 \\
\underline{6x - 24} \\
0
\end{array}
$$

So $p(x) = x^3 + x^2 - 14x - 24 = (x - 4)(x^2 + 5x + 6) = (x - 4)(x + 2)(x + 3)$.

57. **a.** Completing the table:

x	1	5	10	15	20
$C(x)$	2.15	2.75	3.50	4.25	5.00

b. The average cost function is $\bar{C}(x) = \dfrac{2}{x} + 0.15$.

c. Completing the table:

x	1	5	10	15	20
$\bar{C}(x)$	2.15	0.55	0.35	0.28	0.25

d. The average cost function decreases.

e. Sketching the graphs:

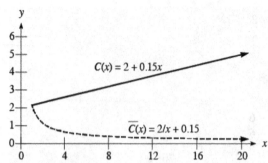

f. For $C(x)$, the domain is $\{x\,|\,1\le x\le 20\}$ and the range is $\{y\,|\,2.15\le y\le 5.00\}$.

For $\overline{C}(x)$, the domain is $\{x\,|\,1\le x\le 20\}$ and the range is $\{y\,|\,0.25\le y\le 2.15\}$.

59. **a.** Evaluating the total cost:

$$T(100)=4.95+0.07(100)=\$11.95$$
$$T(400)=4.95+0.07(400)=\$32.95$$
$$T(500)=4.95+0.07(500)=\$39.95$$

b. The average cost function is given by: $\overline{T}(m)=\dfrac{4.95+0.07m}{m}=0.07+\dfrac{4.95}{m}$

c. Evaluating the average cost:

$$\overline{T}(100)=0.07+\frac{4.95}{100}=\$0.1195$$
$$\overline{T}(100)=0.07+\frac{4.95}{400}\approx\$0.0824$$
$$\overline{T}(100)=0.07+\frac{4.95}{500}=\$0.0799$$

61. Finding the amount of people using Google Chrome: $0.0062(239,893,600)\approx 1,487,340$ people

63. Performing the operations: $\dfrac{2a+10}{a^3}\cdot\dfrac{a^2}{3a+15}=\dfrac{2(a+5)}{a^3}\cdot\dfrac{a^2}{3(a+5)}=\dfrac{2}{3a}$

65. Performing the operations: $\left(x^2-9\right)\left(\dfrac{x+2}{x+3}\right)=(x+3)(x-3)\left(\dfrac{x+2}{x+3}\right)=(x-3)(x+2)$

67. Performing the operations: $\dfrac{2x-7}{x-2}-\dfrac{x-5}{x-2}=\dfrac{2x-7-x+5}{x-2}=\dfrac{x-2}{x-2}=1$

69. Simplifying the expression: $\dfrac{\dfrac{1}{x}-\dfrac{1}{3}}{\dfrac{1}{x}+\dfrac{1}{3}}=\dfrac{\left(\dfrac{1}{x}-\dfrac{1}{3}\right)\cdot 3x}{\left(\dfrac{1}{x}+\dfrac{1}{3}\right)\cdot 3x}=\dfrac{3-x}{3+x}$

71. Solving the equation:

$$\frac{x}{x-3}+\frac{3}{2}=\frac{3}{x-3}$$
$$2(x-3)\left(\frac{x}{x-3}+\frac{3}{2}\right)=2(x-3)\left(\frac{3}{x-3}\right)$$
$$2x+3(x-3)=6$$
$$2x+3x-9=6$$
$$5x=15$$
$$x=3 \quad (\text{does not check})$$

There is no solution (3 does not check).

73. Simplifying: $16(3.5)^2 = 16(12.25) = 196$

75. Simplifying: $\dfrac{180}{45} = 4$

77. Simplifying: $\dfrac{0.0005(200)}{(0.25)^2} = \dfrac{0.1}{0.0625} = 1.6$

79. Solving for k:

$15 = k(5)$
$k = 3$

81. Solving for k:

$50 = \dfrac{k}{48}$
$k = 50 \cdot 48 = 2,400$

5.8 Variation

1. The variation equation is $y = kx$. Substituting $x = 2$ and $y = 10$:

$10 = k \cdot 2$
$k = 5$

So $y = 5x$. Substituting $x = 6$: $y = 5 \cdot 6 = 30$

3. The variation equation is $r = \dfrac{k}{s}$. Substituting $s = 4$ and $r = -3$:

$-3 = \dfrac{k}{4}$
$k = -12$

So $r = \dfrac{-12}{s}$. Substituting $s = 2$: $r = \dfrac{-12}{2} = -6$

5. The variation equation is $d = kr^2$. Substituting $r = 5$ and $d = 10$:

$10 = k \cdot 5^2$
$10 = 25k$
$k = \dfrac{2}{5}$

So $d = \dfrac{2}{5}r^2$. Substituting $r = 10$: $d = \dfrac{2}{5}(10)^2 = \dfrac{2}{5} \cdot 100 = 40$

7. The variation equation is $y = \dfrac{k}{x^2}$. Substituting $x = 3$ and $y = 45$:

$45 = \dfrac{k}{3^2}$
$45 = \dfrac{k}{9}$
$k = 405$

So $y = \dfrac{405}{x^2}$. Substituting $x = 5$: $y = \dfrac{405}{5^2} = \dfrac{405}{25} = \dfrac{81}{5}$

9. The variation equation is $z = kxy^2$. Substituting $x = 3$, $y = 3$, and $z = 54$:

$54 = k(3)(3)^2$
$54 = 27k$
$k = 2$

So $z = 2xy^2$. Substituting $x = 2$ and $y = 4$: $z = 2(2)(4)^2 = 64$

11. The variation equation is $I = \dfrac{k}{w^3}$. Substituting $I = 32$ and $w = \dfrac{1}{2}$:

$$32 = \frac{k}{\left(\dfrac{1}{2}\right)^3}$$

$$32 = \frac{k}{\dfrac{1}{8}}$$

$$k = 4$$

So $I = \dfrac{4}{w^3}$. Substituting $w = \dfrac{1}{3}$: $I = \dfrac{4}{\left(\dfrac{1}{3}\right)^3} = \dfrac{4}{\dfrac{1}{27}} = 108$

13. The variation equation is $z = kyx^2$. Substituting $x = 3, y = 2$, and $z = 72$:

$$72 = k(2)(3)^2$$
$$72 = 18k$$
$$k = 4$$

So $z = 4yx^2$. Substituting $x = 5$ and $y = 3$: $z = 4(3)(5)^2 = 300$

15. The variation equation is $z = kyx^2$. Substituting $x = 1, y = 5$, and $z = 25$:

$$25 = k(5)(1)^2$$
$$25 = 5k$$
$$k = 5$$

So $z = 5yx^2$. Substituting $z = 160$ and $y = 8$:

$$160 = 5(8)x^2$$
$$160 = 40x^2$$
$$x^2 = 4$$
$$x = \pm 2$$

17. The variation equation is $F = \dfrac{km}{d^2}$. Substituting $F = 150, m = 240$, and $d = 8$:

$$150 = \frac{k(240)}{8^2}$$
$$150 = \frac{240k}{64}$$
$$k = \frac{(150)(64)}{240} = 40$$

So $F = \dfrac{40m}{d^2}$. Substituting $m = 360$ and $d = 3$: $F = \dfrac{40(360)}{3^2} = 1,600$

19. The variation equation is $F = \dfrac{km}{d^2}$. Substituting $F = 24, m = 20$, and $d = 5$:

$$24 = \frac{k(20)}{5^2}$$
$$24 = \frac{20k}{25}$$
$$k = \frac{(24)(25)}{20} = 30$$

So $F = \dfrac{30m}{d^2}$. Substituting $m = 40$ and $F = 18.75$:

$$18.75 = \frac{30(40)}{d^2}$$
$$18.75d^2 = 1200$$
$$d^2 = 64$$
$$d = \pm 8$$

21.   Let l represent the length and f represent the force. The variation equation is $l = kf$. Substituting $f = 5$ and $l = 3$:

$$3 = k \cdot 5$$
$$k = \frac{3}{5}$$

So $l = \dfrac{3}{5} f$. Substituting $l = 10$:

$$10 = \frac{3}{5} f$$
$$50 = 3f$$
$$f = \frac{50}{3}$$

The force required is $\dfrac{50}{3}$ pounds.

23.   **a.**   The variation equation is $T = 4P$.

        b.   Graphing the equation:

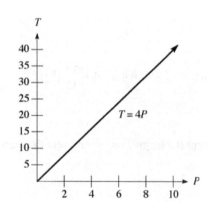

        c.   Substituting $T = 280$:

$$280 = 4P$$
$$P = 70$$

          The pressure is 70 pounds per square inch.

25.   Let v represent the volume and p represent the pressure. The variation equation is $v = \dfrac{k}{p}$.

Substituting $p = 36$ and $v = 25$:

$$25 = \frac{k}{36}$$
$$k = 900$$

The equation is $v = \dfrac{900}{p}$. Substituting $v = 75$:

$$75 = \frac{900}{p}$$
$$75p = 900$$
$$p = 12$$

The pressure is 12 pounds per square inch.

27. **a.** The variation equation is $f = \dfrac{80}{d}$.

b. Graphing the equation:

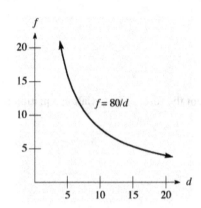

$f = 80/d$

c. Substituting $d = 10$:

$$f = \frac{80}{10}$$
$$f = 8$$

The f-stop is 8.

29. Let A represent the surface area, h represent the height, and r represent the radius. The variation equation is $A = khr$.
Substituting $A = 94$, $r = 3$, and $h = 5$:

$$94 = k(3)(5)$$
$$94 = 15k$$
$$k = \frac{94}{15}$$

The equation is $A = \dfrac{94}{15}hr$. Substituting $r = 2$ and $h = 8$: $A = \dfrac{94}{15}(8)(2) = \dfrac{1504}{15}$.

The surface area is $\dfrac{1504}{15}$ square inches

31. Let R represent the resistance, l represent the length, and d represent the diameter. The variation equation is $R = \dfrac{kl}{d^2}$.

Substituting $R = 10$, $l = 100$, and $d = 0.01$:

$$10 = \frac{k(100)}{(0.01)^2}$$
$$0.001 = 100k$$
$$k = 0.00001$$

The equation is $R = \dfrac{0.00001l}{d^2}$. Substituting $l = 60$ and $d = 0.02$: $R = \dfrac{0.00001(60)}{(0.02)^2} = 1.5$. The resistance is 1.5 ohms.

33. Let P represent the time (period) and L represent the length.

a. The variation equation is $P = k\sqrt{L}$. Substituting $P = 2.1$ and $L = 100$:

$$2.1 = k\sqrt{100}$$
$$2.1 = 10k$$
$$k = 0.21$$

The equation is $P = 0.21\sqrt{L}$.

b. Graphing the equation:

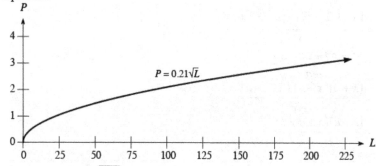

c. Substituting $L = 225$: $P = 0.21\sqrt{225} = 0.21(15) = 3.15$ seconds

35. Multiplying: $0.6(M-70) = 0.6M - 42$

37. Multiplying: $(4x-3)(4x^2-7x+3) = 4x^3 - 28x^2 + 12x - 12x^2 + 21x - 9 = 4x^3 - 40x^2 + 33x - 9$

39. Simplifying: $(4x-3) + (4x^2-7x+3) = 4x^2 - 3x$

41. Simplifying: $(4x^2+3x+2) + (2x^2-5x-6) = 6x^2 - 2x - 4$

43. Simplifying: $4(-1)^2 - 7(-1) = 4(1) + 7 = 4 + 7 = 11$

Chapter 5 Review

1. Reducing the fraction: $\dfrac{2x^2-3xy+y^2}{2x-y} = \dfrac{(2x-y)(x-y)}{2x-y} = x-y$

2. Reducing the fraction: $\dfrac{3x^2-4x-4}{3x^2-x-2} = \dfrac{(3x+2)(x-2)}{(3x+2)(x-1)} = \dfrac{x-2}{x-1}$

3. Finding the speed: $\dfrac{(3.14)(75 \text{ feet})}{70 \text{ seconds}} \cdot \dfrac{60 \text{ seconds}}{1 \text{ minute}} = \dfrac{14{,}130 \text{ feet}}{70 \text{ minutes}} \approx 201.9$ feet/minute

4. **a.** Finding the difference quotient: $\dfrac{f(x+h)-f(x)}{h} = \dfrac{3(x+h)+5-(3x+5)}{h} = \dfrac{3x+3h+5-3x-5}{h} = \dfrac{3h}{h} = 3$

   b. Finding the difference quotient: $\dfrac{f(x)-f(a)}{x-a} = \dfrac{(3x+5)-(3a+5)}{x-a} = \dfrac{3x-3a}{x-a} = \dfrac{3(x-a)}{x-a} = 3$

5. **a.** Finding the difference quotient:

$$\dfrac{f(x+h)-f(x)}{h} = \dfrac{(x+h)^2 + 2(x+h) - 8 - (x^2+2x-8)}{h}$$
$$= \dfrac{x^2 + 2xh + h^2 + 2x + 2h - 8 - x^2 - 2x + 8}{h}$$
$$= \dfrac{2xh + h^2 + 2h}{h}$$
$$= \dfrac{h(2x+h+2)}{h}$$
$$= 2x + h + 2$$

b. Finding the difference quotient:

$$\frac{f(x)-f(a)}{x-a} = \frac{\left(x^2+2x-8\right)-\left(a^2+2a-8\right)}{x-a}$$

$$= \frac{x^2-a^2+2x-2a}{x-a}$$

$$= \frac{(x+a)(x-a)+2(x-a)}{x-a}$$

$$= \frac{(x-a)(x+a+2)}{x-a}$$

$$= x+a+2$$

6. Performing the operations: $\dfrac{x^2-16}{3x+12} \cdot \dfrac{3(x+3)^2}{x^2-x-12} = \dfrac{(x+4)(x-4)}{3(x+4)} \cdot \dfrac{3(x+3)^2}{(x-4)(x+3)} = x+3$

7. Performing the operations:

$$\frac{x^4-81}{2x^2-9x+9} \div \frac{x^2+9}{10x-15} = \frac{x^4-81}{2x^2-9x+9} \cdot \frac{10x-15}{x^2+9} = \frac{\left(x^2+9\right)(x+3)(x-3)}{(2x-3)(x-3)} \cdot \frac{5(2x-3)}{x^2+9} = 5(x+3)$$

8. Performing the operations:

$$\frac{4x^2+6x-4}{2x^2-11x+5} \div \frac{x^3-8}{x^2-7x+10} = \frac{4x^2+6x-4}{2x^2-11x+5} \cdot \frac{x^2-7x+10}{x^3-8}$$

$$= \frac{2(2x-1)(x+2)}{(2x-1)(x-5)} \cdot \frac{(x-2)(x-5)}{(x-2)\left(x^2+2x+4\right)}$$

$$= \frac{2(x+2)}{x^2+2x+4}$$

9. Performing the operations: $\dfrac{3}{14}+\dfrac{9}{20} = \dfrac{3}{14} \cdot \dfrac{10}{10} + \dfrac{9}{20} \cdot \dfrac{7}{7} = \dfrac{30}{140}+\dfrac{63}{140} = \dfrac{93}{140}$

10. Performing the operations: $\dfrac{1}{2}-\dfrac{7}{24}+\dfrac{5}{6} = \dfrac{1}{2} \cdot \dfrac{12}{12}-\dfrac{7}{24}+\dfrac{5}{6} \cdot \dfrac{4}{4} = \dfrac{12}{24}-\dfrac{7}{24}+\dfrac{20}{24} = \dfrac{25}{24}$

11. Performing the operations: $\dfrac{a+7}{a^2-81}+\dfrac{2}{a^2-81} = \dfrac{a+9}{a^2-81} = \dfrac{a+9}{(a+9)(a-9)} = \dfrac{1}{a-9}$

12. Performing the operations:

$$\frac{3}{x-1}+\frac{6}{2x-1} = \frac{3}{x-1} \cdot \frac{2x-1}{2x-1}+\frac{6}{2x-1} \cdot \frac{x-1}{x-1} = \frac{6x-3}{(x-1)(2x-1)}+\frac{6x-6}{(x-1)(2x-1)} = \frac{12x-9}{(x-1)(2x-1)} = \frac{3(4x-3)}{(x-1)(2x-1)}$$

13. Performing the operations:

$$\frac{4x}{x^2+2x-3}-\frac{2x}{x^2-1}=\frac{4x}{(x+3)(x-1)}-\frac{2x}{(x+1)(x-1)}$$

$$=\frac{4x}{(x+3)(x-1)}\cdot\frac{x+1}{x+1}-\frac{2x}{(x+1)(x-1)}\cdot\frac{x+3}{x+3}$$

$$=\frac{4x^2+4x}{(x+3)(x+1)(x-1)}-\frac{2x^2+6x}{(x+3)(x+1)(x-1)}$$

$$=\frac{4x^2+4x-2x^2-6x}{(x+3)(x+1)(x-1)}$$

$$=\frac{2x^2-2x}{(x+3)(x+1)(x-1)}$$

$$=\frac{2x(x-1)}{(x+3)(x+1)(x-1)}$$

$$=\frac{2x}{(x+3)(x+1)}$$

14. Performing the operations:

$$\frac{2x-1}{x^2-1}-\frac{x+4}{x^2+4x+3}=\frac{2x-1}{(x+1)(x-1)}-\frac{x+4}{(x+3)(x+1)}$$

$$=\frac{2x-1}{(x+1)(x-1)}\cdot\frac{x+3}{x+3}-\frac{x+4}{(x+3)(x+1)}\cdot\frac{x-1}{x-1}$$

$$=\frac{2x^2+5x-3}{(x+1)(x-1)(x+3)}-\frac{x^2+3x-4}{(x+1)(x-1)(x+3)}$$

$$=\frac{2x^2+5x-3-x^2-3x+4}{(x+1)(x-1)(x+3)}$$

$$=\frac{x^2+2x+1}{(x+1)(x-1)(x+3)}$$

$$=\frac{(x+1)^2}{(x+1)(x-1)(x+3)}$$

$$=\frac{x+1}{(x-1)(x+3)}$$

15. Simplifying the complex fraction: $\dfrac{4-\dfrac{1}{a+2}}{4+\dfrac{1}{a+2}}=\dfrac{\left(4-\dfrac{1}{a+2}\right)(a+2)}{\left(4+\dfrac{1}{a+2}\right)(a+2)}=\dfrac{4(a+2)-1}{4(a+2)+1}=\dfrac{4a+8-1}{4a+8+1}=\dfrac{4a+7}{4a+9}$

16. Simplifying the complex fraction: $\dfrac{1-\dfrac{16}{x^2}}{1-\dfrac{1}{x}-\dfrac{12}{x^2}}=\dfrac{\left(1-\dfrac{16}{x^2}\right)\bullet x^2}{\left(1-\dfrac{1}{x}-\dfrac{12}{x^2}\right)\bullet x^2}=\dfrac{x^2-16}{x^2-x-12}=\dfrac{(x+4)(x-4)}{(x+3)(x-4)}=\dfrac{x+4}{x+3}$

17. Solving the equation:

$$5 - \frac{2}{x} = \frac{9}{5}$$

$$5x\left(5 - \frac{2}{x}\right) = 5x\left(\frac{9}{5}\right)$$

$$25x - 10 = 9x$$

$$16x = 10$$

$$x = \frac{5}{8}$$

18. Solving the equation:

$$\frac{3x}{x+2} + \frac{3}{2} = \frac{9}{x+1}$$

$$2(x+2)(x+1)\left(\frac{3x}{x+2} + \frac{3}{2}\right) = 2(x+2)(x+1)\left(\frac{9}{x+1}\right)$$

$$6x(x+1) + 3(x+2)(x+1) = 18(x+2)$$

$$6x^2 + 6x + 3x^2 + 9x + 6 = 18x + 36$$

$$9x^2 + 15x + 6 = 18x + 36$$

$$9x^2 - 3x - 30 = 0$$

$$3(3x^2 - x - 10) = 0$$

$$3(3x+5)(x-2) = 0$$

$$x = -\frac{5}{3}, 2$$

19. Solving the equation:

$$\frac{4}{x+5} + \frac{x+6}{8x} = \frac{7}{8}$$

$$8x(x+5)\left(\frac{4}{x+5} + \frac{x+6}{8x}\right) = 8x(x+5)\left(\frac{7}{8}\right)$$

$$32x + (x+6)(x+5) = 7x(x+5)$$

$$32x + x^2 + 11x + 30 = 7x^2 + 35x$$

$$x^2 + 43x + 30 = 7x^2 + 35x$$

$$0 = 6x^2 - 8x - 30$$

$$2(3x^2 - 4x - 15) = 0$$

$$2(3x+5)(x-3) = 0$$

$$x = -\frac{5}{3}, 3$$

20. Solving the equation:

$$1 = \frac{11}{x} - \frac{30}{x^2}$$

$$x^2(1) = x^2\left(\frac{11}{x} - \frac{30}{x^2}\right)$$

$$x^2 = 11x - 30$$

$$x^2 - 11x + 30 = 0$$

$$(x-5)(x-6) = 0$$

$$x = 5, 6$$

21. Let x represent the number. The equation is:

$$\frac{23}{63+x} = \frac{1}{3}$$

$$69 = 63 + x$$

$$x = 6$$

The number is 6.

22. Let x represent the speed of the boat. Since the total time is 11 hours:

$$\frac{36}{x-7} + \frac{36}{x+7} = 11$$

$$(x-7)(x+7)\left(\frac{36}{x-7} + \frac{36}{x+7}\right) = 11(x-7)(x+7)$$

$$36(x+7) + 36(x-7) = 11(x^2 - 49)$$

$$36x + 252 + 36x - 252 = 11x^2 - 539$$

$$0 = 11x^2 - 72x - 539$$

$$0 = (11x+49)(x-11)$$

$$x = 11 \quad \left(x = -\frac{49}{11} \text{ is impossible}\right)$$

The speed of the boat is 11 mph.

23. Let x represent the time to fill the pool with both the pipe and drain open. The rate equation is:

$$\frac{1}{5} - \frac{1}{6} = \frac{1}{x}$$

$$30x\left(\frac{1}{5} - \frac{1}{6}\right) = 30x\left(\frac{1}{x}\right)$$

$$6x - 5x = 30$$

$$x = 30$$

The pool can be filled in 30 hours with both the pipe and drain open.

24. Dividing: $\dfrac{8x^4y^2 - 20x^5y + 28x^2y^3}{4x^2y} = \dfrac{8x^4y^2}{4x^2y} - \dfrac{20x^5y}{4x^2y} + \dfrac{28x^2y^3}{4x^2y} = 2x^2y - 5x^3 + 7y^2$

25. Dividing using long division:

$$
\begin{array}{r}
3x^2 + 2x + 4 \\
3x-5\overline{\smash{\big)}\,9x^3 - 9x^2 + 2x - 12} \\
\underline{9x^3 - 15x^2} \\
6x^2 + 2x \\
\underline{6x^2 - 10x} \\
12x - 12 \\
\underline{12x - 20} \\
8
\end{array}
$$

The quotient is $3x^2 + 2x + 4 + \dfrac{8}{3x-5}$.

26. The variation equation is $y = \dfrac{k}{x^2}$. Substituting $x = 3$ and $y = 6$:

$$6 = \frac{k}{3^2}$$

$$6 = \frac{k}{9}$$

$$k = 54$$

So $y = \dfrac{54}{x^2}$. Substituting $x = 6$: $y = \dfrac{54}{6^2} = \dfrac{54}{36} = \dfrac{3}{2}$

27. The variation equation is $z = kxy^3$. Substituting $x = 4$, $y = 3$, and $z = 216$:

$$216 = k(4)(3)^3$$

$$216 = 108k$$

$$k = 2$$

So $z = 2xy^3$. Substituting $x = 7$ and $y = 2$: $z = 2(7)(2)^3 = 112$

Chapter 5 Cumulative Review

1. Simplifying: $\left(-\dfrac{5}{3}\right)^3 = \left(-\dfrac{5}{3}\right)\left(-\dfrac{5}{3}\right)\left(-\dfrac{5}{3}\right) = -\dfrac{125}{27}$

2. Simplifying: $\left(\dfrac{8}{7}\right)^{-2} = \left(\dfrac{7}{8}\right)^2 = \dfrac{49}{64}$

3. Simplifying: $|-18-32|-90 = |-50|-90 = 50-90 = -40$

4. Simplifying: $3^3 - 6\left(5^2 - 6^2\right) = 27 - 6(25-36) = 27 - 6(-11) = 27 + 66 = 93$

5. Simplifying: $81 \div 18 \cdot 2 = \dfrac{9}{2} \cdot 2 = 9$

6. Simplifying: $36 \div 12 \cdot 4 = 3 \cdot 4 = 12$

7. Simplifying: $\dfrac{2^4 - 5}{11\left(6^2 - 5^2\right)} = \dfrac{16-5}{11(36-25)} = \dfrac{11}{11(11)} = \dfrac{1}{11}$

8. Simplifying: $\dfrac{-5^2(4-4\cdot 2)}{19 + 3^4} = \dfrac{-25(4-8)}{19+81} = \dfrac{-25(-4)}{100} = \dfrac{100}{100} = 1$

9. Computing the value: $-3 \cdot \dfrac{7}{15} - \dfrac{4}{5} = -\dfrac{7}{5} - \dfrac{4}{5} = -\dfrac{11}{5}$

10. Writing in symbols: $2a - 9b > 2a + 9b$

11. Evaluating: $P(10) = 14(10) - 0.01(10)^2 = 140 - 0.01(100) = 140 - 1 = 139$

12. Evaluating: $P(-10) = 14(-10) - 0.01(-10)^2 = -140 - 0.01(100) = -140 - 1 = -141$

13. Evaluating: $Q(10) = \dfrac{5}{4}(10)^2 + \dfrac{1}{5}(10) - 33 = \dfrac{5}{4}(100) + \dfrac{1}{5}(10) - 33 = 125 + 2 - 33 = 94$

14. Evaluating: $Q(-10) = \dfrac{5}{4}(-10)^2 + \dfrac{1}{5}(-10) - 33 = \dfrac{5}{4}(100) + \dfrac{1}{5}(-10) - 33 = 125 - 2 - 33 = 90$

15. Simplifying: $-4(4x+5) - 11x = -16x - 20 - 11x = -27x - 20$

16. Simplifying: $(x+5)^2 - (x-5)^2 = \left(x^2 + 10x + 25\right) - \left(x^2 - 10x + 25\right) = x^2 + 10x + 25 - x^2 + 10x - 25 = 20x$

17. Subtracting:

$$\dfrac{5}{y^2 + y - 6} - \dfrac{4}{y^2 - 4} = \dfrac{5}{(y+3)(y-2)} \cdot \dfrac{y+2}{y+2} - \dfrac{4}{(y+2)(y-2)} \cdot \dfrac{y+3}{y+3}$$

$$= \dfrac{5y+10}{(y+3)(y-2)(y+2)} - \dfrac{4y+12}{(y+3)(y-2)(y+2)}$$

$$= \dfrac{5y+10-4y-12}{(y+3)(y-2)(y+2)}$$

$$= \dfrac{y-2}{(y+3)(y-2)(y+2)}$$

$$= \dfrac{1}{(y+3)(y+2)}$$

18. Subtracting: $\dfrac{x}{y^2 - x^2} + \dfrac{y}{y^2 - x^2} = \dfrac{x+y}{y^2 - x^2} = \dfrac{x+y}{(y+x)(y-x)} = \dfrac{1}{y-x}$

19. Multiplying: $\left(5t^2 + \dfrac{1}{4}\right)\left(4t^2 - \dfrac{1}{5}\right) = 20t^4 - t^2 + t^2 - \dfrac{1}{20} = 20t^4 - \dfrac{1}{20}$

20. Multiplying: $\dfrac{x^2 - 81}{x^2 + 5x + 6} \cdot \dfrac{x+2}{x+9} = \dfrac{(x+9)(x-9)}{(x+2)(x+3)} \cdot \dfrac{x+2}{x+9} = \dfrac{x-9}{x+3}$

21. Dividing: $\dfrac{9x^{7n} - 6x^{4n}}{3x^{2n}} = \dfrac{9x^{7n}}{3x^{2n}} - \dfrac{6x^{4n}}{3x^{2n}} = 3x^{5n} - 2x^{2n}$

22. Dividing using long division:

$$a-1 \overline{\smash{\big)}\,2a^5+0a^4+0a^3+\ a^2+0a-8}$$

Quotient: $2a^4+2a^3+2a^2+3a+3$

$$
\begin{array}{r}
\underline{2a^5-2a^4} \\
2a^4+0a^3 \\
\underline{2a^4-2a^3} \\
2a^3+\ a^2 \\
\underline{2a^3-2a^2} \\
3a^2+0a \\
\underline{3a^2-3a} \\
3a-8 \\
\underline{3a-3} \\
-5
\end{array}
$$

The quotient is $2a^4+2a^3+2a^2+3a+3-\dfrac{5}{a-1}$.

23. Simplifying: $\dfrac{x^{-6}}{x^{-11}}=x^{-6+11}=x^5$

24. Simplifying: $\left(\dfrac{x^{-5}y^{-8}}{x^2y^{-6}}\right)^{-1}=\dfrac{x^2y^{-6}}{x^{-5}y^{-8}}=x^{2+5}y^{-6+8}=x^7y^2$

25. Simplifying: $\dfrac{x^3+3x^2-25x-75}{x^2-2x-15}=\dfrac{x^2(x+3)-25(x+3)}{(x-5)(x+3)}=\dfrac{(x+3)(x+5)(x-5)}{(x-5)(x+3)}=x+5$

26. Simplifying:

$$\dfrac{\dfrac{7a}{4a^3-4}}{\dfrac{14a}{8a-8}}=\dfrac{7a}{4a^3-4}\div\dfrac{14a}{8a-8}$$

$$=\dfrac{7a}{4a^3-4}\cdot\dfrac{8a-8}{14a}$$

$$=\dfrac{7a}{4(a-1)(a^2+a+1)}\cdot\dfrac{8(a-1)}{14a}$$

$$=\dfrac{56a(a-1)}{56a(a-1)(a^2+a+1)}$$

$$=\dfrac{1}{a^2+a+1}$$

27. First find the slope: $m=\dfrac{1-4}{10-5}=\dfrac{-3}{5}=-\dfrac{3}{5}$. Using the point-slope formula:

$$y-4=-\dfrac{3}{5}(x-5)$$

$$y-4=-\dfrac{3}{5}x+3$$

$$y=-\dfrac{3}{5}x+7$$

28. First find the slope: $m=\dfrac{-1-(-1)}{11-3}=\dfrac{0}{8}=0$. Since the line is horizontal, its equation is $y=-1$.

29. Factoring: $396=4\cdot99=(2\cdot2)\cdot(9\cdot11)=(2\cdot2)\cdot(3\cdot3\cdot11)=2^2\cdot3^2\cdot11$

30. Factoring: $x^2 + 3x - 40 = (x+8)(x-5)$

31. Factoring: $x^2 + 2xy - 36 + y^2 = (x+y)^2 - 36 = (x+y+6)(x+y-6)$

32. Factoring: $y^3 - \dfrac{64}{125}x^3 = y^3 - \left(\dfrac{4}{5}x\right)^3 = \left(y - \dfrac{4}{5}x\right)\left(y^2 + \dfrac{4}{5}xy + \dfrac{16}{25}x^2\right)$

33. Solving the equation:
$$\frac{9}{2}x - 6 = 57$$
$$\frac{9}{2}x = 63$$
$$9x = 126$$
$$x = 14$$

34. Solving the equation:
$$9y + 27 = 2y - 8$$
$$7y = -35$$
$$y = -5$$

35. Solving the equation:
$$\frac{2}{3}(9x - 1) - \frac{1}{3} = -7$$
$$6x - \frac{2}{3} - \frac{1}{3} = -7$$
$$6x - 1 = -7$$
$$6x = -6$$
$$x = -1$$

36. Solving the equation:
$$\frac{3}{7}(14x - 4) + \frac{5}{7} = 8$$
$$6x - \frac{12}{7} + \frac{5}{7} = 8$$
$$6x - 1 = 8$$
$$6x = 9$$
$$x = \frac{3}{2}$$

37. Solving the equation:
$$\frac{4}{y-1} = \frac{7}{y+6}$$
$$4(y+6) = 7(y-1)$$
$$4y + 24 = 7y - 7$$
$$-3y = -31$$
$$y = \frac{31}{3}$$

38. Solving the equation:
$$3 - \frac{16}{x} = \frac{12}{x^2}$$
$$x^2\left(3 - \frac{16}{x}\right) = x^2\left(\frac{12}{x^2}\right)$$
$$3x^2 - 16x = 12$$
$$3x^2 - 16x - 12 = 0$$
$$(3x + 2)(x - 6) = 0$$
$$x = -\frac{2}{3}, 6$$

39. Simplifying the second equation:
$$2x + 5y = 17$$
$$7x + 3y = 16$$
Multiply the first equation by 3 and the second equation by –5:
$$6x + 15y = 51$$
$$-35x - 15y = -80$$
Adding yields:
$$-29x = -29$$
$$x = 1$$
Substituting into the first equation:
$$2(1) + 5y = 17$$
$$2 + 5y = 17$$
$$5y = 15$$
$$y = 3$$
The solution is (1,3).

40. Multiply the first equation by 9 and the second equation by 2:
$$27x - 18y = 45$$
$$4x + 18y = 12$$
Adding yields:
$$31x = 57$$
$$x = \frac{57}{31}$$
Substituting into the original second equation:
$$2\left(\frac{57}{31}\right) + 9y = 6$$
$$\frac{114}{31} + 9y = 6$$
$$9y = \frac{72}{31}$$
$$y = \frac{8}{31}$$
The solution is $\left(\frac{57}{31}, \frac{8}{31}\right)$.

41. Solving the inequality:
$$-3(x-2) \le -2(x-6)$$
$$-3x + 6 \le -2x + 12$$
$$-x \le 6$$
$$x \ge -6$$
Graphing the solution set:

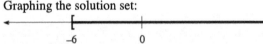

42. Solving the inequality:
$$|x-4| + 3 < 5$$
$$|x-4| < 2$$
$$-2 < x - 4 < 2$$
$$2 < x < 6$$
Graphing the solution set:

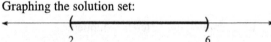

43. Graphing the line:

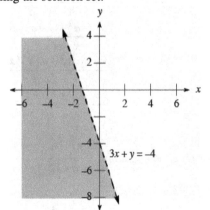

44. Shading the solution set:

45. Evaluating the function: $(f-g)(3) = f(3) - g(3) = 7 - 3 = 4$

46. Evaluating the function: $(f+g)(-2) = f(-2) + g(-2) = 2 + 8 = 10$

47. Evaluating the function: $(f \circ g)(-1) = f\big[g(-1)\big] = f(3) = 7$

48. Evaluating the function: $(g \circ f)(-1) = g\big[f(-1)\big] = g(3) = 3$

Chapter 5 Test

1. Reducing the fraction: $\dfrac{x^2+2xy+y^2}{x+y}=\dfrac{(x+y)^2}{x+y}=x+y$

2. Reducing the fraction: $\dfrac{4x^2-4x-3}{2x^2-x-1}=\dfrac{(2x+1)(2x-3)}{(2x+1)(x-1)}=\dfrac{2x-3}{x-1}$

3. Finding the speed: $\dfrac{(3.14)(65\text{ feet})}{50\text{ seconds}}=\dfrac{204.1\text{ feet}}{50\text{ seconds}}\approx4.1\text{ feet/second}$

4.   **a.**   Finding the difference quotient: $\dfrac{f(x+h)-f(x)}{h}=\dfrac{8(x+h)-5-(8x-5)}{h}=\dfrac{8x+8h-5-8x+5}{h}=\dfrac{8h}{h}=8$

     b.   Finding the difference quotient: $\dfrac{f(x)-f(a)}{x-a}=\dfrac{(8x-5)-(8a-5)}{x-a}=\dfrac{8x-8a}{x-a}=\dfrac{8(x-a)}{x-a}=8$

5.   **a.**   Finding the difference quotient:

$$\begin{aligned}\frac{f(x+h)-f(x)}{h}&=\frac{(x+h)^2+(x+h)-6-\left(x^2+x-6\right)}{h}\\&=\frac{x^2+2xh+h^2+x+h-6-x^2-x+6}{h}\\&=\frac{2xh+h^2+h}{h}\\&=\frac{h(2x+h+1)}{h}\\&=2x+h+1\end{aligned}$$

     b.   Finding the difference quotient:

$$\begin{aligned}\frac{f(x)-f(a)}{x-a}&=\frac{\left(x^2+x-6\right)-\left(a^2+a-6\right)}{x-a}\\&=\frac{x^2-a^2+x-a}{x-a}\\&=\frac{(x+a)(x-a)+1(x-a)}{x-a}\\&=\frac{(x-a)(x+a+1)}{x-a}\\&=x+a+1\end{aligned}$$

6. Performing the operations: $\dfrac{a^2-9}{4a+12}\cdot\dfrac{12(a+2)^2}{a^2-a-6}=\dfrac{(a+3)(a-3)}{4(a+3)}\cdot\dfrac{12(a+2)^2}{(a-3)(a+2)}=3(a+2)$

7. Performing the operations:

$$\frac{a^4-16}{2a^2+a-6}\div\frac{a^2+4}{8a-12}=\frac{a^4-16}{2a^2+a-6}\cdot\frac{8a-12}{a^2+4}=\frac{\left(a^2+4\right)(a+2)(a-2)}{(2a-3)(a+2)}\cdot\frac{4(2a-3)}{a^2+4}=4(a-2)$$

8. Performing the operations:

$$\begin{aligned}\frac{2x^2+3x+1}{2x^2+6x+18}\div\frac{2x^2-5x-3}{x^3-27}&=\frac{2x^2+3x+1}{2x^2+6x+18}\cdot\frac{x^3-27}{2x^2-5x-3}\\&=\frac{(2x+1)(x+1)}{2\left(x^2+3x+9\right)}\cdot\frac{(x-3)\left(x^2+3x+9\right)}{(2x+1)(x-3)}\\&=\frac{x+1}{2}\end{aligned}$$

---

9. Performing the operations: $\dfrac{3}{10} + \dfrac{6}{25} = \dfrac{3}{10} \cdot \dfrac{5}{5} + \dfrac{6}{25} \cdot \dfrac{2}{2} = \dfrac{15}{50} + \dfrac{12}{50} = \dfrac{27}{50}$

10. Performing the operations: $\dfrac{1}{2} - \dfrac{5}{32} + \dfrac{3}{16} = \dfrac{1}{2} \cdot \dfrac{16}{16} - \dfrac{5}{32} + \dfrac{3}{16} \cdot \dfrac{2}{2} = \dfrac{16}{32} - \dfrac{5}{32} + \dfrac{6}{32} = \dfrac{17}{32}$

11. Performing the operations: $\dfrac{a+2}{a^2-25} - \dfrac{7}{a^2-25} = \dfrac{a-5}{a^2-25} = \dfrac{a-5}{(a+5)(a-5)} = \dfrac{1}{a+5}$

12. Performing the operations:

$$\dfrac{2}{x+1} + \dfrac{4}{2x-1} = \dfrac{2}{x+1} \cdot \dfrac{2x-1}{2x-1} + \dfrac{4}{2x-1} \cdot \dfrac{x+1}{x+1} = \dfrac{4x-2}{(x+1)(2x-1)} + \dfrac{4x+4}{(x+1)(2x-1)} = \dfrac{8x+2}{(x+1)(2x-1)} = \dfrac{2(4x+1)}{(x+1)(2x-1)}$$

13. Performing the operations:

$$\dfrac{5x}{x^2+3x-4} - \dfrac{4x}{x^2+2x-3} = \dfrac{5x}{(x+4)(x-1)} - \dfrac{4x}{(x+3)(x-1)}$$

$$= \dfrac{5x}{(x+4)(x-1)} \cdot \dfrac{x+3}{x+3} - \dfrac{4x}{(x+3)(x-1)} \cdot \dfrac{x+4}{x+4}$$

$$= \dfrac{5x^2+15x}{(x+4)(x+3)(x-1)} - \dfrac{4x^2+16x}{(x+4)(x+3)(x-1)}$$

$$= \dfrac{5x^2+15x-4x^2-16x}{(x+4)(x+3)(x-1)}$$

$$= \dfrac{x^2-x}{(x+4)(x+3)(x-1)}$$

$$= \dfrac{x(x-1)}{(x+4)(x+3)(x-1)}$$

$$= \dfrac{x}{(x+4)(x+3)}$$

14. Performing the operations:

$$\dfrac{2x+4}{x^2-10x-39} - \dfrac{x+2}{x^2-18x+65} = \dfrac{2x+4}{(x-13)(x+3)} - \dfrac{x+2}{(x-13)(x-5)}$$

$$= \dfrac{2x+4}{(x-13)(x+3)} \cdot \dfrac{x-5}{x-5} - \dfrac{x+2}{(x-13)(x-5)} \cdot \dfrac{x+3}{x+3}$$

$$= \dfrac{2x^2-6x-20}{(x-13)(x+3)(x-5)} - \dfrac{x^2+5x+6}{(x-13)(x+3)(x-5)}$$

$$= \dfrac{2x^2-6x-20-x^2-5x-6}{(x-13)(x+3)(x-5)}$$

$$= \dfrac{x^2-11x-26}{(x-13)(x+3)(x-5)}$$

$$= \dfrac{(x-13)(x+2)}{(x-13)(x+3)(x-5)}$$

$$= \dfrac{x+2}{(x+3)(x-5)}$$

15. Simplifying the complex fraction: $\dfrac{2 - \dfrac{1}{a+6}}{2 + \dfrac{1}{a+6}} = \dfrac{\left(2 - \dfrac{1}{a+6}\right)(a+6)}{\left(2 + \dfrac{1}{a+6}\right)(a+6)} = \dfrac{2(a+6)-1}{2(a+6)+1} = \dfrac{2a+12-1}{2a+12+1} = \dfrac{2a+11}{2a+13}$

16. Simplifying the complex fraction: $\dfrac{1-\dfrac{25}{x^2}}{1+\dfrac{7}{x}+\dfrac{10}{x^2}} = \dfrac{\left(1-\dfrac{25}{x^2}\right)\cdot x^2}{\left(1+\dfrac{7}{x}+\dfrac{10}{x^2}\right)\cdot x^2} = \dfrac{x^2-25}{x^2+7x+10} = \dfrac{(x+5)(x-5)}{(x+5)(x+2)} = \dfrac{x-5}{x+2}$

17. Solving the equation:

$$5+\frac{2}{x}=\frac{6}{5}$$
$$5x\left(5+\frac{2}{x}\right)=5x\left(\frac{6}{5}\right)$$
$$25x+10=6x$$
$$19x=-10$$
$$x=-\frac{10}{19}$$

18. Solving the equation:

$$\frac{2x}{x+4}-3=\frac{-8}{x+4}$$
$$(x+4)\left(\frac{2x}{x+4}-3\right)=(x+4)\left(\frac{-8}{x+4}\right)$$
$$2x-3(x+4)=-8$$
$$2x-3x-12=-8$$
$$-x-12=-8$$
$$-x=4$$
$$x=-4 \quad \text{(impossible)}$$

There is no solution to the equation.

19. Solving the equation:

$$\frac{9}{y+3}+\frac{y+4}{7y}=\frac{1}{7}$$
$$7y(y+3)\left(\frac{9}{y+3}+\frac{y+4}{7y}\right)=7y(y+3)\left(\frac{1}{7}\right)$$
$$63y+(y+3)(y+4)=y(y+3)$$
$$63y+y^2+7y+12=y^2+3y$$
$$y^2+70y+12=y^2+3y$$
$$70y+12=3y$$
$$67y=-12$$
$$y=-\frac{12}{67}$$

20. Solving the equation:

$$1-\frac{10}{x}=-\frac{21}{x^2}$$
$$x^2\left(1-\frac{10}{x}\right)=x^2\left(-\frac{21}{x^2}\right)$$
$$x^2-10x=-21$$
$$x^2-10x+21=0$$
$$(x-3)(x-7)=0$$
$$x=3,7$$

21. Let x represent the number. The equation is:

$$\frac{13}{54+x}=\frac{1}{4}$$
$$52=54+x$$
$$x=-2$$

The number is –2.

22. Let x represent the speed of the boat. Since the total time is 11 hours:

$$\frac{24}{x-5}+\frac{24}{x+5}=14$$
$$(x-5)(x+5)\left(\frac{24}{x-5}+\frac{24}{x+5}\right)=14(x-5)(x+5)$$
$$24(x+5)+24(x-5)=14\left(x^2-25\right)$$
$$24x+120+24x-120=14x^2-350$$
$$0=14x^2-48x-350$$
$$0=(14x+50)(x-7)$$
$$x=7 \quad \left(x=-\frac{50}{14} \text{ is impossible}\right)$$

The speed of the boat is 7 mph.

23. Let x represent the time to fill the pool with both the pipe and drain open. The rate equation is:

$$\frac{1}{6} - \frac{1}{10} = \frac{2}{3} \cdot \frac{1}{x}$$

$$30x\left(\frac{1}{6} - \frac{1}{10}\right) = 30x\left(\frac{2}{3x}\right)$$

$$5x - 3x = 20$$

$$2x = 20$$

$$x = 10$$

The pool can be filled in 10 hours with both the pipe and drain open.

24. Dividing: $\dfrac{6x^4y + 33x^3y^2 - 6x^2y^3}{3x^2y} = \dfrac{6x^4y}{3x^2y} + \dfrac{33x^3y^2}{3x^2y} - \dfrac{6x^2y^3}{3x^2y} = 2x^2 + 11xy - 2y^2$

25. Dividing using long division:

$$
\require{enclose}
\begin{array}{r}
x^2 - 3x + 2 \\
4x+3 \enclose{longdiv}{4x^3 - 9x^2 - x + 8} \\
\underline{4x^3 + 3x^2} \\
-12x^2 - x \\
\underline{-12x^2 - 9x} \\
8x + 8 \\
\underline{8x + 6} \\
2
\end{array}
$$

The quotient is $x^2 - 3x + 2 + \dfrac{2}{4x+3}$.

26. The variation equation is $y = \dfrac{k}{x^2}$. Substituting $x = 2$ and $y = 7$:

$$7 = \frac{k}{2^2}$$

$$7 = \frac{k}{4}$$

$$k = 28$$

So $y = \dfrac{28}{x^2}$. Substituting $x = 14$: $y = \dfrac{28}{14^2} = \dfrac{28}{196} = \dfrac{1}{7}$

27. The variation equation is $z = kxy^2$. Substituting $x = 6$, $y = 3$, and $z = 27$:

$$27 = k(6)(3)^2$$

$$27 = 54k$$

$$k = \frac{1}{2}$$

So $z = \dfrac{1}{2}xy^2$. Substituting $z = 50$ and $y = 4$:

$$50 = \frac{1}{2}(x)(4)^2$$

$$50 = 8x$$

$$x = \frac{25}{4}$$

Chapter 6
Rational Exponents and Radicals

6.1 Rational Exponents

1. Finding the root: $\sqrt{144} = 12$

3. Finding the root: $\sqrt{-144}$ is not a real number

5. Finding the root: $-\sqrt{49} = -7$

7. Finding the root: $\sqrt[3]{-27} = -3$

9. Finding the root: $\sqrt[4]{16} = 2$

11. Finding the root: $\sqrt[4]{-16}$ is not a real number

13. Finding the root: $\sqrt{0.04} = 0.2$

15. Finding the root: $\sqrt[3]{0.008} = 0.2$

17. Simplifying: $\sqrt{36a^8} = 6a^4$

19. Simplifying: $\sqrt[3]{27a^{12}} = 3a^4$

21. Simplifying: $\sqrt[3]{x^3 y^6} = xy^2$

23. Simplifying: $\sqrt[5]{32x^{10}y^5} = 2x^2 y$

25. Simplifying: $\sqrt[4]{16a^{12}b^{20}} = 2a^3 b^5$

27. Simplifying: $\sqrt[3]{-27x^9 y^{12}} = -3x^3 y^4$

29. Writing as an exponent: $\sqrt[5]{x^4} = x^{4/5}$

31. Writing as an exponent: $\sqrt[3]{n^2} = n^{2/3}$

33. Writing as an exponent: $\sqrt[6]{a^3} = a^{3/6} = a^{1/2}$

35. Writing as an exponent: $\sqrt[8]{m^5} = m^{5/8}$

37. Writing as a root and simplifying: $36^{1/2} = \sqrt{36} = 6$

39. Writing as a root and simplifying: $-9^{1/2} = -\sqrt{9} = -3$

41. Writing as a root and simplifying: $8^{1/3} = \sqrt[3]{8} = 2$

43. Writing as a root and simplifying: $(-8)^{1/3} = \sqrt[3]{-8} = -2$

45. Writing as a root and simplifying: $32^{1/5} = \sqrt[5]{32} = 2$

47. Writing as a root and simplifying: $\left(\dfrac{81}{25}\right)^{1/2} = \sqrt{\dfrac{81}{25}} = \dfrac{9}{5}$

49. Writing as a root and simplifying: $\left(\dfrac{64}{125}\right)^{1/3} = \sqrt[3]{\dfrac{64}{125}} = \dfrac{4}{5}$

51. Writing as a root and simplifying: $\left(\dfrac{16}{81}\right)^{1/4} = \sqrt[4]{\dfrac{16}{81}} = \dfrac{2}{3}$

53. Simplifying: $27^{2/3} = \left(27^{1/3}\right)^2 = 3^2 = 9$

55. Simplifying: $25^{3/2} = \left(25^{1/2}\right)^3 = 5^3 = 125$

57. Simplifying: $16^{3/4} = \left(16^{1/4}\right)^3 = 2^3 = 8$

59. Simplifying: $(-27)^{2/3} = \left((-27)^{1/3}\right)^2 = (-3)^2 = 9$

61. Simplifying: $27^{-1/3} = \left(27^{1/3}\right)^{-1} = 3^{-1} = \dfrac{1}{3}$

63. Simplifying: $81^{-3/4} = \left(81^{1/4}\right)^{-3} = 3^{-3} = \dfrac{1}{3^3} = \dfrac{1}{27}$

65. Simplifying: $\left(\dfrac{25}{36}\right)^{-1/2} = \left(\dfrac{36}{25}\right)^{1/2} = \dfrac{6}{5}$

67. Simplifying: $\left(\dfrac{81}{16}\right)^{-3/4} = \left(\dfrac{16}{81}\right)^{3/4} = \left[\left(\dfrac{16}{81}\right)^{1/4}\right]^3 = \left(\dfrac{2}{3}\right)^3 = \dfrac{8}{27}$

69. Simplifying: $16^{1/2} + 27^{1/3} = 4 + 3 = 7$

71. Simplifying: $8^{-2/3} + 4^{-1/2} = \left(8^{1/3}\right)^{-2} + \left(4^{1/2}\right)^{-1} = 2^{-2} + 2^{-1} = \dfrac{1}{4} + \dfrac{1}{2} = \dfrac{3}{4}$

73. Using properties of exponents: $x^{3/5} \cdot x^{1/5} = x^{3/5+1/5} = x^{4/5}$

75. Using properties of exponents: $\left(a^{3/4}\right)^{4/3} = a^{3/4 \cdot 4/3} = a$

77. Using properties of exponents: $\dfrac{x^{1/5}}{x^{3/5}} = x^{1/5-3/5} = x^{-2/5} = \dfrac{1}{x^{2/5}}$

79. Using properties of exponents: $\dfrac{x^{5/6}}{x^{2/3}} = x^{5/6-2/3} = x^{5/6-4/6} = x^{1/6}$

81. Using properties of exponents: $\left(a^{2/3}b^{1/2}c^{1/4}\right)^{1/3} = a^{2/3 \cdot 1/3}b^{1/2 \cdot 1/3}c^{1/4 \cdot 1/3} = a^{2/9}b^{1/6}c^{1/12}$

83. Using properties of exponents: $\left(x^{3/5}y^{5/6}z^{1/3}\right)^{3/5} = x^{3/5 \cdot 3/5}y^{5/6 \cdot 3/5}z^{1/3 \cdot 3/5} = x^{9/25}y^{1/2}z^{1/5}$

85. Using properties of exponents: $\dfrac{a^{3/4}b^2}{a^{7/8}b^{1/4}} = a^{3/4-7/8}b^{2-1/4} = a^{6/8-7/8}b^{8/4-1/4} = a^{-1/8}b^{7/4} = \dfrac{b^{7/4}}{a^{1/8}}$

87. Using properties of exponents: $\dfrac{\left(y^{2/3}\right)^{3/4}}{\left(y^{1/3}\right)^{3/5}} = \dfrac{y^{1/2}}{y^{1/5}} = y^{1/2-1/5} = y^{5/10-2/10} = y^{3/10}$

89. Using properties of exponents: $\left(\dfrac{x^{-1/2}}{y^{1/4}}\right)^4 = \dfrac{x^{-1/2 \cdot 4}}{y^{1/4 \cdot 4}} = \dfrac{x^{-2}}{y} = \dfrac{1}{x^2 y}$

91. Using properties of exponents: $\left(\dfrac{a^{-1/4}}{b^{1/2}}\right)^8 = \dfrac{a^{-1/4 \cdot 8}}{b^{1/2 \cdot 8}} = \dfrac{a^{-2}}{b^4} = \dfrac{1}{a^2 b^4}$

93. Using properties of exponents: $\dfrac{\left(r^{-2}s^{1/3}\right)^6}{r^8 s^{3/2}} = \dfrac{r^{-12}s^2}{r^8 s^{3/2}} = r^{-12-8}s^{2-3/2} = r^{-20}s^{1/2} = \dfrac{s^{1/2}}{r^{20}}$

95. Using properties of exponents: $\dfrac{\left(25a^6 b^4\right)^{1/2}}{\left(8a^{-9}b^3\right)^{-1/3}} = \dfrac{25^{1/2}a^3 b^2}{8^{-1/3}a^3 b^{-1}} = \dfrac{5}{1/2}a^{3-3}b^{2+1} = 10b^3$

97. Simplifying each expression:

$$\left(9^{1/2} + 4^{1/2}\right)^2 = (3+2)^2 = 5^2 = 25$$
$$9 + 4 = 13$$

Note that the values are not equal.

99. Rewriting with exponents: $\sqrt{\sqrt{a}} = \sqrt{a^{1/2}} = \left(a^{1/2}\right)^{1/2} = a^{1/4} = \sqrt[4]{a}$

101. Substituting $r = 250$: $v = \left(\dfrac{5 \cdot 250}{2}\right)^{1/2} = 625^{1/2} = 25$. The maximum speed is 25 mph.

103. Using a calculator: $\dfrac{1+\sqrt{5}}{2} \approx 1.618$

105. a. Each side of the square is: $60 + 300 + 60 = 420$ picometers

b. Let d represent the length of the diagonal. Using the Pythagorean theorem:

$$420^2 + 420^2 = d^2$$
$$d^2 = 352{,}800$$
$$d = \sqrt{352{,}800} \approx 594 \text{ picometers}$$

c. Converting to meters: $594 \text{ pm} \cdot \dfrac{1 \text{ m}}{10^{12} \text{ pm}} = 5.94 \times 10^{-10} \text{ m}$

107. See the completed table below:

Pyramid Name	Location/Culture	b (ft)	h (ft)	Slant height (ft)	Volume (ft^3)
Temple of Kukulkan	Mexico/Maya	181	98	133	1,070,000
Temple IV at Tecal	Guatemala/Maya	118	187	196	868,000
Pyramid of the Sun	Mexico/Aztec	733	246	441	44,058,000
Great Pyramid of Khufu	Gizal/Egypt	755	455	591	86,454,000
Luxor Hotel	Las Vegas/Modern	600	350	461	42,000,000
Transamerica Pyramid	San Francisco/Modern	175	850	854	8,677,000

109. The longest slant height is the Transamerica Pyramid in San Francisco.

111. Simplifying: $\sqrt{25} = 5$
113. Simplifying: $\sqrt{6^2} = 6$

115. Simplifying: $\sqrt{16x^4 y^2} = 4x^2 y$
117. Simplifying: $\sqrt{(5y)^2} = 5y$

119. Simplifying: $\sqrt[3]{27} = 3$
121. Simplifying: $\sqrt[3]{2^3} = 2$

123. Simplifying: $\sqrt[3]{8a^3 b^3} = 2ab$
125. Simplifying: $\sqrt[4]{625x^8 y^4} = 5x^2 y$

127. Filling in the blank: $50 = 25 \cdot 2$
129. Filling in the blank: $48x^4 y^3 = 48x^4 y^2 \cdot y$

131. Filling in the blank: $12x^7 y^6 = 4x^6 y^6 \cdot 3x$
133. Filling in the blank: $10x^2 y^5 = 2xy^4 \cdot 5xy$

6.2 Simplifying Radicals

1. Simplifying the radical: $\sqrt{8} = \sqrt{4 \cdot 2} = 2\sqrt{2}$
3. Simplifying the radical: $\sqrt{98} = \sqrt{49 \cdot 2} = 7\sqrt{2}$

5. Simplifying the radical: $\sqrt{288} = \sqrt{144 \cdot 2} = 12\sqrt{2}$
7. Simplifying the radical: $\sqrt{80} = \sqrt{16 \cdot 5} = 4\sqrt{5}$

9. Simplifying the radical: $\sqrt{48} = \sqrt{16 \cdot 3} = 4\sqrt{3}$
11. Simplifying the radical: $\sqrt{675} = \sqrt{225 \cdot 3} = 15\sqrt{3}$

13. Simplifying the radical: $\sqrt[3]{54} = \sqrt[3]{27 \cdot 2} = 3\sqrt[3]{2}$
15. Simplifying the radical: $\sqrt[3]{128} = \sqrt[3]{64 \cdot 2} = 4\sqrt[3]{2}$

17. Simplifying the radical: $\sqrt[3]{432} = \sqrt[3]{216 \cdot 2} = 6\sqrt[3]{2}$
19. Simplifying the radical: $\sqrt[5]{64} = \sqrt[5]{32 \cdot 2} = 2\sqrt[5]{2}$

21. Simplifying the radical: $\sqrt{18x^3} = \sqrt{9x^2 \cdot 2x} = 3x\sqrt{2x}$

23. Simplifying the radical: $\sqrt[4]{32y^7} = \sqrt[4]{16y^4 \cdot 2y^3} = 2y\sqrt[4]{2y^3}$

25. Simplifying the radical: $\sqrt[3]{40x^4 y^7} = \sqrt[3]{8x^3 y^6 \cdot 5xy} = 2xy^2 \sqrt[3]{5xy}$

27. Simplifying the radical: $\sqrt{48a^2 b^3 c^4} = \sqrt{16a^2 b^2 c^4 \cdot 3b} = 4abc^2 \sqrt{3b}$

29. Simplifying the radical: $\sqrt[3]{48a^2 b^3 c^4} = \sqrt[3]{8b^3 c^3 \cdot 6a^2 c} = 2bc\sqrt[3]{6a^2 c}$

31. Simplifying the radical: $\sqrt[5]{64x^8 y^{12}} = \sqrt[5]{32x^5 y^{10} \cdot 2x^3 y^2} = 2xy^2 \sqrt[5]{2x^3 y^2}$

33. Simplifying the radical: $\sqrt[5]{243x^7 y^{10} z^5} = \sqrt[5]{243x^5 y^{10} z^5 \cdot x^2} = 3xy^2 z\sqrt[5]{x^2}$

35. Simplifying the radical: $\sqrt[3]{250x^5 y^{10}} = \sqrt[3]{125x^3 y^9 \cdot 2x^2 y} = 5xy^3 \sqrt[3]{2x^2 y}$

37. Simplifying the radical: $\sqrt[3]{-27x^{10}y^{13}} = \sqrt[3]{-27x^9y^{12} \cdot xy} = -3x^3y^4\sqrt[3]{xy}$

39. Substituting into the expression: $\sqrt{b^2 - 4ac} = \sqrt{(-6)^2 - 4(2)(3)} = \sqrt{36 - 24} = \sqrt{12} = 2\sqrt{3}$

41. Substituting into the expression: $\sqrt{b^2 - 4ac} = \sqrt{(2)^2 - 4(1)(6)} = \sqrt{4 - 24} = \sqrt{-20}$, which is not a real number

43. Substituting into the expression: $\sqrt{b^2 - 4ac} = \sqrt{\left(-\dfrac{1}{2}\right)^2 - 4\left(\dfrac{1}{2}\right)\left(-\dfrac{5}{4}\right)} = \sqrt{\dfrac{1}{4} + \dfrac{5}{2}} = \sqrt{\dfrac{11}{4}} = \dfrac{\sqrt{11}}{2}$

45. Rationalizing the denominator: $\dfrac{2}{\sqrt{3}} = \dfrac{2}{\sqrt{3}} \cdot \dfrac{\sqrt{3}}{\sqrt{3}} = \dfrac{2\sqrt{3}}{3}$

47. Rationalizing the denominator: $\dfrac{5}{\sqrt{6}} = \dfrac{5}{\sqrt{6}} \cdot \dfrac{\sqrt{6}}{\sqrt{6}} = \dfrac{5\sqrt{6}}{6}$

49. Rationalizing the denominator: $\sqrt{\dfrac{1}{2}} = \dfrac{1}{\sqrt{2}} \cdot \dfrac{\sqrt{2}}{\sqrt{2}} = \dfrac{\sqrt{2}}{2}$

51. Rationalizing the denominator: $\sqrt{\dfrac{1}{5}} = \dfrac{1}{\sqrt{5}} \cdot \dfrac{\sqrt{5}}{\sqrt{5}} = \dfrac{\sqrt{5}}{5}$

53. Rationalizing the denominator: $\dfrac{4}{\sqrt[3]{2}} = \dfrac{4}{\sqrt[3]{2}} \cdot \dfrac{\sqrt[3]{4}}{\sqrt[3]{4}} = \dfrac{4\sqrt[3]{4}}{2} = 2\sqrt[3]{4}$

55. Rationalizing the denominator: $\dfrac{2}{\sqrt[3]{9}} = \dfrac{2}{\sqrt[3]{9}} \cdot \dfrac{\sqrt[3]{3}}{\sqrt[3]{3}} = \dfrac{2\sqrt[3]{3}}{3}$

57. Rationalizing the denominator: $\sqrt[4]{\dfrac{3}{2x^2}} = \dfrac{\sqrt[4]{3}}{\sqrt[4]{2x^2}} \cdot \dfrac{\sqrt[4]{8x^2}}{\sqrt[4]{8x^2}} = \dfrac{\sqrt[4]{24x^2}}{2x}$

59. Rationalizing the denominator: $\sqrt[4]{\dfrac{8}{y}} = \dfrac{\sqrt[4]{8}}{\sqrt[4]{y}} \cdot \dfrac{\sqrt[4]{y^3}}{\sqrt[4]{y^3}} = \dfrac{\sqrt[4]{8y^3}}{y}$

61. Rationalizing the denominator: $\sqrt[3]{\dfrac{4x}{3y}} = \dfrac{\sqrt[3]{4x}}{\sqrt[3]{3y}} \cdot \dfrac{\sqrt[3]{9y^2}}{\sqrt[3]{9y^2}} = \dfrac{\sqrt[3]{36xy^2}}{3y}$

63. Rationalizing the denominator: $\sqrt[3]{\dfrac{2x}{9y}} = \dfrac{\sqrt[3]{2x}}{\sqrt[3]{9y}} \cdot \dfrac{\sqrt[3]{3y^2}}{\sqrt[3]{3y^2}} = \dfrac{\sqrt[3]{6xy^2}}{3y}$

65. Rationalizing the denominator: $\sqrt[4]{\dfrac{1}{8x^3}} = \dfrac{1}{\sqrt[4]{8x^3}} \cdot \dfrac{\sqrt[4]{2x}}{\sqrt[4]{2x}} = \dfrac{\sqrt[4]{2x}}{2x}$

67. Rationalizing the denominator: $\sqrt[4]{\dfrac{9}{8x^2}} = \dfrac{\sqrt[4]{9}}{\sqrt[4]{8x^2}} \cdot \dfrac{\sqrt[4]{2x^2}}{\sqrt[4]{2x^2}} = \dfrac{\sqrt[4]{18x^2}}{2x}$

69. Simplifying: $\sqrt{\dfrac{27x^3}{5y}} = \dfrac{\sqrt{27x^3}}{\sqrt{5y}} \cdot \dfrac{\sqrt{5y}}{\sqrt{5y}} = \dfrac{\sqrt{135x^3y}}{5y} = \dfrac{3x\sqrt{15xy}}{5y}$

71. Simplifying: $\sqrt{\dfrac{75x^3y^2}{2z}} = \dfrac{\sqrt{75x^3y^2}}{\sqrt{2z}} \cdot \dfrac{\sqrt{2z}}{\sqrt{2z}} = \dfrac{\sqrt{150x^3y^2z}}{2z} = \dfrac{5xy\sqrt{6xz}}{2z}$

73. Simplifying: $\sqrt[3]{\dfrac{16a^4b^3}{9c}} = \dfrac{\sqrt[3]{16a^4b^3}}{\sqrt[3]{9c}} \cdot \dfrac{\sqrt[3]{3c^2}}{\sqrt[3]{3c^2}} = \dfrac{\sqrt[3]{48a^4b^3c^2}}{3c} = \dfrac{2ab\sqrt[3]{6ac^2}}{3c}$

75. Simplifying: $\sqrt[3]{\dfrac{8x^3y^6}{9z}} = \dfrac{\sqrt[3]{8x^3y^6}}{\sqrt[3]{9z}} \cdot \dfrac{\sqrt[3]{3z^2}}{\sqrt[3]{3z^2}} = \dfrac{\sqrt[3]{24x^3y^6z^2}}{3z} = \dfrac{2xy^2\sqrt[3]{3z^2}}{3z}$

77. Simplifying: $\sqrt{25x^2} = 5|x|$ 79. Simplifying: $\sqrt{27x^3y^2} = \sqrt{9x^2y^2 \cdot 3x} = 3|xy|\sqrt{3x}$

81. Simplifying: $\sqrt{x^2 - 10x + 25} = \sqrt{(x-5)^2} = |x-5|$ 83. Simplifying: $\sqrt{4x^2 + 12x + 9} = \sqrt{(2x+3)^2} = |2x+3|$

85. Simplifying: $\sqrt{4a^4 + 16a^3 + 16a^2} = \sqrt{4a^2\left(a^2 + 4a + 4\right)} = \sqrt{4a^2\left(a+2\right)^2} = 2|a(a+2)|$

87. Simplifying: $\sqrt{4x^3 - 8x^2} = \sqrt{4x^2\left(x-2\right)} = 2|x|\sqrt{x-2}$

89. Substituting $a = 9$ and $b = 16$:
$$\sqrt{a+b} = \sqrt{9+16} = \sqrt{25} = 5$$
$$\sqrt{a} + \sqrt{b} = \sqrt{9} + \sqrt{16} = 3 + 4 = 7$$
Thus $\sqrt{a+b} \neq \sqrt{a} + \sqrt{b}$.

91. Substituting $w = 10$ and $l = 15$: $d = \sqrt{l^2 + w^2} = \sqrt{15^2 + 10^2} = \sqrt{225 + 100} = \sqrt{325} = \sqrt{25 \cdot 13} = 5\sqrt{13}$ feet

93.   a.   Substituting $k = 1$: $d = \sqrt{8000k + k^2} = \sqrt{8000(1) + (1)^2} = \sqrt{8001} \approx 89.4$ miles

     b.   Substituting $k = 2$: $d = \sqrt{8000k + k^2} = \sqrt{8000(2) + (2)^2} = \sqrt{16,004} \approx 126.5$ miles

     c.   Substituting $k = 3$: $d = \sqrt{8000k + k^2} = \sqrt{8000(3) + (3)^2} = \sqrt{24,009} \approx 154.9$ miles

95. Answers will vary.

97. The terms are $f(1) = \sqrt{2}, f(\sqrt{2}) = \sqrt{3}, \ldots$ So $f(a_{10}) = \sqrt{11}$ and $f(a_{100}) = \sqrt{101}$.

99. Simplifying: $5x - 4x + 6x = 7x$ 101. Simplifying: $35xy^2 - 8xy^2 = 27xy^2$

103. Simplifying: $\dfrac{1}{2}x + \dfrac{1}{3}x = \dfrac{3}{6}x + \dfrac{2}{6}x = \dfrac{5}{6}x$ 105. Simplifying: $5(x+1)^2 - 12(x+1)^2 = -7(x+1)^2$

107. Simplifying: $\sqrt{18} = \sqrt{9 \cdot 2} = 3\sqrt{2}$ 109. Simplifying: $\sqrt{75xy^3} = \sqrt{25y^2 \cdot 3xy} = 5y\sqrt{3xy}$

111. Simplifying: $\sqrt[3]{8a^4b^2} = \sqrt[3]{8a^3 \cdot ab^2} = 2a\sqrt[3]{ab^2}$ 113. Simplifying: $\sqrt[4]{32x^8y^5} = \sqrt[4]{16x^8y^4 \cdot 2y} = 2x^2y\sqrt[4]{2y}$

6.3 Addition and Subtraction of Radical Expressions

1. Combining radicals: $3\sqrt{5} + 4\sqrt{5} = 7\sqrt{5}$ 3. Combining radicals: $3x\sqrt{7} - 4x\sqrt{7} = -x\sqrt{7}$

5. Combining radicals: $5\sqrt[3]{10} - 4\sqrt[3]{10} = \sqrt[3]{10}$ 7. Combining radicals: $8\sqrt[5]{6} - 2\sqrt[5]{6} + 3\sqrt[5]{6} = 9\sqrt[5]{6}$

9. Combining radicals: $3x\sqrt{2} - 4x\sqrt{2} + x\sqrt{2} = 0$

11. Combining radicals: $\sqrt{20} - \sqrt{80} + \sqrt{45} = 2\sqrt{5} - 4\sqrt{5} + 3\sqrt{5} = \sqrt{5}$

13. Combining radicals: $4\sqrt{8} - 2\sqrt{50} - 5\sqrt{72} = 8\sqrt{2} - 10\sqrt{2} - 30\sqrt{2} = -32\sqrt{2}$

15. Combining radicals: $5x\sqrt{8} + 3\sqrt{32x^2} - 5\sqrt{50x^2} = 10x\sqrt{2} + 12x\sqrt{2} - 25x\sqrt{2} = -3x\sqrt{2}$

17. Combining radicals: $5\sqrt{5y} + \sqrt{18y} = 5\sqrt{5y} + 3\sqrt{2y}$

19. Combining radicals: $5\sqrt[3]{16} - 4\sqrt[3]{54} = 10\sqrt[3]{2} - 12\sqrt[3]{2} = -2\sqrt[3]{2}$

21. Combining radicals: $\sqrt[3]{x^4y^2} + 7x\sqrt[3]{xy^2} = x\sqrt[3]{xy^2} + 7x\sqrt[3]{xy^2} = 8x\sqrt[3]{xy^2}$

23. Combining radicals: $5a^2\sqrt{27ab^3} - 6b\sqrt{12a^5b} = 15a^2b\sqrt{3ab} - 12a^2b\sqrt{3ab} = 3a^2b\sqrt{3ab}$

25. Combining radicals: $\sqrt[3]{24a^5b^4} + \sqrt[3]{81a^8b^4} = 2ab\sqrt[3]{3a^2b} + 3a^2b\sqrt[3]{3a^2b} = \left(2ab + 3a^2b\right)\sqrt[3]{3a^2b}$

27. Combining radicals: $b\sqrt[3]{24a^5b} + 3a\sqrt[3]{81a^2b^4} = 2ab\sqrt[3]{3a^2b} + 9ab\sqrt[3]{3a^2b} = 11ab\sqrt[3]{3a^2b}$

29. Combining radicals: $5x\sqrt[4]{3y^5} + y\sqrt[4]{243x^4y} + \sqrt[4]{48x^4y^5} = 5xy\sqrt[4]{3y} + 3xy\sqrt[4]{3y} + 2xy\sqrt[4]{3y} = 10xy\sqrt[4]{3y}$

31. Combining radicals: $\dfrac{\sqrt{2}}{2} + \dfrac{1}{\sqrt{2}} = \dfrac{\sqrt{2}}{2} + \dfrac{1}{\sqrt{2}} \cdot \dfrac{\sqrt{2}}{\sqrt{2}} = \dfrac{\sqrt{2}}{2} + \dfrac{\sqrt{2}}{2} = \sqrt{2}$

33. Combining radicals: $\dfrac{\sqrt{5}}{3} + \dfrac{1}{\sqrt{5}} = \dfrac{\sqrt{5}}{3} + \dfrac{1}{\sqrt{5}} \cdot \dfrac{\sqrt{5}}{\sqrt{5}} = \dfrac{\sqrt{5}}{3} + \dfrac{\sqrt{5}}{5} = \dfrac{5\sqrt{5}}{15} + \dfrac{3\sqrt{5}}{15} = \dfrac{8\sqrt{5}}{15}$

35. Combining radicals: $\sqrt{x} - \dfrac{1}{\sqrt{x}} = \sqrt{x} - \dfrac{1}{\sqrt{x}} \cdot \dfrac{\sqrt{x}}{\sqrt{x}} = \sqrt{x} - \dfrac{\sqrt{x}}{x} = \dfrac{x\sqrt{x}}{x} - \dfrac{\sqrt{x}}{x} = \dfrac{(x-1)\sqrt{x}}{x}$

37. Combining radicals: $\dfrac{\sqrt{18}}{6} + \sqrt{\dfrac{1}{2}} + \dfrac{\sqrt{2}}{2} = \dfrac{3\sqrt{2}}{6} + \dfrac{1}{\sqrt{2}} \cdot \dfrac{\sqrt{2}}{\sqrt{2}} + \dfrac{\sqrt{2}}{2} = \dfrac{\sqrt{2}}{2} + \dfrac{\sqrt{2}}{2} + \dfrac{\sqrt{2}}{2} = \dfrac{3\sqrt{2}}{2}$

39. Combining radicals: $\sqrt{6} - \sqrt{\dfrac{2}{3}} + \sqrt{\dfrac{1}{6}} = \sqrt{6} - \dfrac{\sqrt{2}}{\sqrt{3}} \cdot \dfrac{\sqrt{3}}{\sqrt{3}} + \dfrac{1}{\sqrt{6}} \cdot \dfrac{\sqrt{6}}{\sqrt{6}} = \sqrt{6} - \dfrac{\sqrt{6}}{3} + \dfrac{\sqrt{6}}{6} = \dfrac{6\sqrt{6}}{6} - \dfrac{2\sqrt{6}}{6} + \dfrac{\sqrt{6}}{6} = \dfrac{5\sqrt{6}}{6}$

41. Combining radicals: $\sqrt[3]{25} + \dfrac{3}{\sqrt[3]{5}} = \sqrt[3]{25} + \dfrac{3}{\sqrt[3]{5}} \cdot \dfrac{\sqrt[3]{25}}{\sqrt[3]{25}} = \sqrt[3]{25} + \dfrac{3\sqrt[3]{25}}{5} = \dfrac{5\sqrt[3]{25}}{5} + \dfrac{3\sqrt[3]{25}}{5} = \dfrac{8\sqrt[3]{25}}{5}$

43. Combining radicals:
$\dfrac{\sqrt{45}}{10} + \sqrt{\dfrac{1}{5}} + \dfrac{\sqrt{5}}{5} = \dfrac{3\sqrt{5}}{10} + \dfrac{1}{\sqrt{5}} \cdot \dfrac{\sqrt{5}}{\sqrt{5}} + \dfrac{\sqrt{5}}{5} = \dfrac{3\sqrt{5}}{10} + \dfrac{\sqrt{5}}{5} + \dfrac{\sqrt{5}}{5} = \dfrac{3\sqrt{5}}{10} + \dfrac{2\sqrt{5}}{5} = \dfrac{3\sqrt{5}}{10} + \dfrac{4\sqrt{5}}{10} = \dfrac{7\sqrt{5}}{10}$

45. Using a calculator:
$\sqrt{12} \approx 3.464 \qquad 2\sqrt{3} \approx 3.464$

47. It is equal to the decimal approximation for $\sqrt{50}$:
$\sqrt{8} + \sqrt{18} \approx 7.071 \approx \sqrt{50} \qquad \sqrt{26} \approx 5.099$

49. Correcting the right side: $3\sqrt{2x} + 5\sqrt{2x} = 8\sqrt{2x}$

51. Correcting the right side: $\sqrt{9+16} = \sqrt{25} = 5$

53. Answers will vary.

55. Answers will vary.

57. Answers will vary.

59. Using x as the length of the sides, the hypotenuse d is given by:
$$x^2 + x^2 = d^2$$
$$d^2 = 2x^2$$
$$d = x\sqrt{2}$$
Therefore the ratio is: $\dfrac{x\sqrt{2}}{x} = \sqrt{2}$

61. a. Since the diagonal of the base is $5\sqrt{2}$, the ratio is: $\dfrac{5\sqrt{2}}{5} = \sqrt{2}$

   b. Since the area of the base is 25, the ratio is: $\dfrac{25}{5\sqrt{2}} = \dfrac{5}{\sqrt{2}}$

   c. Since the area of the base is 25 and the perimeter is 20, the ratio is: $\dfrac{25}{20} = \dfrac{5}{4}$

63. Simplifying: $3 \cdot 2 = 6$

65. Simplifying: $(x+y)(4x-y) = 4x^2 - xy + 4xy - y^2 = 4x^2 + 3xy - y^2$

67. Simplifying: $(x+3)^2 = x^2 + 2(3x) + 3^2 = x^2 + 6x + 9$

69. Simplifying: $(x-2)(x+2) = x^2 - 2^2 = x^2 - 4$

71. Simplifying: $2\sqrt{18} = 2\sqrt{9 \cdot 2} = 2 \cdot 3\sqrt{2} = 6\sqrt{2}$

73. Simplifying: $\left(\sqrt{6}\right)^2 = 6$

75. Simplifying: $\left(3\sqrt{x}\right)^2 = 9x$

77. Simplifying: $\left(4\sqrt{3x}\right)^2 = 16(3x) = 48x$

79. Rationalizing the denominator: $\dfrac{\sqrt{3}}{\sqrt{2}} = \dfrac{\sqrt{3}}{\sqrt{2}} \cdot \dfrac{\sqrt{2}}{\sqrt{2}} = \dfrac{\sqrt{6}}{2}$

81. Rationalizing the denominator: $\dfrac{\sqrt{6}}{\sqrt{8}} = \dfrac{\sqrt{6}}{\sqrt{8}} \cdot \dfrac{\sqrt{2}}{\sqrt{2}} = \dfrac{\sqrt{12}}{\sqrt{16}} = \dfrac{2\sqrt{3}}{4} = \dfrac{\sqrt{3}}{2}$

6.4 Multiplication and Division of Radical Expressions

1. Multiplying: $\sqrt{6}\sqrt{3} = \sqrt{18} = 3\sqrt{2}$ 3. Multiplying: $\left(2\sqrt{3}\right)\left(5\sqrt{7}\right) = 10\sqrt{21}$

5. Multiplying: $\left(4\sqrt{6}\right)\left(2\sqrt{15}\right)\left(3\sqrt{10}\right) = 24\sqrt{900} = 24 \cdot 30 = 720$

7. Multiplying: $\left(3\sqrt[3]{3}\right)\left(6\sqrt[3]{9}\right) = 18\sqrt[3]{27} = 18 \cdot 3 = 54$ 9. Multiplying: $\sqrt{3}\left(\sqrt{2} - 3\sqrt{3}\right) = \sqrt{6} - 3\sqrt{9} = \sqrt{6} - 9$

11. Multiplying: $6\sqrt[3]{4}\left(2\sqrt[3]{2} + 1\right) = 12\sqrt[3]{8} + 6\sqrt[3]{4} = 24 + 6\sqrt[3]{4}$

13. Multiplying: $\left(\sqrt{3} + \sqrt{2}\right)\left(3\sqrt{3} - \sqrt{2}\right) = 3\sqrt{9} - \sqrt{6} + 3\sqrt{6} - \sqrt{4} = 9 + 2\sqrt{6} - 2 = 7 + 2\sqrt{6}$

15. Multiplying: $\left(\sqrt{x} + 5\right)\left(\sqrt{x} - 3\right) = x - 3\sqrt{x} + 5\sqrt{x} - 15 = x + 2\sqrt{x} - 15$

17. Multiplying: $\left(3\sqrt{6} + 4\sqrt{2}\right)\left(\sqrt{6} + 2\sqrt{2}\right) = 3\sqrt{36} + 4\sqrt{12} + 6\sqrt{12} + 8\sqrt{4} = 18 + 8\sqrt{3} + 12\sqrt{3} + 16 = 34 + 20\sqrt{3}$

19. Multiplying: $\left(\sqrt{3} + 4\right)^2 = \left(\sqrt{3} + 4\right)\left(\sqrt{3} + 4\right) = \sqrt{9} + 4\sqrt{3} + 4\sqrt{3} + 16 = 19 + 8\sqrt{3}$

21. Multiplying: $\left(\sqrt{x} - 3\right)^2 = \left(\sqrt{x} - 3\right)\left(\sqrt{x} - 3\right) = x - 3\sqrt{x} - 3\sqrt{x} + 9 = x - 6\sqrt{x} + 9$

23. Multiplying: $\left(2\sqrt{a} - 3\sqrt{b}\right)^2 = \left(2\sqrt{a} - 3\sqrt{b}\right)\left(2\sqrt{a} - 3\sqrt{b}\right) = 4a - 6\sqrt{ab} - 6\sqrt{ab} + 9b = 4a - 12\sqrt{ab} + 9b$

25. Multiplying: $\left(\sqrt{x-4} + 2\right)^2 = \left(\sqrt{x-4} + 2\right)\left(\sqrt{x-4} + 2\right) = x - 4 + 2\sqrt{x-4} + 2\sqrt{x-4} + 4 = x + 4\sqrt{x-4}$

27. Multiplying: $\left(\sqrt{x-5} - 3\right)^2 = \left(\sqrt{x-5} - 3\right)\left(\sqrt{x-5} - 3\right) = x - 5 - 3\sqrt{x-5} - 3\sqrt{x-5} + 9 = x + 4 - 6\sqrt{x-5}$

29. Multiplying: $\left(\sqrt{3} - \sqrt{2}\right)\left(\sqrt{3} + \sqrt{2}\right) = \left(\sqrt{3}\right)^2 - \left(\sqrt{2}\right)^2 = 3 - 2 = 1$

31. Multiplying: $\left(\sqrt{a} + 7\right)\left(\sqrt{a} - 7\right) = \left(\sqrt{a}\right)^2 - (7)^2 = a - 49$

33. Multiplying: $\left(5 - \sqrt{x}\right)\left(5 + \sqrt{x}\right) = (5)^2 - \left(\sqrt{x}\right)^2 = 25 - x$

35. Multiplying: $\left(\sqrt{x-4} + 2\right)\left(\sqrt{x-4} - 2\right) = \left(\sqrt{x-4}\right)^2 - (2)^2 = x - 4 - 4 = x - 8$

37. Multiplying: $\left(\sqrt{3} + 1\right)^3 = \left(\sqrt{3} + 1\right)\left(3 + 2\sqrt{3} + 1\right) = \left(\sqrt{3} + 1\right)\left(4 + 2\sqrt{3}\right) = 4\sqrt{3} + 4 + 6 + 2\sqrt{3} = 10 + 6\sqrt{3}$

39. Multiplying: $\left(\sqrt{3} - 3\right)^3 = \left(\sqrt{3} - 3\right)\left(3 - 6\sqrt{3} + 9\right) = \left(\sqrt{3} - 3\right)\left(12 - 6\sqrt{3}\right) = 12\sqrt{3} - 18 - 36 + 18\sqrt{3} = -54 + 30\sqrt{3}$

41. Rationalizing the denominator: $\dfrac{\sqrt{2}}{\sqrt{6} - \sqrt{2}} = \dfrac{\sqrt{2}}{\sqrt{6} - \sqrt{2}} \cdot \dfrac{\sqrt{6} + \sqrt{2}}{\sqrt{6} + \sqrt{2}} = \dfrac{\sqrt{12} + 2}{6 - 2} = \dfrac{2\sqrt{3} + 2}{4} = \dfrac{1 + \sqrt{3}}{2}$

43. Rationalizing the denominator: $\dfrac{\sqrt{5}}{\sqrt{5} + 1} = \dfrac{\sqrt{5}}{\sqrt{5} + 1} \cdot \dfrac{\sqrt{5} - 1}{\sqrt{5} - 1} = \dfrac{5 - \sqrt{5}}{5 - 1} = \dfrac{5 - \sqrt{5}}{4}$

45. Rationalizing the denominator: $\dfrac{\sqrt{x}}{\sqrt{x} - 3} = \dfrac{\sqrt{x}}{\sqrt{x} - 3} \cdot \dfrac{\sqrt{x} + 3}{\sqrt{x} + 3} = \dfrac{x + 3\sqrt{x}}{x - 9}$

47. Rationalizing the denominator: $\dfrac{\sqrt{5}}{2\sqrt{5} - 3} = \dfrac{\sqrt{5}}{2\sqrt{5} - 3} \cdot \dfrac{2\sqrt{5} + 3}{2\sqrt{5} + 3} = \dfrac{2\sqrt{25} + 3\sqrt{5}}{20 - 9} = \dfrac{10 + 3\sqrt{5}}{11}$

49. Rationalizing the denominator: $\dfrac{3}{\sqrt{x} - \sqrt{y}} = \dfrac{3}{\sqrt{x} - \sqrt{y}} \cdot \dfrac{\sqrt{x} + \sqrt{y}}{\sqrt{x} + \sqrt{y}} = \dfrac{3\sqrt{x} + 3\sqrt{y}}{x - y}$

51. Rationalizing the denominator: $\dfrac{\sqrt{6}+\sqrt{2}}{\sqrt{6}-\sqrt{2}} = \dfrac{\sqrt{6}+\sqrt{2}}{\sqrt{6}-\sqrt{2}} \cdot \dfrac{\sqrt{6}+\sqrt{2}}{\sqrt{6}+\sqrt{2}} = \dfrac{6+2\sqrt{12}+2}{6-2} = \dfrac{8+4\sqrt{3}}{4} = 2+\sqrt{3}$

53. Rationalizing the denominator: $\dfrac{\sqrt{7}-2}{\sqrt{7}+2} = \dfrac{\sqrt{7}-2}{\sqrt{7}+2} \cdot \dfrac{\sqrt{7}-2}{\sqrt{7}-2} = \dfrac{7-4\sqrt{7}+4}{7-4} = \dfrac{11-4\sqrt{7}}{3}$

55. Rationalizing the denominator: $\dfrac{\sqrt{a}+\sqrt{b}}{\sqrt{a}-\sqrt{b}} = \dfrac{\sqrt{a}+\sqrt{b}}{\sqrt{a}-\sqrt{b}} \cdot \dfrac{\sqrt{a}+\sqrt{b}}{\sqrt{a}+\sqrt{b}} = \dfrac{a+2\sqrt{ab}+b}{a-b}$

57. Rationalizing the denominator: $\dfrac{\sqrt{x}+2}{\sqrt{x}-2} = \dfrac{\sqrt{x}+2}{\sqrt{x}-2} \cdot \dfrac{\sqrt{x}+2}{\sqrt{x}+2} = \dfrac{x+4\sqrt{x}+4}{x-4}$

59. Rationalizing the denominator:
$\dfrac{2\sqrt{3}-\sqrt{7}}{3\sqrt{3}+\sqrt{7}} = \dfrac{2\sqrt{3}-\sqrt{7}}{3\sqrt{3}+\sqrt{7}} \cdot \dfrac{3\sqrt{3}-\sqrt{7}}{3\sqrt{3}-\sqrt{7}} = \dfrac{18-3\sqrt{21}-2\sqrt{21}+7}{27-7} = \dfrac{25-5\sqrt{21}}{20} = \dfrac{5-\sqrt{21}}{4}$

61. Rationalizing the denominator: $\dfrac{3\sqrt{x}+2}{1+\sqrt{x}} = \dfrac{3\sqrt{x}+2}{1+\sqrt{x}} \cdot \dfrac{1-\sqrt{x}}{1-\sqrt{x}} = \dfrac{3\sqrt{x}+2-3x-2\sqrt{x}}{1-x} = \dfrac{\sqrt{x}-3x+2}{1-x}$

63. Rationalizing the denominator: $\dfrac{2\sqrt{x}-1}{1-3\sqrt{x}} = \dfrac{2\sqrt{x}-1}{1-3\sqrt{x}} \cdot \dfrac{1+3\sqrt{x}}{1+3\sqrt{x}} = \dfrac{2\sqrt{x}+6x-1-3\sqrt{x}}{1-9x} = \dfrac{6x-\sqrt{x}-1}{1-9x}$

65. Simplifying the product: $\left(\sqrt[3]{2}+\sqrt[3]{3}\right)\left(\sqrt[3]{4}-\sqrt[3]{6}+\sqrt[3]{9}\right) = \sqrt[3]{8}-\sqrt[3]{12}+\sqrt[3]{18}+\sqrt[3]{12}-\sqrt[3]{18}+\sqrt[3]{27} = 2+3 = 5$

67. The correct statement is: $5\left(2\sqrt{3}\right) = 10\sqrt{3}$

69. The correct statement is: $\left(\sqrt{x}+3\right)^2 = \left(\sqrt{x}+3\right)\left(\sqrt{x}+3\right) = x+6\sqrt{x}+9$

71. The correct statement is: $\left(5\sqrt{3}\right)^2 = \left(5\sqrt{3}\right)\left(5\sqrt{3}\right) = 25 \cdot 3 = 75$

73. The correct statement is: $\left(x+\sqrt{3}\right)^2 = x^2+2x\sqrt{3}+3$

75. Substituting $h = 50$: $t = \dfrac{\sqrt{100-50}}{4} = \dfrac{\sqrt{50}}{4} = \dfrac{5\sqrt{2}}{4}$ seconds

Substituting $h = 0$: $t = \dfrac{\sqrt{100-0}}{4} = \dfrac{\sqrt{100}}{4} = \dfrac{10}{4} = \dfrac{5}{2}$ seconds

77. Since the large rectangle is a golden rectangle and $AC = 6$, then $CE = 6\left(\dfrac{1+\sqrt{5}}{2}\right) = 3+3\sqrt{5}$. Since $CD = 6$, then

$DE = 3+3\sqrt{5}-6 = 3\sqrt{5}-3$. Now computing the ratio:
$$\dfrac{EF}{DE} = \dfrac{6}{3\sqrt{5}-3} \cdot \dfrac{3\sqrt{5}+3}{3\sqrt{5}+3} = \dfrac{18\left(\sqrt{5}+1\right)}{45-9} = \dfrac{18\left(\sqrt{5}+1\right)}{36} = \dfrac{1+\sqrt{5}}{2}$$
Therefore the smaller rectangle $BDEF$ is also a golden rectangle.

79. Since the large rectangle is a golden rectangle and $AC = 2x$, then $CE = 2x\left(\dfrac{1+\sqrt{5}}{2}\right) = x\left(1+\sqrt{5}\right)$. Since $CD = 2x$, then

$DE = x\left(1+\sqrt{5}\right)-2x = x\left(-1+\sqrt{5}\right)$. Now computing the ratio:
$$\dfrac{EF}{DE} = \dfrac{2x}{x\left(-1+\sqrt{5}\right)} = \dfrac{2}{-1+\sqrt{5}} \cdot \dfrac{-1-\sqrt{5}}{-1-\sqrt{5}} = \dfrac{-2\left(\sqrt{5}+1\right)}{1-5} = \dfrac{-2\left(\sqrt{5}+1\right)}{-4} = \dfrac{1+\sqrt{5}}{2}$$

Therefore the smaller rectangle $BDEF$ is also a golden rectangle.

81. Simplifying: $\left(t+5\right)^2 = t^2+2\left(5t\right)+5^2 = t^2+10t+25$

83. Simplifying: $\sqrt{x} \cdot \sqrt{x} = \sqrt{x^2} = x$

85. Solving the equation:

$$3x + 4 = 5^2$$
$$3x + 4 = 25$$
$$3x = 21$$
$$x = 7$$

87. Solving the equation:

$$t^2 + 7t + 12 = 0$$
$$(t + 4)(t + 3) = 0$$
$$t = -4, -3$$

89. Solving the equation:

$$t^2 + 10t + 25 = t + 7$$
$$t^2 + 9t + 18 = 0$$
$$(t + 6)(t + 3) = 0$$
$$t = -6, -3$$

91. Solving the equation:

$$(x + 4)^2 = x + 6$$
$$x^2 + 8x + 16 = x + 6$$
$$x^2 + 7x + 10 = 0$$
$$(x + 5)(x + 2) = 0$$
$$x = -5, -2$$

93. Substituting $x = 7$: $\sqrt{3(7) + 4} = \sqrt{25} = 5$. Yes, it is a solution.

95. Substituting $t = -6$:

$$-6 + 5 = \sqrt{-6 + 7}$$
$$-1 = 1$$

No, it is not a solution.

97. Finding the percentages:

North America: $0.49(50) = 24.5$ million

Asia: $0.14(50) = 7$ million

Africa: $0.01(50) = 0.5$ million $= 500,000$

Landmark Review

1. Finding the root: $\sqrt{81} = 9$

2. Finding the root: $-\sqrt{81} = -9$

3. Finding the root: $\sqrt{-81}$ is not a real number

4. Finding the root: $\sqrt[3]{-27} = -3$

5. Simplifying: $\sqrt[3]{x^6 y^{12}} = x^2 y^4$

6. Simplifying: $64^{1/2} = \sqrt{64} = 8$

7. Simplifying: $\left(\dfrac{16}{25}\right)^{-1/2} = \left(\dfrac{25}{16}\right)^{1/2} = \dfrac{5}{4}$

8. Simplifying: $81^{1/2} + 100^{1/2} = \sqrt{81} + \sqrt{100} = 9 + 10 = 19$

9. Simplifying: $\sqrt{164} = \sqrt{4 \cdot 41} = 2\sqrt{41}$

10. Simplifying: $\sqrt{18x^5 y^6} = \sqrt{9x^4 y^6 \cdot 2x} = 3x^2 y^3 \sqrt{2x}$

11. Simplifying: $\sqrt[5]{486 x^{12} y^{10} z^{18}} = \sqrt[5]{243 x^{10} y^{10} z^{15} \cdot 2x^2 z^3} = 3x^2 y^2 z^3 \sqrt[5]{2x^2 z^3}$

12. Simplifying: $\dfrac{4}{\sqrt{5}} = \dfrac{4}{\sqrt{5}} \cdot \dfrac{\sqrt{5}}{\sqrt{5}} = \dfrac{4\sqrt{5}}{5}$

13. Simplifying: $6\sqrt{150} - 4\sqrt{150} + 3\sqrt{216} = 6\sqrt{25 \cdot 6} - 4\sqrt{25 \cdot 6} + 3\sqrt{36 \cdot 6} = 30\sqrt{6} - 20\sqrt{6} + 18\sqrt{6} = 28\sqrt{6}$

14. Simplifying: $\dfrac{\sqrt{2}}{3} + \dfrac{1}{\sqrt{2}} = \dfrac{\sqrt{2}}{3} + \dfrac{1}{\sqrt{2}} \cdot \dfrac{\sqrt{2}}{\sqrt{2}} = \dfrac{\sqrt{2}}{3} + \dfrac{\sqrt{2}}{2} = \dfrac{2\sqrt{2}}{6} + \dfrac{3\sqrt{2}}{6} = \dfrac{5\sqrt{2}}{6}$

15. Multiplying: $\sqrt{6}\sqrt{2} = \sqrt{12} = 2\sqrt{3}$

16. Multiplying: $\left(3\sqrt{5}\right)\left(2\sqrt{10}\right)\left(4\sqrt{8}\right) = 24\sqrt{400} = 24 \cdot 20 = 480$

17. Multiplying: $\left(2\sqrt{3} + 3\sqrt{2}\right)\left(\sqrt{3} + 4\sqrt{2}\right) = 2\sqrt{9} + 8\sqrt{6} + 3\sqrt{6} + 12\sqrt{4} = 6 + 11\sqrt{6} + 24 = 30 + 11\sqrt{6}$

18. Multiplying: $\left(\sqrt{5} - 1\right)^2 = \left(\sqrt{5} - 1\right)\left(\sqrt{5} - 1\right) = \sqrt{25} - \sqrt{5} - \sqrt{5} + 1 = 6 - 2\sqrt{5}$

19. Rationalizing the denominator: $\dfrac{\sqrt{2}}{\sqrt{6}-\sqrt{2}} = \dfrac{\sqrt{2}}{\sqrt{6}-\sqrt{2}} \cdot \dfrac{\sqrt{6}+\sqrt{2}}{\sqrt{6}+\sqrt{2}} = \dfrac{\sqrt{12}+2}{6-2} = \dfrac{2\sqrt{3}+2}{4} = \dfrac{1+\sqrt{3}}{2}$

20. Rationalizing the denominator: $\dfrac{\sqrt{5}+3}{\sqrt{5}-3} = \dfrac{\sqrt{5}+3}{\sqrt{5}-3} \cdot \dfrac{\sqrt{5}+3}{\sqrt{5}+3} = \dfrac{5+6\sqrt{5}+9}{5-9} = \dfrac{14+6\sqrt{5}}{-4} = \dfrac{-7-3\sqrt{5}}{2}$

6.5 Radical Equations and Functions

1. Solving the equation:
$$\sqrt{2x+1} = 3$$
$$\left(\sqrt{2x+1}\right)^2 = 3^2$$
$$2x+1 = 9$$
$$2x = 8$$
$$x = 4$$

3. Solving the equation:
$$\sqrt{4x+1} = -5$$
$$\left(\sqrt{4x+1}\right)^2 = (-5)^2$$
$$4x+1 = 25$$
$$4x = 24$$
$$x = 6$$
Since this value does not check, there is no solution.

5. Solving the equation:
$$\sqrt{2y-1} = 3$$
$$\left(\sqrt{2y-1}\right)^2 = 3^2$$
$$2y-1 = 9$$
$$2y = 10$$
$$y = 5$$

7. Solving the equation:
$$\sqrt{5x-7} = -1$$
$$\left(\sqrt{5x-7}\right)^2 = (-1)^2$$
$$5x-7 = 1$$
$$5x = 8$$
$$x = \frac{8}{5}$$
Since this value does not check, there is no solution.

9. Solving the equation:
$$\sqrt{2x-3}-2 = 4$$
$$\sqrt{2x-3} = 6$$
$$\left(\sqrt{2x-3}\right)^2 = 6^2$$
$$2x-3 = 36$$
$$2x = 39$$
$$x = \frac{39}{2}$$

11. Solving the equation:
$$\sqrt{4a+1}+3 = 2$$
$$\sqrt{4a+1} = -1$$
$$\left(\sqrt{4a+1}\right)^2 = (-1)^2$$
$$4a+1 = 1$$
$$4a = 0$$
$$a = 0$$
Since this value does not check, there is no solution.

13. Solving the equation:
$$\sqrt[4]{3x+1} = 2$$
$$\left(\sqrt[4]{3x+1}\right)^4 = 2^4$$
$$3x+1 = 16$$
$$3x = 15$$
$$x = 5$$

15. Solving the equation:
$$\sqrt[3]{2x-5} = 1$$
$$\left(\sqrt[3]{2x-5}\right)^3 = 1^3$$
$$2x-5 = 1$$
$$2x = 6$$
$$x = 3$$

17. Solving the equation:
$$\sqrt[3]{3a+5} = -3$$
$$\left(\sqrt[3]{3a+5}\right)^3 = (-3)^3$$
$$3a+5 = -27$$
$$3a = -32$$
$$a = -\frac{32}{3}$$

19. Solving the equation:
$$\sqrt{y-3} = y-3$$
$$\left(\sqrt{y-3}\right)^2 = (y-3)^2$$
$$y-3 = y^2-6y+9$$
$$0 = y^2-7y+12$$
$$0 = (y-3)(y-4)$$
$$y = 3, 4$$

21. Solving the equation:
$$\sqrt{a+2} = a+2$$
$$\left(\sqrt{a+2}\right)^2 = (a+2)^2$$
$$a+2 = a^2 + 4a + 4$$
$$0 = a^2 + 3a + 2$$
$$0 = (a+2)(a+1)$$
$$a = -2, -1$$

23. Solving the equation:
$$\sqrt{2x+4} = \sqrt{1-x}$$
$$\left(\sqrt{2x+4}\right)^2 = \left(\sqrt{1-x}\right)^2$$
$$2x+4 = 1-x$$
$$3x = -3$$
$$x = -1$$

25. Solving the equation:
$$\sqrt{4a+7} = -\sqrt{a+2}$$
$$\left(\sqrt{4a+7}\right)^2 = \left(-\sqrt{a+2}\right)^2$$
$$4a+7 = a+2$$
$$3a = -5$$
$$a = -\frac{5}{3}$$

Since this value does not check, there is no solution.

27. Solving the equation:
$$\sqrt[4]{5x-8} = \sqrt[4]{4x-1}$$
$$\left(\sqrt[4]{5x-8}\right)^4 = \left(\sqrt[4]{4x-1}\right)^4$$
$$5x-8 = 4x-1$$
$$x = 7$$

29. Solving the equation:
$$x+1 = \sqrt{5x+1}$$
$$(x+1)^2 = \left(\sqrt{5x+1}\right)^2$$
$$x^2 + 2x + 1 = 5x + 1$$
$$x^2 - 3x = 0$$
$$x(x-3) = 0$$
$$x = 0, 3$$

31. Solving the equation:
$$t+5 = \sqrt{2t+9}$$
$$(t+5)^2 = \left(\sqrt{2t+9}\right)^2$$
$$t^2 + 10t + 25 = 2t + 9$$
$$t^2 + 8t + 16 = 0$$
$$(t+4)^2 = 0$$
$$t = -4$$

33. Solving the equation:
$$\sqrt{y-8} = \sqrt{8-y}$$
$$\left(\sqrt{y-8}\right)^2 = \left(\sqrt{8-y}\right)^2$$
$$y-8 = 8-y$$
$$2y = 16$$
$$y = 8$$

35. Solving the equation:
$$\sqrt[3]{3x+5} = \sqrt[3]{5-2x}$$
$$\left(\sqrt[3]{3x+5}\right)^3 = \left(\sqrt[3]{5-2x}\right)^3$$
$$3x+5 = 5-2x$$
$$5x = 0$$
$$x = 0$$

37. Solving the equation:
$$\sqrt{x-8} = \sqrt{x} - 2$$
$$\left(\sqrt{x-8}\right)^2 = \left(\sqrt{x} - 2\right)^2$$
$$x-8 = x - 4\sqrt{x} + 4$$
$$-12 = -4\sqrt{x}$$
$$\sqrt{x} = 3$$
$$x = 9$$

39. Solving the equation:
$$\sqrt{x+1} = \sqrt{x} + 1$$
$$\left(\sqrt{x+1}\right)^2 = \left(\sqrt{x} + 1\right)^2$$
$$x+1 = x + 2\sqrt{x} + 1$$
$$0 = 2\sqrt{x}$$
$$\sqrt{x} = 0$$
$$x = 0$$

41. Solving the equation:
$$\sqrt{x+8} = \sqrt{x-4} + 2$$
$$\left(\sqrt{x+8}\right)^2 = \left(\sqrt{x-4} + 2\right)^2$$
$$x+8 = x - 4 + 4\sqrt{x-4} + 4$$
$$8 = 4\sqrt{x-4}$$
$$\sqrt{x-4} = 2$$
$$x - 4 = 4$$
$$x = 8$$

43. Solving the equation:
$$\sqrt{x-5} - 3 = \sqrt{x-8}$$
$$\left(\sqrt{x-5} - 3\right)^2 = \left(\sqrt{x-8}\right)^2$$
$$x - 5 - 6\sqrt{x-5} + 9 = x - 8$$
$$-6\sqrt{x-5} = -12$$
$$\sqrt{x-5} = 2$$
$$x - 5 = 4$$
$$x = 9$$

Since this value does not check, there is no solution.

45. Solving the equation:

$$\sqrt{x+4} = 2 - \sqrt{2x}$$
$$\left(\sqrt{x+4}\right)^2 = \left(2 - \sqrt{2x}\right)^2$$
$$x + 4 = 4 - 4\sqrt{2x} + 2x$$
$$-x = -4\sqrt{2x}$$
$$(-x)^2 = \left(-4\sqrt{2x}\right)^2$$
$$x^2 = 32x$$
$$x^2 - 32x = 0$$
$$x(x - 32) = 0$$
$$x = 0, 32$$

The solution is 0 (32 does not check).

47. Solving the equation:

$$\sqrt{2x+4} = \sqrt{x+3} + 1$$
$$\left(\sqrt{2x+4}\right)^2 = \left(\sqrt{x+3} + 1\right)^2$$
$$2x + 4 = x + 3 + 2\sqrt{x+3} + 1$$
$$x = 2\sqrt{x+3}$$
$$x^2 = \left(2\sqrt{x+3}\right)^2$$
$$x^2 = 4x + 12$$
$$x^2 - 4x - 12 = 0$$
$$(x - 6)(x + 2) = 0$$
$$x = -2, 6$$

The solution is 6 (–2 does not check).

49. Solving the equation:

$$\sqrt{2x-5} + \sqrt{3x-5} = \sqrt{2x+3}$$
$$\left(\sqrt{2x-5} + \sqrt{3x-5}\right)^2 = \left(\sqrt{2x+3}\right)^2$$
$$2x - 5 + 2\sqrt{(2x-5)(3x-5)} + 3x - 5 = 2x + 3$$
$$2\sqrt{(2x-5)(3x-5)} + 5x - 10 = 2x + 3$$
$$2\sqrt{(2x-5)(3x-5)} = 13 - 3x$$
$$\left(2\sqrt{(2x-5)(3x-5)}\right)^2 = (13 - 3x)^2$$
$$4(2x-5)(3x-5) = (13 - 3x)^2$$
$$24x^2 - 100x + 100 = 169 - 78x + 9x^2$$
$$15x^2 - 22x - 69 = 0$$
$$(15x + 23)(x - 3) = 0$$
$$x = 3 \quad \left(x = -\frac{23}{15} \text{ does not check}\right)$$

51. Solving the equation:

$$\sqrt{2a-2} + \sqrt{4a+3} = \sqrt{2a+5}$$
$$\left(\sqrt{2a-2} + \sqrt{4a+3}\right)^2 = \left(\sqrt{2a+5}\right)^2$$
$$2a - 2 + 2\sqrt{(2a-2)(4a+3)} + 4a + 3 = 2a + 5$$
$$2\sqrt{(2a-2)(4a+3)} + 6a + 1 = 2a + 5$$
$$2\sqrt{(2a-2)(4a+3)} = 4 - 4a$$
$$\sqrt{(2a-2)(4a+3)} = 2 - 2a$$
$$\left(\sqrt{(2a-2)(4a+3)}\right)^2 = (2 - 2a)^2$$
$$(2a-2)(4a+3) = (2 - 2a)^2$$
$$8a^2 - 2a - 6 = 4 - 8a + 4a^2$$
$$4a^2 + 6a - 10 = 0$$
$$2a^2 + 3a - 5 = 0$$
$$(2a + 5)(a - 1) = 0$$
$$a = 1 \quad \left(a = -\frac{5}{2} \text{ does not check}\right)$$

53. Solving the equation:

$$\sqrt{4x-5} - \sqrt{x-5} = \sqrt{3x-4}$$
$$\left(\sqrt{4x-5} - \sqrt{x-5}\right)^2 = \left(\sqrt{3x-4}\right)^2$$
$$4x-5-2\sqrt{(4x-5)(x-5)} + x-5 = 3x-4$$
$$-2\sqrt{(4x-5)(x-5)} + 5x-10 = 3x-4$$
$$-2\sqrt{(4x-5)(x-5)} = 6-2x$$
$$\sqrt{(4x-5)(x-5)} = x-3$$
$$\left(\sqrt{(4x-5)(x-5)}\right)^2 = (x-3)^2$$
$$(4x-5)(x-5) = (x-3)^2$$
$$4x^2 - 25x + 25 = x^2 - 6x + 9$$
$$3x^2 - 19x + 16 = 0$$
$$(3x-16)(x-1) = 0$$
$$x = \frac{16}{3} \quad (x = 1 \text{ does not check})$$

55. Solving for h:

$$t = \frac{\sqrt{100-h}}{4}$$
$$4t = \sqrt{100-h}$$
$$16t^2 = 100 - h$$
$$h = 100 - 16t^2$$

57. Solving for L:

$$2 = 2\left(\frac{22}{7}\right)\sqrt{\frac{L}{32}}$$
$$\frac{7}{22} = \sqrt{\frac{L}{32}}$$
$$\left(\frac{7}{22}\right)^2 = \frac{L}{32}$$
$$L = 32\left(\frac{7}{22}\right)^2 \approx 3.24 \text{ feet}$$

59. Solving the proportion:

$$\frac{\sqrt{x+1}}{l} = \frac{3}{10}$$
$$3l = 10\sqrt{x+1}$$
$$l = \frac{10}{3}\sqrt{x+1}$$

61. The width is $\sqrt{25} = 5$ meters.

63. Solving the equation:

$$\sqrt{x} = 50$$
$$x = 2500$$

The plume is 2,500 meters down river.

65. The range of values is $0 \le y \le 100$.

67. Graphing the equation:

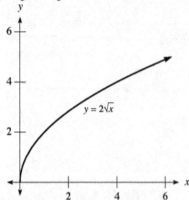

$y = 2\sqrt{x}$

69. Graphing the equation:

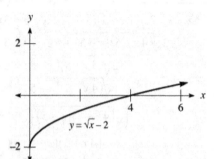

$y = \sqrt{x} - 2$

71. Graphing the equation:

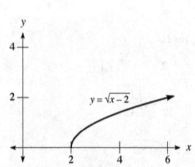

$y = \sqrt{x - 2}$

73. Graphing the equation:

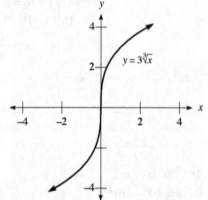

$y = 3\sqrt[3]{x}$

75. Graphing the equation:

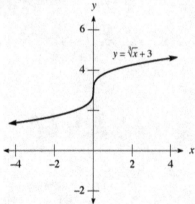

$y = \sqrt[3]{x} + 3$

77. Graphing the equation:

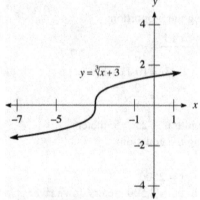

$y = \sqrt[3]{x + 3}$

79. Simplifying: $\sqrt{25} = 5$

81. Simplifying: $\sqrt{12} = \sqrt{4 \cdot 3} = 2\sqrt{3}$

83. Simplifying: $(-1)^{15} = -1$

85. Simplifying: $(-1)^{50} = 1$

87. Solving the equation:

$$3x = 12$$
$$x = 4$$

89. Solving the equation:
$$4x - 3 = 5$$
$$4x = 8$$
$$x = 2$$

91. Performing the operations: $(3 + 4x) + (7 - 6x) = 10 - 2x$

93. Performing the operations: $(7 + 3x) - (5 + 6x) = 7 + 3x - 5 - 6x = 2 - 3x$

95. Performing the operations: $(3 - 4x)(2 + 5x) = 6 + 15x - 8x - 20x^2 = 6 + 7x - 20x^2$

97. Performing the operations: $2x(4-6x) = 8x - 12x^2$

99. Performing the operations: $(2+3x)^2 = 2^2 + 2(2)(3x) + (3x)^2 = 4 + 12x + 9x^2$

101. Performing the operations: $(2-3x)(2+3x) = 2^2 - (3x)^2 = 4 - 9x^2$

6.6 Complex Numbers

1. Writing in terms of i: $\sqrt{-36} = 6i$

3. Writing in terms of i: $-\sqrt{-25} = -5i$

5. Writing in terms of i: $\sqrt{-72} = 6i\sqrt{2}$

7. Writing in terms of i: $-\sqrt{-12} = -2i\sqrt{3}$

9. Rewriting the expression: $i^{28} = \left(i^4\right)^7 = (1)^7 = 1$

11. Rewriting the expression: $i^{26} = i^{24}i^2 = \left(i^4\right)^6 i^2 = (1)^6 (-1) = -1$

13. Rewriting the expression: $i^{75} = i^{72}i^3 = \left(i^4\right)^{18} i^2 i = (1)^{18} (-1)i = -i$

15. Rewriting the expression: $(-i)^{12} = \left(i^4\right)^3 = (1)^3 = 1$

17. Setting real and imaginary parts equal:

$$\begin{aligned} 2x &= 6 & 3y &= -3 \\ x &= 3 & y &= -1 \end{aligned}$$

19. Setting real and imaginary parts equal:

$$\begin{aligned} & & 10y &= -5 \\ -x &= 2 & & \\ x &= -2 & y &= -\frac{1}{2} \end{aligned}$$

21. Setting real and imaginary parts equal:

$$\begin{aligned} 2x &= -16 & -2y &= 10 \\ x &= -8 & y &= -5 \end{aligned}$$

23. Setting real and imaginary parts equal:

$$\begin{aligned} 2x - 4 &= 10 & -6y &= -3 \\ 2x &= 14 & & \\ x &= 7 & y &= \frac{1}{2} \end{aligned}$$

25. Setting real and imaginary parts equal:

$$\begin{aligned} 7x - 1 &= 2 & 5y + 2 &= 4 \\ 7x &= 3 & 5y &= 2 \\ x &= \frac{3}{7} & y &= \frac{2}{5} \end{aligned}$$

27. Combining the numbers: $(2+3i)+(3+6i) = 5 + 9i$

29. Combining the numbers: $(3-5i)+(2+4i) = 5 - i$

31. Combining the numbers: $(5+2i)-(3+6i) = 5 + 2i - 3 - 6i = 2 - 4i$

33. Combining the numbers: $(3-5i)-(2+i) = 3 - 5i - 2 - i = 1 - 6i$

35. Combining the numbers: $[(3+2i)-(6+i)]+(5+i) = 3 + 2i - 6 - i + 5 + i = 2 + 2i$

37. Combining the numbers: $[(7-i)-(2+4i)]-(6+2i) = 7 - i - 2 - 4i - 6 - 2i = -1 - 7i$

39. Combining the numbers:

$$(3+2i)-[(3-4i)-(6+2i)] = (3+2i)-(3-4i-6-2i) = (3+2i)-(-3-6i) = 3+2i+3+6i = 6+8i$$

41. Combining the numbers: $(4-9i)+[(2-7i)-(4+8i)] = (4-9i)+(2-7i-4-8i) = (4-9i)+(-2-15i) = 2 - 24i$

43. Finding the product: $3i(4+5i) = 12i + 15i^2 = -15 + 12i$

45. Finding the product: $6i(4-3i) = 24i - 18i^2 = 18 + 24i$

47. Finding the product: $(3+2i)(4+i) = 12 + 8i + 3i + 2i^2 = 12 + 11i - 2 = 10 + 11i$

49. Finding the product: $(4+9i)(3-i) = 12 + 27i - 4i - 9i^2 = 12 + 23i + 9 = 21 + 23i$

51. Finding the product: $(1+i)^3 = (1+i)(1+i)^2 = (1+i)(1+2i-1) = (1+i)(2i) = -2 + 2i$

---

53. Finding the product: $(2-i)^3 = (2-i)(2-i)^2 = (2-i)(4-4i-1) = (2-i)(3-4i) = 6-11i-4 = 2-11i$

55. Finding the product: $(2+5i)^2 = (2+5i)(2+5i) = 4+10i+10i-25 = -21+20i$

57. Finding the product: $(1-i)^2 = (1-i)(1-i) = 1-i-i-1 = -2i$

59. Finding the product: $(3-4i)^2 = (3-4i)(3-4i) = 9-12i-12i-16 = -7-24i$

61. Finding the product: $(2+i)(2-i) = 4-i^2 = 4+1 = 5$

63. Finding the product: $(6-2i)(6+2i) = 36-4i^2 = 36+4 = 40$

65. Finding the product: $(2+3i)(2-3i) = 4-9i^2 = 4+9 = 13$

67. Finding the product: $(10+8i)(10-8i) = 100-64i^2 = 100+64 = 164$

69. Finding the product: $(\sqrt{3}+2i)(\sqrt{3}-2i) = 3-4i^2 = 3+4 = 7$

71. Finding the quotient: $\dfrac{2-3i}{i} = \dfrac{2-3i}{i} \cdot \dfrac{i}{i} = \dfrac{2i+3}{-1} = -3-2i$

73. Finding the quotient: $\dfrac{5+2i}{-i} = \dfrac{5+2i}{-i} \cdot \dfrac{i}{i} = \dfrac{5i-2}{1} = -2+5i$

75. Finding the quotient: $\dfrac{4}{2-3i} = \dfrac{4}{2-3i} \cdot \dfrac{2+3i}{2+3i} = \dfrac{8+12i}{4+9} = \dfrac{8+12i}{13} = \dfrac{8}{13} + \dfrac{12}{13}i$

77. Finding the quotient: $\dfrac{6}{-3+2i} = \dfrac{6}{-3+2i} \cdot \dfrac{-3-2i}{-3-2i} = \dfrac{-18-12i}{9+4} = \dfrac{-18-12i}{13} = -\dfrac{18}{13} - \dfrac{12}{13}i$

79. Finding the quotient: $\dfrac{2+3i}{2-3i} = \dfrac{2+3i}{2-3i} \cdot \dfrac{2+3i}{2+3i} = \dfrac{4+12i-9}{4+9} = \dfrac{-5+12i}{13} = -\dfrac{5}{13} + \dfrac{12}{13}i$

81. Finding the quotient: $\dfrac{5+4i}{3+6i} = \dfrac{5+4i}{3+6i} \cdot \dfrac{3-6i}{3-6i} = \dfrac{15-18i+24}{9+36} = \dfrac{39-18i}{45} = \dfrac{13}{15} - \dfrac{2}{5}i$

83. Dividing to find R: $R = \dfrac{80+20i}{-6+2i} = \dfrac{80+20i}{-6+2i} \cdot \dfrac{-6-2i}{-6-2i} = \dfrac{-480-280i+40}{36+4} = \dfrac{-440-280i}{40} = (-11-7i)$ ohms

85. Solving the equation:

$$\dfrac{t}{3} - \dfrac{1}{2} = -1$$
$$6\left(\dfrac{t}{3} - \dfrac{1}{2}\right) = 6(-1)$$
$$2t - 3 = -6$$
$$2t = -3$$
$$t = -\dfrac{3}{2}$$

87. Solving the equation:

$$2 + \dfrac{5}{y} = \dfrac{3}{y^2}$$
$$y^2\left(2 + \dfrac{5}{y}\right) = y^2\left(\dfrac{3}{y^2}\right)$$
$$2y^2 + 5y = 3$$
$$2y^2 + 5y - 3 = 0$$
$$(2y-1)(y+3) = 0$$
$$y = -3, \dfrac{1}{2}$$

89. Let x represent the number. The equation is:

$$x + \dfrac{1}{x} = \dfrac{41}{20}$$
$$20x\left(x + \dfrac{1}{x}\right) = 20x\left(\dfrac{41}{20}\right)$$
$$20x^2 + 20 = 41x$$
$$20x^2 - 41x + 20 = 0$$
$$(5x-4)(4x-5) = 0$$
$$x = \dfrac{4}{5}, \dfrac{5}{4}$$

The number is either $\dfrac{5}{4}$ or $\dfrac{4}{5}$.

91. Finding the slope: $m = \dfrac{7.50 - 5.39}{2009 - 2000} = \dfrac{2.11}{9} \approx 0.234$

Using the point-slope formula:
$$y - 5.39 = 0.234(x - 2000)$$
$$y - 5.39 = 0.234x - 468$$
$$y = 0.234x - 462.61$$

Substituting $x = 2015$: $y = 0.234(2015) - 462.61 = \$8.90$

Chapter 6 Review

1. Simplifying: $27^{-2/3} = \left(27^{1/3}\right)^{-2} = 3^{-2} = \dfrac{1}{3^2} = \dfrac{1}{9}$

2. Simplifying: $\left(\dfrac{144}{49}\right)^{-1/2} = \left(\dfrac{49}{144}\right)^{1/2} = \dfrac{7}{12}$

3. Simplifying: $x^{2/3} \cdot x^{1/5} = x^{2/3+1/5} = x^{10/15+3/15} = x^{13/15}$

4. Simplifying: $\dfrac{\left(a^{1/4}b\right)^{-2}}{\left(a^{3/2}b^6\right)^{-1}} = \dfrac{a^{-1/2}b^{-2}}{a^{-3/2}b^{-6}} = a^{-1/2+3/2}b^{-2+6} = ab^4$

5. Simplifying: $\sqrt{49x^8y^{12}} = 7x^4y^6$

6. Simplifying: $\sqrt[3]{27x^6y^{12}} = 3x^2y^4$

7. Simplifying: $\dfrac{\left(49a^8b^{10}\right)^{1/2}}{\left(27a^{15}b^3\right)^{1/3}} = \dfrac{7a^4b^5}{3a^5b} = \dfrac{7b^4}{3a}$

8. Simplifying: $\dfrac{\left(x^{1/n}y^{2/n}\right)^n}{\left(x^{1/n}y^n\right)^{n^2}} = \dfrac{xy^2}{x^n y^{n^3}} = x^{1-n}y^{2-n^3}$

9. Simplifying: $\sqrt{50x^3y^7} = \sqrt{25x^2y^6 \cdot 2xy} = 5xy^3\sqrt{2xy}$

10. Simplifying: $\sqrt[3]{135x^5y^7} = \sqrt[3]{27x^3y^6 \cdot 5x^2y} = 3xy^2\sqrt[3]{5x^2y}$

11. Simplifying: $\sqrt{\dfrac{5}{7}} = \dfrac{\sqrt{5}}{\sqrt{7}} \cdot \dfrac{\sqrt{7}}{\sqrt{7}} = \dfrac{\sqrt{35}}{7}$

12. Simplifying: $\sqrt{\dfrac{12a^3b^5}{5c^2}} = \dfrac{2ab^2\sqrt{3ab}}{c\sqrt{5}} \cdot \dfrac{\sqrt{5}}{\sqrt{5}} = \dfrac{2ab^2\sqrt{15ab}}{5c}$

13. Rationalizing the denominator: $\dfrac{3}{\sqrt{5}-2} = \dfrac{3}{\sqrt{5}-2} \cdot \dfrac{\sqrt{5}+2}{\sqrt{5}+2} = \dfrac{3\sqrt{5}+6}{5-4} = 3\sqrt{5}+6$

14. Rationalizing the denominator: $\dfrac{\sqrt{x}-\sqrt{5}}{\sqrt{x}+\sqrt{5}} = \dfrac{\sqrt{x}-\sqrt{5}}{\sqrt{x}+\sqrt{5}} \cdot \dfrac{\sqrt{x}-\sqrt{5}}{\sqrt{x}-\sqrt{5}} = \dfrac{x-\sqrt{5x}-\sqrt{5x}+5}{x-5} = \dfrac{x-2\sqrt{5x}+5}{x-5}$

15. Combining: $\dfrac{3}{x^{1/3}} + x^{2/3} = \dfrac{3}{x^{1/3}} + x^{2/3} \cdot \dfrac{x^{1/3}}{x^{1/3}} = \dfrac{3+x}{x^{1/3}}$

16. Combining: $\dfrac{x^4}{\left(x^4-6\right)^{1/2}} - \left(x^4-6\right)^{1/2} = \dfrac{x^4}{\left(x^4-6\right)^{1/2}} - \left(x^4-6\right)^{1/2} \cdot \dfrac{\left(x^4-6\right)^{1/2}}{\left(x^4-6\right)^{1/2}} = \dfrac{x^4-x^4+6}{\left(x^4-6\right)^{1/2}} = \dfrac{6}{\left(x^4-6\right)^{1/2}} = \dfrac{6\sqrt{x^4-6}}{x^4-6}$

17. Combining: $2\sqrt{12} - 2\sqrt{48} = 4\sqrt{3} - 8\sqrt{3} = -4\sqrt{3}$

18. Combining: $3\sqrt[3]{40a^3b^5} - a\sqrt[3]{5b^5} = 6ab\sqrt[3]{5b^2} - ab\sqrt[3]{5b^2} = 5ab\sqrt[3]{5b^2}$

19. Multiplying: $3a^{5/2}\left(2a^{3/2} - a^{7/2}\right) = 6a^{8/2} - 3a^{12/2} = 6a^4 - 3a^6$

20. Multiplying: $\left(3a^{4/5} - 2\right)^2 = \left(3a^{4/5} - 2\right)\left(3a^{4/5} - 2\right) = 9a^{8/5} - 6a^{4/5} - 6a^{4/5} + 4 = 9a^{8/5} - 12a^{4/5} + 4$

21. Multiplying: $\left(\sqrt{x}-3\right)\left(\sqrt{x}+5\right)=x-3\sqrt{x}+5\sqrt{x}-15=x+2\sqrt{x}-15$

22. Multiplying: $\left(4\sqrt{3}-\sqrt{5}\right)^2=\left(4\sqrt{3}-\sqrt{5}\right)\left(4\sqrt{3}-\sqrt{5}\right)=48-4\sqrt{15}-4\sqrt{15}+5=53-8\sqrt{15}$

23. Solving the equation:
$$\sqrt{x+7}=x-5$$
$$\left(\sqrt{x+7}\right)^2=(x-5)^2$$
$$x+7=x^2-10x+25$$
$$0=x^2-11x+18$$
$$0=(x-2)(x-9)$$
$$x=9 \quad (x=2 \text{ doesn't check})$$

24. Solving the equation:
$$\sqrt[3]{5x+4}=4$$
$$\left(\sqrt[3]{5x+4}\right)^3=(4)^3$$
$$5x+4=64$$
$$5x=60$$
$$x=12$$

25. Solving the equation:
$$\sqrt{x+8}=\sqrt{x-16}+4$$
$$\left(\sqrt{x+8}\right)^2=\left(\sqrt{x-16}+4\right)^2$$
$$x+8=x-16+8\sqrt{x-16}+16$$
$$x+8=x+8\sqrt{x-16}$$
$$\sqrt{x-16}=1$$
$$x-16=1$$
$$x=17$$

26. Graphing the equation:

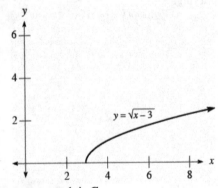

27. Graphing the equation:

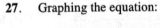
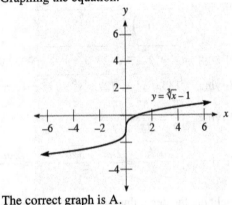

28. The correct graph is C.

29. The correct graph is A.

30. The correct graph is D.

31. The correct graph is B.

32. The correct graph is E.

33. The correct graph is F.

34. Setting the real and imaginary parts equal:
$$-(2x-3)=5 \qquad\qquad 4y-3=9$$
$$2x-3=-5 \qquad\qquad\quad 4y=12$$
$$2x=-2 \qquad\qquad\qquad y=3$$
$$x=-1$$

35. Performing the operations:
$$(5+3i)-\left[(4-2i)-(3+7i)\right]=(5+3i)-(4-2i-3-7i)=(5+3i)-(1-9i)=5+3i-1+9i=4+12i$$

36. Performing the operations: $(3-2i)(4+3i)=12+9i-8i+6=18+i$

37. Performing the operations: $(5-3i)^2=(5-3i)(5-3i)=25-15i-15i-9=16-30i$

38. Performing the operations: $\dfrac{4i-1}{4i+1}=\dfrac{4i-1}{4i+1}\cdot\dfrac{4i-1}{4i-1}=\dfrac{-16-8i+1}{-16-1}=\dfrac{-15-8i}{-17}=\dfrac{15}{17}+\dfrac{8}{17}i$

39. Rewriting the exponent: $i^{39}=i^{38}\cdot i=\left(i^2\right)^{19}\cdot i=(-1)^{19}\cdot i=-i$

Chapter 6 Cumulative Review

1. Simplifying: $2-[1+4(8-9)]=2-[1+4(-1)]=2-(1-4)=2+3=5$

2. Simplifying: $3+21\div7+4\cdot2=3+3+8=14$

3. Simplifying: $5+(7-3)^2-(4+1)^2=5+(4)^2-(5)^2=5+16-25=-4$

4. Simplifying: $\sqrt[4]{128}=\sqrt[4]{2^4\cdot8}=2\sqrt[4]{8}$

5. Simplifying: $27^{2/3}+25^{1/2}=\left(27^{1/3}\right)^2+25^{1/2}=(3)^2+5=9+5=14$

6. Simplifying: $\dfrac{1-\dfrac{4}{5}}{1+\dfrac{1}{5}}=\dfrac{1-\dfrac{4}{5}}{1+\dfrac{1}{5}}\cdot\dfrac{5}{5}=\dfrac{5-4}{5+1}=\dfrac{1}{6}$

7. Simplifying: $\left(-\dfrac{8}{125}\right)^{-1/3}=\left(-\dfrac{125}{8}\right)^{1/3}=-\dfrac{5}{2}$

8. Simplifying: $32+[4-9\div3(6-9)]=32+[4-9\div3(-3)]=32+[4-3(-3)]=32+(4+9)=32+13=45$

9. Reducing to lowest terms: $\dfrac{104}{117}=\dfrac{2\cdot2\cdot2\cdot13}{3\cdot3\cdot13}=\dfrac{2\cdot2\cdot2}{3\cdot3}=\dfrac{8}{9}$

10. Reducing to lowest terms: $\dfrac{18x^2-21xy-15y^2}{6x+3y}=\dfrac{3\left(6x^2-7xy-5y^2\right)}{3(2x+y)}=\dfrac{3(3x-5y)(2x+y)}{3(2x+y)}=3x-5y$

11. Reducing to lowest terms: $\dfrac{x^2+x-2}{x^2+5x+6}=\dfrac{(x-1)(x+2)}{(x+3)(x+2)}=\dfrac{x-1}{x+3}$

12. Reducing to lowest terms: $\dfrac{4a^8b^{-2}}{16a^3b^{-8}}=\dfrac{1}{4}a^{8-3}b^{-2+8}=\dfrac{1}{4}a^5b^6=\dfrac{a^5b^6}{4}$

13. Multiplying: $\left(3\sqrt{x}-5\right)\left(\sqrt{x}+1\right)=3x-5\sqrt{x}+3\sqrt{x}-5=3x-2\sqrt{x}-5$

14. Multiplying: $(8+2i)(6-i)=48+12i-8i-2i^2=48+4i+2=50+4i$

15. Dividing: $\dfrac{3-i}{3-2i}=\dfrac{3-i}{3-2i}\cdot\dfrac{3+2i}{3+2i}=\dfrac{9-3i+6i-2i^2}{9-4i^2}=\dfrac{9+3i+2}{9+4}=\dfrac{11+3i}{13}=\dfrac{11}{13}+\dfrac{3}{13}i$

16. Dividing: $\dfrac{\sqrt{5}}{2-\sqrt{5}}=\dfrac{\sqrt{5}}{2-\sqrt{5}}\cdot\dfrac{2+\sqrt{5}}{2+\sqrt{5}}=\dfrac{2\sqrt{5}+5}{4-5}=\dfrac{2\sqrt{5}+5}{-1}=-2\sqrt{5}-5$

17. Multiplying: $(4x+2y)(7x-y)=28x^2-4xy+14xy-2y^2=28x^2+10xy-2y^2$

18. Multiplying: $\left(16x^2-9\right)\cdot\dfrac{x-7}{4x-3}=\dfrac{(4x+3)(4x-3)}{1}\cdot\dfrac{x-7}{4x-3}=(4x+3)(x-7)=4x^2-25x-21$

19. Dividing: $\dfrac{24x^7y^{-3}}{5x^2y^4}\div\dfrac{6x^2y^2}{25x^3y}=\dfrac{24x^7y^{-3}}{5x^2y^4}\cdot\dfrac{25x^3y}{6x^2y^2}=\dfrac{24\cdot25x^{10}y^{-2}}{5\cdot6x^4y^6}=\dfrac{20x^6}{y^8}$

20. Dividing: $\dfrac{\sqrt{x}-\sqrt{y}}{\sqrt{x}+\sqrt{y}}=\dfrac{\sqrt{x}-\sqrt{y}}{\sqrt{x}+\sqrt{y}}\cdot\dfrac{\sqrt{x}-\sqrt{y}}{\sqrt{x}-\sqrt{y}}=\dfrac{x-2\sqrt{xy}+y}{x-y}$

21. Solving the equation:

$$\frac{1}{2} + \frac{2}{a+3} = \frac{1}{a+3}$$

$$2(a+3)\left(\frac{1}{2} + \frac{2}{a+3}\right) = 2(a+3)\left(\frac{1}{a+3}\right)$$

$$a + 3 + 4 = 2$$

$$a + 7 = 2$$

$$a = -5$$

22. Solving the equation:

$$\sqrt{5-x} = x - 5$$

$$\left(\sqrt{5-x}\right)^2 = (x-5)^2$$

$$5 - x = x^2 - 10x + 25$$

$$0 = x^2 - 9x + 20$$

$$0 = (x-4)(x-5)$$

$$x = 4, 5$$

23. Solving the equation:

$$(3x+4)^2 = 7$$

$$3x + 4 = \pm\sqrt{7}$$

$$3x = -4 \pm \sqrt{7}$$

$$x = \frac{-4 \pm \sqrt{7}}{3}$$

24. Solving the equation:

$$0.02x^2 + 0.07x = 0.04$$

$$2x^2 + 7x = 4$$

$$2x^2 + 7x - 4 = 0$$

$$(2x-1)(x+4) = 0$$

$$x = \frac{1}{2}, -4$$

25. Solving the equation:

$$\sqrt{x-7} = 7 - \sqrt{x}$$

$$\left(\sqrt{x-7}\right)^2 = \left(7 - \sqrt{x}\right)^2$$

$$x - 7 = 49 - 14\sqrt{x} + x$$

$$-14\sqrt{x} = -56$$

$$\sqrt{x} = 4$$

$$x = 16$$

26. Solving the equation:

$$3x^3 - 4x = -4x^2$$

$$3x^3 + 4x^2 - 4x = 0$$

$$x\left(3x^2 + 4x - 4\right) = 0$$

$$x(3x-2)(x+2) = 0$$

$$x = -2, 0, \frac{2}{3}$$

27. Solving the equation:

$$\frac{1}{10}x^2 + \frac{2}{5}x = \frac{1}{2}$$

$$10\left(\frac{1}{10}x^2 + \frac{2}{5}x\right) = 10\left(\frac{1}{2}\right)$$

$$x^2 + 4x = 5$$

$$x^2 + 4x - 5 = 0$$

$$(x+5)(x-1) = 0$$

$$x = -5, 1$$

28. Solving the equation:

$$\frac{1}{8}(16x-2) + \frac{1}{4} = 6$$

$$2x - \frac{1}{4} + \frac{1}{4} = 6$$

$$2x = 6$$

$$x = 3$$

29. Solving the equation:

$$|8x-9| - 4 = 3$$

$$|8x-9| = 7$$

$$8x - 9 = -7, 7$$

$$8x = 2, 16$$

$$x = \frac{1}{4}, 2$$

30. Solving the equation:

$$\sqrt[3]{15-4x} = -1$$

$$\left(\sqrt[3]{15-4x}\right)^3 = (-1)^3$$

$$15 - 4x = -1$$

$$-4x = -16$$

$$x = 4$$

31. Solving the inequality:

$$-1 \le \frac{x}{5} - 5 \le 1$$

$$4 \le \frac{x}{5} \le 6$$

$$20 \le x \le 30$$

32. Solving the inequality:

$$|7x+2| > 3$$

$$\begin{array}{lll} 7x + 2 < -3 & \text{or} & 7x + 2 > 3 \\ 7x < -5 & & 7x > 1 \\ x < -\dfrac{5}{7} & & x > \dfrac{1}{7} \end{array}$$

Graphing the solution set:

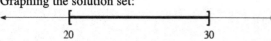

Graphing the solution set:

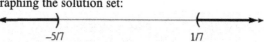

33. Multiply the first equation by 5 and the second equation by 6:
$$-45x + 30y = 150$$
$$24x - 30y = -150$$
Adding yields:
$$-21x = 0$$
$$x = 0$$
Substituting into the first equation:
$$-9(0) + 6y = 30$$
$$6y = 30$$
$$y = 5$$
The solution is $(0, 5)$.

34. Multiply the first equation by 3 and the second equation by 5:
$$6x + 15y = -69$$
$$35x - 15y = 110$$
Adding yields:
$$41x = 41$$
$$x = 1$$
Substituting into the first equation:
$$2(1) + 5y = -23$$
$$2 + 5y = -23$$
$$5y = -25$$
$$y = -5$$
The solution is $(1, -5)$.

35. Graphing the line:

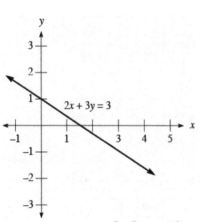

36. Graphing the inequality:

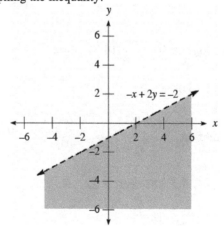

37. Finding the slope: $m = \dfrac{-5 - 7}{-8 - (-5)} = \dfrac{-12}{-3} = 4$

38. Finding the slope: $m = \dfrac{2 - 13}{5 - 6} = \dfrac{-11}{-1} = 11$

39. Rationalizing the denominator: $\dfrac{6}{\sqrt[4]{27}} = \dfrac{6}{\sqrt[4]{27}} \cdot \dfrac{\sqrt[4]{3}}{\sqrt[4]{3}} = \dfrac{6\sqrt[4]{3}}{\sqrt[4]{81}} = \dfrac{6\sqrt[4]{3}}{3} = 2\sqrt[4]{3}$

40. Rationalizing the denominator: $\dfrac{5}{\sqrt{7} - 3} = \dfrac{5}{\sqrt{7} - 3} \cdot \dfrac{\sqrt{7} + 3}{\sqrt{7} + 3} = \dfrac{5\sqrt{7} + 15}{7 - 9} = \dfrac{-5\sqrt{7} - 15}{2}$

41. Factoring: $81a^4 - 256b^4 = \left(9a^2\right)^2 - \left(16b^2\right)^2 = \left(9a^2 - 16b^2\right)\left(9a^2 + 16b^2\right) = (3a - 4b)(3a + 4b)\left(9a^2 + 16b^2\right)$

42. Factoring: $24a^4 - 44a^2 - 28 = 4(6a^4 - 11a^2 - 7) = 4(3a^2 - 7)(2a^2 + 1)$

43. The variation equation is $y = \dfrac{k}{\sqrt{x}}$. Substituting $y = -1$ and $x = 9$:

$$-1 = \frac{k}{\sqrt{9}}$$
$$-1 = \frac{k}{3}$$
$$k = -3$$

So the equation is $y = \dfrac{-3}{\sqrt{x}}$. Substituting $x = 16$: $y = \dfrac{-3}{\sqrt{16}} = -\dfrac{3}{4}$

44. The variation equation is $z = kxy^3$. Substituting $z = -32, x = 4$ and $y = 2$:

$$-32 = k(4)(2)^3$$
$$-32 = 32k$$
$$k = -1$$

So the equation is $z = -xy^3$. Substituting $x = 2$ and $y = 3$: $z = -(2)(3)^3 = -54$

45. Evaluating the function: $f(b) = 2b + 2$

46. Evaluating the function: $(g - f)(3) = g(3) - f(3) = (3^2 + 3) - (2 \cdot 3 + 2) = 12 - 8 = 4$

47. Evaluating the function: $(g \circ f)(1) = g[f(1)] = g(2 \cdot 1 + 2) = g(4) = 4^2 + 4 = 20$

48. Evaluating the function: $(f \circ g)(-1) = f[g(-1)] = f((-1)^2 - 1) = f(0) = 2 \cdot 0 + 2 = 2$

49. Subtracting: $\$175{,}750{,}800 - \$256{,}308{,}000 = -\$80{,}557{,}200$

50. Subtracting: $\$591{,}262{,}700 - \$152{,}630{,}700 = \$438{,}632{,}000$

Chapter 6 Test

1. Simplifying: $16^{-3/4} = (16^{1/4})^{-3} = 2^{-3} = \dfrac{1}{2^3} = \dfrac{1}{8}$ **2.** Simplifying: $\left(\dfrac{81}{64}\right)^{-1/2} = \left(\dfrac{64}{81}\right)^{1/2} = \dfrac{8}{9}$

3. Simplifying: $x^{1/7} \cdot x^{-2/3} = x^{1/7 - 2/3} = x^{3/21 - 14/21} = x^{-11/21} = \dfrac{1}{x^{11/21}}$

4. Simplifying: $\dfrac{(a^{1/3}b^2)^{-1}}{(a^{2/5}b^{-5})^{-2}} = \dfrac{a^{-1/3}b^{-2}}{a^{-4/5}b^{10}} = a^{-1/3 + 4/5}b^{-2-10} = a^{7/15}b^{-12} = \dfrac{a^{7/15}}{b^{12}}$

5. Simplifying: $\sqrt{25x^6y^{20}} = 5x^3y^{10}$ **6.** Simplifying: $\sqrt[4]{81x^4y^{20}} = 3xy^5$

7. Simplifying: $\dfrac{(8a^{12}b^3)^{1/3}}{(49a^{12}b^8)^{1/2}} = \dfrac{2a^4b}{7a^6b^4} = \dfrac{2}{7a^2b^3}$ **8.** Simplifying: $\dfrac{(x^{1/n}y^n)^{n^2}}{(x^n y^{1/n})^{n^2}} = \dfrac{x^n y^{n^3}}{x^{n^3} y^n} = x^{n-n^3} y^{n^3-n}$

9. Simplifying: $\sqrt{27x^5y^3} = \sqrt{9x^4y^2 \cdot 3xy} = 3x^2y\sqrt{3xy}$

10. Simplifying: $\sqrt[3]{128x^2y^7} = \sqrt[3]{64y^6 \cdot 2x^2y} = 4y^2\sqrt[3]{2x^2y}$

11. Simplifying: $\sqrt{\dfrac{3}{5}} = \dfrac{\sqrt{3}}{\sqrt{5}} \cdot \dfrac{\sqrt{5}}{\sqrt{5}} = \dfrac{\sqrt{15}}{5}$

12. Simplifying: $\sqrt{\dfrac{8a^2b^7}{7c}} = \dfrac{2ab^3\sqrt{2b}}{\sqrt{7c}} \cdot \dfrac{\sqrt{7c}}{\sqrt{7c}} = \dfrac{2ab^3\sqrt{14bc}}{7c}$

13. Rationalizing the denominator: $\dfrac{7}{\sqrt{2}+1} = \dfrac{7}{\sqrt{2}+1} \cdot \dfrac{\sqrt{2}-1}{\sqrt{2}-1} = \dfrac{7\sqrt{2}-7}{2-1} = 7\sqrt{2}-7$

14. Rationalizing the denominator: $\dfrac{\sqrt{x}+\sqrt{3}}{\sqrt{x}-\sqrt{3}} = \dfrac{\sqrt{x}+\sqrt{3}}{\sqrt{x}-\sqrt{3}} \cdot \dfrac{\sqrt{x}+\sqrt{3}}{\sqrt{x}+\sqrt{3}} = \dfrac{x+\sqrt{3x}+\sqrt{3x}+3}{x-3} = \dfrac{x+2\sqrt{3x}+3}{x-3}$

15. Combining: $\dfrac{5}{x^{1/2}} - x^{1/2} = \dfrac{5}{x^{1/2}} - x^{1/2} \cdot \dfrac{x^{1/2}}{x^{1/2}} = \dfrac{5-x}{x^{1/2}} \cdot \dfrac{x^{1/2}}{x^{1/2}} = \dfrac{5\sqrt{x}-x\sqrt{x}}{x}$

16. Combining:

$$\dfrac{x^3}{\left(x^3-17\right)^{1/2}} - \left(x^3-17\right)^{1/2} = \dfrac{x^3}{\left(x^3-17\right)^{1/2}} - \left(x^3-17\right)^{1/2} \cdot \dfrac{\left(x^3-17\right)^{1/2}}{\left(x^3-17\right)^{1/2}} = \dfrac{x^3-x^3+17}{\left(x^3-17\right)^{1/2}} = \dfrac{17}{\left(x^3-17\right)^{1/2}} = \dfrac{17\sqrt{x^3-17}}{x^3-17}$$

17. Combining: $3\sqrt{8} - 2\sqrt{18} = 6\sqrt{2} - 6\sqrt{2} = 0$

18. Combining: $4\sqrt[3]{32a^6b^3} - 5a^2\sqrt[3]{4b^3} = 8a^2b\sqrt[3]{4} - 5a^2b\sqrt[3]{4} = 3a^2b\sqrt[3]{4}$

19. Multiplying: $4a^{3/2}\left(a^{5/2} - 3a^{1/2}\right) = 4a^{8/2} - 12a^{4/2} = 4a^4 - 12a^2$

20. Multiplying: $\left(2a^{5/2} - 3\right)^2 = \left(2a^{5/2} - 3\right)\left(2a^{5/2} - 3\right) = 4a^5 - 6a^{5/2} - 6a^{5/2} + 9 = 4a^5 - 12a^{5/2} + 9$

21. Multiplying: $\left(\sqrt{x}-1\right)\left(\sqrt{x}+5\right) = x - \sqrt{x} + 5\sqrt{x} - 5 = x + 4\sqrt{x} - 5$

22. Multiplying: $\left(2\sqrt{3} - \sqrt{2}\right)^2 = \left(2\sqrt{3} - \sqrt{2}\right)\left(2\sqrt{3} - \sqrt{2}\right) = 12 - 2\sqrt{6} - 2\sqrt{6} + 2 = 14 - 4\sqrt{6}$

23. Solving the equation:

$$\sqrt{2x-3} = x-3$$
$$\left(\sqrt{2x-3}\right)^2 = (x-3)^2$$
$$2x-3 = x^2 - 6x + 9$$
$$0 = x^2 - 8x + 12$$
$$0 = (x-2)(x-6)$$
$$x = 6 \quad (x = 2 \text{ doesn't check})$$

24. Solving the equation:

$$\sqrt[3]{4x-2} = -2$$
$$\left(\sqrt[3]{4x-2}\right)^3 = (-2)^3$$
$$4x-2 = -8$$
$$4x = -6$$
$$x = -\dfrac{3}{2}$$

25. Solving the equation:

$$\sqrt{x+6} = \sqrt{x-9} + 3$$
$$\left(\sqrt{x+6}\right)^2 = \left(\sqrt{x-9}+3\right)^2$$
$$x+6 = x-9 + 6\sqrt{x-9} + 9$$
$$x+6 = x + 6\sqrt{x-9}$$
$$\sqrt{x-9} = 1$$
$$x-9 = 1$$
$$x = 10$$

26. Graphing the equation:

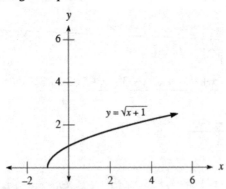

$y = \sqrt{x+1}$

27. Graphing the equation:

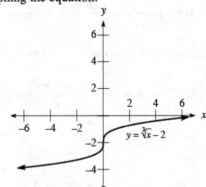

$y = \sqrt[3]{x} - 2$

28. The correct graph is E.
30. The correct graph is A.
32. The correct graph is D.

29. The correct graph is F.
31. The correct graph is B.
33. The correct graph is C.

34. Setting the real and imaginary parts equal:

$$-(x-2) = 4 \qquad\qquad 7y+1 = 8$$
$$x-2 = -4 \qquad\qquad 7y = 7$$
$$x = -2 \qquad\qquad y = 1$$

35. Performing the operations:

$$(2+i) - \left[(5-2i) - (3+4i)\right] = (2+i) - (5-2i-3-4i) = (2+i) - (2-6i) = 2+i-2+6i = 7i$$

36. Performing the operations: $(5+3i)(2-i) = 10+6i-5i+3 = 13+i$

37. Performing the operations: $(3-6i)^2 = (3-6i)(3-6i) = 9-18i-18i-36 = -27-36i$

38. Performing the operations: $\dfrac{3i+2}{3i-2} = \dfrac{3i+2}{3i-2} \cdot \dfrac{3i+2}{3i+2} = \dfrac{-9+12i+4}{-9-4} = \dfrac{-5+12i}{-13} = \dfrac{5}{13} - \dfrac{12}{13}i$

39. Rewriting the exponent: $i^{36} = \left(i^2\right)^{18} = (-1)^{18} = 1$

Chapter 7
Quadratic Equations and Functions

7.1 Completing the Square

1. Solving the equation:
$$x^2 = 25$$
$$x = \pm\sqrt{25} = \pm 5$$

3. Solving the equation:
$$a^2 = -9$$
$$a = \pm\sqrt{-9} = \pm 3i$$

5. Solving the equation:
$$y^2 = \frac{3}{4}$$
$$y = \pm\sqrt{\frac{3}{4}} = \pm\frac{\sqrt{3}}{2}$$

7. Solving the equation:
$$x^2 + 12 = 0$$
$$x^2 = -12$$
$$x = \pm\sqrt{-12} = \pm 2i\sqrt{3}$$

9. Solving the equation:
$$4a^2 - 45 = 0$$
$$4a^2 = 45$$
$$a^2 = \frac{45}{4}$$
$$a = \pm\sqrt{\frac{45}{4}} = \pm\frac{3\sqrt{5}}{2}$$

11. Solving the equation:
$$(2y-1)^2 = 25$$
$$2y-1 = \pm\sqrt{25} = \pm 5$$
$$2y-1 = -5, 5$$
$$2y = -4, 6$$
$$y = -2, 3$$

13. Solving the equation:
$$(2a+3)^2 = -9$$
$$2a+3 = \pm\sqrt{-9} = \pm 3i$$
$$2a = -3 \pm 3i$$
$$a = \frac{-3 \pm 3i}{2}$$

15. Solving the equation:
$$(5x+2)^2 = -8$$
$$5x+2 = \pm\sqrt{-2} = \pm 2i\sqrt{2}$$
$$5x = -2 \pm 2i\sqrt{2}$$
$$x = \frac{-2 \pm 2i\sqrt{2}}{5}$$

17. Solving the equation:
$$x^2 + 8x + 16 = -27$$
$$(x+4)^2 = -27$$
$$x+4 = \pm\sqrt{-27} = \pm 3i\sqrt{3}$$
$$x = -4 \pm 3i\sqrt{3}$$

19. Solving the equation:
$$4a^2 - 12a + 9 = -4$$
$$(2a-3)^2 = -4$$
$$2a-3 = \pm\sqrt{-4} = \pm 2i$$
$$2a = 3 \pm 2i$$
$$a = \frac{3 \pm 2i}{2}$$

21. Completing the square: $x^2 + 12x + 36 = (x+6)^2$

23. Completing the square: $x^2 - 4x + 4 = (x-2)^2$

25. Completing the square: $a^2 - 10a + 25 = (a-5)^2$

27. Completing the square: $x^2 + 5x + \dfrac{25}{4} = \left(x+\dfrac{5}{2}\right)^2$

29. Completing the square: $y^2 - 7y + \dfrac{49}{4} = \left(y-\dfrac{7}{2}\right)^2$

31. Completing the square: $x^2 + \dfrac{1}{2}x + \dfrac{1}{16} = \left(x+\dfrac{1}{4}\right)^2$

33. Completing the square: $x^2 + \dfrac{2}{3}x + \dfrac{1}{9} = \left(x + \dfrac{1}{3}\right)^2$

35. Solving the equation:
$$x^2 + 4x = 12$$
$$x^2 + 4x + 4 = 12 + 4$$
$$(x+2)^2 = 16$$
$$x + 2 = \pm\sqrt{16} = \pm 4$$
$$x + 2 = -4, 4$$
$$x = -6, 2$$

37. Solving the equation:
$$x^2 + 12x = -27$$
$$x^2 + 12x + 36 = -27 + 36$$
$$(x+6)^2 = 9$$
$$x + 6 = \pm\sqrt{9} = \pm 3$$
$$x + 6 = -3, 3$$
$$x = -9, -3$$

39. Solving the equation:
$$a^2 - 2a + 5 = 0$$
$$a^2 - 2a + 1 = -5 + 1$$
$$(a-1)^2 = -4$$
$$a - 1 = \pm\sqrt{-4} = \pm 2i$$
$$a = 1 \pm 2i$$

41. Solving the equation:
$$y^2 - 8y + 1 = 0$$
$$y^2 - 8y + 16 = -1 + 16$$
$$(y-4)^2 = 15$$
$$y - 4 = \pm\sqrt{15}$$
$$y = 4 \pm \sqrt{15}$$

43. Solving the equation:
$$x^2 - 5x - 3 = 0$$
$$x^2 - 5x + \frac{25}{4} = 3 + \frac{25}{4}$$
$$\left(x - \frac{5}{2}\right)^2 = \frac{37}{4}$$
$$x - \frac{5}{2} = \pm\frac{\sqrt{37}}{2}$$
$$x = \frac{5 \pm \sqrt{37}}{2}$$

45. Solving the equation:
$$2x^2 - 4x - 8 = 0$$
$$x^2 - 2x - 4 = 0$$
$$x^2 - 2x + 1 = 4 + 1$$
$$(x-1)^2 = 5$$
$$x - 1 = \pm\sqrt{5}$$
$$x = 1 \pm \sqrt{5}$$

47. Solving the equation:
$$3t^2 - 8t + 1 = 0$$
$$t^2 - \frac{8}{3}t + \frac{1}{3} = 0$$
$$t^2 - \frac{8}{3}t + \frac{16}{9} = -\frac{1}{3} + \frac{16}{9}$$
$$\left(t - \frac{4}{3}\right)^2 = \frac{13}{9}$$
$$t - \frac{4}{3} = \pm\sqrt{\frac{13}{9}} = \pm\frac{\sqrt{13}}{3}$$
$$t = \frac{4 \pm \sqrt{13}}{3}$$

49. Solving the equation:
$$4x^2 - 3x + 5 = 0$$
$$x^2 - \frac{3}{4}x + \frac{5}{4} = 0$$
$$x^2 - \frac{3}{4}x + \frac{9}{64} = -\frac{5}{4} + \frac{9}{64}$$
$$\left(x - \frac{3}{8}\right)^2 = -\frac{71}{64}$$
$$x - \frac{3}{8} = \pm\sqrt{-\frac{71}{64}} = \pm\frac{i\sqrt{71}}{8}$$
$$x = \frac{3 \pm i\sqrt{71}}{8}$$

51. Solving the equation:
$$3x^2 + 4x - 1 = 0$$
$$x^2 + \frac{4}{3}x - \frac{1}{3} = 0$$
$$x^2 + \frac{4}{3}x + \frac{4}{9} = \frac{1}{3} + \frac{4}{9}$$
$$\left(x + \frac{2}{3}\right)^2 = \frac{7}{9}$$
$$x + \frac{2}{3} = \pm\sqrt{\frac{7}{9}} = \pm\frac{\sqrt{7}}{3}$$
$$x = \frac{-2 \pm \sqrt{7}}{3}$$

53. Solving the equation:
$$2x^2 - 10x = 11$$
$$x^2 - 5x = \frac{11}{2}$$
$$x^2 - 5x + \frac{25}{4} = \frac{11}{2} + \frac{25}{4}$$
$$\left(x - \frac{5}{2}\right)^2 = \frac{47}{4}$$
$$x - \frac{5}{2} = \pm\sqrt{\frac{47}{4}} = \pm\frac{\sqrt{47}}{2}$$
$$x = \frac{5 \pm \sqrt{47}}{2}$$

55. Solving the equation:
$$4x^2 - 10x + 11 = 0$$
$$x^2 - \frac{5}{2}x + \frac{11}{4} = 0$$
$$x^2 - \frac{5}{2}x + \frac{25}{16} = -\frac{11}{4} + \frac{25}{16}$$
$$\left(x - \frac{5}{4}\right)^2 = -\frac{19}{16}$$
$$x - \frac{5}{4} = \pm\sqrt{-\frac{19}{16}} = \pm\frac{i\sqrt{19}}{4}$$
$$x = \frac{5 \pm i\sqrt{19}}{4}$$

57. Solving the equation:
$$27x^2 - 90x + 71 = 0$$
$$x^2 - \frac{10}{3}x + \frac{71}{27} = 0$$
$$x^2 - \frac{10}{3}x + \frac{25}{9} = -\frac{71}{27} + \frac{25}{9}$$
$$\left(x - \frac{5}{3}\right)^2 = \frac{4}{27}$$
$$x - \frac{5}{3} = \pm\sqrt{\frac{4}{27}} = \pm\frac{2}{3\sqrt{3}}$$
$$x - \frac{5}{3} = \pm\frac{2}{3\sqrt{3}} \cdot \frac{\sqrt{3}}{\sqrt{3}}$$
$$x - \frac{5}{3} = \pm\frac{2\sqrt{3}}{9}$$
$$x = \frac{15 \pm 2\sqrt{3}}{9}$$

59. **a.** No, it cannot be solved by factoring.
   b. Solving the equation:
$$x^2 = -9$$
$$x = \pm\sqrt{-9}$$
$$x = \pm 3i$$

61. **a.** Solving by factoring:
$$x^2 - 6x = 0$$
$$x(x - 6) = 0$$
$$x = 0, 6$$

   b. Solving by completing the square:
$$x^2 - 6x = 0$$
$$x^2 - 6x + 9 = 0 + 9$$
$$(x - 3)^2 = 9$$
$$x - 3 = \pm\sqrt{9}$$
$$x - 3 = -3, 3$$
$$x = 0, 6$$

63. **a.** Solving by factoring:
$$x^2 + 2x = 35$$
$$x^2 + 2x - 35 = 0$$
$$(x + 7)(x - 5) = 0$$
$$x = -7, 5$$

   b. Solving by completing the square:
$$x^2 + 2x = 35$$
$$x^2 + 2x + 1 = 35 + 1$$
$$(x + 1)^2 = 36$$
$$x + 1 = \pm\sqrt{36}$$
$$x + 1 = -6, 6$$
$$x = -7, 5$$

65. Substituting: $x^2 - 6x - 7 = \left(-3 + \sqrt{2}\right)^2 - 6\left(-3 + \sqrt{2}\right) - 7 = 9 - 6\sqrt{2} + 2 + 18 - 6\sqrt{2} - 7 = 22 - 12\sqrt{2}$

No, $x = -3 + \sqrt{2}$ is not a solution to the equation.

67. **a.** Solving the equation:
$$5x - 7 = 0$$
$$5x = 7$$
$$x = \frac{7}{5}$$

b. Solving the equation:
$$5x - 7 = 8$$
$$5x = 15$$
$$x = 3$$

c. Solving the equation:
$$(5x - 7)^2 = 8$$
$$5x - 7 = \pm\sqrt{8}$$
$$5x - 7 = \pm 2\sqrt{2}$$
$$5x = 7 \pm 2\sqrt{2}$$
$$x = \frac{7 \pm 2\sqrt{2}}{5}$$

d. Solving the equation:
$$\sqrt{5x - 7} = 8$$
$$\left(\sqrt{5x - 7}\right)^2 = (8)^2$$
$$5x - 7 = 64$$
$$5x = 71$$
$$x = \frac{71}{5}$$

e. Solving the equation:
$$\frac{5}{2} - \frac{7}{2x} = \frac{4}{x}$$
$$2x\left(\frac{5}{2} - \frac{7}{2x}\right) = 2x\left(\frac{4}{x}\right)$$
$$5x - 7 = 8$$
$$5x = 15$$
$$x = 3$$

69. Finding the x-intercepts:
$$x^2 - 4x - 5 = 0$$
$$(x + 1)(x - 4) = 0$$
$$x = -1, 4$$

71. Finding the x-intercepts:
$$x^2 + 3x - 5 = 0$$
$$x^2 + 3x + \frac{9}{4} = 5 + \frac{9}{4}$$
$$\left(x + \frac{3}{2}\right)^2 = \frac{29}{4}$$
$$x + \frac{3}{2} = \pm\sqrt{\frac{29}{4}} = \frac{\pm\sqrt{29}}{2}$$
$$x = \frac{-3 \pm \sqrt{29}}{2}$$

73. Finding the x-intercepts:
$$x^2 - 7x - 9 = 0$$
$$x^2 - 7x + \frac{49}{4} = 9 + \frac{49}{4}$$
$$\left(x - \frac{7}{2}\right)^2 = \frac{85}{4}$$
$$x - \frac{7}{2} = \pm\sqrt{\frac{85}{4}} = \frac{\pm\sqrt{85}}{2}$$
$$x = \frac{7 \pm \sqrt{85}}{2}$$

75. Finding the x-intercepts:
$$x^2 + 4x + 9 = 0$$
$$x^2 + 4x + 4 = -9 + 4$$
$$(x + 2)^2 = -5$$
$$x + 2 = \pm\sqrt{-5} = \pm i\sqrt{5}$$
$$x = -2 \pm i\sqrt{5}$$

Since the solutions aren't real, there are no x-intercepts.

77. Finding the x-intercepts:

$$2x^2 + 3x - 4 = 0$$

$$x^2 + \frac{3}{2}x - 2 = 0$$

$$x^2 + \frac{3}{2}x + \frac{9}{16} = 2 + \frac{9}{16}$$

$$\left(x + \frac{3}{4}\right)^2 = \frac{41}{16}$$

$$x + \frac{3}{4} = \pm\sqrt{\frac{41}{16}} = \frac{\pm\sqrt{41}}{4}$$

$$x = \frac{-3 \pm \sqrt{41}}{4}$$

79. Finding the x-intercepts:

$$4x^2 + 4x - 11 = 0$$

$$x^2 + x - \frac{11}{4} = 0$$

$$x^2 + x + \frac{1}{4} = \frac{11}{4} + \frac{1}{4}$$

$$\left(x + \frac{1}{2}\right)^2 = 3$$

$$x + \frac{1}{2} = \pm\sqrt{3} = \frac{\pm 2\sqrt{3}}{2}$$

$$x = \frac{-1 \pm 2\sqrt{3}}{2}$$

81. The other two sides are $\dfrac{\sqrt{3}}{2}$ inch, 1 inch.

83. The hypotenuse is $\sqrt{2}$ inches.

85. Let x represent the horizontal distance. Using the Pythagorean theorem:

$$x^2 + 120^2 = 790^2$$

$$x^2 + 14400 = 624100$$

$$x^2 = 609700$$

$$x = \sqrt{609700} \approx 781 \text{ feet}$$

87. Solving for r:

$$3456 = 3000(1 + r)^2$$

$$(1 + r)^2 = 1.152$$

$$1 + r = \sqrt{1.152}$$

$$r = \sqrt{1.152} - 1 \approx 0.073$$

The annual interest rate is 7.3%.

89. Its length is $20\sqrt{2} \approx 28$ feet.

91. Simplifying: $49 - 4(6)(-5) = 49 + 120 = 169$

93. Simplifying: $(-27)^2 - 4(0.1)(1,700) = 729 - 680 = 49$

95. Simplifying: $-7 + \dfrac{169}{12} = -\dfrac{84}{12} + \dfrac{169}{12} = \dfrac{85}{12}$

97. Simplifying: $\dfrac{-4 + \sqrt{36}}{2} = \dfrac{-4 + 6}{2} = \dfrac{2}{2} = 1$

99. Factoring: $27t^3 - 8 = (3t - 2)(9t^2 + 6t + 4)$

101. Factoring: $2x^3 + 54 = 2(x^3 + 27) = 2(x + 3)(x^2 - 3x + 9)$

103. **a.** Finding the percentage: $0.503(2,000) = 1,006$ volunteers

     b. Finding the percentage: $0.173(2,000) = 346$ volunteers

7.2 The Quadratic Formula

1. Solving the equation:
$$x^2 + 5x + 6 = 0$$
$$(x+3)(x+2) = 0$$
$$x = -3, -2$$

3. Using the quadratic formula: $x = \dfrac{4 \pm \sqrt{(-4)^2 - 4(1)(1)}}{2(1)} = \dfrac{4 \pm \sqrt{16-4}}{2} = \dfrac{4 \pm \sqrt{12}}{2} = \dfrac{4 \pm 2\sqrt{3}}{2} = 2 \pm \sqrt{3}$

5. Solving the equation:
$$\frac{1}{6}x^2 - \frac{1}{2}x + \frac{1}{3} = 0$$
$$x^2 - 3x + 2 = 0$$
$$(x-1)(x-2) = 0$$
$$x = 1, 2$$

7. Solving the equation:
$$\frac{x^2}{2} + 1 = \frac{2x}{3}$$
$$3x^2 + 6 = 4x$$
$$3x^2 - 4x + 6 = 0$$
$$x = \frac{4 \pm \sqrt{16-72}}{6} = \frac{4 \pm \sqrt{-56}}{6} = \frac{4 \pm 2i\sqrt{14}}{6} = \frac{2 \pm i\sqrt{14}}{3}$$

9. Solving the equation:
$$y^2 - 5y = 0$$
$$y(y-5) = 0$$
$$y = 0, 5$$

11. Solving the equation:
$$30x^2 + 40x = 0$$
$$10x(3x+4) = 0$$
$$x = -\frac{4}{3}, 0$$

13. Solving the equation:
$$\frac{2t^2}{3} - t = -\frac{1}{6}$$
$$4t^2 - 6t = -1$$
$$4t^2 - 6t + 1 = 0$$
$$t = \frac{6 \pm \sqrt{36-16}}{8} = \frac{6 \pm \sqrt{20}}{8} = \frac{6 \pm 2\sqrt{5}}{8} = \frac{3 \pm \sqrt{5}}{4}$$

15. Solving the equation:
$$0.01x^2 + 0.06x - 0.08 = 0$$
$$x^2 + 6x - 8 = 0$$
$$x = \frac{-6 \pm \sqrt{36+32}}{2} = \frac{-6 \pm \sqrt{68}}{2} = \frac{-6 \pm 2\sqrt{17}}{2} = -3 \pm \sqrt{17}$$

17. Solving the equation:
$$2x + 3 = -2x^2$$
$$2x^2 + 2x + 3 = 0$$
$$x = \frac{-2 \pm \sqrt{4-24}}{4} = \frac{-2 \pm \sqrt{-20}}{4} = \frac{-2 \pm 2i\sqrt{5}}{4} = \frac{-1 \pm i\sqrt{5}}{2}$$

19. Solving the equation:

$$100x^2 - 200x + 100 = 0$$
$$100\left(x^2 - 2x + 1\right) = 0$$
$$100\left(x - 1\right)^2 = 0$$
$$x = 1$$

21. Solving the equation:

$$\frac{1}{2}r^2 = \frac{1}{6}r - \frac{2}{3}$$
$$3r^2 = r - 4$$
$$3r^2 - r + 4 = 0$$
$$r = \frac{1 \pm \sqrt{1 - 48}}{6} = \frac{1 \pm \sqrt{-47}}{6} = \frac{1 \pm i\sqrt{47}}{6}$$

23. Solving the equation:

$$(x - 3)(x - 5) = 1$$
$$x^2 - 8x + 15 = 1$$
$$x^2 - 8x + 14 = 0$$
$$x = \frac{8 \pm \sqrt{64 - 56}}{2} = \frac{8 \pm \sqrt{8}}{2} = \frac{8 \pm 2\sqrt{2}}{2} = 4 \pm \sqrt{2}$$

25. Solving the equation:

$$(x + 3)^2 + (x - 8)(x - 1) = 16$$
$$x^2 + 6x + 9 + x^2 - 9x + 8 = 16$$
$$2x^2 - 3x + 1 = 0$$
$$(2x - 1)(x - 1) = 0$$
$$x = \frac{1}{2}, 1$$

27. Solving the equation:

$$\frac{x^2}{3} - \frac{5x}{6} = \frac{1}{2}$$
$$2x^2 - 5x = 3$$
$$2x^2 - 5x - 3 = 0$$
$$(2x + 1)(x - 3) = 0$$
$$x = -\frac{1}{2}, 3$$

29. Solving the equation:

$$\sqrt{x} = x - 1$$
$$\left(\sqrt{x}\right)^2 = (x - 1)^2$$
$$x = x^2 - 2x + 1$$
$$x^2 - 3x + 1 = 0$$
$$x = \frac{3 \pm \sqrt{9 - 4}}{2} = \frac{3 \pm \sqrt{5}}{2}$$
$$x = \frac{3 + \sqrt{5}}{2} \qquad \left(x = \frac{3 - \sqrt{5}}{2} \text{ does not check}\right)$$

31. Solving the equation:

$$\frac{1}{x+1}-\frac{1}{x}=\frac{1}{2}$$

$$2x(x+1)\left(\frac{1}{x+1}-\frac{1}{x}\right)=2x(x+1)\cdot\frac{1}{2}$$

$$2x-(2x+2)=x^2+x$$

$$2x-2x-2=x^2+x$$

$$x^2+x+2=0$$

$$x=\frac{-1\pm\sqrt{1-8}}{2}=\frac{-1\pm\sqrt{-7}}{2}=\frac{-1\pm i\sqrt{7}}{2}$$

33. Solving the equation:

$$\frac{1}{y-1}+\frac{1}{y+1}=1$$

$$(y+1)(y-1)\left(\frac{1}{y-1}+\frac{1}{y+1}\right)=(y+1)(y-1)\cdot 1$$

$$y+1+y-1=y^2-1$$

$$2y=y^2-1$$

$$y^2-2y-1=0$$

$$y=\frac{2\pm\sqrt{4+4}}{2}=\frac{2\pm\sqrt{8}}{2}=\frac{2\pm 2\sqrt{2}}{2}=1\pm\sqrt{2}$$

35. Solving the equation:

$$\frac{1}{x+2}+\frac{1}{x+3}=1$$

$$(x+2)(x+3)\left(\frac{1}{x+2}+\frac{1}{x+3}\right)=(x+2)(x+3)\cdot 1$$

$$x+3+x+2=x^2+5x+6$$

$$2x+5=x^2+5x+6$$

$$x^2+3x+1=0$$

$$x=\frac{-3\pm\sqrt{9-4}}{2}=\frac{-3\pm\sqrt{5}}{2}$$

37. Solving the equation:

$$\frac{6}{r^2-1}-\frac{1}{2}=\frac{1}{r+1}$$

$$2(r+1)(r-1)\left(\frac{6}{(r+1)(r-1)}-\frac{1}{2}\right)=2(r+1)(r-1)\cdot\frac{1}{r+1}$$

$$12-(r^2-1)=2r-2$$

$$12-r^2+1=2r-2$$

$$r^2+2r-15=0$$

$$(r+5)(r-3)=0$$

$$r=-5,3$$

39. Solving the equation:

$$\frac{1}{x^2-4}+\frac{x}{x-2}=2$$

$$(x+2)(x-2)\left(\frac{1}{(x+2)(x-2)}+\frac{x}{x-2}\right)=(x+2)(x-2)\cdot 2$$

$$1+x(x+2)=2\left(x^2-4\right)$$

$$1+x^2+2x=2x^2-8$$

$$x^2-2x-9=0$$

$$x=\frac{2\pm\sqrt{4+36}}{2}=\frac{2\pm\sqrt{40}}{2}=\frac{2\pm2\sqrt{10}}{2}=1\pm\sqrt{10}$$

41. Solving the equation:

$$2-\frac{3}{x}=\frac{1}{x^2}$$

$$2x^2-3x=1$$

$$2x^2-3x=1$$

$$2x^2-3x-1=0$$

$$x=\frac{3\pm\sqrt{9+8}}{4}=\frac{3\pm\sqrt{17}}{4}$$

43. Solving the equation:

$$x^3-8=0$$

$$(x-2)\left(x^2+2x+4\right)=0$$

$$x=2 \quad\text{or}\quad x=\frac{-2\pm\sqrt{4-16}}{2}=\frac{-2\pm\sqrt{-12}}{2}=\frac{-2\pm2i\sqrt{3}}{2}=-1\pm i\sqrt{3}$$

$$x=2,-1\pm i\sqrt{3}$$

45. Solving the equation:

$$8a^3+27=0$$

$$(2a+3)\left(4a^2-6a+9\right)=0$$

$$a=-\frac{3}{2} \quad\text{or}\quad a=\frac{6\pm\sqrt{36-144}}{8}=\frac{6\pm\sqrt{-108}}{8}=\frac{6\pm6i\sqrt{3}}{8}=\frac{3\pm3i\sqrt{3}}{4}$$

$$a=-\frac{3}{2},\frac{3\pm3i\sqrt{3}}{4}$$

47. Solving the equation:

$$125t^3-1=0$$

$$(5t-1)\left(25t^2+5t+1\right)=0$$

$$t=\frac{1}{5} \quad\text{or}\quad t=\frac{-5\pm\sqrt{25-100}}{50}=\frac{-5\pm\sqrt{-75}}{50}=\frac{-5\pm5i\sqrt{3}}{50}=\frac{-1\pm i\sqrt{3}}{10}$$

$$t=\frac{1}{5},\frac{-1\pm i\sqrt{3}}{10}$$

49. Solving the equation:

$$2x^3+2x^2+3x=0$$

$$x\left(2x^2+2x+3\right)=0$$

$$x=0 \quad\text{or}\quad x=\frac{-2\pm\sqrt{4-24}}{4}=\frac{-2\pm\sqrt{-20}}{4}=\frac{-2\pm2i\sqrt{5}}{4}=\frac{-1\pm i\sqrt{5}}{2}$$

$$x=0,\frac{-1\pm i\sqrt{5}}{2}$$

51. Solving the equation:

$$3y^4 = 6y^3 - 6y^2$$
$$3y^4 - 6y^3 + 6y^2 = 0$$
$$3y^2\left(y^2 - 2y + 2\right) = 0$$

$$y = 0 \qquad \text{or} \qquad y = \frac{2 \pm \sqrt{4-8}}{2} = \frac{2 \pm \sqrt{-4}}{2} = \frac{2 \pm 2i}{2} = 1 \pm i$$

$$y = 0, 1 \pm i$$

53. Solving the equation:

$$6t^5 + 4t^4 = -2t^3$$
$$6t^5 + 4t^4 + 2t^3 = 0$$
$$2t^3\left(3t^2 + 2t + 1\right) = 0$$

$$t = 0 \qquad \text{or} \qquad t = \frac{-2 \pm \sqrt{4-12}}{6} = \frac{-2 \pm \sqrt{-8}}{6} = \frac{-2 \pm 2i\sqrt{2}}{6} = \frac{-1 \pm i\sqrt{2}}{3}$$

$$t = 0, \frac{-1 \pm i\sqrt{2}}{3}$$

55. The expressions from **a** and **b** are equivalent, since: $\dfrac{6 + 2\sqrt{3}}{4} = \dfrac{2\left(3 + \sqrt{3}\right)}{4} = \dfrac{3 + \sqrt{3}}{2}$

57. **a.** Solving by factoring:

$$3x^2 - 5x = 0$$
$$x(3x - 5) = 0$$
$$x = 0, \frac{5}{3}$$

b. Using the quadratic formula: $x = \dfrac{5 \pm \sqrt{(-5)^2 - 4(3)(0)}}{2(3)} = \dfrac{5 \pm \sqrt{25 - 0}}{6} = \dfrac{5 \pm 5}{6} = 0, \dfrac{5}{3}$

59. No, it cannot be solved by factoring. Using the quadratic formula:

$$x = \frac{4 \pm \sqrt{(-4)^2 - 4(1)(7)}}{2(1)} = \frac{4 \pm \sqrt{16 - 28}}{2} = \frac{4 \pm \sqrt{-12}}{2} = \frac{4 \pm 2i\sqrt{3}}{2} = 2 \pm i\sqrt{3}$$

61. Substituting: $x^2 + 2x = (-1 + i)^2 + 2(-1 + i) = 1 - 2i + i^2 - 2 + 2i = 1 - 2i - 1 - 2 + 2i = -2$

Yes, $x = -1 + i$ is a solution to the equation.

63. Finding the fixed points:

$$x^2 - 3x = x$$
$$x^2 - 4x = 0$$
$$x(x - 4) = 0$$
$$x = 0, 4$$

65. Finding the fixed points:

$$x(1.4 - x) = x$$
$$1.4x - x^2 = x$$
$$0.4x - x^2 = 0$$
$$x(0.4 - x) = 0$$
$$x = 0, 0.4$$

67. Finding the fixed points:

$$x^2 + 5x + 2 = x$$
$$x^2 + 4x + 2 = 0$$

$$x = \frac{-4 \pm \sqrt{16 - 8}}{2} = \frac{-4 \pm \sqrt{8}}{2} = \frac{-4 \pm 2\sqrt{2}}{2} = -2 \pm \sqrt{2}$$

69. Finding the fixed points:

$$\frac{x+3}{x} = x$$
$$x + 3 = x^2$$
$$x^2 - x - 3 = 0$$
$$x = \frac{1 \pm \sqrt{1+12}}{2} = \frac{1 \pm \sqrt{13}}{2}$$

71. Finding the fixed points:

$$\frac{2x^2 - 6}{x} = x$$
$$2x^2 - 6 = x^2$$
$$x^2 = 6$$
$$x = \pm\sqrt{6}$$

73. Substituting $s = 74$:

$$5t + 16t^2 = 74$$
$$16t^2 + 5t - 74 = 0$$
$$(t-2)(16t + 37) = 0$$
$$t = 2 \qquad \left(t = -\frac{37}{16} \text{ is impossible}\right)$$

It will take 2 seconds for the object to fall 74 feet.

75. Since profit is revenue minus the cost, the equation is:

$$100x - 0.5x^2 - (60x + 300) = 300$$
$$100x - 0.5x^2 - 60x - 300 = 300$$
$$-0.5x^2 + 40x - 600 = 0$$
$$x^2 - 80x + 1,200 = 0$$
$$(x - 20)(x - 60) = 0$$
$$x = 20, 60$$

The weekly profit is \$300 if 20 items or 60 items are sold.

77. Let x represent the width of strip being cut off. After removing the strip, the overall area is 80% of its original area. The equation is:

$$(10.5 - 2x)(8.2 - 2x) = 0.80(10.5 \times 8.2)$$
$$86.1 - 37.4x + 4x^2 = 68.88$$
$$4x^2 - 37.4x + 17.22 = 0$$
$$x = \frac{37.4 \pm \sqrt{(-37.4)^2 - 4(4)(17.22)}}{8} = \frac{37.4 \pm \sqrt{1123.24}}{8} \approx \frac{37.4 \pm 33.5}{8} \approx 0.49, 8.86$$

The width of strip is 0.49 centimeter (8.86 cm is impossible).

79. **a.** The two equations are: $l + w = 10, lw = 15$

b. Since $l = 10 - w$, the equation is:

$$w(10 - w) = 15$$
$$10w - w^2 = 15$$
$$w^2 - 10w + 15 = 0$$
$$w = \frac{10 \pm \sqrt{100 - 60}}{2} = \frac{10 \pm \sqrt{40}}{2} = \frac{10 \pm 2\sqrt{10}}{2} = 5 \pm \sqrt{10} \approx 1.84, 8.16$$

The length and width are 8.16 yards and 1.84 yards.

c. Two answers are possible because either dimension (long or short) may be considered the length.

81. Evaluating $b^2 - 4ac$: $b^2 - 4ac = (-3)^2 - 4(1)(-40) = 9 + 160 = 169$

83. Evaluating $b^2 - 4ac$: $b^2 - 4ac = 12^2 - 4(4)(9) = 144 - 144 = 0$

85. Solving the equation:

$$k^2 - 144 = 0$$
$$(k + 12)(k - 12) = 0$$
$$k = -12, 12$$

87. Multiplying: $(x-3)(x+2) = x^2 + 2x - 3x - 6 = x^2 - x - 6$

89. Multiplying:

$$(x-3)(x-3)(x+2) = \left(x^2 - 6x + 9\right)(x+2)$$
$$= x^3 - 6x^2 + 9x + 2x^2 - 12x + 18$$
$$= x^3 - 4x^2 - 3x + 18$$

7.3 The Discriminant and Multiplicity

1. Computing the discriminant: $D = (-6)^2 - 4(1)(5) = 36 - 20 = 16$. The equation will have two rational solutions.

3. First write the equation as $4x^2 - 4x + 1 = 0$. Computing the discriminant: $D = (-4)^2 - 4(4)(1) = 16 - 16 = 0$
The equation will have one rational solution.

5. Computing the discriminant: $D = 1^2 - 4(1)(-1) = 1 + 4 = 5$. The equation will have two irrational solutions.

7. First write the equation as $2y^2 - 3y - 1 = 0$. Computing the discriminant: $D = (-3)^2 - 4(2)(-1) = 9 + 8 = 17$
The equation will have two irrational solutions.

9. Computing the discriminant: $D = 0^2 - 4(1)(-9) = 36$. The equation will have two rational solutions.

11. First write the equation as $5a^2 - 4a - 5 = 0$. Computing the discriminant: $D = (-4)^2 - 4(5)(-5) = 16 + 100 = 116$
The equation will have two irrational solutions.

13. Setting the discriminant equal to 0:

$$(-k)^2 - 4(1)(25) = 0$$
$$k^2 - 100 = 0$$
$$k^2 = 100$$
$$k = \pm 10$$

15. First write the equation as $x^2 - kx + 36 = 0$. Setting the discriminant equal to 0:

$$(-k)^2 - 4(1)(36) = 0$$
$$k^2 - 144 = 0$$
$$k^2 = 144$$
$$k = \pm 12$$

17. Setting the discriminant equal to 0:

$$(-12)^2 - 4(4)(k) = 0$$
$$144 - 16k = 0$$
$$16k = 144$$
$$k = 9$$

19. First write the equation as $kx^2 - 40x - 25 = 0$. Setting the discriminant equal to 0:

$$(-40)^2 - 4(k)(-25) = 0$$
$$1600 + 100k = 0$$
$$100k = -1600$$
$$k = -16$$

21. Setting the discriminant equal to 0:

$$(-k)^2 - 4(3)(2) = 0$$
$$k^2 - 24 = 0$$
$$k^2 = 24$$
$$k = \pm\sqrt{24} = \pm 2\sqrt{6}$$

23. Setting the discriminant equal to 0:

$$k^2 - 4(3)(k) = 0$$
$$k^2 - 12k = 0$$
$$k(k-12) = 0$$
$$k = 0, 12$$

25. Writing the equation:

$$(x-5)(x-2) = 0$$
$$x^2 - 7x + 10 = 0$$

27. Writing the equation:

$$(t+3)(t-6) = 0$$
$$t^2 - 3t - 18 = 0$$

29. Writing the equation:
$$(y-2)(y+2)(y-4)=0$$
$$\left(y^2-4\right)(y-4)=0$$
$$y^3-4y^2-4y+16=0$$

31. Writing the equation:
$$(2x-1)(x-3)=0$$
$$2x^2-7x+3=0$$

33. Writing the equation:
$$(4t+3)(t-3)=0$$
$$4t^2-9t-9=0$$

35. Writing the equation:
$$(x-3)(x+3)(6x-5)=0$$
$$\left(x^2-9\right)(6x-5)=0$$
$$6x^3-5x^2-54x+45=0$$

37. Writing the equation:
$$(2a+1)(5a-3)=0$$
$$10a^2-a-3=0$$

39. Writing the equation:
$$(3x+2)(3x-2)(x-1)=0$$
$$\left(9x^2-4\right)(x-1)=0$$
$$9x^3-9x^2-4x+4=0$$

41. Writing the equation:
$$(x-2)(x+2)(x-3)(x+3)=0$$
$$\left(x^2-4\right)\left(x^2-9\right)=0$$
$$x^4-13x^2+36=0$$

43. Starting with the solutions:
$$x=\pm\sqrt{7}$$
$$x^2=\left(\pm\sqrt{7}\right)^2$$
$$x^2=7$$
$$x^2-7=0$$

45. Starting with the solutions:
$$x=\pm5i$$
$$x^2=\left(\pm5i\right)^2$$
$$x^2=-25$$
$$x^2+25=0$$

47. Starting with the solutions:
$$x=1\pm i$$
$$x-1=\pm i$$
$$(x-1)^2=(\pm i)^2$$
$$x^2-2x+1=-1$$
$$x^2-2x+2=0$$

49. Starting with the solutions:
$$x=-2\pm3i$$
$$x+2=\pm3i$$
$$(x+2)^2=(\pm3i)^2$$
$$x^2+4x+4=-9$$
$$x^2+4x+13=0$$

51. Starting with the solutions:
$$x=-4\pm3i$$
$$x+4=\pm3i$$
$$(x+4)^2=(\pm3i)^2$$
$$x^2+8x+16=-9$$
$$x^2+8x+25=0$$

53. Starting with the solutions:
$$x=\frac{-2\pm5i}{4}$$
$$4x=-2\pm5i$$
$$(4x+2)^2=(\pm5i)^2$$
$$16x^2+16x+4=-25$$
$$16x^2+16x+29=0$$

55. Starting with the solutions:
$$x=-1\pm\sqrt{6}$$
$$x+1=\pm\sqrt{6}$$
$$(x+1)^2=\left(\pm\sqrt{6}\right)^2$$
$$x^2+2x+1=6$$
$$x^2+2x-5=0$$

57. Starting with the solutions:
$$x=\frac{-4\pm\sqrt{2}}{3}$$
$$3x=-4\pm\sqrt{2}$$
$$(3x+4)^2=\left(\pm\sqrt{2}\right)^2$$
$$9x^2+24x+16=2$$
$$9x^2+24x+14=0$$

59. Starting with the solutions:
$$x=\frac{3\pm i\sqrt{5}}{7}$$
$$7x=3\pm i\sqrt{5}$$
$$(7x-3)^2=\left(\pm i\sqrt{5}\right)^2$$
$$49x^2-42x+9=-5$$
$$49x^2-42x+14=0$$
$$7x^2-6x+2=0$$

61. Starting with the solutions:
$$(x-3)(x+5)^2 = 0$$
$$(x-3)(x^2+10x+25)=0$$
$$x^3+10x^2+25x-3x^2-30x-75=0$$
$$x^3+7x^2-5x-75=0$$

63. Starting with the solutions:
$$(x-3)^2(x+3)^2 = 0$$
$$(x^2-6x+9)(x^2+6x+9)=0$$
$$x^4+6x^3+9x^2-6x^3-36x^2-54x+9x^2+54x+81=0$$
$$x^4-18x^2+81=0$$

65. First use long division to find the other factor:

$$
\begin{array}{r}
x^2+3x+2 \\
x+3\,\overline{)\,x^3+6x^2+11x+6} \\
\underline{x^3+3x^2} \\
3x^2+11x \\
\underline{3x^2+9x} \\
2x+6 \\
\underline{2x+6} \\
0
\end{array}
$$

So $x^3+6x^2+11x+6=(x+3)(x^2+3x+2)=(x+3)(x+2)(x+1)$. Therefore the solutions are $-3, -2$, and -1.

67. First use long division to find the other factor:

$$
\begin{array}{r}
y^2+2y-8 \\
y+3\,\overline{)\,y^3+5y^2-2y-24} \\
\underline{y^3+3y^2} \\
2y^2-2y \\
\underline{2y^2+6y} \\
-8y-24 \\
\underline{-8y-24} \\
0
\end{array}
$$

So $y^3+5y^2-2y-24=(y+3)(y^2+2y-8)=(y+3)(y+4)(y-2)$. Therefore the solutions are $-4, -3$, and 2.

69. First write the equation as $x^3-5x^2+8x-6=0$. Using long division to find the other factor:

$$
\begin{array}{r}
x^2-2x+2 \\
x-3\,\overline{)\,x^3-5x^2+8x-6} \\
\underline{x^3-3x^2} \\
-2x^2+8x \\
\underline{-2x^2+6x} \\
2x-6 \\
\underline{2x-6} \\
0
\end{array}
$$

So $x^3-5x^2+8x-6=(x-3)(x^2-2x-2)$. One solution is 3, and the others can be found using the quadratic

formula: $x=\dfrac{2\pm\sqrt{(-2)^2-4(1)(2)}}{2(1)}=\dfrac{2\pm\sqrt{4-8}}{2}=\dfrac{2\pm\sqrt{-4}}{2}=\dfrac{2\pm2i}{2}=1\pm i$

71. First write the equation as $t^3 - 13t^2 + 65t - 125 = 0$. Using long division to find the other factor:

$$\begin{array}{r} t^2 - 8t + 25 \\ t - 5 \overline{\smash{\big)}\ t^3 - 13t^2 + 65t - 125} \\ \underline{t^3 - 5t^2} \\ -8t^2 + 65t \\ \underline{-8t^2 + 40t} \\ 25t - 125 \\ \underline{25t - 125} \\ 0 \end{array}$$

So $t^3 - 13t^2 + 65t - 125 = (t-5)(t^2 - 8t + 25)$. One solution is 5, and the others can be found using the quadratic

formula: $t = \dfrac{8 \pm \sqrt{(-8)^2 - 4(1)(25)}}{2(1)} = \dfrac{8 \pm \sqrt{64 - 100}}{2} = \dfrac{8 \pm \sqrt{-36}}{2} = \dfrac{8 \pm 6i}{2} = 4 \pm 3i$

73. Simplifying: $(x+3)^2 - 2(x+3) - 8 = x^2 + 6x + 9 - 2x - 6 - 8 = x^2 + 4x - 5$

75. Simplifying: $(2a-3)^2 - 9(2a-3) + 20 = 4a^2 - 12a + 9 - 18a + 27 + 20 = 4a^2 - 30a + 56$

77. Simplifying:
$$2(4a+2)^2 - 3(4a+2) - 20 = 2(16a^2 + 16a + 4) - 3(4a+2) - 20$$
$$= 32a^2 + 32a + 8 - 12a - 6 - 20$$
$$= 32a^2 + 20a - 18$$

79. Solving the equation:
$$x^2 = \frac{1}{4}$$
$$x = \pm\sqrt{\frac{1}{4}} = \pm\frac{1}{2}$$

81. Since $\sqrt{x} \geq 0$, this equation has no solution.

83. Solving the equation:
$$x + 3 = 4$$
$$x = 1$$

85. Solving the equation:
$$y^2 - 2y - 8 = 0$$
$$(y+2)(y-4) = 0$$
$$y = -2, 4$$

87. Solving the equation:
$$4y^2 + 7y - 2 = 0$$
$$(4y-1)(y+2) = 0$$
$$y = -2, \frac{1}{4}$$

89. Solving the equation:
$$12x^2 = x + 1$$
$$12x^2 - x - 1 = 0$$
$$(4x+1)(3x-1) = 0$$
$$x = -\frac{1}{4}, \frac{1}{3}$$

91. **a.** Far Side is four and forty-seven hundredths.
b. Peanuts is three and eighty-five hundredths.

Landmark Review

1. Solving the equation:

$$x^2 = 9$$
$$x = \pm\sqrt{9} = \pm 3$$

2. Solving the equation:

$$y^2 = \frac{3}{4}$$
$$y = \pm\sqrt{\frac{3}{4}} = \pm\frac{\sqrt{3}}{2}$$

3. Solving the equation:

$$(x+3)^2 = 16$$
$$x + 3 = \pm\sqrt{16} = \pm 4$$
$$x + 3 = -4, 4$$
$$x = -7, 1$$

4. Solving the equation:

$$y^2 - 6y + 9 = 25$$
$$(y-3)^2 = 25$$
$$y - 3 = \pm\sqrt{25} = \pm 5$$
$$y - 3 = -5, 5$$
$$y = -2, 8$$

5. Solving the equation:

$$x^2 + 8x = 9$$
$$x^2 + 8x - 9 = 0$$
$$(x+9)(x-1) = 0$$
$$x = -9, 1$$

6. Solving the equation:

$$y^2 + 10y = -24$$
$$y^2 + 10y + 24 = 0$$
$$(y+6)(y+4) = 0$$
$$y = -6, -4$$

7. Solving the equation:

$$x^2 + 6x = 16$$
$$x^2 + 6x - 16 = 0$$
$$(x+8)(x-2) = 0$$
$$x = -8, 2$$

8. Solving the equation:

$$3x^2 + 9x - 12 = 0$$
$$3(x^2 + 3x - 4) = 0$$
$$3(x+4)(x-1) = 0$$
$$x = -4, 1$$

9. Using the quadratic formula: $x = \dfrac{-5 \pm \sqrt{(5)^2 - 4(1)(-3)}}{2(1)} = \dfrac{-5 \pm \sqrt{25+12}}{2} = \dfrac{-5 \pm \sqrt{37}}{2}$

10. Using the quadratic formula: $x = \dfrac{-1 \pm \sqrt{(1)^2 - 4(1)(8)}}{2(1)} = \dfrac{-1 \pm \sqrt{1-32}}{2} = \dfrac{-1 \pm i\sqrt{31}}{2}$

11. First write the equation as $2y^2 - 4y - 12 = 0$, or $y^2 - 2y - 6 = 0$

Using the quadratic formula: $y = \dfrac{2 \pm \sqrt{(-2)^2 - 4(1)(-6)}}{2(1)} = \dfrac{2 \pm \sqrt{4+24}}{2} = \dfrac{2 \pm \sqrt{28}}{2} = \dfrac{2 \pm 2\sqrt{7}}{2} = 1 \pm \sqrt{7}$

12. First write the equation as $3x^2 + 9x - 9 = 0$, or $x^2 + 3x - 3 = 0$

Using the quadratic formula: $x = \dfrac{-3 \pm \sqrt{(3)^2 - 4(1)(-3)}}{2(1)} = \dfrac{-3 \pm \sqrt{9+12}}{2} = \dfrac{-3 \pm \sqrt{21}}{2}$

13. Computing the discriminant: $D = (4)^2 - 4(1)(-5) = 16 + 20 = 36$. The equation will have two rational solutions.

14. Computing the discriminant: $D = (2)^2 - 4(1)(-5) = 4 + 20 = 24$. The equation will have two irrational solutions.

15. First write the equation as $2x^2 + 3x + 3 = 0$. Computing the discriminant: $D = (3)^2 - 4(3)(2) = 9 - 24 = -15$
The equation will have two non-real complex solutions.

16. Computing the discriminant: $D = (5)^2 - 4(6)(1) = 25 - 24 = 1$. The equation will have two rational solutions.

17. Writing the equation:

$$(x+6)(x+2) = 0$$
$$x^2 + 8x + 12 = 0$$

18. Writing the equation:

$$(x-3)(x+3)(x-5) = 0$$
$$(x^2 - 9)(x-5) = 0$$
$$x^3 - 5x^2 - 9x + 45 = 0$$

7.4 Equations Quadratic in Form

1. Solving the equation:

$$(x-3)^2 + 3(x-3) + 2 = 0$$
$$(x-3+2)(x-3+1) = 0$$
$$(x-1)(x-2) = 0$$
$$x = 1, 2$$

3. Solving the equation:

$$2(x+4)^2 + 5(x+4) - 12 = 0$$
$$[2(x+4) - 3][(x+4) + 4] = 0$$
$$(2x+5)(x+8) = 0$$
$$x = -8, -\frac{5}{2}$$

5. Solving the equation:

$$x^4 - 6x^2 - 27 = 0$$
$$(x^2 - 9)(x^2 + 3) = 0$$
$$x^2 = 9, -3$$
$$x = \pm 3, \pm i\sqrt{3}$$

7. Solving the equation:

$$x^4 + 9x^2 = -20$$
$$x^4 + 9x^2 + 20 = 0$$
$$(x^2 + 4)(x^2 + 5) = 0$$
$$x^2 = -4, -5$$
$$x = \pm 2i, \pm i\sqrt{5}$$

9. Solving the equation:

$$(2a-3)^2 - 9(2a-3) = -20$$
$$(2a-3)^2 - 9(2a-3) + 20 = 0$$
$$(2a-3-4)(2a-3-5) = 0$$
$$(2a-7)(2a-8) = 0$$
$$a = \frac{7}{2}, 4$$

11. Solving the equation:

$$2(4a+2)^2 = 3(4a+2) + 20$$
$$2(4a+2)^2 - 3(4a+2) - 20 = 0$$
$$[2(4a+2) + 5][(4a+2) - 4] = 0$$
$$(8a+9)(4a-2) = 0$$
$$a = -\frac{9}{8}, \frac{1}{2}$$

13. Solving the equation:

$$6t^4 = -t^2 + 5$$
$$6t^4 + t^2 - 5 = 0$$
$$(6t^2 - 5)(t^2 + 1) = 0$$
$$t^2 = \frac{5}{6}, -1$$
$$t = \pm\sqrt{\frac{5}{6}} = \pm\frac{\sqrt{30}}{6}, \pm i$$

15. Solving the equation:

$$9x^4 - 49 = 0$$
$$(3x^2 - 7)(3x^2 + 7) = 0$$
$$x^2 = \frac{7}{3}, -\frac{7}{3}$$
$$x = \pm\sqrt{\frac{7}{3}}, \pm\sqrt{-\frac{7}{3}}$$
$$t = \pm\frac{\sqrt{21}}{3}, \pm\frac{i\sqrt{21}}{3}$$

17. Solving the equation:

$$x - 7\sqrt{x} + 10 = 0$$
$$(\sqrt{x} - 5)(\sqrt{x} - 2) = 0$$
$$\sqrt{x} = 2, 5$$
$$x = 4, 25$$

Both values check in the original equation.

19. Solving the equation:

$$t - 2\sqrt{t} - 15 = 0$$
$$(\sqrt{t} - 5)(\sqrt{t} + 3) = 0$$
$$\sqrt{t} = -3, 5$$
$$t = 9, 25$$

Only $t = 25$ checks in the original equation.

21. Solving the equation:
$$6x + 11\sqrt{x} = 35$$
$$6x + 11\sqrt{x} - 35 = 0$$
$$\left(3\sqrt{x} - 5\right)\left(2\sqrt{x} + 7\right) = 0$$
$$\sqrt{x} = \frac{5}{3}, -\frac{7}{2}$$
$$x = \frac{25}{9}, \frac{49}{4}$$

Only $x = \dfrac{25}{9}$ checks in the original equation.

23. Solving the equation:
$$\left(a - 2\right) - 11\sqrt{a - 2} + 30 = 0$$
$$\left(\sqrt{a-2} - 6\right)\left(\sqrt{a-2} - 5\right) = 0$$
$$\sqrt{a-2} = 5, 6$$
$$a - 2 = 25, 36$$
$$a = 27, 38$$

25. Solving the equation:
$$\left(2x + 1\right) - 8\sqrt{2x+1} + 15 = 0$$
$$\left(\sqrt{2x+1} - 3\right)\left(\sqrt{2x+1} - 5\right) = 0$$
$$\sqrt{2x+1} = 3, 5$$
$$2x + 1 = 9, 25$$
$$2x = 8, 24$$
$$x = 4, 12$$

27. Solving for t:
$$16t^2 - vt - h = 0$$
$$t = \frac{v \pm \sqrt{v^2 - 4(16)(-h)}}{32} = \frac{v \pm \sqrt{v^2 + 64h}}{32}$$

29. Solving for x:
$$kx^2 + 8x + 4 = 0$$
$$x = \frac{-8 \pm \sqrt{64 - 16k}}{2k} = \frac{-8 \pm 4\sqrt{4 - k}}{2k} = \frac{-4 \pm 2\sqrt{4 - k}}{k}$$

31. Solving for x:
$$x^2 + 2xy + y^2 = 0$$
$$x = \frac{-2y \pm \sqrt{4y^2 - 4y^2}}{2} = \frac{-2y}{2} = -y$$

33. Solving for t (note that $t > 0$):
$$16t^2 - 8t - h = 0$$
$$t = \frac{8 + \sqrt{64 + 64h}}{32} = \frac{8 + 8\sqrt{1 + h}}{32} = \frac{1 + \sqrt{1 + h}}{4}$$

35. Solving when $h = 16.5$:
$$16t^2 - 8t - 16.5 = 0$$
$$t = \frac{8 + \sqrt{(-8)^2 - 4(16)(-16.5)}}{2(16)} = \frac{8 + \sqrt{64 + 1056}}{32} = \frac{8 + \sqrt{1120}}{32} \approx 1.30 \text{ seconds}$$

Solving when $h = 24.7$:
$$16t^2 - 8t - 24.7 = 0$$
$$t = \frac{8 + \sqrt{(-8)^2 - 4(16)(-24.7)}}{2(16)} = \frac{8 + \sqrt{64 + 1580.8}}{32} = \frac{8 + \sqrt{1644.8}}{32} \approx 1.52 \text{ seconds}$$

Solving when $h = 33$:

$$16t^2 - 8t - 33 = 0$$

$$t = \frac{8 + \sqrt{(-8)^2 - 4(16)(-33)}}{2(16)} = \frac{8 + \sqrt{64 + 2112}}{32} = \frac{8 + \sqrt{2176}}{32} \approx 1.71 \text{ seconds}$$

37. **a.** The equation of the arch is $f(x) = ax(x - 400)$. Solving for a:

$$230 = a(200)(200 - 400)$$
$$230 = -40{,}000a$$
$$a = -\frac{23}{4{,}000}$$

So the equation of the arch is $f(x) = -\dfrac{23}{4{,}000}x(x - 400) = -\dfrac{23}{4{,}000}\left(x^2 - 400x\right)$.

b. The equation of the arch is $f(x) = ax(x - 290)$. Solving for a:

$$77 = a(145)(145 - 290)$$
$$77 = -21{,}025a$$
$$a = -\frac{77}{21{,}025}$$

So the equation of the arch is $f(x) = -\dfrac{77}{21{,}025}x(x - 290) = -\dfrac{77}{21{,}025}\left(x^2 - 290x\right)$.

c. The equation of the arch is $f(x) = ax(x - 250)$. Solving for a:

$$400 = a(125)(200 - 250)$$
$$400 = -15{,}625a$$
$$a = -\frac{16}{625}$$

So the equation of the arch is $f(x) = -\dfrac{16}{625}x(x - 250) = -\dfrac{16}{625}\left(x^2 - 250x\right)$.

d. The equation of the arch is $f(x) = ax(x - 275)$. Solving for a:

$$246 = a(137.5)(137.5 - 275)$$
$$246 = -18{,}906.25a$$
$$a = -\frac{246}{18{,}906.25} = -\frac{984}{75{,}625}$$

So the equation of the arch is $f(x) = -\dfrac{984}{75{,}625}x(x - 275) = -\dfrac{984}{75{,}625}\left(x^2 - 275x\right)$.

39. Using the Pythagorean theorem:

$$x^2 + (x+2)^2 = (x+4)^2$$
$$x^2 + x^2 + 4x + 4 = x^2 + 8x + 16$$
$$x^2 - 4x - 12 = 0$$
$$(x-6)(x+2) = 0$$
$$x = 6 \qquad (x = -2 \text{ is impossible})$$

So the area is: $A = \dfrac{1}{2}(6)(8) = 24$

41. **a.** The equation is $l + 2w = 160$.

b. The area is: $A = w \cdot l = w(160 - 2w) = -2w^2 + 160w$

c. Completing the table:

w	0	10	20	30	40	50	60	70	80
A	0	1,400	2,400	3,000	3,200	3,000	2,400	1,400	0

d. The maximum area is 3,200 square yards.

43. Evaluating when $x = 1$: $y = 3(1)^2 - 6(1) + 1 = 3 - 6 + 1 = -2$

45. Evaluating: $P(135) = -0.1(135)^2 + 27(135) - 500 = -1,822.5 + 3,645 - 500 = 1,322.5$

47. Solving the equation:
$$0 = a(80)^2 + 70$$
$$0 = 6400a + 70$$
$$6400a = -70$$
$$a = -\frac{7}{640}$$

49. Solving the equation:
$$x^2 - 6x + 5 = 0$$
$$(x - 1)(x - 5) = 0$$
$$x = 1, 5$$

51. Solving the equation:
$$-x^2 - 2x + 3 = 0$$
$$x^2 + 2x - 3 = 0$$
$$(x + 3)(x - 1) = 0$$
$$x = -3, 1$$

53. Solving the equation:
$$2x^2 - 6x + 5 = 0$$
$$x = \frac{6 \pm \sqrt{(-6)^2 - 4(2)(5)}}{2(2)} = \frac{6 \pm \sqrt{36 - 40}}{4} = \frac{6 \pm \sqrt{-4}}{4} = \frac{6 \pm 2i}{4} = \frac{3 \pm i}{2} = \frac{3}{2} \pm \frac{1}{2}i$$

55. Completing the square: $x^2 - 6x + 9 = (x - 3)^2$

57. Completing the square: $y^2 + 2y + 1 = (y + 1)^2$

7.5 Graphing Quadratic Functions

1. First complete the square: $f(x) = x^2 + 2x - 3 = (x^2 + 2x + 1) - 1 - 3 = (x + 1)^2 - 4$

The x-intercepts are $-3, 1$ and the vertex is $(-1, -4)$. Graphing the parabola:

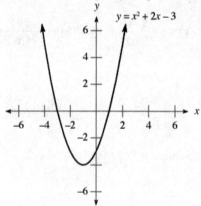

3. First complete the square: $f(x) = -x^2 - 4x + 5 = -\left(x^2 + 4x + 4\right) + 4 + 5 = -(x+2)^2 + 9$

The x-intercepts are $-5, 1$ and the vertex is $(-2, 9)$. Graphing the parabola:

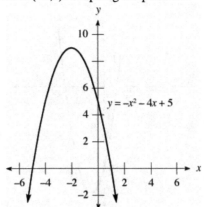

5. The x-intercepts are $-1, 1$ and the vertex is $(0, -1)$. Graphing the parabola:

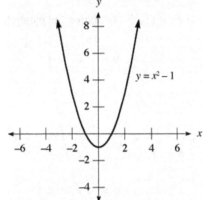

7. The x-intercepts are $-3, 3$ and the vertex is $(0, 9)$. Graphing the parabola:

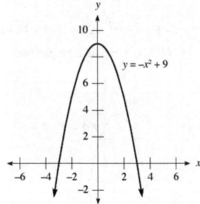

9. First complete the square: $f(x) = 2x^2 - 4x - 6 = 2\left(x^2 - 2x + 1\right) - 2 - 6 = 2(x-1)^2 - 8$

The x-intercepts are $-1, 3$ and the vertex is $(1, -8)$. Graphing the parabola:

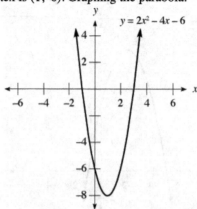

11. First complete the square: $f(x) = x^2 - 2x - 4 = \left(x^2 - 2x + 1\right) - 1 - 4 = (x-1)^2 - 5$

The x-intercepts are $1 \pm \sqrt{5}$ and the vertex is $(1, -5)$. Graphing the parabola:

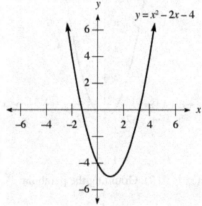

13. First complete the square: $f(x) = -x^2 - 2x + 3 = -\left(x^2 + 2x + 1\right) + 1 + 3 = -(x+1)^2 + 4$

The x-intercepts are $-3, 1$ and the vertex is $(-1, 4)$. Graphing the parabola:

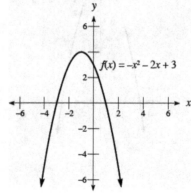

15. The vertex is (1,3) and the *y*-intercept is 5. Graphing the parabola:

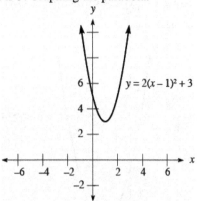

$y = 2(x - 1)^2 + 3$

17. The vertex is (–2,4) and the *x*-intercepts are –4 and 0. Graphing the parabola:

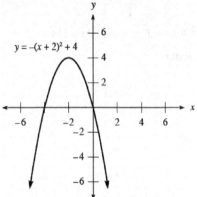

$y = -(x + 2)^2 + 4$

19. The vertex is (2,–4) and the *y*-intercept is –2. Graphing the parabola:

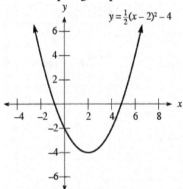

$y = \frac{1}{2}(x - 2)^2 - 4$

21. The vertex is (4,–1) and the *y*-intercept is –33. Graphing the parabola:

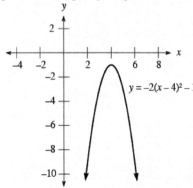

$y = -2(x - 4)^2 - 1$

23. First complete the square: $f(x) = x^2 - 4x - 4 = \left(x^2 - 4x + 4\right) - 4 - 4 = (x-2)^2 - 8$

The vertex is $(2, -8)$. Graphing the parabola:

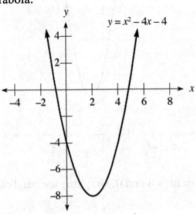

25. First complete the square: $f(x) = -x^2 + 2x - 5 = -\left(x^2 - 2x + 1\right) + 1 - 5 = -(x-1)^2 - 4$

The vertex is $(1, -4)$. Graphing the parabola:

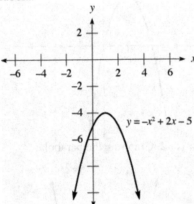

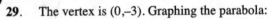

27. The vertex is $(0, 1)$. Graphing the parabola:

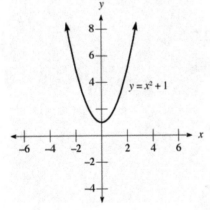

29. The vertex is $(0, -3)$. Graphing the parabola:

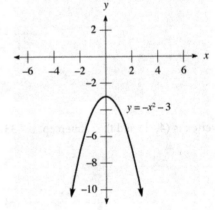

31. First complete the square: $g(x) = 3x^2 + 4x + 1 = 3\left(x^2 + \dfrac{4}{3}x + \dfrac{4}{9}\right) + 1 - \dfrac{4}{3} = 3\left(x + \dfrac{2}{3}\right)^2 - \dfrac{1}{3}$

The vertex is $\left(-\dfrac{2}{3}, -\dfrac{1}{3}\right)$. Graphing the parabola:

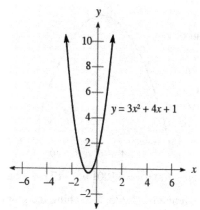

$y = 3x^2 + 4x + 1$

33. First complete the square: $g(x) = -2x^2 + 8x - 3 = -2\left(x^2 - 4x + 4\right) - 3 + 8 = -2(x-2)^2 + 5$

The vertex is $(2,5)$. Graphing the parabola:

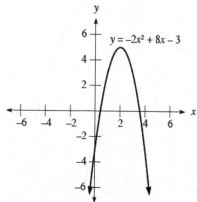

$y = -2x^2 + 8x - 3$

35. Completing the square: $f(x) = x^2 - 6x + 5 = \left(x^2 - 6x + 9\right) - 9 + 5 = (x-3)^2 - 4$

The vertex is $(3,-4)$, which is the lowest point on the graph.

37. Completing the square: $f(x) = -x^2 + 2x + 8 = -\left(x^2 - 2x + 1\right) + 1 + 8 = -(x-1)^2 + 9$

The vertex is $(1,9)$, which is the highest point on the graph.

39. Completing the square: $f(x) = -x^2 + 4x + 12 = -\left(x^2 - 4x + 4\right) + 4 + 12 = -(x-2)^2 + 16$

The vertex is $(2,16)$, which is the highest point on the graph.

41. Completing the square: $f(x) = -x^2 - 8x = -\left(x^2 + 8x + 16\right) + 16 = -(x+4)^2 + 16$

The vertex is $(-4,16)$, which is the highest point on the graph.

43. First complete the square:

$$P(x) = -0.002x^2 + 3.5x - 800 = -0.002\left(x^2 - 1750x + 765,625\right) + 1,531.25 - 800 = -0.002(x-875)^2 + 731.25$$

It must sell 875 patterns to obtain a maximum profit of \$731.25.

45. The ball is in her hand at times 0 sec and 2 sec.

Completing the square: $h(t) = -16t^2 + 32t = -16\left(t^2 - 2t + 1\right) + 16 = -16(t-1)^2 + 16$

The maximum height of the ball is 16 feet.

47. Completing the square: $R = xp = 1200p - 100p^2 = -100\left(p^2 - 12p + 36\right) + 3600 = -100\left(p - 6\right)^2 + 3600$

The price is $6.00 and the maximum revenue is $3,600. Sketching the graph:

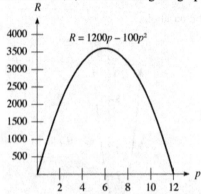

49. Completing the square: $R = xp = 1700p - 100p^2 = -100\left(p^2 - 17p + 72.25\right) + 7225 = -100\left(p - 8.5\right)^2 + 7225$

The price is $8.50 and the maximum revenue is $7,225. Sketching the graph:

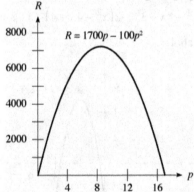

51. The equation is given on the graph:

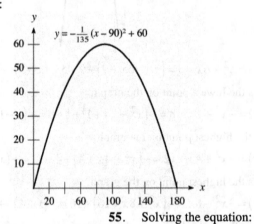

53. Solving the equation:

$$x^2 - 2x - 8 = 0$$
$$(x - 4)(x + 2) = 0$$
$$x = -2, 4$$

55. Solving the equation:

$$6x^2 - x = 2$$
$$6x^2 - x - 2 = 0$$
$$(2x + 1)(3x - 2) = 0$$
$$x = -\frac{1}{2}, \frac{2}{3}$$

57. Solving the equation:
$$x^2 - 6x + 9 = 0$$
$$(x-3)^2 = 0$$
$$x = 3$$

59. Solving the equation:
$$x - \frac{4}{x} = 0$$
$$x^2 - 4 = 0$$
$$(x+2)(x-2) = 0$$
$$x = -2, 2$$

7.6 Polynomial and Rational Inequalities

1. Factoring the inequality:
$$x^2 + x - 6 > 0$$
$$(x+3)(x-2) > 0$$

Forming the sign chart:

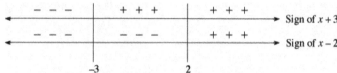

The solution set is $x < -3$ or $x > 2$. Graphing the solution set:

3. Factoring the inequality:
$$x^2 - x - 12 \le 0$$
$$(x+3)(x-4) \le 0$$

Forming the sign chart:

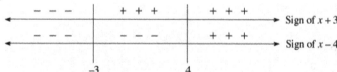

The solution set is $-3 \le x \le 4$. Graphing the solution set:

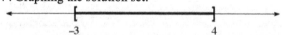

5. Factoring the inequality:
$$x^2 + 5x \ge -6$$
$$x^2 + 5x + 6 \ge 0$$
$$(x+2)(x+3) \ge 0$$

Forming the sign chart:

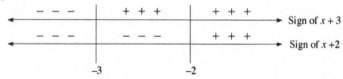

The solution set is $x \le -3$ or $x \ge -2$. Graphing the solution set:

7.   Factoring the inequality:

$$6x^2 < 5x - 1$$
$$6x^2 - 5x + 1 < 0$$
$$(3x - 1)(2x - 1) < 0$$

Forming the sign chart:

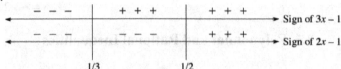

The solution set is $\dfrac{1}{3} < x < \dfrac{1}{2}$. Graphing the solution set:

9.   Factoring the inequality:

$$x^2 - 9 < 0$$
$$(x + 3)(x - 3) < 0$$

Forming the sign chart:

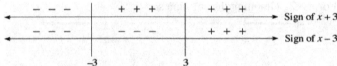

The solution set is $-3 < x < 3$. Graphing the solution set:

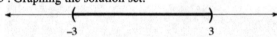

11.   Factoring the inequality:

$$4x^2 - 9 \geq 0$$
$$(2x + 3)(2x - 3) \geq 0$$

Forming the sign chart:

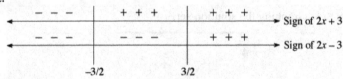

The solution set is $x \leq -\dfrac{3}{2}$ or $x \geq \dfrac{3}{2}$. Graphing the solution set:

13.   Factoring the inequality:

$$2x^2 - x - 3 < 0$$
$$(2x - 3)(x + 1) < 0$$

Forming the sign chart:

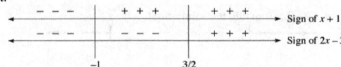

The solution set is $-1 < x < \dfrac{3}{2}$. Graphing the solution set:

15. Factoring the inequality:

$$x^2 - 4x - 5 \geq -8$$
$$x^2 - 4x + 3 \geq 0$$
$$(x-3)(x-1) \geq 0$$

Forming the sign chart:

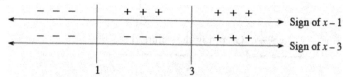

The solution set is $x \leq 1$ or $x \geq 3$. Graphing the solution set:

17. Factoring the inequality:

$$x^2 + 3x - 4 \geq -4 + 2x$$
$$x^2 + x \geq 0$$
$$x(x+1) \geq 0$$

Forming the sign chart:

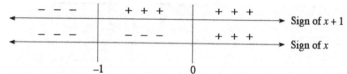

The solution set is $x \leq -1$ or $x \geq 0$. Graphing the solution set:

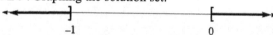

19. Factoring the inequality:

$$x^2 - 4x + 4 \geq 0$$
$$(x-2)^2 \geq 0$$

Since this inequality is always true, the solution set is all real numbers. Graphing the solution set:

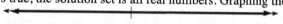

21. Factoring the inequality:

$$x^2 - 10x + 25 < 0$$
$$(x-5)^2 < 0$$

Since this inequality is never true, there is no solution.

23. Forming the sign chart:

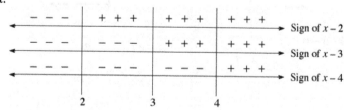

The solution set is $2 < x < 3$ or $x > 4$. Graphing the solution set:

25. Forming the sign chart:

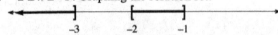

The solution set is $x \le -3$ or $-2 \le x \le -1$. Graphing the solution set:

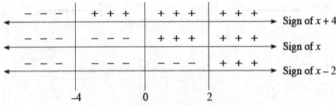

27. Forming the sign chart:

The solution set is $-4 \le x \le 0$ or $x \ge 2$. Graphing the solution set:

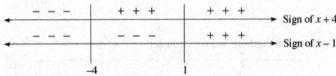

29. Forming the sign chart:

The solution set is $-4 < x \le 1$. Graphing the solution set:

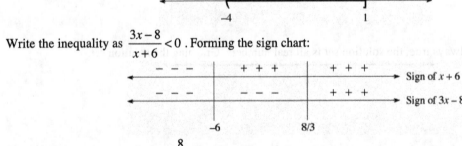

31. Write the inequality as $\dfrac{3x-8}{x+6} < 0$. Forming the sign chart:

The solution set is $x < -6$ or $x > \dfrac{8}{3}$. Graphing the solution set:

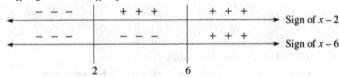

33. Write the inequality as $\dfrac{4+x-6}{x-6} < 0$, or $\dfrac{x-2}{x-6} < 0$. Forming the sign chart:

The solution set is $x < 2$ or $x > 6$. Graphing the solution set:

35. Forming the sign chart:

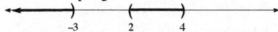

The solution set is $x < -3$ or $2 < x < 4$. Graphing the solution set:

37. Simplify the inequality:
$$\frac{2}{x-4} - \frac{1}{x-3} < 0$$
$$\frac{2(x-3)-1(x-4)}{(x-4)(x-3)} < 0$$
$$\frac{2x-6-x+4}{(x-4)(x-3)} < 0$$
$$\frac{x-2}{(x-4)(x-3)} < 0$$

Forming the sign chart:

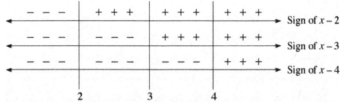

The solution set is $2 < x < 3$ or $x > 4$. Graphing the solution set:

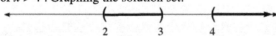

39. Simplify the inequality:
$$\frac{x+7}{2x+12} + \frac{6}{x^2-36} \le 0$$
$$\frac{x+7}{2(x+6)} + \frac{6}{(x+6)(x-6)} \le 0$$
$$\frac{(x+7)(x-6)+6\cdot 2}{2(x+6)(x-6)} \le 0$$
$$\frac{x^2+x-42+12}{2(x+6)(x-6)} \le 0$$
$$\frac{x^2+x-30}{2(x+6)(x-6)} \le 0$$
$$\frac{(x+6)(x-5)}{2(x+6)(x-6)} \le 0$$
$$\frac{x-5}{2(x-6)} \le 0$$

Forming the sign chart:

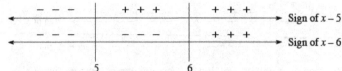

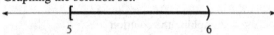

The solution set is $5 \le x < 6$. Graphing the solution set:

41. Simplify the inequality:

$$\frac{x+1}{4x-4} \le \frac{1}{x^2-1}$$

$$\frac{x+1}{4x-4} - \frac{1}{x^2-1} \le 0$$

$$\frac{x+1}{4(x-1)} - \frac{1}{(x+1)(x-1)} \le 0$$

$$\frac{(x+1)(x+1)-1\cdot4}{4(x+1)(x-1)} \le 0$$

$$\frac{x^2+2x+1-4}{4(x+1)(x-1)} \le 0$$

$$\frac{x^2+2x-3}{4(x+1)(x-1)} \le 0$$

$$\frac{(x+3)(x-1)}{4(x+1)(x-1)} \le 0$$

$$\frac{x+3}{4(x+1)} \le 0$$

Forming the sign chart:

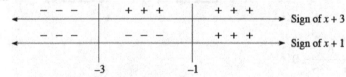

The solution set is $-3 \le x < -1$. Graphing the solution set:

43. **a.** The solution set is $-2 < x < 2$. In interval notation, this is $(-2, 2)$.

   b. The solution set is $x < -2$ or $x > 2$. In interval notation, this is $(-\infty, -2) \cup (2, \infty)$.

   c. The solution set is $x = -2, 2$.

45. **a.** The solution set is $-2 < x < 5$. In interval notation, this is $(-2, 5)$.

   b. The solution set is $x < -2$ or $x > 5$. In interval notation, this is $(-\infty, -2) \cup (5, \infty)$.

   c. The solution set is $x = -2, 5$.

47. **a.** The solution set is $x < -1$ or $1 < x < 3$. In interval notation, this is $(-\infty, -1) \cup (1, 3)$.

   b. The solution set is $-1 < x < 1$ or $x > 3$. In interval notation, this is $(-1, 1) \cup (3, \infty)$.

   c. The solution set is $x = -1, 1, 3$.

49. Setting the denominator equal to 0:
$$x^2 - 3x - 4 = 0$$
$$(x-4)(x+1) = 0$$
$$x = -1, 4$$
The domain is $\{x \mid x \neq -1, 4\}$.

51. The quantity inside the radical must be non-negative:
$$x^2 - 7x \geq 0$$
$$x(x-7) \geq 0$$
Forming the sign chart:

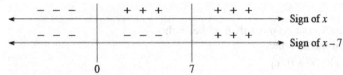

The domain is $\{x \mid x \leq 0 \text{ or } x \geq 7\}$.

53. The quantity inside the radical must be non-negative:
$$2x^2 - 5x - 3 \geq 0$$
$$(2x+1)(x-3) \geq 0$$
Forming the sign chart:

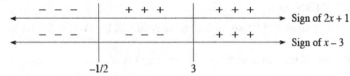

The domain is $\left\{x \mid x \leq -\dfrac{1}{2} \text{ or } x \geq 3\right\}$.

55. The quantity inside the radical must be positive:
$$5x^2 - 17x + 6 > 0$$
$$(5x-2)(x-3) > 0$$
Forming the sign chart:

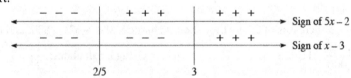

The domain is $\left\{x \mid x < \dfrac{2}{5} \text{ or } x > 3\right\}$.

57. Let w represent the width and $2w + 3$ represent the length. Using the area formula:
$$w(2w+3) \geq 44$$
$$2w^2 + 3w \geq 44$$
$$2w^2 + 3w - 44 \geq 0$$
$$(2w+11)(w-4) \geq 0$$
Forming the sign chart:

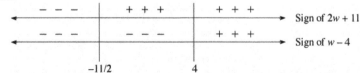

The width is at least 4 inches.

59. Solving the inequality:
$$1300p - 100p^2 \geq 4000$$
$$-100p^2 + 1300p - 4000 \geq 0$$
$$p^2 - 13p + 40 \leq 0$$
$$(p-8)(p-5) \leq 0$$

Forming the sign chart:

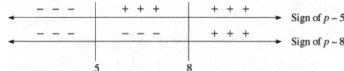

She should charge at least $5 but no more than $8 per radio.

61. Completing the square on the income:
$$y = (10{,}000 - 200x)(100 + 10x)$$
$$= 2{,}000(50 - x)(10 + x)$$
$$= 2{,}000(-x^2 + 40x + 500)$$
$$= -2{,}000(x^2 - 40x) + 1{,}000{,}000$$
$$= -2{,}000(x^2 - 40x + 400) + 800{,}000 + 1{,}000{,}000$$
$$= -2{,}000(x - 20)^2 + 1{,}800{,}000$$

The union should have 20 increases of $10, so their new dues should be $100 + 20($10) = $300, and their income will be $1,800,000.

63. Let x represent the number of $2 increases in price. Completing the square on the income:
$$y = (40 - 2x)(20 + 2x)$$
$$= -4(x - 20)(x + 10)$$
$$= -4(x^2 - 10x - 200)$$
$$= -4(x^2 - 10x) + 800$$
$$= -4(x^2 - 10x + 25) + 100 + 800$$
$$= -4(x - 5)^2 + 900$$

The business should have 5 increases of $2, so they should charge $20 + 5($2) = $30, and their income will be $900.

65. Using a calculator: $\dfrac{50{,}000}{32{,}000} = 1.5625$

67. Using a calculator: $\dfrac{1}{2}\left(\dfrac{4.5926}{1.3876} - 2\right) \approx 0.6549$

69. Solving the equation:
$$2\sqrt{3t - 1} = 2$$
$$\sqrt{3t - 1} = 1$$
$$\left(\sqrt{3t - 1}\right)^2 = (1)^2$$
$$3t - 1 = 1$$
$$3t = 2$$
$$t = \frac{2}{3}$$

The solution is $\dfrac{2}{3}$.

70. Solving the equation:
$$\sqrt{x + 3} = x - 3$$
$$\left(\sqrt{x + 3}\right)^2 = (x - 3)^2$$
$$x + 3 = x^2 - 6x + 9$$
$$0 = x^2 - 7x + 6$$
$$0 = (x - 6)(x - 1)$$
$$x = 1, 6 \qquad (x = 1 \text{ does not check})$$

The solution is 6.

73. Graphing the equation:

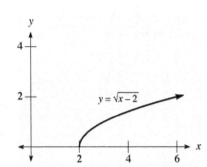

75. Graphing the equation:

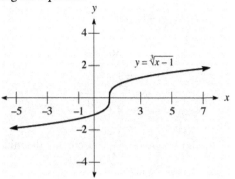

Chapter 7 Review

1. Solving the equation:
$$(3x+4)^2 = 25$$
$$3x+4 = \pm 5$$
$$3x+4 = -5, 5$$
$$3x = -9, 1$$
$$x = -3, \frac{1}{3}$$

2. Solving the equation:
$$(2x-3)^2 = -18$$
$$2x-3 = \pm\sqrt{-18}$$
$$2x-3 = \pm 3i\sqrt{2}$$
$$2x = 3 \pm 3i\sqrt{2}$$
$$x = \frac{3 \pm 3i\sqrt{2}}{2}$$

3. Solving the equation:
$$y^2 - 6y + 9 = 36$$
$$(y-3)^2 = 36$$
$$y-3 = \pm 6$$
$$y-3 = -6, 6$$
$$y = -3, 9$$

4. Solving the equation:
$$(x-4)(x+7) = -10$$
$$x^2 + 3x - 28 = -10$$
$$x^2 + 3x - 18 = 0$$
$$(x+6)(x-3) = 0$$
$$x = -6, 3$$

5. Solving the equation:
$$125t^3 - 64 = 0$$
$$(5x-4)(25x^2 + 20x + 16) = 0$$
$$x = \frac{4}{5}, \frac{-20 \pm \sqrt{400 - 1{,}600}}{50} = \frac{-20 \pm \sqrt{-1{,}200}}{50} = \frac{-20 \pm 20i\sqrt{3}}{50} = \frac{-2 \pm 2i\sqrt{3}}{5}$$

6. Solving the equation:
$$\frac{1}{a} - \frac{1}{3} = \frac{1}{a-2}$$
$$3a(a-2)\left(\frac{1}{a} - \frac{1}{3}\right) = 3a(a-2)\left(\frac{1}{a-2}\right)$$
$$3(a-2) - a(a-2) = 3a$$
$$3a - 6 - a^2 + 2a = 3a$$
$$a^2 - 2a + 6 = 0$$
$$a = \frac{2 \pm \sqrt{4 - 24}}{2} = \frac{2 \pm \sqrt{-20}}{2} = \frac{2 \pm 2i\sqrt{5}}{2} = 1 \pm i\sqrt{5}$$

7. Solving for r:
$$36(r-4)^2 = A$$
$$(r-4)^2 = \frac{A}{36}$$
$$r-4 = \pm\frac{\sqrt{A}}{6}$$
$$r = 4 \pm \frac{\sqrt{A}}{6}$$

8. Solving by completing the square:
$$x^2 - 8x = -13$$
$$x^2 - 8x + 16 = -13 + 16$$
$$(x-4)^2 = 3$$
$$x - 4 = \pm\sqrt{3}$$
$$x = 4 \pm \sqrt{3}$$

9. The shorter side is $\frac{12}{2} = 6$ cm and the middle side is $6\sqrt{3}$ cm.

10. Solving the equation:
$$48t - 16t^2 = 20$$
$$-16t^2 + 48t - 20 = 0$$
$$4t^2 - 12t + 5 = 0$$
$$(2t-1)(2t-5) = 0$$
$$t = \frac{1}{2}, \frac{5}{2}$$

The object will be 20 feet above the ground after $\frac{1}{2}$ sec or $\frac{5}{2}$ sec.

11. Setting the revenue equal to the cost:
$$161x - 0.5x^2 = 10x + 300$$
$$-0.5x^2 + 151x - 300 = 0$$
$$x^2 - 302x + 600 = 0$$
$$(x-2)(x-300) = 0$$
$$x = 2, 300$$

The company must sell 2 or 300 watches to break even.

12. First write the equation as $3x^2 + 18x + k = 0$. Setting the discriminant equal to 0:
$$(18)^2 - 4(3)(k) = 0$$
$$324 - 12k = 0$$
$$12k = 324$$
$$k = 27$$

13. First write the equation as $3x^2 + 16x - 35 = 0$. Finding the discriminant: $D = (16)^2 - 4(3)(-35) = 256 + 420 = 676$

Since the discriminant is a perfect square $\left(26^2 = 676\right)$, the equation has two rational solutions.

14. Finding the equation:
$$(x-3)(5x+3) = 0$$
$$5x^2 - 12x - 9 = 0$$

15. Finding the equation:
$$(x+4)(x-4)(x-3) = 0$$
$$\left(x^2 - 16\right)(x-3) = 0$$
$$x^3 - 3x^2 - 16x + 48 = 0$$

16. Solving the equation:
$$4x^4 - 11x^2 - 45 = 0$$
$$\left(x^2 - 5\right)\left(4x^2 + 9\right) = 0$$
$$x^2 = 5, -\frac{9}{4}$$
$$x = \pm\sqrt{5}, \pm\frac{3}{2}i$$

17. Solving the equation:
$$(3x+2)^2 - 4(3x+2) - x - 6 = 0$$
$$9x^2 + 12x + 4 - 12x - 8 - x - 6 = 0$$
$$9x^2 - x - 10 = 0$$
$$(9x-10)(x+1) = 0$$
$$x = -1, \frac{10}{9}$$

18. Solving the equation:

$$2t - 5\sqrt{t} - 3 = 0$$
$$\left(2\sqrt{t} + 1\right)\left(\sqrt{t} - 3\right) = 0$$
$$\sqrt{t} = -\frac{1}{2}, 3$$
$$t = \frac{1}{4}, 9$$

Since $t = \frac{1}{4}$ does not check, the solution is 9.

19. Solving for t:

$$16t^2 - 12t - h = 0$$
$$t = \frac{12 + \sqrt{144 - 4(16)(-h)}}{32} = \frac{12 + \sqrt{144 + 64h}}{32} = \frac{12 + 4\sqrt{9 + 4h}}{32} = \frac{3 + \sqrt{9 + 4h}}{8}$$

Note that only the positive answer was given here since t represents time, thus $t > 0$.

20. Completing the square: $y = x^2 - 4x - 6 = \left(x^2 - 4x + 4\right) - 4 - 6 = (x - 2)^2 - 10$

The vertex is $(2, -10)$. Graphing the parabola:

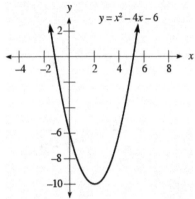

21. Completing the square: $y = -x^2 - 2x + 4 = -\left(x^2 + 2x + 1\right) + 1 + 4 = -(x + 1)^2 + 5$

The vertex is $(-1, 5)$. Graphing the parabola:

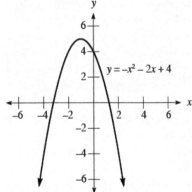

22. The vertex is $(4, -3)$, the x-intercepts are $(3, 0)$ and $(5, 0)$, and the parabola is pointed up, so the equation is: $y = 3(x - 4)^2 - 3$

23. Finding the profit and completing the square:

$$P = 26x - 0.4x^2 - 4x - 200$$
$$= -0.4x^2 + 22x - 200$$
$$= -0.4\left(x^2 - 55x + 756.25\right) + 302.5 - 200$$
$$= -0.4\left(x - 27.5\right)^2 + 102.5$$

The maximum weekly profit is $102.50, obtained by selling 27.5 items per week.

24. Factoring the inequality:

$$x^2 + 3x - 10 \le 0$$
$$(x+5)(x-2) \le 0$$

Forming a sign chart:

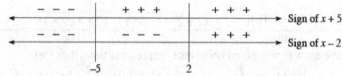

The solution set is $-5 \le x \le 2$. Graphing the solution set:

25. Factoring the inequality:

$$3x^2 - 8x > 3$$
$$3x^2 - 8x - 3 > 0$$
$$(3x+1)(x-3) > 0$$

Forming a sign chart:

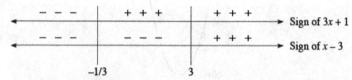

The solution set is $x < -\dfrac{1}{3}$ or $x > 3$. Graphing the solution set:

26. **a.** The solution is $x < -3$ or $-1 < x < 2$.
    b. The solution is $-3 < x < -1$ or $x > 2$.
    c. The solution is $x = -3, -1, 2$.

Chapter 7 Cumulative Review

1. Simplifying: $6 - 36 \div 6 + 2 \cdot 2 = 6 - 6 + 4 = 4$

2. Simplifying: $5(13-17)^2 - 2(16-17)^2 = 5(-4)^2 - 2(-1)^2 = 5(16) - 2(1) = 80 - 2 = 78$

3. Simplifying: $\left(-\dfrac{5}{2}\right)^3 = \left(-\dfrac{5}{2}\right)\left(-\dfrac{5}{2}\right)\left(-\dfrac{5}{2}\right) = -\dfrac{125}{8}$

4. Simplifying: $\left(-\dfrac{3}{4}\right)^2 = \left(-\dfrac{3}{4}\right)\left(-\dfrac{3}{4}\right) = \dfrac{9}{16}$

5. Simplifying: $3 + 2x - 5(3x-2) = 3 + 2x - 15x + 10 = -13x + 13$

6. Simplifying: $7 - 2[4x - 3(x+1)] = 7 - 2(4x - 3x - 3) = 7 - 2(x - 3) = 7 - 2x + 6 = -2x + 13$

7. Simplifying: $\left(\dfrac{x^{-3}y^{-3}}{x^{-2}y^4}\right)^{-1} = \dfrac{x^3 y^3}{x^2 y^{-4}} = x^{3-2} y^{3+4} = xy^7$

8. Simplifying: $\left(\dfrac{a^{-2}b^{-1}}{a^5 b^{-2}}\right)^{-3} = \dfrac{a^6 b^3}{a^{-15} b^6} = a^{6+15} b^{3-6} = a^{21} b^{-3} = \dfrac{a^{21}}{b^3}$

9. Simplifying: $\sqrt[3]{54} = \sqrt[3]{27 \cdot 2} = 3\sqrt[3]{2}$

10. Simplifying: $\sqrt{32x^5} = \sqrt{16x^4 \cdot 2x} = 4x^2 \sqrt{2x}$

11. Simplifying: $64^{-2/3} - 16^{-1/2} = \left(64^{1/3}\right)^{-2} - \left(16^{1/2}\right)^{-1} = 4^{-2} - 4^{-1} = \dfrac{1}{16} - \dfrac{1}{4} = \dfrac{1}{16} - \dfrac{4}{16} = -\dfrac{3}{16}$

12. Simplifying: $\left(\dfrac{125}{8}\right)^{-2/3} = \left[\left(\dfrac{125}{8}\right)^{1/3}\right]^{-2} = \left(\dfrac{5}{2}\right)^{-2} = \left(\dfrac{2}{5}\right)^2 = \dfrac{4}{25}$

13. Simplifying: $\dfrac{\frac{4}{7} - 1}{\frac{4}{7} + 1} = \dfrac{\frac{4}{7} - 1}{\frac{4}{7} + 1} \cdot \dfrac{7}{7} = \dfrac{4-7}{4+7} = -\dfrac{3}{11}$

14. Simplifying: $\dfrac{\frac{1}{8} + 3}{1 - \frac{3}{2}} = \dfrac{\frac{1}{8} + 3}{1 - \frac{3}{2}} \cdot \dfrac{8}{8} = \dfrac{1+24}{8-12} = -\dfrac{25}{4}$

15. Reducing the fraction: $\dfrac{3x^2 - 17xy - 28y^2}{3x + 4y} = \dfrac{(3x+4y)(x-7y)}{3x+4y} = x - 7y$

16. Reducing the fraction: $\dfrac{x^2 - x - 20}{x+4} = \dfrac{(x+4)(x-5)}{x+4} = x - 5$

17. Dividing: $\dfrac{-4+i}{i} = \dfrac{-4+i}{i} \cdot \dfrac{-i}{-i} = \dfrac{4i - i^2}{-i^2} = \dfrac{4i+1}{1} = 1 + 4i$

18. Dividing: $\dfrac{4+2i}{5-i} = \dfrac{4+2i}{5-i} \cdot \dfrac{5+i}{5+i} = \dfrac{20 + 14i + 2i^2}{25+1} = \dfrac{18 + 14i}{26} = \dfrac{9+7i}{13} = \dfrac{9}{13} + \dfrac{7}{13}i$

19. Solving the equation:

$$\dfrac{5}{4}x + 3 = 8$$
$$\dfrac{5}{4}x = 5$$
$$5x = 20$$
$$x = 4$$

20. Solving the equation:

$$\dfrac{1}{3}a + \dfrac{3}{4} = 5$$
$$12\left(\dfrac{1}{3}a + \dfrac{3}{4}\right) = 12(5)$$
$$4a + 9 = 60$$
$$4a = 51$$
$$a = \dfrac{51}{4}$$

21. Solving the equation:
$$|a| + 4 = 7$$
$$|a| = 3$$
$$a = \pm 3$$

22. Since $|a + 1| \geq 0$, there is no solution to the equation.

23. Solving the equation:

$$\frac{x}{4} + \frac{15}{4x} = -2$$
$$4x\left(\frac{x}{4} + \frac{15}{4x}\right) = 4x(-2)$$
$$x^2 + 15 = -8x$$
$$x^2 + 8x + 15 = 0$$
$$(x + 5)(x + 3) = 0$$
$$x = -5, -3$$

24. Solving the equation:

$$-\frac{1}{3} + \frac{a}{a+2} = \frac{2}{a+2}$$
$$3(a+2)\left(-\frac{1}{3} + \frac{a}{a+2}\right) = 3(a+2)\left(\frac{2}{a+2}\right)$$
$$-(a+2) + 3a = 3 \cdot 2$$
$$-a - 2 + 3a = 6$$
$$2a - 2 = 6$$
$$2a = 8$$
$$a = 4$$

25. Solving the equation:
$$(2x - 3)^2 = 8$$
$$2x - 3 = \pm\sqrt{8}$$
$$2x - 3 = \pm 2\sqrt{2}$$
$$2x = 3 \pm 2\sqrt{2}$$
$$x = \frac{3 \pm 2\sqrt{2}}{2}$$

26. Solving the equation:
$$4x^3 + x = 9x^2$$
$$4x^3 - 9x^2 + x = 0$$
$$x(4x^2 - 9x + 1) = 0$$
$$x = 0, \frac{9 \pm \sqrt{81 - 16}}{8} = \frac{9 \pm \sqrt{65}}{8}$$

27. Solving the equation:
$$\frac{1}{10}x^2 - \frac{1}{2}x + \frac{2}{5} = 0$$
$$x^2 - 5x + 4 = 0$$
$$(x - 1)(x - 4) = 0$$
$$x = 1, 4$$

28. Solving the equation:
$$0.09a^2 + 0.02a = -0.04$$
$$0.09a^2 + 0.02a + 0.04 = 0$$
$$9a^2 + 2a + 4 = 0$$
$$a = \frac{-2 \pm \sqrt{(2)^2 - 4(9)(4)}}{2(9)} = \frac{-2 \pm \sqrt{4 - 144}}{18} = \frac{-2 \pm \sqrt{-140}}{18} = \frac{-2 \pm 2i\sqrt{35}}{18} = \frac{-1 \pm i\sqrt{35}}{9}$$

29. Solving the equation:
$$\sqrt{y + 4} = y + 4$$
$$\left(\sqrt{y+4}\right)^2 = (y+4)^2$$
$$y + 4 = y^2 + 8y + 16$$
$$0 = y^2 + 7y + 12$$
$$0 = (y + 4)(y + 3)$$
$$y = -4, -3$$
Both values check in the original equation.

30. Solving the equation:
$$\sqrt{x - 5} = 5 - \sqrt{x}$$
$$\left(\sqrt{x-5}\right)^2 = \left(5 - \sqrt{x}\right)^2$$
$$x - 5 = 25 - 10\sqrt{x} + x$$
$$-10\sqrt{x} = -30$$
$$\sqrt{x} = 3$$
$$x = 9$$
This value checks in the original equation.

31. Solving the equation:
$$x + 5\sqrt{x} - 24 = 0$$
$$\left(\sqrt{x} - 3\right)\left(\sqrt{x} + 8\right) = 0$$
$$\sqrt{x} = -8, 3$$
$$x = 64, 9$$

Only $x = 9$ checks in the original equation.

32. Solving the equation:
$$x^{2/3} - x^{1/3} = 30$$
$$x^{2/3} - x^{1/3} - 30 = 0$$
$$\left(x^{1/3} - 6\right)\left(x^{1/3} + 5\right) = 0$$
$$x^{1/3} = -5, 6$$
$$x = -125, 216$$

Both values check in the original equation.

33. Solving the inequality:
$$-5 \le \frac{1}{3}x + 7 \le 1$$
$$-12 \le \frac{1}{3}x \le -6$$
$$-36 \le x \le -18$$

Graphing the solution set:

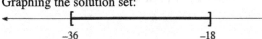

34. Solving the inequality:
$$|3x + 2| \ge 1$$
$$3x + 2 \le -1 \quad \text{or} \quad 3x + 2 \ge 1$$
$$3x \le -3 \qquad\qquad 3x \ge -1$$
$$x \le -1 \qquad\qquad x \ge -\frac{1}{3}$$

Graphing the solution set:

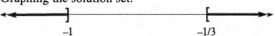

35. Factoring the inequality:
$$x^2 - 3x < 18$$
$$x^2 - 3x - 18 < 0$$
$$(x + 3)(x - 6) < 0$$

Forming the sign chart:

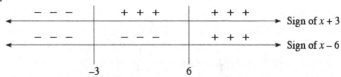

The solution set is $-3 < x < 6$. Graphing the solution set:

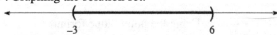

36. Forming the sign chart:

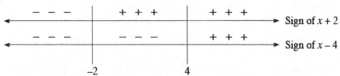

The solution set is $x < -2$ or $x \ge 4$. Graphing the solution set:

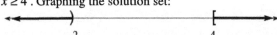

37. Multiply the first equation by 2:
$$14x - 6y = 86$$
$$-14x + 6y = -5$$

Adding yields $0 = 81$, which is false. There is no solution (lines are parallel).

38. Multiplying the first equation by 3 and the second equation by 2:
$$-6x + 12y = 24$$
$$6x - 12y = 16$$

Adding yields $0 = 40$, which is false. There is no solution (lines are parallel).

39. Graphing the line:

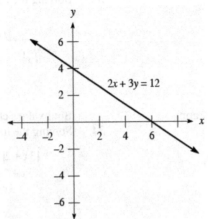

40. Completing the square: $y = -x^2 + 4x - 3 = -\left(x^2 - 4x + 4\right) + 4 - 3 = -\left(x - 2\right)^2 + 1$. Graphing the parabola:

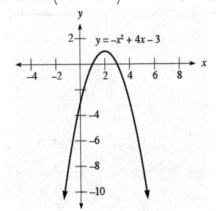

41. First find the slope: $m = \dfrac{\dfrac{1}{4} - \dfrac{13}{4}}{-\dfrac{3}{2} - \dfrac{1}{2}} = \dfrac{-3}{-2} = \dfrac{3}{2}$. Using the point-slope formula:

$$y - \frac{13}{4} = \frac{3}{2}\left(x - \frac{1}{2}\right)$$
$$y - \frac{13}{4} = \frac{3}{2}x - \frac{3}{4}$$
$$y = \frac{3}{2}x + \frac{5}{2}$$

42. Solving for y:
$$2x + 8y = 17$$
$$8y = -2x + 17$$
$$y = -\frac{1}{4}x + \frac{17}{8}$$

So the perpendicular slope is 4. Using the point-slope formula:
$$y - 2 = 4(x - 1)$$
$$y - 2 = 4x - 4$$
$$y = 4x - 2$$

43. Factoring completely: $x^2 - 6x + 9 - y^2 = (x - 3)^2 - y^2 = (x - 3 + y)(x - 3 - y)$

44. Factoring completely: $(x - 3)^2 + 5(x - 4) - 1 = x^2 - 6x + 9 + 5x - 20 - 1 = x^2 - x - 12 = (x + 3)(x - 4)$

45. Rationalizing the denominator: $\dfrac{6}{\sqrt[3]{4}} = \dfrac{6}{\sqrt[3]{4}} \cdot \dfrac{\sqrt[3]{2}}{\sqrt[3]{2}} = \dfrac{6\sqrt[3]{2}}{2} = 3\sqrt[3]{2}$

46. Rationalizing the denominator: $\dfrac{\sqrt{3}}{\sqrt{3}-\sqrt{5}} = \dfrac{\sqrt{3}}{\sqrt{3}-\sqrt{5}} \cdot \dfrac{\sqrt{3}+\sqrt{5}}{\sqrt{3}+\sqrt{5}} = \dfrac{3+\sqrt{15}}{3-5} = -\dfrac{3+\sqrt{15}}{2}$

47. The set is $\{1,4\}$.   **48.**   The set is $\{2,8\}$.

49. Let x represent the largest angle, $\dfrac{3}{10}x$ represent the smallest angle, and $\dfrac{3}{10}x+20$ represent the remaining angle.

The equation is:

$$x + \frac{3}{10}x + \frac{3}{10}x + 20 = 180$$
$$\frac{8}{5}x + 20 = 180$$
$$\frac{8}{5}x = 160$$
$$8x = 800$$
$$x = 100$$
$$\frac{3}{10}x = 30$$
$$\frac{3}{10}x + 20 = 50$$

The angles are $30°, 50°$, and $100°$.

50. Completing the table:

	Dollars Invested at 3%	Dollars Invested at 2%
Number of	x	$6,000 - x$
Interest on	$0.03(x)$	$0.02(6,000 - x)$

The equation is:

$$0.03(x) + 0.02(6,000 - x) = 145$$
$$0.03x + 120 - 0.02x = 145$$
$$0.01x + 120 = 145$$
$$0.01x = 25$$
$$x = 2,500$$
$$6,000 - x = 3,500$$

There is $2,500 invested at 3% and $3,500 invested at 2%.

51. The variation equation is $y = kx^2$. Substituting $y = -4$ and $x = -\dfrac{2}{3}$:

$$-4 = k\left(-\frac{2}{3}\right)^2$$
$$k = -4 \cdot \frac{9}{4} = -9$$

So the equation is $y = -9x^2$. Substituting $x = \dfrac{5}{9}$: $y = -9\left(\dfrac{5}{9}\right)^2 = -9 \cdot \dfrac{25}{81} = -\dfrac{25}{9}$

52. The variation equation is $w = \dfrac{k}{\sqrt{c}}$. Substituting $w = 8$ and $c = 4$:

$$8 = \dfrac{k}{\sqrt{4}}$$
$$8 = \dfrac{k}{2}$$
$$k = 16$$

So the equation is $w = \dfrac{16}{\sqrt{c}}$. Substituting $c = 16$: $w = \dfrac{16}{\sqrt{16}} = \dfrac{16}{4} = 4$

53. Finding the amount: $0.77(426{,}350) = 328{,}290$ people

54. Finding the amount: $0.09(426{,}350) = 38{,}372$ people

Chapter 7 Test

1. Solving the equation:

$$(2x - 3)^2 = 36$$
$$2x - 3 = \pm 6$$
$$2x - 3 = -6, 6$$
$$2x = -3, 9$$
$$x = -\dfrac{3}{2}, \dfrac{9}{2}$$

2. Solving the equation:

$$(4x + 1)^2 = -12$$
$$4x + 1 = \pm\sqrt{-12}$$
$$4x + 1 = \pm 2i\sqrt{3}$$
$$4x = -1 \pm 2i\sqrt{3}$$
$$x = \dfrac{-1 \pm 2i\sqrt{3}}{4}$$

3. Solving the equation:

$$y^2 + 8y + 16 = -25$$
$$(y + 4)^2 = -25$$
$$y + 4 = \pm 5i$$
$$y = -4 \pm 5i$$

4. Solving the equation:

$$(x + 4)(x + 6) = -3$$
$$x^2 + 10x + 24 = -3$$
$$x^2 + 10x + 27 = 0$$

$$x = \dfrac{-10 \pm \sqrt{(10)^2 - 4(1)(27)}}{2(1)} = \dfrac{-10 \pm \sqrt{100 - 108}}{2} = \dfrac{-10 \pm \sqrt{-8}}{2} = \dfrac{-10 \pm 2i\sqrt{2}}{2} = -5 \pm i\sqrt{2}$$

5. Solving the equation:

$$64t^3 - 27 = 0$$
$$(4t - 3)(16t^2 + 12t + 9) = 0$$

$$t = \dfrac{3}{4}, \dfrac{-12 \pm \sqrt{144 - 576}}{32} = \dfrac{-12 \pm \sqrt{-432}}{32} = \dfrac{-12 \pm 12i\sqrt{3}}{32} = \dfrac{-3 \pm 3i\sqrt{3}}{8}$$

6. Solving the equation:

$$\frac{1}{a}-\frac{1}{2}=\frac{1}{a-1}$$

$$2a(a-1)\left(\frac{1}{a}-\frac{1}{2}\right)=2a(a-1)\left(\frac{1}{a-1}\right)$$

$$2(a-1)-a(a-1)=2a$$

$$2a-2-a^2+a=2a$$

$$a^2-a+2=0$$

$$a=\frac{1\pm\sqrt{1-8}}{2}=\frac{1\pm\sqrt{-7}}{2}=\frac{1\pm i\sqrt{7}}{2}$$

7. Solving for r:

$$49(r-7)^2=A$$

$$(r-7)^2=\frac{A}{49}$$

$$r-7=\pm\frac{\sqrt{A}}{7}$$

$$r=7\pm\frac{\sqrt{A}}{7}$$

8. Solving by completing the square:

$$x^2-6x=-11$$

$$x^2-6x+9=-11+9$$

$$(x-3)^2=-2$$

$$x-3=\pm\sqrt{-2}$$

$$x-3=\pm i\sqrt{2}$$

$$x=3\pm i\sqrt{2}$$

9. The shorter side is $\frac{8}{2}=4$ m and the middle side is $4\sqrt{3}$ m.

10. Solving the equation:

$$32t-16t^2=7$$

$$-16t^2+32t-7=0$$

$$16t^2-32t+7=0$$

$$(4t-1)(4t-7)=0$$

$$t=\frac{1}{4},\frac{7}{4}$$

The object will be 7 feet above the ground after $\frac{1}{4}$ sec or $\frac{7}{4}$ sec.

11. Setting the revenue equal to the cost:

$$30x-0.2x^2=9x+100$$

$$-0.2x^2+21x-100=0$$

$$x^2-105x+500=0$$

$$(x-5)(x-100)=0$$

$$x=5,100$$

The company must sell 5 or 100 letter openers to break even.

12. First write the equation as $kx^2+16x+8=0$. Setting the discriminant equal to 0:

$$(16)^2-4(k)(8)=0$$

$$256-32k=0$$

$$32k=256$$

$$k=8$$

13. First write the equation as $5x^2-3x+7=0$. Finding the discriminant: $D=(-3)^2-4(5)(7)=9-140=-131$

Since the discriminant is negative, the equation has two non-real complex solutions.

14. Finding the equation:

$$(x+7)(2x-5)=0$$

$$2x^2+9x-35=0$$

15. Finding the equation:

$$(x+3)(x-3)(x-5)=0$$

$$(x^2-9)(x-5)=0$$

$$x^3-5x^2-9x+45=0$$

16. Solving the equation:
$$16x^4 - 39x^2 - 27 = 0$$
$$\left(x^2 - 3\right)\left(16x^2 + 9\right) = 0$$
$$x^2 = 3, -\frac{9}{16}$$
$$x = \pm\sqrt{3}, \pm\frac{3}{4}i$$

17. Solving the equation:
$$(2t+1)^2 - 6(2t+1) - t + 7 = 0$$
$$4t^2 + 4t + 1 - 12t - 6 - t + 7 = 0$$
$$4t^2 - 9t + 2 = 0$$
$$(4t-1)(t-2) = 0$$
$$t = \frac{1}{4}, 2$$

18. Solving the equation:
$$3t - 7\sqrt{t} + 2 = 0$$
$$\left(3\sqrt{t} - 1\right)\left(\sqrt{t} - 2\right) = 0$$
$$\sqrt{t} = \frac{1}{3}, 2$$
$$t = \frac{1}{9}, 4$$

Both values check in the original equation.

19. Solving for t:
$$16t^2 - 10t - h = 0$$
$$t = \frac{10 + \sqrt{100 - 4(16)(-h)}}{32} = \frac{10 + \sqrt{100 + 64h}}{32} = \frac{10 + 2\sqrt{25 + 16h}}{32} = \frac{5 + \sqrt{25 + 16h}}{16}$$

Note that only the positive answer was given here since t represents time, thus $t > 0$.

20. Completing the square: $y = x^2 - 2x + 1 = (x-1)^2$

The vertex is $(1,0)$. Graphing the parabola:

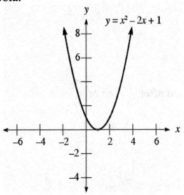

21. Completing the square: $y = -x^2 + 4x - 2 = -\left(x^2 - 4x + 4\right) + 4 - 2 = -(x-2)^2 + 2$

The vertex is $(2,2)$. Graphing the parabola:

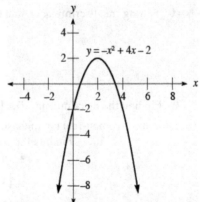

22. The vertex is (2,4), the x-intercepts are (0,0) and (4,0), and the parabola is pointed down, so the equation is: $y = -(x-2)^2 + 4$

23. Finding the profit and completing the square:
$$P = 30x - 0.2x^2 - 4x - 200$$
$$= -0.2x^2 + 26x - 200$$
$$= -0.2\left(x^2 - 130x + 4225\right) + 845 - 200$$
$$= -0.2(x-65)^2 + 645$$

The maximum weekly profit is $645, obtained by selling 65 items per week.

24. Factoring the inequality:
$$x^2 - 3x - 4 \le 0$$
$$(x-4)(x+1) \le 0$$

Forming a sign chart:

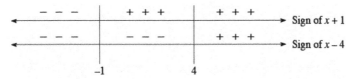

The solution set is $-1 \le x \le 4$. Graphing the solution set:

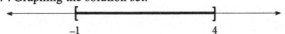

25. Factoring the inequality:
$$2x^2 + 3x > 2$$
$$2x^2 + 3x - 2 > 0$$
$$(2x-1)(x+2) > 0$$

Forming a sign chart:

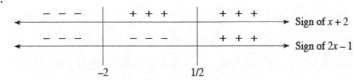

The solution set is $x < -2$ or $x > \dfrac{1}{2}$. Graphing the solution set:

26. **a.** The solution is $-2 < x < -1$ or $x > 1$.
    b. The solution is $x < -2$ or $-1 < x < 1$.
    c. The solution is $x = -2, -1, 1$.

Chapter 8
Exponential and Logarithmic Functions

8.1 Exponential Functions and Applications

1. Evaluating: $g(0) = \left(\dfrac{1}{2}\right)^0 = 1$

3. Evaluating: $g(-1) = \left(\dfrac{1}{2}\right)^{-1} = 2$

5. Evaluating: $f(-3) = 3^{-3} = \dfrac{1}{27}$

7. Evaluating: $f(2) + g(-2) = 3^2 + \left(\dfrac{1}{2}\right)^{-2} = 9 + 4 = 13$

9. Evaluating: $f(-1) + g(1) = 4^{-1} + \left(\dfrac{1}{3}\right)^1 = \dfrac{1}{4} + \dfrac{1}{3} = \dfrac{3}{12} + \dfrac{4}{12} = \dfrac{7}{12}$

11. Evaluating: $\dfrac{f(-2)}{g(1)} = \dfrac{4^{-2}}{\left(\dfrac{1}{3}\right)^1} = \dfrac{1}{16} \div \dfrac{1}{3} = \dfrac{3}{16}$

13. Evaluating: $\dfrac{f(3) - f(2)}{3 - 2} = \dfrac{4^3 - 4^2}{3 - 2} = \dfrac{64 - 16}{1} = 48$

15. Evaluating: $\dfrac{f(-1) - g(-2)}{-1 - (-2)} = \dfrac{4^{-1} - \left(\dfrac{1}{3}\right)^{-2}}{-1 + 2} = \dfrac{\dfrac{1}{4} - 9}{1} = \dfrac{1}{4} - \dfrac{36}{4} = -\dfrac{35}{4}$

17. Simplifying: $\dfrac{f(x) - f(2)}{x - 2} = \dfrac{3^x - 3^2}{x - 2} = \dfrac{3^x - 9}{x - 2}$

19. Simplifying: $\dfrac{f(x) - f(3)}{x - 3} = \dfrac{3^x - 3^3}{x - 3} = \dfrac{3^x - 27}{x - 3}$

21. Simplifying: $\dfrac{f(x+h) - f(x)}{h} = \dfrac{3^{x+h} - 3^x}{h} = \dfrac{3^x\left(3^h - 1\right)}{h}$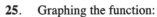

23. Graphing the function:

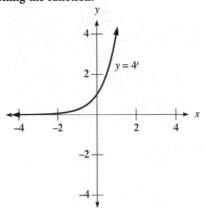

25. Graphing the function:

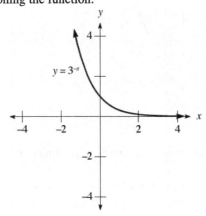

27. Graphing the function:

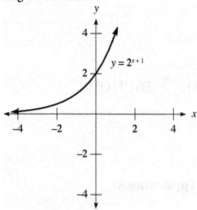

$y = 2^{x+1}$

29. Graphing the function:

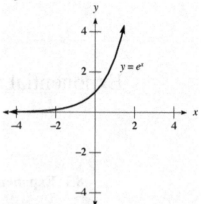

$y = e^x$

31. Graphing the function:

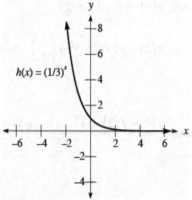

$h(x) = (1/3)^x$

33. Graphing the function:

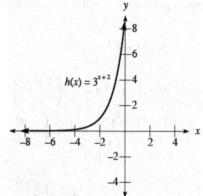

$h(x) = 3^{x+2}$

35. Graphing the functions:

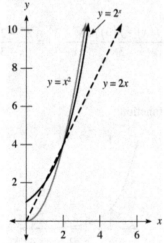

$y = 2^x$

$y = x^2$ $y = 2x$

37. Graphing the functions:

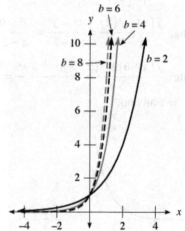

$b = 6$

$b = 4$

$b = 8$

$b = 2$

39. The equation is: $h(n) = 6\left(\dfrac{2}{3}\right)^n$. Substituting $n = 5$: $h(5) = 6\left(\dfrac{2}{3}\right)^5 \approx 0.79$ feet

41. From a graph, $Q(t) = 0.5$ when $t \approx 4.27$ days.

43. **a.** The equation is $A(t) = 1,200\left(1 + \dfrac{0.06}{4}\right)^{4t}$.

  b. Substitute $t = 8$: $A(8) = 1,200\left(1 + \dfrac{0.06}{4}\right)^{32} \approx \$1,932.39$

  c. Using a graphing calculator, the time is approximately 11.6 years.

  d. Substitute $t = 8$ into the compound interest formula: $A(8) = 1,200\,e^{0.06 \times 8} \approx \$1,939.29$

45. **a.** The function is given by: $A(t) = 5,400\left(1 + \dfrac{0.05}{4}\right)^{4t}$

  b. Substitute $t = 5$: $A(5) = 5,400\left(1 + \dfrac{0.05}{4}\right)^{20} \approx \$6,923.00$

  c. Substitute $t = 8$: $A(8) = 5,400\left(1 + \dfrac{0.05}{4}\right)^{32} \approx \$8,023$. It will take about 8 years.

  d. Using $A(t) = 5,400\,e^{0.05t}$: $A(5) = 5,400\,e^{0.05(5)} \approx \$6,933.74$

47. Finding the function values:
$$f(1) = 50 \cdot 4^1 = 200 \text{ bacteria}$$
$$f(2) = 50 \cdot 4^2 = 800 \text{ bacteria}$$
$$f(3) = 50 \cdot 4^3 = 3,200 \text{ bacteria}$$

49. **a.** Substitute $t = 3.5$: $V(5) = 450,000\,(1 - 0.30)^5 \approx \$129,138.48$

  b. The domain is $\{t \mid 0 \le t \le 6\}$.

  c. Sketching the graph:

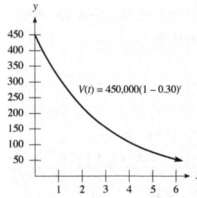

  d. The range is $\{V(t) \mid 52,942.05 \le V(t) \le 450,000\}$.

  e. From the graph, the crane will be worth \$85,000 after approximately 4.7 years, or 4 years 8 months.

51. Graphing the function:

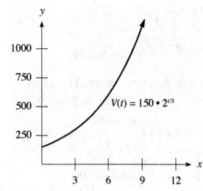

$V(t) = 150 \cdot 2^{t/3}$

53. **a.** Evaluating when $t = 25$: $C(25) = 0.10e^{0.0576(25)} \approx \$0.42$

b. Evaluating when $t = 40$: $C(40) = 0.10e^{0.0576(40)} \approx \$1.00$

c. Evaluating when $t = 50$: $C(50) = 0.10e^{0.0576(50)} \approx \$1.78$

d. Evaluating when $t = 90$: $C(90) = 0.10e^{0.0576(90)} \approx \$17.84$

55. Using the model: $B(3) = 0.798 \cdot 1.164^3 \approx 1,258,525$ bankruptcies
The predicted model is 58,474 less bankruptcies less than the actual amount.

57. **a.** Evaluating when $t = 5$: $A(5) = 5,000,000e^{-0.598(5)} \approx 231,437$ cells

b. Evaluating when $t = 10$: $A(10) = 5,000,000e^{-0.598(10)} \approx 12,644$ cells

c. Evaluating when $t = 20$: $A(10) = 5,000,000e^{-0.598(20)} \approx 32$ cells

59. The domain is $\{-2, 2\}$ and the range is $\{3, 6, 8\}$. This is not a function.

61. First find where the denominator is equal to 0:
$$x^2 + 2x - 35 = 0$$
$$(x + 7)(x - 5) = 0$$
$$x = -7, 5$$
The domain is $\{x \mid x \neq -7, 5\}$.

63. Evaluating the function: $f(0) = 2(0)^2 - 18 = 0 - 18 = -18$

65. Simplifying the function: $\dfrac{g(x+h) - g(x)}{h} = \dfrac{2(x+h) - 6 - (2x-6)}{h} = \dfrac{2x + 2h - 6 - 2x + 6}{h} = \dfrac{2h}{h} = 2$

67. First find the slope: $m = \dfrac{80.00 - 10.75}{2011 - 1981} = \dfrac{69.25}{30}$

Using the point-slope formula:
$$y - 80 = \frac{69.25}{30}(x - 2011)$$
$$y - 80 = 2.308x - 4,642.06$$
$$y = 2.308x - 4,562.06$$

69. **a.** $f(0) = 1$ **b.** $f(-1) = \dfrac{1}{3}$

c. $f(1) = 3$ **d.** $g(0) = 1$

e. $g(1) = \dfrac{1}{2}$ **f.** $g(-1) = 2$

g. $f[g(0)] = f(1) = 3$ **h.** $g[f(0)] = g(1) = \dfrac{1}{2}$

71. Solving for y:

$$x = 2y - 3$$
$$2y = x + 3$$
$$y = \frac{x+3}{2}$$

73. Solving for y:

$$x = y^2 - 2$$
$$y^2 = x + 2$$
$$y = \pm\sqrt{x+2}$$

75. Solving for y:

$$x = \frac{y-4}{y-2}$$
$$x(y-2) = y - 4$$
$$xy - 2x = y - 4$$
$$xy - y = 2x - 4$$
$$y(x-1) = 2x - 4$$
$$y = \frac{2x-4}{x-1}$$

77. Solving for y:

$$x = \sqrt{y-3}$$
$$x^2 = y - 3$$
$$y = x^2 + 3$$

8.2 Inverse Functions

1. Let $y = f(x)$. Switch x and y and solve for y:

$$3y - 1 = x$$
$$3y = x + 1$$
$$y = \frac{x+1}{3}$$

The inverse is $f^{-1}(x) = \frac{x+1}{3}$.

3. Let $y = f(x)$. Switch x and y and solve for y:

$$y^3 = x$$
$$y = \sqrt[3]{x}$$

The inverse is $f^{-1}(x) = \sqrt[3]{x}$.

5. Let $y = f(x)$. Switch x and y and solve for y:

$$\frac{y-3}{y-1} = x$$
$$y - 3 = xy - x$$
$$y - xy = 3 - x$$
$$y(1-x) = 3 - x$$
$$y = \frac{3-x}{1-x} = \frac{x-3}{x-1}$$

The inverse is $f^{-1}(x) = \frac{x-3}{x-1}$.

7. Let $y = f(x)$. Switch x and y and solve for y:

$$\frac{y-3}{4} = x$$
$$y - 3 = 4x$$
$$y = 4x + 3$$

The inverse is $f^{-1}(x) = 4x + 3$.

9. Let $y = f(x)$. Switch x and y and solve for y:

$$\frac{1}{2}y - 3 = x$$
$$y - 6 = 2x$$
$$y = 2x + 6$$

The inverse is $f^{-1}(x) = 2x + 6$.

11. Let $y = f(x)$. Switch x and y and solve for y:

$$\frac{2}{3}y - 3 = x$$
$$2y - 9 = 3x$$
$$2y = 3x + 9$$
$$y = \frac{3}{2}x + \frac{9}{2}$$

The inverse is $f^{-1}(x) = \frac{3}{2}x + \frac{9}{2}$.

13. Let $y = f(x)$. Switch x and y and solve for y:

$$y^3 - 4 = x$$
$$y^3 = x + 4$$
$$y = \sqrt[3]{x + 4}$$

The inverse is $f^{-1}(x) = \sqrt[3]{x + 4}$.

15. Let $y = f(x)$. Switch x and y and solve for y:

$$\frac{4y - 3}{2y + 1} = x$$
$$4y - 3 = 2xy + x$$
$$4y - 2xy = x + 3$$
$$y(4 - 2x) = x + 3$$
$$y = \frac{x + 3}{4 - 2x}$$

The inverse is $f^{-1}(x) = \frac{x + 3}{4 - 2x}$.

17. Let $y = f(x)$. Switch x and y and solve for y:

$$\frac{2y + 1}{3y + 1} = x$$
$$2y + 1 = 3xy + x$$
$$2y - 3xy = x - 1$$
$$y(2 - 3x) = x - 1$$
$$y = \frac{x - 1}{2 - 3x} = \frac{1 - x}{3x - 2}$$

The inverse is $f^{-1}(x) = \frac{1 - x}{3x - 2}$.

19. Let $y = f(x)$. Switch x and y and solve for y:

$$\sqrt[3]{3y - 2} = x$$
$$3y - 2 = x^3$$
$$3y = x^3 + 2$$
$$y = \frac{x^3 + 2}{3}$$

The inverse is $f^{-1}(x) = \frac{x^3 + 2}{3}$.

21. Finding the inverse:

$$2y - 1 = x$$
$$2y = x + 1$$
$$y = \frac{x + 1}{2}$$

The inverse is $y^{-1} = \frac{x + 1}{2}$. Graphing each curve:

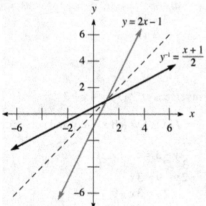

23. Finding the inverse:

$$y^2 - 3 = x$$
$$y^2 = x + 3$$
$$y = \pm\sqrt{x + 3}$$

The inverse is $y^{-1} = \pm\sqrt{x + 3}$. Graphing each curve:

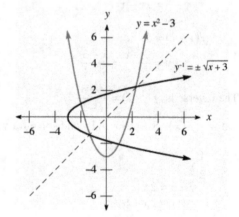

25. Finding the inverse:

$$y^2 - 2y - 3 = x$$
$$y^2 - 2y + 1 = x + 3 + 1$$
$$(y - 1)^2 = x + 4$$
$$y - 1 = \pm\sqrt{x + 4}$$
$$y = 1 \pm \sqrt{x + 4}$$

The inverse is $y^{-1} = 1 \pm \sqrt{x+4}$. Graphing each curve:

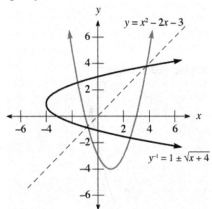

27. The inverse is $x = 3^y$. Graphing each curve:

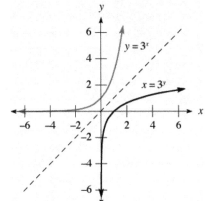

29. The inverse is $x = 4$. Graphing each curve:

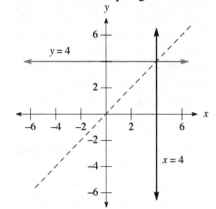

31. Finding the inverse:
$$\frac{1}{2}y^3 = x$$
$$y^3 = 2x$$
$$y = \sqrt[3]{2x}$$

The inverse is $y^{-1} = \sqrt[3]{2x}$. Graphing each curve:

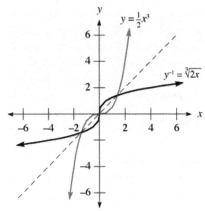

33. Finding the inverse:
$$\frac{1}{2}y + 2 = x$$
$$y + 4 = 2x$$
$$y = 2x - 4$$

The inverse is $y^{-1} = 2x - 4$. Graphing each curve:

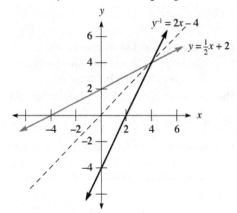

35. Finding the inverse:

$$\sqrt{y+2} = x$$
$$y+2 = x^2$$
$$y = x^2 - 2$$

The inverse is $y^{-1} = x^2 - 2, x \geq 0$. Graphing each curve:

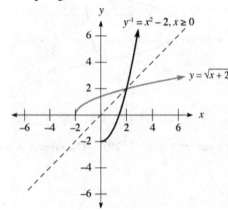

37. Finding the inverse:

$$\sqrt[3]{y} + 4 = x$$
$$\sqrt[3]{y} = x - 4$$
$$y = (x-4)^3$$

The inverse is $y^{-1} = (x-4)^3$. Graphing each curve:

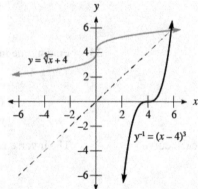

39. **a.** Yes, this function is one-to-one.
   b. No, this function is not one-to-one.
   c. Yes, this function is one-to-one.

41. The inverse is $\{(4,1),(5,2),(7,3)\}$. Yes, the inverse does represent a function.

43. The inverse is $\{(A,a),(B,b),(C,c)\}$. Yes, the inverse does represent a function.

45. **a.** Evaluating the function: $f(2) = 3(2) - 2 = 6 - 2 = 4$

   b. Evaluating the function: $f^{-1}(2) = \dfrac{2+2}{3} = \dfrac{4}{3}$

   c. Evaluating the function: $f\left(f^{-1}(2)\right) = f\left(\dfrac{4}{3}\right) = 3\left(\dfrac{4}{3}\right) - 2 = 4 - 2 = 2$

   d. Evaluating the function: $f^{-1}\left(f(2)\right) = f^{-1}(4) = \dfrac{4+2}{3} = \dfrac{6}{3} = 2$

47. Let $y = f(x)$. Switch x and y and solve for y:

$$\frac{1}{y} = x$$

$$y = \frac{1}{x}$$

The inverse is $f^{-1}(x) = \frac{1}{x}$.

49. **a.** $3x$ **b.** $3x + 2$

      c. $x - 2$ **d.** $\dfrac{x-2}{3}$

The inverse is $f^{-1}(x) = 7(x + 2) = 7x + 14$.

51. **a.** The value is –3.   **b.** The value is –6.
      c. The value is 2.   **d.** The value is 3.
      e. The value is –2.   **f.** The value is 3.
      g. They are inverses of each other.

53. **a.** Substituting: $C(-64) = \dfrac{5(-64 - 32)}{9} = \dfrac{-480}{9} \approx -53.3°C$

      b. Finding the inverse:

$$C = \frac{5(F - 32)}{9}$$

$$9C = 5(F - 32)$$

$$\frac{9}{5}C = F - 32$$

$$F(C) = \frac{9}{5}C + 32$$

      c. Substituting: $F(0) = \dfrac{9}{5}(0) + 32 = 32°F$

55. Setting the functions equal:

$$\frac{9}{5}C + 32 = C$$

$$9C + 160 = 5C$$

$$4C = -160$$

$$C = -40°$$

57. **a.** Substituting $t = 20$: $s(20) = 16(20) + 249.4 = \$569.40$ billion

      b. Finding the inverse:

$$s = 16t + 249.4$$

$$16t = s - 249.4$$

$$t(s) = \frac{s - 249.4}{16}$$

      c. Substitute $s = 507$: $t(507) = \dfrac{507 - 249.4}{16} \approx 16$.

The payments will reach $507 billion in the year 2006.

59. **a.** Substituting $m = 4520$: $f = \dfrac{22(4520)}{15} \approx 6{,}629$ feet per second

b. Finding the inverse:
$$f = \frac{22m}{15}$$
$$15f = 22m$$
$$m(f) = \frac{15f}{22}$$

c. Substituting $f = 2$: $m(2) = \dfrac{15(2)}{22} \approx 1.36$ mph

61. Solving the equation:
$$(2x-1)^2 = 25$$
$$2x - 1 = \pm\sqrt{25}$$
$$2x - 1 = -5, 5$$
$$2x = -4, 6$$
$$x = -2, 3$$

63. The number is 25, since $x^2 - 10x + 25 = (x-5)^2$.

65. Solving the equation:
$$x^2 - 10x + 8 = 0$$
$$x^2 - 10x + 25 = -8 + 25$$
$$(x-5)^2 = 17$$
$$x - 5 = \pm\sqrt{17}$$
$$x = 5 \pm \sqrt{17}$$

67. Solving the equation:
$$3x^2 - 6x + 6 = 0$$
$$x^2 - 2x + 2 = 0$$
$$x^2 - 2x + 1 = -2 + 1$$
$$(x-1)^2 = -1$$
$$x - 1 = \pm i$$
$$x = 1 \pm i$$

69. Finding the inverse:
$$3y + 5 = x$$
$$3y = x - 5$$
$$y = \frac{x-5}{3}$$

So $f^{-1}(x) = \dfrac{x-5}{3}$. Now verifying the inverse: $f\left[f^{-1}(x)\right] = f\left(\dfrac{x-5}{3}\right) = 3\left(\dfrac{x-5}{3}\right) + 5 = x - 5 + 5 = x$

71. Finding the inverse:
$$y^3 + 1 = x$$
$$y^3 = x - 1$$
$$y = \sqrt[3]{x-1}$$

So $f^{-1}(x) = \sqrt[3]{x-1}$. Now verifying the inverse: $f\left[f^{-1}(x)\right] = f\left(\sqrt[3]{x-1}\right) = \left(\sqrt[3]{x-1}\right)^3 + 1 = x - 1 + 1 = x$

73. Finding the inverse:
$$\frac{y-4}{y-2} = x$$
$$y - 4 = xy - 2x$$
$$y - xy = 4 - 2x$$
$$y(1-x) = 4 - 2x$$
$$y = \frac{4-2x}{1-x} = \frac{2x-4}{x-1}$$

So $f^{-1}(x) = \dfrac{2x-4}{x-1}$. Now verifying the inverse:

$$f\left[f^{-1}(x)\right] = f\left(\frac{2x-4}{x-1}\right) = \frac{\dfrac{2x-4}{x-1}-4}{\dfrac{2x-4}{x-1}-2} = \frac{2x-4-4(x-1)}{2x-4-2(x-1)} = \frac{2x-4-4x+4}{2x-4-2x+2} = \frac{-2x}{-2} = x$$

75. Finding the inverse:
$$\frac{2y-3}{y+2} = x$$
$$2y-3 = xy+2x$$
$$2y-xy = 2x+3$$
$$y(2-x) = 2x+3$$
$$y = \frac{2x+3}{2-x}$$

So $f^{-1}(x) = \dfrac{2x+3}{2-x}$. Now verifying the inverse:

$$f\left[f^{-1}(x)\right] = f\left(\frac{2x+3}{2-x}\right) = \frac{2\left(\dfrac{2x+3}{2-x}\right)-3}{\dfrac{2x+3}{2-x}+2} = \frac{2(2x+3)-3(2-x)}{2x+3+2(2-x)} = \frac{4x+6-6+3x}{2x+3+4-2x} = \frac{7x}{7} = x$$

77. **a.** From the graph: $f(0) = 1$ **b.** From the graph: $f(1) = 2$

   c. From the graph: $f(2) = 5$ **d.** From the graph: $f^{-1}(1) = 0$

   e. From the graph: $f^{-1}(2) = 1$ **f.** From the graph: $f^{-1}(5) = 2$

   g. From the graph: $f^{-1}(f(2)) = 2$ **h.** From the graph: $f\left(f^{-1}(5)\right) = 5$

79. The amount of EURO Clark started with is: $E(1000) = 0.73539(1000) = 735.39$ EURO

   Since he spent 694 EURO, he has left: $735.39 - 694 = 41.39$ EURO

   Converting back to dollars: $D(41.39) = \dfrac{41.39}{0.73539} = \$56.28$

81. Solving the equation:
$$f(3x+2) = 3$$
$$3x+2 = f^{-1}(3)$$
$$3x+2 = -6$$
$$3x = -8$$
$$x = -\frac{8}{3}$$

83. Finding the inverse:
$$\frac{ay+b}{cy+d} = x$$
$$ay+b = cxy+dx$$
$$ay-cxy = dx-b$$
$$y(a-cx) = dx-b$$
$$y = \frac{dx-b}{a-cx} = \frac{b-dx}{cx-a}$$

So $f^{-1}(x) = \dfrac{b-dx}{cx-a}$.

85. Verifying the inverse:

$$f\left[f^{-1}(x)\right] = f\left(\frac{ax+5}{3x-a}\right) = \frac{a\left(\dfrac{ax+5}{3x-a}\right)+5}{3\left(\dfrac{ax+5}{3x-a}\right)-a} = \frac{a(ax+5)+5(3x-a)}{3(ax+5)-a(3x-a)} = \frac{a^2x+5a+15x-5a}{3ax+15-3ax+a^2} = \frac{x(a^2+15)}{a^2+15} = x$$

87. Simplifying: $3^{-2} = \dfrac{1}{3^2} = \dfrac{1}{9}$ 89. Simplifying: $\left(\dfrac{1}{2}\right)^4 = \dfrac{1}{2^4} = \dfrac{1}{16}$

91. Solving the equation:
$$2 = 3x$$
$$x = \frac{2}{3}$$

93. Solving the equation:
$$4 = x^3$$
$$x = \sqrt[3]{4}$$

95. Completing the statement: $8 = 2^3$

97. Completing the statement: $10,000 = 10^4$

99. Completing the statement: $81 = 3^4$

101. Completing the statement: $6 = 6^1$

103. Completing the statement: $27 = \left(\frac{1}{3}\right)^{-3}$

105. Completing the statement: $\frac{1}{16} = 2^{-4}$

8.3 Logarithmic Functions and Applications

1. Writing in logarithmic form: $\log_2 16 = 4$

3. Writing in logarithmic form: $\log_5 125 = 3$

5. Writing in logarithmic form: $\log_{10} 0.01 = -2$

7. Writing in logarithmic form: $\log_2 \frac{1}{32} = -5$

9. Writing in logarithmic form: $\log_{1/2} 8 = -3$

11. Writing in logarithmic form: $\log_3 27 = 3$

13. Writing in exponential form: $10^2 = 100$

15. Writing in exponential form: $2^6 = 64$

17. Writing in exponential form: $8^0 = 1$

19. Writing in exponential form: $10^{-3} = 0.001$

21. Writing in exponential form: $6^2 = 36$

23. Writing in exponential form: $5^{-2} = \frac{1}{25}$

25. Solving the equation:
$$\log_3 x = 2$$
$$x = 3^2 = 9$$

27. Solving the equation:
$$\log_5 x = -3$$
$$x = 5^{-3} = \frac{1}{125}$$

29. Solving the equation:
$$\log_2 16 = x$$
$$2^x = 16$$
$$x = 4$$

31. Solving the equation:
$$\log_8 2 = x$$
$$8^x = 2$$
$$x = \frac{1}{3}$$

33. Solving the equation:
$$\log_x 4 = 2$$
$$x^2 = 4$$
$$x = 2$$

35. Solving the equation:
$$\log_x 5 = 3$$
$$x^3 = 5$$
$$x = \sqrt[3]{5}$$

37. Solving the equation:
$$\log_5 25 = x$$
$$5^x = 25$$
$$x = 2$$

39. Solving the equation:
$$\log_x 36 = 2$$
$$x^2 = 36$$
$$x = 6$$

41. Solving the equation:
$$\log_8 4 = x$$
$$8^x = 4$$
$$2^{3x} = 2^2$$
$$3x = 2$$
$$x = \frac{2}{3}$$

43. Solving the equation:
$$\log_9 \frac{1}{3} = x$$
$$9^x = \frac{1}{3}$$
$$3^{2x} = 3^{-1}$$
$$2x = -1$$
$$x = -\frac{1}{2}$$

45. Solving the equation:

$$\log_8 x = -2$$
$$x = 8^{-2} = \frac{1}{64}$$

47. Solving the equation:

$$\log_{16} 8 = x$$
$$16^x = 8$$
$$2^{4x} = 2^3$$
$$4x = 3$$
$$x = \frac{3}{4}$$

49. Sketching the graph:

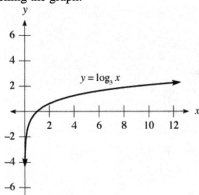

51. Sketching the graph:

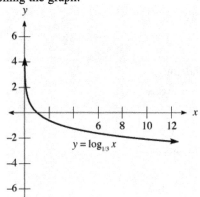

53. Sketching the graph:

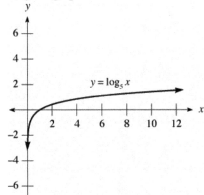

55. Sketching the graph:

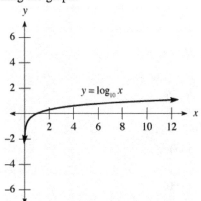

57. The function is $f(x) = 3^x$.

59. The function is $f(x) = \log_{1/3} x$.

61. Simplifying the logarithm:

$$x = \log_2 16$$
$$2^x = 16$$
$$x = 4$$

63. Simplifying the logarithm:

$$x = \log_{25} 125$$
$$25^x = 125$$
$$5^{2x} = 5^3$$
$$2x = 3$$
$$x = \frac{3}{2}$$

65. Simplifying the logarithm:

$$x = \log_{10} 1000$$
$$10^x = 1000$$
$$x = 3$$

67. Simplifying the logarithm:

$$x = \log_3 3$$
$$3^x = 3$$
$$x = 1$$

69. Simplifying the logarithm:
$$x = \log_5 1$$
$$5^x = 1$$
$$x = 0$$

71. Simplifying the logarithm:
$$x = \log_{17} 1$$
$$17^x = 1$$
$$x = 0$$

73. Simplifying the logarithm:
$$x = \log_{16} 4$$
$$16^x = 4$$
$$4^{2x} = 4^1$$
$$2x = 1$$
$$x = \frac{1}{2}$$

75. Simplifying the logarithm:
$$x = \log_{100} 1000$$
$$100^x = 1000$$
$$10^{2x} = 10^3$$
$$2x = 3$$
$$x = \frac{3}{2}$$

77. First find $\log_2 8$:
$$x = \log_2 8$$
$$2^x = 8$$
$$x = 3$$
Now find $\log_3 3$:

$$x = \log_3 3$$
$$3^x = 3$$
$$x = 1$$

79. First find $\log_3 81$:
$$x = \log_3 81$$
$$3^x = 81$$
$$x = 4$$
Now find $\log_{1/2} 4$:
$$x = \log_{1/2} 4$$
$$\left(\frac{1}{2}\right)^x = 4$$
$$2^{-x} = 2^2$$
$$x = -2$$

81. First find $\log_6 6$:
$$x = \log_6 6$$
$$6^x = 6$$
$$x = 1$$
Now find $\log_3 1$:
$$x = \log_3 1$$
$$3^x = 1$$
$$x = 0$$

83. First find $\log_2 16$:
$$x = \log_2 16$$
$$2^x = 16$$
$$x = 4$$
Now find $\log_2 4$:
$$x = \log_2 4$$
$$2^x = 4$$
$$x = 2$$
Now find $\log_4 2$:
$$x = \log_4 2$$
$$4^x = 2$$
$$2^{2x} = 2$$
$$2x = 1$$
$$x = \frac{1}{2}$$

85. Completing the table:

Prefix	Multiplying Factor	$\log_{10}$ (Multiplying Factor)
Nano	0.000000001	–9
Micro	0.000001	–6
Deci	0.1	–1
Giga	1,000,000,000	9
Peta	1,000,000,000,000,000	15

87. Using the relationship $M = \log_{10} T$:

$$M = \log_{10} 100$$
$$10^M = 100$$
$$M = 2$$

89. It is 10^8 times as large.

91. Since $M \geq 5$, there are 800 + 120 + 18 + 1 = 939 earthquakes.

93. Note that 1 GB = (1,024)(1,024) MB = 1,048,576 MB.

   a. The number of novels is: $\dfrac{4(1,048,576)}{400} \approx 10,486$ novels

   b. The number of novels is: $\dfrac{512(1,024)}{400} \approx 1,311$ novels

   c. The number of novels is: $\dfrac{2(1,048,576)}{400} \approx 5,243$ novels

95. Simplifying: $8^{2/3} = \left(8^{1/3}\right)^2 = \left(\sqrt[3]{8}\right)^2 = 2^2 = 4$ **97.** Simplifying: $16^{3/4} = \left(16^{1/4}\right)^3 = \left(\sqrt[4]{16}\right)^3 = 2^3 = 8$

99. Simplifying: $(-27)^{2/3} = \left((-27)^{1/3}\right)^2 = \left(\sqrt[3]{-27}\right)^2 = (-3)^2 = 9$

101. Simplifying: $27^{-2/3} = \left(27^{1/3}\right)^{-2} = \left(\sqrt[3]{27}\right)^{-2} = 3^{-2} = \dfrac{1}{9}$

103. Solving the equation:

$$(x+2)(x) = 2^3$$
$$x^2 + 2x = 8$$
$$x^2 + 2x - 8 = 0$$
$$(x+4)(x-2) = 0$$
$$x = -4, 2$$

105. Solving the equation:

$$\frac{x-2}{x+1} = 9$$
$$x - 2 = 9(x+1)$$
$$x - 2 = 9x + 9$$
$$-8x = 11$$
$$x = -\frac{11}{8}$$

107. Writing in exponential form: $2^3 = (x+2)(x)$

109. Writing in exponential form: $3^4 = \dfrac{x-2}{x+1}$

Landmark Review

1. Evaluating: $g(0) = \left(\dfrac{1}{3}\right)^0 = 1$

2. Evaluating: $f(-1) = 3^{-1} = \dfrac{1}{3}$

3. Evaluating: $f(-2) + g(2) = 3^{-2} + \left(\dfrac{1}{3}\right)^2 = \dfrac{1}{9} + \dfrac{1}{9} = \dfrac{2}{9}$

4. Evaluating: $\dfrac{f(-3) - g(-2)}{-3-2} = \dfrac{3^{-3} - \left(\dfrac{1}{3}\right)^{-2}}{-5} = \dfrac{\dfrac{1}{27} - 9}{-5} = \dfrac{1-243}{-135} = \dfrac{242}{135}$

5. Graphing the function:

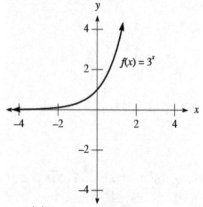

6. Graphing the function:

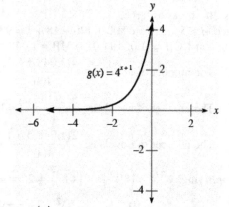

7. Let $y = f(x)$. Switch x and y and solve for y:

$$5y - 2 = x$$
$$5y = x + 2$$
$$y = \dfrac{x+2}{5}$$

The inverse is $f^{-1}(x) = \dfrac{x+2}{5}$.

8. Let $y = f(x)$. Switch x and y and solve for y:

$$2y^3 - 2 = x$$
$$2y^3 = x + 2$$
$$y^3 = \dfrac{x+2}{2}$$
$$y = \sqrt[3]{\dfrac{x+2}{2} \cdot \dfrac{4}{4}}$$
$$y = \dfrac{\sqrt[3]{4x+8}}{2}$$

The inverse is $f^{-1}(x) = \dfrac{\sqrt[3]{4x+8}}{2}$.

9. Finding the inverse:

$$2y + 3 = x$$
$$2y = x - 3$$
$$y = \frac{x-3}{2}$$

The inverse is $y^{-1} = \frac{x-3}{2}$. Graphing each curve:

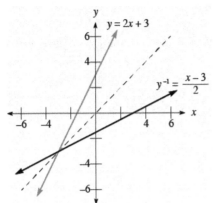

10. Finding the inverse:

$$2^y = x$$
$$y = \log_2 x$$

The inverse is $y^{-1} = \log_2 x$. Graphing each curve:

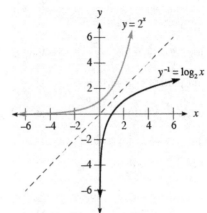

11. Writing in logarithmic form: $\log_2 16 = 4$

12. Writing in logarithmic form: $\log_4 16 = 2$

13. Writing in exponential form: $3^{-2} = \frac{1}{9}$

14. Writing in exponential form: $7^2 = 49$

15. Solving the equation:

$$\log_5 x = 2$$
$$x = 5^2$$
$$x = 25$$

16. Solving the equation:

$$\log_x \frac{1}{64} = -2$$
$$x^{-2} = \frac{1}{64}$$
$$x = 8$$

17. Solving the equation:

$$\log_x 3 = 5$$
$$x^5 = 3$$
$$x = 3^{1/5} = \sqrt[5]{3}$$

18. Solving the equation:

$$\log_{25} \frac{1}{5} = x$$
$$25^x = \frac{1}{5}$$
$$x = -\frac{1}{2}$$

8.4 Properties of Logarithms

1. Using properties of logarithms: $\log_3 4x = \log_3 4 + \log_3 x$

3. Using properties of logarithms: $\log_6 \frac{5}{x} = \log_6 5 - \log_6 x$

5. Using properties of logarithms: $\log_2 y^5 = 5\log_2 y$

7. Using properties of logarithms: $\log_9 \sqrt[3]{z} = \log_9 z^{1/3} = \frac{1}{3}\log_9 z$

9. Using properties of logarithms: $\log_6 x^2 y^4 = \log_6 x^2 + \log_6 y^4 = 2\log_6 x + 4\log_6 y$

11. Using properties of logarithms: $\log_5 \sqrt{x} \cdot y^4 = \log_5 x^{1/2} + \log_5 y^4 = \frac{1}{2}\log_5 x + 4\log_5 y$

13. Using properties of logarithms: $\log_b \frac{xy}{z} = \log_b xy - \log_b z = \log_b x + \log_b y - \log_b z$

15. Using properties of logarithms: $\log_{10} \dfrac{4}{xy} = \log_{10} 4 - \log_{10} xy = \log_{10} 4 - \log_{10} x - \log_{10} y$

17. Using properties of logarithms: $\log_{10} \dfrac{x^2 y}{\sqrt{z}} = \log_{10} x^2 + \log_{10} y - \log_{10} z^{1/2} = 2\log_{10} x + \log_{10} y - \dfrac{1}{2} \log_{10} z$

19. Using properties of logarithms: $\log_{10} \dfrac{x^3 \sqrt{y}}{z^4} = \log_{10} x^3 + \log_{10} y^{1/2} - \log_{10} z^4 = 3\log_{10} x + \dfrac{1}{2}\log_{10} y - 4\log_{10} z$

21. Using properties of logarithms:

$$\log_b \sqrt[3]{\dfrac{x^2 y}{z^4}} = \log_b \dfrac{x^{2/3} y^{1/3}}{z^{4/3}} = \log_b x^{2/3} + \log_b y^{1/3} - \log_b z^{4/3} = \dfrac{2}{3}\log_b x + \dfrac{1}{3}\log_b y - \dfrac{4}{3}\log_b z$$

23. Using properties of logarithms:

$$\log_3 \sqrt[3]{\dfrac{x^2 y}{z^6}} = \log_3 \dfrac{x^{2/3} y^{1/3}}{z^2} = \log_3 x^{2/3} + \log_3 y^{1/3} - \log_3 z^2 = \dfrac{2}{3}\log_3 x + \dfrac{1}{3}\log_3 y - 2\log_3 z$$

25. Using properties of logarithms:

$$\log_a \dfrac{4x^5}{9a^2} = \log_a 4x^5 - \log_a 9a^2$$

$$= \log_a 2^2 + \log_a x^5 - \log_a 3^2 - \log_a a^2$$

$$= 2\log_a 2 + 5\log_a x - 2\log_a 3 - 2$$

27. Using properties of logarithms:

$$\log_b \dfrac{9x^3}{64b^2} = \log_b 9x^3 - \log_b 64b^2$$

$$= \log_b 3^2 + \log_b x^3 - \log_b 2^6 - \log_b b^2$$

$$= 2\log_b 3 + 3\log_b x - 6\log_b 2 - 2$$

29. Writing as a single logarithm: $\log_b x + \log_b z = \log_b xz$

31. Writing as a single logarithm: $2\log_3 x - 3\log_3 y = \log_3 x^2 - \log_3 y^3 = \log_3 \dfrac{x^2}{y^3}$

33. Writing as a single logarithm: $\dfrac{1}{2}\log_{10} x + \dfrac{1}{3}\log_{10} y = \log_{10} x^{1/2} + \log_{10} y^{1/3} = \log_{10}\left(\sqrt{x}\,\sqrt[3]{y}\right)$

35. Writing as a single logarithm: $3\log_2 x + \dfrac{1}{2}\log_2 y - \log_2 z = \log_2 x^3 + \log_2 y^{1/2} - \log_2 z = \log_2\left(\dfrac{x^3 \sqrt{y}}{z}\right)$

37. Writing as a single logarithm: $\dfrac{1}{2}\log_2 x - 3\log_2 y - 4\log_2 z = \log_2 x^{1/2} - \log_2 y^3 - \log_2 z^4 = \log_2\left(\dfrac{\sqrt{x}}{y^3 z^4}\right)$

39. Writing as a single logarithm:

$$\dfrac{3}{2}\log_{10} x - \dfrac{3}{4}\log_{10} y - \dfrac{4}{5}\log_{10} z = \log_{10} x^{3/2} - \log_{10} y^{3/4} - \log_{10} z^{4/5} = \log_{10}\left(\dfrac{x^{3/2}}{y^{3/4} z^{4/5}}\right)$$

41. Writing as a single logarithm:

$$\dfrac{1}{2}\log_5 x + \dfrac{2}{3}\log_5 y - 4\log_5 z = \log_5 x^{1/2} + \log_5 y^{2/3} - \log_5 z^4 = \log_5\left(\dfrac{\sqrt{x}\cdot \sqrt[3]{y^2}}{z^4}\right)$$

43. Writing as a single logarithm:

$$\log_3\left(x^2 - 16\right) - 2\log_3(x+4) = \log_3\left(x^2 - 16\right) - \log_3(x+4)^2 = \log_3 \dfrac{(x+4)(x-4)}{(x+4)^2} = \log_3\left(\dfrac{x-4}{x+4}\right)$$

45. Solving the equation:

$$\log_2 x + \log_2 3 = 1$$
$$\log_2 3x = 1$$
$$3x = 2^1$$
$$3x = 2$$
$$x = \frac{2}{3}$$

47. Solving the equation:

$$\log_3 x - \log_3 2 = 2$$
$$\log_3 \frac{x}{2} = 2$$
$$\frac{x}{2} = 3^2$$
$$\frac{x}{2} = 9$$
$$x = 18$$

49. Solving the equation:

$$\log_3 x + \log_3 (x-2) = 1$$
$$\log_3 (x^2 - 2x) = 1$$
$$x^2 - 2x = 3^1$$
$$x^2 - 2x - 3 = 0$$
$$(x-3)(x+1) = 0$$
$$x = 3, -1$$

The solution is 3 (–1 does not check).

51. Solving the equation:

$$\log_3 (x+3) - \log_3 (x-1) = 1$$
$$\log_3 \frac{x+3}{x-1} = 1$$
$$\frac{x+3}{x-1} = 3^1$$
$$x+3 = 3x-3$$
$$-2x = -6$$
$$x = 3$$

53. Solving the equation:

$$\log_2 x + \log_2 (x-2) = 3$$
$$\log_2 (x^2 - 2x) = 3$$
$$x^2 - 2x = 2^3$$
$$x^2 - 2x - 8 = 0$$
$$(x-4)(x+2) = 0$$
$$x = 4, -2$$

The solution is 4 (–2 does not check).

55. Solving the equation:

$$\log_8 x + \log_8 (x-3) = \frac{2}{3}$$
$$\log_8 (x^2 - 3x) = \frac{2}{3}$$
$$x^2 - 3x = 8^{2/3}$$
$$x^2 - 3x - 4 = 0$$
$$(x-4)(x+1) = 0$$
$$x = 4, -1$$

The solution is 4 (–1 does not check).

57. Solving the equation:

$$\log_3 (x+2) - \log_3 x = 1$$
$$\log_3 \frac{x+2}{x} = 1$$
$$\frac{x+2}{x} = 3^1$$
$$x+2 = 3x$$
$$2x = 2$$
$$x = 1$$

59. Solving the equation:

$$\log_2 (x+1) + \log_2 (x+2) = 1$$
$$\log_2 (x^2 + 3x + 2) = 1$$
$$x^2 + 3x + 2 = 2^1$$
$$x^2 + 3x = 0$$
$$x(x+3) = 0$$
$$x = 0, -3$$

The solution is 0 (–3 does not check).

61. Solving the equation:
$$\log_9 \sqrt{x} + \log_9 \sqrt{2x+3} = \frac{1}{2}$$
$$\log_9 \sqrt{2x^2 + 3x} = \frac{1}{2}$$
$$\sqrt{2x^2 + 3x} = 9^{1/2}$$
$$2x^2 + 3x = 9$$
$$2x^2 + 3x - 9 = 0$$
$$(2x - 3)(x + 3) = 0$$
$$x = \frac{3}{2}, -3$$

The solution is $\frac{3}{2}$ (−3 does not check).

63. Solving the equation:
$$4\log_3 x - \log_3 x^2 = 6$$
$$4\log_3 x - 2\log_3 x = 6$$
$$2\log_3 x = 6$$
$$\log_3 x = 3$$
$$x = 3^3$$
$$x = 27$$

65. Solving the equation:
$$\log_5 \sqrt{x} + \log_5 \sqrt{6x+5} = 1$$
$$\log_5 \sqrt{6x^2 + 5x} = 1$$
$$\frac{1}{2}\log_5 \left(6x^2 + 5x\right) = 1$$
$$\log_5 \left(6x^2 + 5x\right) = 2$$
$$6x^2 + 5x = 5^2$$
$$6x^2 + 5x - 25 = 0$$
$$(3x - 5)(2x + 5) = 0$$
$$x = \frac{5}{3}, -\frac{5}{2}$$

The solution is $\frac{5}{3}$ ($-\frac{5}{2}$ does not check).

67. Rewriting the formula:
$$D = 10\log_{10}\left(\frac{I}{I_0}\right)$$
$$D = 10\left(\log_{10} I - \log_{10} I_0\right)$$

69.
a. Finding the value: $\log_{10} 40 = \log_{10}(8 \cdot 5) = \log_{10} 8 + \log_{10} 5 = 0.903 + 0.699 = 1.602$

b. Finding the value: $\log_{10} 320 = \log_{10}\left(8^2 \cdot 5\right) = \log_{10} 8^2 + \log_{10} 5 = 2\log_{10} 8 + \log_{10} 5 = 2(0.903) + 0.699 = 2.505$

c. Finding the value:
$$\log_{10} 1600 = \log_{10}\left(8^2 \cdot 5^2\right) = \log_{10} 8^2 + \log_{10} 5^2 = 2\log_{10} 8 + 2\log_{10} 5 = 2(0.903) + 2(0.699) = 3.204$$

71. Rewriting the equation: $\text{pH} = 6.1 + \log_{10}\left(\frac{x}{y}\right) = 6.1 + \log_{10} x - \log_{10} y$

73. Solving for M: $M = 0.21\log_{10}\frac{1}{10^{-12}} = 0.21\log_{10} 10^{12} = 0.21(12) = 2.52$

75. Simplifying: $5^0 = 1$

77. Simplifying: $\log_3 3 = \log_3 3^1 = 1$

79. Simplifying: $\log_b b^4 = 4$

81. Simplifying: $4^{\log_4 x} = x$

83. Using a calculator: $10^{-5.6} \approx 2.5 \times 10^{-6}$

85. Using a calculator: $\dfrac{2.00 \times 10^8}{3.96 \times 10^6} \approx 51$

8.5 Common and Natural Logarithms with Applications

1. Evaluating the logarithm: $\log 378 \approx 2.5775$

3. Evaluating the logarithm: $\log 37.8 \approx 1.5775$

5. Evaluating the logarithm: $\log 3,780 \approx 3.5775$

7. Evaluating the logarithm: $\log 0.0378 \approx -1.4225$

9. Evaluating the logarithm: $\log 37,800 \approx 4.5775$

11. Evaluating the logarithm: $\log 600 \approx 2.7782$

13. Evaluating the logarithm: $\log 2,010 \approx 3.3032$

15. Evaluating the logarithm: $\log 0.00971 \approx -2.0128$

17. Evaluating the logarithm: $\log 0.0314 \approx -1.5031$

19. Evaluating the logarithm: $\log 0.399 \approx -0.3990$

21. Solving for x:
$$\log x = 2.8802$$
$$x = 10^{2.8802} \approx 759$$

23. Solving for x:
$$\log x = -2.1198$$
$$x = 10^{-2.1198} \approx 0.00759$$

25. Solving for x:
$$\log x = 3.1553$$
$$x = 10^{3.1553} \approx 1,430$$

27. Solving for x:
$$\log x = -5.3497$$
$$x = 10^{-5.3497} \approx 0.00000447$$

29. Solving for x:
$$\log x = -7.0372$$
$$x = 10^{-7.0372} \approx 0.0000000918$$

31. Solving for x:
$$\log x = 10$$
$$x = 10^{10}$$

33. Solving for x:
$$\log x = -10$$
$$x = 10^{-10}$$

35. Solving for x:
$$\log x = 20$$
$$x = 10^{20}$$

37. Solving for x:
$$\log x = -2$$
$$x = 10^{-2} = \frac{1}{100}$$

39. Solving for x:
$$\log x = \log_2 8$$
$$\log x = 3$$
$$x = 10^3 = 1,000$$

41. Solving for x:
$$\ln x = 1$$
$$x = e^{-1} = \frac{1}{e}$$

43. Solving for x:
$$\log x = 2\log 5$$
$$\log x = \log 5^2$$
$$x = 25$$

45. Solving for x:
$$\ln x = -3\ln 2$$
$$\ln x = \ln 2^{-3}$$
$$x = \frac{1}{8}$$

47. Solving for x:
$$\ln x = 4\ln 3$$
$$\ln x = \ln 3^4$$
$$x = 81$$

49. Simplifying the logarithm: $\ln e = \ln e^1 = 1$

51. Simplifying the logarithm: $\ln e^5 = 5$

53. Simplifying the logarithm: $\ln e^x = x$

55. Simplifying the logarithm: $\log 10,000 = \log 10^4 = 4$

57. Simplifying the logarithm: $\ln \dfrac{1}{e^3} = \log e^{-3} = -3$

59. Simplifying the logarithm: $\log \sqrt{1000} = \log 10^{3/2} = \dfrac{3}{2}$

61. Using properties of logarithms: $\ln 10e^{3t} = \ln 10 + \ln e^{3t} = 3t + \ln 10$

63. Using properties of logarithms: $\ln Ae^{-2t} = \ln A + \ln e^{-2t} = -2t + \ln A$

65. Using properties of logarithms: $\log\left[100(1.01)^{3t}\right] = \log 10^2 + \log 1.01^{3t} = 2 + 3t\log 1.01$

67. Using properties of logarithms: $\ln\left(Pe^{rt}\right) = \ln P + \ln e^{rt} = \ln P + rt$

69. Using properties of logarithms: $-\log\left(4.2 \times 10^{-3}\right) = -\log 4.2 - \log 10^{-3} = 3 - \log 4.2$

71. Using properties of logarithms: $-\log\left(3.4 \times 10^4\right) = -\log 3.4 - \log 10^4 = -4 - \log 3.4$

73. Evaluating the logarithm: $\ln 15 = \ln(3 \cdot 5) = \ln 3 + \ln 5 = 1.0986 + 1.6094 = 2.7080$

75. Evaluating the logarithm: $\ln\dfrac{1}{3} = \ln 3^{-1} = -\ln 3 = -1.0986$

77. Evaluating the logarithm: $\ln 9 = \ln 3^2 = 2\ln 3 = 2(1.0986) = 2.1972$

79. Evaluating the logarithm: $\ln 16 = \ln 2^4 = 4\ln 2 = 4(0.6931) = 2.7724$

81. For the 1906 earthquake:
$$\log T = 8.3$$
$$T = 10^{8.3} = 1.995\times10^8$$
For the atomic bomb test:
$$\log T = 5.0$$
$$T = 10^{5.0} = 1\times10^5$$

Dividing the two values: $\dfrac{1.995\times10^8}{1\times10^5} \approx 2000$. San Francisco earthquake was approximately 2,000 times greater.

83. Completing the table:

Date	Location	Magnitude (M)	Energy Level (T)
5/22/1960	Chile	9.5	3.16×10^9
3/28/1964	Alaska	9.2	1.58×10^9
12/26/2004	Indonesia	9.1	1.26×10^9
3/11/2001	Japan	9.0	1.00×10^9

85. Completing the table:

x	$(1+x)^{1/x}$
1	2
0.5	2.25
0.1	2.5937
0.01	2.7048
0.001	2.7169
0.0001	2.7181
0.00001	2.7183

87. It appears to approach e.

89. Substituting $s = 15$:
$$5\ln x = 15$$
$$\ln x = 3$$
$$x = e^3 \approx 20$$
Approximately 15% of students enrolled are in the age range in the year 2009.

91. Computing the pH: $\text{pH} = -\log\left(6.50\times10^{-4}\right) \approx 3.19$

93. Finding the concentration:
$$4.75 = -\log\left[H^+\right]$$
$$-4.75 = \log\left[H^+\right]$$
$$\left[H^+\right] = 10^{-4.75} \approx 1.78\times10^{-5}$$

95. Finding the concentration:
$$5.5 = \log T$$
$$T = 10^{5.5} \approx 3.16\times10^5$$

97. Finding the magnitude:
$$8.3 = \log T$$
$$T = 10^{8.3} \approx 2.00\times10^8$$

99. Completing the table:

Location	Date	Magnitude (M)	Shockwave (T)
Moresby Island	January 23	4.0	1.00×10^4
Vancouver Island	April 30	5.3	1.99×10^5
Quebec City	June 29	3.2	1.58×10^3
Mould Bay	November 13	5.2	1.58×10^5
St. Lawrence	December 14	3.7	5.01×10^3

101. Finding the rate of depreciation:

$$\log(1-r) = \frac{1}{5}\log\frac{4500}{9000}$$
$$\log(1-r) \approx -0.0602$$
$$1-r \approx 10^{-0.0602}$$
$$r = 1 - 10^{-0.0602}$$
$$r \approx 0.129 = 12.9\%$$

103. Finding the rate of depreciation:

$$\log(1-r) = \frac{1}{5}\log\frac{5750}{7550}$$
$$\log(1-r) \approx -0.0237$$
$$1-r \approx 10^{-0.0237}$$
$$r = 1 - 10^{-0.0237}$$
$$r \approx 0.053 = 5.3\%$$

105. Solving the equation:

$$5(2x+1) = 12$$
$$10x + 5 = 12$$
$$10x = 7$$
$$x = \frac{7}{10}$$

107. Solving the equation:

$$3^x = \frac{1}{27}$$
$$3^x = 3^{-3}$$
$$x = -3$$

109. Using a calculator: $\dfrac{100,000}{32,000} = 3.1250$

111. Using a calculator: $\dfrac{1}{2}\left(\dfrac{-0.6931}{1.4289} + 3\right) \approx 1.2575$

113. Rewriting the logarithm: $\log 1.05^t = t \log 1.05$

115. Rewriting the logarithm: $\log 1.045^{2t} = 2t \log 1.045$

117. Simplifying: $\ln e^{0.05t} = 0.05t$

119. Simplifying: $\ln e^{-0.0042t} = -0.0042t$

121. Using a calculator: $\dfrac{\ln 10}{0.0015} \approx 1,535.06$

123. Using a calculator: $\dfrac{\ln 2}{\ln 1.043} \approx 16.46$

8.6 Exponential Equations, Change of Base, and Applications

1. Solving the equation:

$$3^x = 5$$
$$\ln 3^x = \ln 5$$
$$x \ln 3 = \ln 5$$
$$x = \frac{\ln 5}{\ln 3} \approx 1.4650$$

3. Solving the equation:

$$5^x = 3$$
$$\ln 5^x = \ln 3$$
$$x \ln 5 = \ln 3$$
$$x = \frac{\ln 3}{\ln 5} \approx 0.6826$$

5. Solving the equation:

$$5^{-x} = 12$$
$$\ln 5^{-x} = \ln 12$$
$$-x \ln 5 = \ln 12$$
$$x = -\frac{\ln 12}{\ln 5} \approx -1.5440$$

7. Solving the equation:

$$12^{-x} = 5$$
$$\ln 12^{-x} = \ln 5$$
$$-x \ln 12 = \ln 5$$
$$x = -\frac{\ln 5}{\ln 12} \approx -0.6477$$

9. Solving the equation:

$$8^{x+1} = 4$$
$$2^{3x+3} = 2^2$$
$$3x + 3 = 2$$
$$3x = -1$$
$$x = -\frac{1}{3}$$

11. Solving the equation:

$$4^{x-1} = 4$$
$$4^{x-1} = 4^1$$
$$x - 1 = 1$$
$$x = 2$$

13. Solving the equation:

$$3^{2x+1} = 2$$
$$\ln 3^{2x+1} = \ln 2$$
$$(2x+1)\ln 3 = \ln 2$$
$$2x + 1 = \frac{\ln 2}{\ln 3}$$
$$2x = \frac{\ln 2}{\ln 3} - 1$$
$$x = \frac{1}{2}\left(\frac{\ln 2}{\ln 3} - 1\right) \approx -0.1845$$

15. Solving the equation:

$$3^{1-2x} = 2$$
$$\ln 3^{1-2x} = \ln 2$$
$$(1-2x)\ln 3 = \ln 2$$
$$1 - 2x = \frac{\ln 2}{\ln 3}$$
$$-2x = \frac{\ln 2}{\ln 3} - 1$$
$$x = \frac{1}{2}\left(1 - \frac{\ln 2}{\ln 3}\right) \approx 0.1845$$

17. Solving the equation:

$$15^{3x-4} = 10$$
$$\ln 15^{3x-4} = \ln 10$$
$$(3x-4)\ln 15 = \ln 10$$
$$3x - 4 = \frac{\ln 10}{\ln 15}$$
$$3x = \frac{\ln 10}{\ln 15} + 4$$
$$x = \frac{1}{3}\left(\frac{\ln 10}{\ln 15} + 4\right) \approx 1.6168$$

19. Solving the equation:

$$6^{5-2x} = 4$$
$$\ln 6^{5-2x} = \ln 4$$
$$(5-2x)\ln 6 = \ln 4$$
$$5 - 2x = \frac{\ln 4}{\ln 6}$$
$$-2x = \frac{\ln 4}{\ln 6} - 5$$
$$x = \frac{1}{2}\left(5 - \frac{\ln 4}{\ln 6}\right) \approx 2.1131$$

21. Solving the equation:

$$3^{-4x} = 81$$
$$3^{-4x} = 3^4$$
$$-4x = 4$$
$$x = -1$$

23. Solving the equation:

$$5^{3x-2} = 15$$
$$\ln 5^{3x-2} = \ln 15$$
$$(3x-2)\ln 5 = \ln 15$$
$$3x - 2 = \frac{\ln 15}{\ln 5}$$
$$3x = \frac{\ln 15}{\ln 5} + 2$$
$$x = \frac{1}{3}\left(\frac{\ln 15}{\ln 5} + 2\right) \approx 1.2275$$

25. Solving the equation:

$$64^x = 16^{x-3}$$
$$4^{3x} = 4^{2(x-3)}$$
$$3x = 2x - 6$$
$$x = -6$$

27. Solving the equation:

$$8^a = 16^{2a+5}$$
$$2^{3a} = 2^{4(2a+5)}$$
$$3a = 8a + 20$$
$$-5a = 20$$
$$a = -4$$

29. Solving the equation:
$$16^{x+1} = 8^{3x-2}$$
$$2^{4(x+1)} = 2^{3(3x-2)}$$
$$4x + 4 = 9x - 6$$
$$-5x = -10$$
$$x = 2$$

31. Solving the equation:
$$27^{3b-5} = 81^{2b-3}$$
$$3^{3(3b-5)} = 3^{4(2b-3)}$$
$$9b - 15 = 8b - 12$$
$$b = 3$$

33. Solving the equation:
$$100e^{3t} = 250$$
$$e^{3t} = \frac{5}{2}$$
$$3t = \ln\frac{5}{2}$$
$$t = \frac{1}{3}\ln\frac{5}{2} \approx 0.3054$$

35. Solving the equation:
$$1200\left(1 + \frac{0.072}{4}\right)^{4t} = 25000$$
$$\left(1 + \frac{0.072}{4}\right)^{4t} = \frac{125}{6}$$
$$\ln\left(1 + \frac{0.072}{4}\right)^{4t} = \ln\frac{125}{6}$$
$$4t\ln\left(1 + \frac{0.072}{4}\right) = \ln\frac{125}{6}$$
$$t = \frac{\ln\dfrac{125}{6}}{4\ln\left(1 + \dfrac{0.072}{4}\right)} \approx 42.5528$$

37. Solving the equation:
$$50e^{-0.0742t} = 32$$
$$e^{-0.0742t} = \frac{16}{25}$$
$$-0.0742t = \ln\frac{16}{25}$$
$$t = \frac{\ln\dfrac{16}{25}}{-0.0742} \approx 6.0147$$

39. Evaluating the logarithm: $\log_8 16 = \dfrac{\log 16}{\log 8} = \dfrac{\log 2^4}{\log 2^3} = \dfrac{4}{3}$

41. Evaluating the logarithm: $\log_{16} 8 = \dfrac{\log 8}{\log 16} = \dfrac{\log 2^3}{\log 2^4} = \dfrac{3}{4}$

43. Evaluating the logarithm: $\log_7 15 = \dfrac{\log 15}{\log 7} \approx 1.3917$

45. Evaluating the logarithm: $\log_{15} 7 = \dfrac{\log 7}{\log 15} \approx 0.7186$

47. Evaluating the logarithm: $\log_8 240 = \dfrac{\log 240}{\log 8} \approx 2.6356$

49. Evaluating the logarithm: $\log_4 321 = \dfrac{\log 321}{\log 4} \approx 4.1632$

51. Evaluating the logarithm: $\ln 345 \approx 5.8435$

53. Evaluating the logarithm: $\ln 0.345 \approx -1.0642$

55. Evaluating the logarithm: $\ln 10 \approx 2.3026$

57. Evaluating the logarithm: $\ln 45,000 \approx 10.7144$

59. Using the compound interest formula:

$$500\left(1+\frac{0.06}{2}\right)^{2t}=1000$$

$$\left(1+\frac{0.06}{2}\right)^{2t}=2$$

$$\ln\left(1+\frac{0.06}{2}\right)^{2t}=\ln 2$$

$$2t\ln\left(1+\frac{0.06}{2}\right)=\ln 2$$

$$t=\frac{\ln 2}{2\ln\left(1+\frac{0.06}{2}\right)}\approx 11.72$$

It will take 11.72 years.

61. Using the compound interest formula:

$$1000\left(1+\frac{0.12}{6}\right)^{6t}=3000$$

$$\left(1+\frac{0.12}{6}\right)^{6t}=3$$

$$\ln\left(1+\frac{0.12}{6}\right)^{6t}=\ln 3$$

$$6t\ln\left(1+\frac{0.12}{6}\right)=\ln 3$$

$$t=\frac{\ln 3}{6\ln\left(1+\frac{0.12}{6}\right)}\approx 9.25$$

It will take 9.25 years.

63. Using the compound interest formula:

$$P\left(1+\frac{0.08}{4}\right)^{4t}=2P$$

$$\left(1+\frac{0.08}{4}\right)^{4t}=2$$

$$\ln\left(1+\frac{0.08}{4}\right)^{4t}=\ln 2$$

$$4t\ln\left(1+\frac{0.08}{4}\right)=\ln 2$$

$$t=\frac{\ln 2}{4\ln\left(1+\frac{0.08}{4}\right)}\approx 8.75$$

It will take 8.75 years.

65. Using the compound interest formula:

$$25\left(1+\frac{0.06}{2}\right)^{2t}=75$$

$$\left(1+\frac{0.06}{2}\right)^{2t}=3$$

$$\ln\left(1+\frac{0.06}{2}\right)^{2t}=\ln 3$$

$$2t\ln\left(1+\frac{0.06}{2}\right)=\ln 3$$

$$t=\frac{\ln 3}{2\ln\left(1+\frac{0.06}{2}\right)}\approx 18.58$$

It was invested 18.58 years ago.

67. Using the continuous interest formula:

$$500e^{0.06t}=1000$$

$$e^{0.06t}=2$$

$$0.06t=\ln 2$$

$$t=\frac{\ln 2}{0.06}\approx 11.55$$

It will take 11.55 years.

69. Using the continuous interest formula:

$$500e^{0.06t}=1500$$

$$e^{0.06t}=3$$

$$0.06t=\ln 3$$

$$t=\frac{\ln 3}{0.06}\approx 18.31$$

It will take 18.31 years.

71. Using the continuous interest formula:

$$1000e^{0.08t}=2500$$

$$e^{0.08t}=2.5$$

$$0.08t=\ln 2.5$$

$$t=\frac{\ln 2.5}{0.08}\approx 11.45$$

It will take 11.45 years.

73. Using the population model:

$$32000e^{0.05t}=64000$$

$$e^{0.05t}=2$$

$$0.05t=\ln 2$$

$$t=\frac{\ln 2}{0.05}\approx 13.9$$

The city will reach 64,000 toward the end of the year 2018 (October).

75. Using the exponential model:

$$466 \cdot 1.035^t = 900$$

$$1.035^t = \frac{900}{466}$$

$$\ln 1.035^t = \ln \frac{900}{466}$$

$$t \ln 1.035 = \ln \frac{900}{466}$$

$$t = \frac{\ln \frac{900}{466}}{\ln 1.035} \approx 19$$

In the year 2009 it is predicted that 900 million passengers will travel by airline.

77. Using the exponential model:

$$78.16(1.11)^t = 800$$

$$1.11^t = \frac{800}{78.16}$$

$$\ln 1.11^t = \ln \frac{800}{78.16}$$

$$t \ln 1.11 = \ln \frac{800}{78.16}$$

$$t = \frac{\ln \frac{800}{78.16}}{\ln 1.11} \approx 22$$

In the year 1992 it was estimated that \$800 billion will be spent on health care expenditures.

79. Using the compound interest formula:

$$20,972 \left(1 + \frac{0.07}{2}\right)^{2t} = 41,944$$

$$\left(1 + \frac{0.07}{2}\right)^{2t} = 2$$

$$\ln \left(1 + \frac{0.07}{2}\right)^{2t} = \ln 2$$

$$2t \ln \left(1 + \frac{0.07}{2}\right) = \ln 2$$

$$t = \frac{\ln 2}{2 \ln \left(1 + \frac{0.07}{2}\right)} \approx 10.07$$

It will take 10.07 years for the money to double.

81. Using the exponential formula:

$$0.10 e^{0.0576t} = 1.00$$

$$e^{0.0576t} = 10$$

$$0.0576t = \ln 10$$

$$t = \frac{\ln 10}{0.0576} \approx 40$$

A Coca Cola will cost \$1.00 in the year 2000.

83.   **a.**   The exponential model is $A(t) = 75 + (200 - 75)e^{-kt} = 75 + 125e^{-kt}$. Finding k:

$$75 + 125e^{-k(5)} = 180$$

$$125e^{-5k} = 105$$

$$e^{-5k} = 0.84$$

$$-5k = \ln 0.84$$

$$k = \frac{\ln 0.84}{-5} \approx 0.0349$$

b.   Using $A(t) = 75 + 125e^{-0.0349t}$: $A(15) = 75 + 125e^{-0.0349(15)} \approx 149.1°$

c. Using $A(t) = 75 + 125e^{-0.0349t}$:

$$75 + 125e^{-0.0349t} = 100$$
$$125e^{-0.0349t} = 25$$
$$e^{-0.0349t} = 0.2$$
$$-0.0349t = \ln 0.2$$
$$t = \frac{\ln 0.2}{-0.0349} \approx 46.1 \text{ minutes}$$

85. Completing the square: $y = 2x^2 + 8x - 15 = 2(x^2 + 4x + 4) - 8 - 15 = 2(x+2)^2 - 23$. The lowest point is $(-2, -23)$.

87. Completing the square: $y = 12x - 4x^2 = -4\left(x^2 - 3x + \frac{9}{4}\right) + 9 = -4\left(x - \frac{3}{2}\right)^2 + 9$. The highest point is $\left(\frac{3}{2}, 9\right)$.

89. Completing the square: $y = 64t - 16t^2 = -16(t^2 - 4t + 4) + 64 = -16(t-2)^2 + 64$

The object reaches a maximum height after 2 seconds, and the maximum height is 64 feet.

Chapter 8 Review

1. Graphing the function:

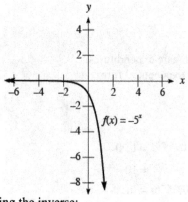

2. Graphing the function:

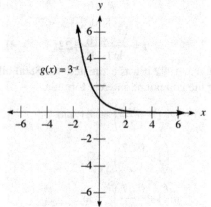

3. Finding the inverse:

$$\frac{1}{3}y + \frac{4}{3} = x$$
$$y + 4 = 3x$$
$$y = 3x - 4$$

The inverse is $f^{-1}(x) = 3x - 4$. Sketching the graphs:

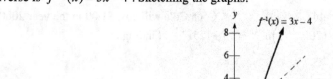

4. Graphing the function and its inverse (which is not a function):

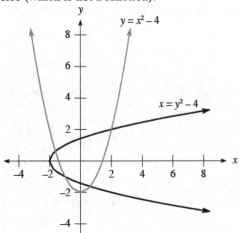

5. Solving for x:

$$\log_4 x = 3$$
$$x = 4^3 = 64$$

6. Solving for x:

$$\log_x 16 = 4$$
$$x^4 = 16$$
$$x = 2$$

7. Graphing the function:

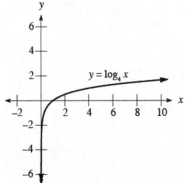

8. Graphing the function:

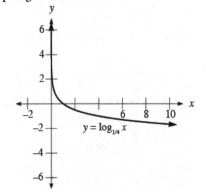

9. Evaluating the logarithm:

$$x = \log_{16} 4$$
$$16^x = 4$$
$$4^{2x} = 4^1$$
$$2x = 1$$
$$x = \frac{1}{2}$$

10. Evaluating the logarithm: $\log_8 24 = \dfrac{\ln 24}{\ln 8} \approx 1.53$

11. Evaluating the logarithm: $\log 57,300 \approx 4.76$

12. Evaluating the logarithm: $\log 0.0507 \approx -1.29$

13. Evaluating the logarithm: $\ln 27.4 \approx 3.31$

14. Evaluating the logarithm: $\ln 0.024 \approx -3.73$

15. Expanding the logarithm: $\log_3 \dfrac{5x^3}{y} = \log_3 5 + \log_3 x^3 - \log_3 y = \log_3 5 + 3\log_3 x - \log_3 y$

16. Expanding the logarithm: $\log \dfrac{\sqrt{x}}{y^5 \sqrt[3]{z}} = \log \dfrac{x^{1/2}}{y^5 z^{1/3}} = \log x^{1/2} - \log y^5 - \log z^{1/3} = \dfrac{1}{2}\log x - 5\log y - \dfrac{1}{3}\log z$

17. Writing as a single logarithm: $\dfrac{1}{2}\log_4 x + 3\log_4 y = \log_4 x^{1/2} + \log_4 y^3 = \log_4 \left(x^{1/2} y^3\right) = \log_4 \left(y^3 \sqrt{x}\right)$

18. Writing as a single logarithm: $3\log x - 4\log y + \dfrac{1}{2}\log z = \log x^3 - \log y^4 + \log z^{1/2} = \log\left(\dfrac{x^3\sqrt{z}}{y^4}\right)$

19. Solving for x:
$$\log x = 2.6532$$
$$x = 10^{2.6532} \approx 449.987$$

20. Solving for x:
$$\log x = -1.2518$$
$$x = 10^{-1.2518} \approx 0.056$$

21. Solving for x:
$$2^x = 5$$
$$\ln 2^x = \ln 5$$
$$x\ln 2 = \ln 5$$
$$x = \dfrac{\ln 5}{\ln 2} \approx 2.322$$

22. Solving for x:
$$4^{2x-3} = 64$$
$$4^{2x-3} = 4^3$$
$$2x - 3 = 3$$
$$2x = 6$$
$$x = 3$$

23. Solving for x:
$$\log_4 x + \log_4 2 = 3$$
$$\log_4 2x = 3$$
$$2x = 4^3$$
$$2x = 64$$
$$x = 32$$

24. Solving for x:
$$\log_2 x + \log_2 (x-2) = 3$$
$$\log_2 (x^2 - 2x) = 3$$
$$x^2 - 2x = 2^3$$
$$x^2 - 2x - 8 = 0$$
$$(x-4)(x+2) = 0$$
$$x = 4, -2$$
The solution is 4 (-2 does not check).

25. Finding the pH: $\text{pH} = -\log\left(9.3\times 10^{-6}\right) \approx 5.03$

26. Using the compound interest formula: $A = 400\left(1 + \dfrac{0.06}{4}\right)^{4\cdot 7} = 400(1.015)^{28} \approx \$606.89$

There will be \$606.89 in the account after 7 years.

27. Using the compound interest formula:
$$600\left(1 + \dfrac{0.09}{4}\right)^{4t} = 2400$$
$$\left(1 + \dfrac{0.09}{4}\right)^{4t} = 4$$
$$\ln(1.0225)^{4t} = \ln 4$$
$$4t\ln 1.0225 = \ln 4$$
$$t = \dfrac{\ln 4}{4\ln 1.0225} \approx 15.6 \text{ years}$$
It will take 15.6 years for the account to reach \$2,400.

28. No, since both $x = 4$ and $x = 6$ have been assigned the value 2, the function is not one-to-one.
29. Yes, this function is one-to-one.
30. Yes, this function is one-to-one.
31. Yes, this function is one-to-one.
32. Since this function does not pass the horizontal line test, it is not one-to-one.
33. Since this function does not pass the horizontal line test, it is not one-to-one.

Chapter 8 Cumulative Review

1. Simplifying: $-3-2\left[4+8(-1-5)\right]=-3-2\left[4+8(-6)\right]=-3-2(4-48)=-3-2(-44)=-3+88=85$

2. Simplifying: $4(3x+1)-7(2x-2)=12x+4-14x+14=-2x+18$

3. Simplifying: $\dfrac{8}{3}\div\dfrac{1}{6}\cdot\dfrac{3}{2}=\dfrac{8}{3}\cdot\dfrac{6}{1}\cdot\dfrac{3}{2}=\dfrac{48}{2}=24$

4. Simplifying: $\dfrac{8}{3}-\dfrac{1}{6}+\dfrac{3}{2}=\dfrac{16}{6}-\dfrac{1}{6}+\dfrac{9}{6}=\dfrac{24}{6}=4$

5. Simplifying: $4\sqrt{32}-3\sqrt{8}+2\sqrt{18}=4\sqrt{16\cdot2}-3\sqrt{4\cdot2}+2\sqrt{9\cdot2}=16\sqrt{2}-6\sqrt{2}+6\sqrt{2}=16\sqrt{2}$

6. Simplifying: $\left(\sqrt{5}+3\sqrt{3}\right)\left(2\sqrt{5}+\sqrt{3}\right)=2\sqrt{25}+6\sqrt{15}+\sqrt{15}+3\sqrt{9}=10+6\sqrt{15}+\sqrt{15}+9=19+7\sqrt{15}$

7. Simplifying: $\left[(5+i)-(2-3i)\right]-(2-5i)=(5+i-2+3i)-(2-5i)=3+4i-2+5i=1+9i$

8. Simplifying: $\dfrac{(1+i)^2}{2}=\dfrac{1+2i+i^2}{2}=\dfrac{1+2i-1}{2}=\dfrac{2i}{2}=i$

9. Simplifying: $\log_{13}\left(\log_{17}17\right)=\log_{13}1=0$

10. Simplifying: $\log_9\left[\log_3\left(\log_2 8\right)\right]=\log_9\left[\log_3\left(\log_2 2^3\right)\right]=\log_9\left(\log_3 3\right)=\log_9 1=0$

11. Simplifying: $\dfrac{1-\dfrac{1}{x-2}}{1+\dfrac{1}{x-2}}=\dfrac{1-\dfrac{1}{x-2}}{1+\dfrac{1}{x-2}}\cdot\dfrac{x-2}{x-2}=\dfrac{x-2-1}{x-2+1}=\dfrac{x-3}{x-1}$

12. Simplifying: $1-\dfrac{x}{1-\dfrac{1}{x}}=1-\dfrac{x}{1-\dfrac{1}{x}}\cdot\dfrac{x}{x}=1-\dfrac{x^2}{x-1}=\dfrac{x-1}{x-1}-\dfrac{x^2}{x-1}=\dfrac{-x^2+x-1}{x-1}=\dfrac{x^2-x+1}{1-x}$

13. Reducing the fraction: $\dfrac{137}{274}=\dfrac{1\cdot137}{2\cdot137}=\dfrac{1}{2}$

14. Reducing the fraction: $\dfrac{216}{168}=\dfrac{9\cdot24}{7\cdot24}=\dfrac{9}{7}$

15. Multiplying: $\left(4t^2+\dfrac{1}{5}\right)\left(5t^2-\dfrac{1}{4}\right)=20t^4+t^2-t^2-\dfrac{1}{20}=20t^4-\dfrac{1}{20}$

16. Multiplying: $(5x+3)\left(x^2-5x+3\right)=5x^3-25x^2+15x+3x^2-15x+9=5x^3-22x^2+9$

17. Using long division:

$$\begin{array}{r}
x-5 \\
x-1\overline{\smash{)}x^2-6x+3} \\
\underline{x^2-x} \\
-5x+3 \\
\underline{-5x+5} \\
-2
\end{array}$$

The quotient is $x-5-\dfrac{2}{x-1}$.

18. Using long division:

$$\begin{array}{r}
4x+5 \\
3x+2\overline{\smash{)}12x^2+23x-3} \\
\underline{12x^2+8x} \\
15x-3 \\
\underline{15x+10} \\
-13
\end{array}$$

The quotient is $4x+5-\dfrac{13}{3x+2}$.

19. Subtracting:

$$\frac{6}{(x+3)(x-3)} - \frac{5}{(x+3)(x-2)} = \frac{6}{(x+3)(x-3)} \cdot \frac{x-2}{x-2} - \frac{5}{(x+3)(x-2)} \cdot \frac{x-3}{x-3}$$

$$= \frac{6x-12}{(x+3)(x-3)(x-2)} - \frac{5x-15}{(x+3)(x-3)(x-2)}$$

$$= \frac{x+3}{(x+3)(x-3)(x-2)}$$

$$= \frac{1}{(x-3)(x-2)}$$

20. Adding:

$$\frac{3}{6x^2-5x-4} + \frac{1}{6x^2-11x+4} = \frac{3}{(3x-4)(2x+1)} \cdot \frac{2x-1}{2x-1} + \frac{1}{(3x-4)(2x-1)} \cdot \frac{2x+1}{2x+1}$$

$$= \frac{6x-3}{(3x-4)(2x+1)(2x-1)} + \frac{2x+1}{(3x-4)(2x+1)(2x-1)}$$

$$= \frac{8x-2}{(3x-4)(2x+1)(2x-1)}$$

$$= \frac{2(4x-1)}{(3x-4)(2x+1)(2x-1)}$$

21. Solving the equation:

$$8 - 5(3x+2) = 4$$
$$8 - 15x - 10 = 4$$
$$-15x - 2 = 4$$
$$-15x = 6$$
$$x = -\frac{2}{5}$$

22. Solving the equation:

$$\frac{3}{4}(12x-7) + \frac{1}{4} = 13$$
$$3(12x-7) + 1 = 52$$
$$36x - 21 + 1 = 52$$
$$36x - 20 = 52$$
$$36x = 72$$
$$x = 2$$

23. Solving the equation:

$$32x^2 = 4x + 3$$
$$32x^2 - 4x - 3 = 0$$
$$(8x-3)(4x+1) = 0$$
$$x = -\frac{1}{4}, \frac{3}{8}$$

24. Solving the equation:

$$4x - 4 = x^2$$
$$x^2 - 4x + 4 = 0$$
$$(x-2)^2 = 0$$
$$x = 2$$

25. Solving the equation:

$$\frac{1}{x+2} + \frac{1}{x-5} = 1$$
$$(x+2)(x-5)\left(\frac{1}{x+2} + \frac{1}{x-5}\right) = (x+2)(x-5) \cdot 1$$
$$x - 5 + x + 2 = x^2 - 3x - 10$$
$$2x - 3 = x^2 - 3x - 10$$
$$x^2 - 5x - 7 = 0$$
$$x = \frac{5 \pm \sqrt{25+28}}{2} = \frac{5 \pm \sqrt{53}}{2}$$

26. Solving the equation:
$$\frac{1}{(x+3)(x-2)}+\frac{4}{(x+2)(x-2)}=\frac{-2}{(x+2)(x+3)}$$
$$(x+2)+4(x+3)=-2(x-2)$$
$$x+2+4x+12=-2x+4$$
$$5x+14=-2x+4$$
$$7x=-10$$
$$x=-\frac{10}{7}$$

27. Solving the equation:
$$x-4\sqrt{x}-5=0$$
$$\left(\sqrt{x}-5\right)\left(\sqrt{x}+1\right)=0$$
$$\sqrt{x}=-1,5$$
$$x=1,25$$

Only $x = 25$ checks in the original equation.

28. Solving the equation:
$$2(3y+1)^2+(3y+1)-10=0$$
$$\left[2(3y+1)+5\right]\left[(3y+1)-2\right]=0$$
$$(6y+7)(3y-1)=0$$
$$y=-\frac{7}{6},\frac{1}{3}$$

29. Solving the equation:
$$\log_4 x=4$$
$$x=4^4=256$$

30. Solving the equation:
$$\log_x 0.2=-1$$
$$x^{-1}=0.2$$
$$x=5$$

31. Solving the equation:
$$\log_6(x+2)-\log_6(x+5)=1$$
$$\log_6\frac{x+2}{x+5}=1$$
$$\frac{x+2}{x+5}=6^1$$
$$x+2=6x+30$$
$$-5x=28$$
$$x=-\frac{28}{5}\text{ (impossible)}$$

There is no solution to the equation.

32. Solving the equation:
$$\log_3(x-1)+\log_3(x-6)=2$$
$$\log_3\left(x^2-7x+6\right)=2$$
$$x^2-7x+6=3^2$$
$$x^2-7x+6=9$$
$$x^2-7x-3=0$$
$$x=\frac{7\pm\sqrt{49+12}}{2}=\frac{7\pm\sqrt{61}}{2}$$

Only $x=\dfrac{7+\sqrt{61}}{2}$ checks in the original equation.

33. Multiply the first equation by 2:
$$-2x+10y=38$$
$$2x-9y=-34$$
Adding yields: $y=4$

Substituting into the first equation:
$$-x+5(4)=19$$
$$-x+20=19$$
$$-x=-1$$
$$x=1$$
The solution is $(1,4)$.

34. Multiply the first equation by 2:
$$8x+14y=48$$
$$-8x-9y=-48$$
Adding yields:
$$5y=0$$
$$y=0$$
Substituting into the first equation:
$$4x+7(0)=24$$
$$4x=24$$
$$x=6$$
The solution is $(6,0)$.

35. Multiply the second equation by –1 and add it to the first equation:
$$x+3y=-12$$
$$-x+3z=4$$
Adding yields the equation $3y+3z=-8$. So the system becomes:
$$3y+3z=-8$$
$$y+3z=0$$
Multiplying the second equation by –1:
$$3y+3z=-8$$
$$-y-3z=0$$
Adding yields:
$$2y=-8$$
$$y=-4$$
Substituting to find x:
$$x+3(-4)=-12$$
$$x-12=-12$$
$$x=0$$
Substituting to find z:
$$-(0)+3z=4$$
$$3z=4$$
$$z=\frac{4}{3}$$
The solution is $\left(0,-4,\frac{4}{3}\right)$.

36. Multiply the second equation by –1 and add it to the first equation:

$$6x - y + 9z = 0$$
$$-6x - 6y - 9z = 0$$

Adding yields:

$$-7y = 0$$
$$y = 0$$

Substituting $y = 0$, the first and third equations becomes:

$$6x + 9z = 0$$
$$8x + z = -11$$

Multiplying the second equation by –9:

$$6x + 9z = 0$$
$$-72x - 9z = 99$$

Adding yields:

$$-66x = 99$$
$$x = -\frac{3}{2}$$

Substituting to find z:

$$6\left(-\frac{3}{2}\right) - 0 + 9z = 0$$
$$-9 + 9z = 0$$
$$9z = 9$$
$$z = 1$$

The solution is $\left(-\frac{3}{2}, 0, 1\right)$.

37. Graphing the line:

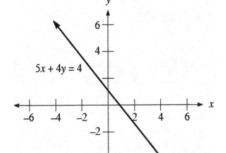

38. Graphing the line:

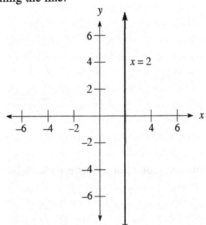

39. Written in symbols: $8 - y = -3x$

40. Written in symbols: $2a - 3b < 2a + 3b$

41. Writing in scientific notation: $0.00000129 = 1.29 \times 10^{-6}$

42. Writing in scientific notation: $83,000,000 = 8.3 \times 10^{7}$

43. Factoring completely: $64x^3 + 27 = (4x)^3 + (3)^3 = (4x + 3)(16x^2 - 12x + 9)$

44. Factoring completely: $48a^4 + 36a^2 + 6 = 6(8a^4 + 6a^2 + 1) = 6(4a^2 + 1)(2a^2 + 1)$

45. The domain is $\{3, 5\}$ and the range is $\{-4, -2, -1\}$. This is not a function.

46. The domain is $\{1, 2, 3\}$ and the range is $\{1, 2\}$. This is a function.

47. Finding the total in scientific notation: $2.638 \times 10^8 + 1.702 \times 10^8 = \$4.34 \times 10^8$

48. Finding the difference: $583.5 - 317.8 = \$265.7$ million

Chapter 8 Test

1. Graphing the function:

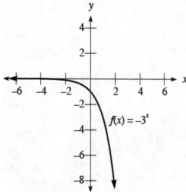

2. Graphing the function:

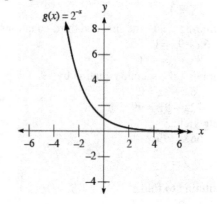

3. Finding the inverse:

$$\frac{1}{2}y + \frac{3}{2} = x$$
$$y + 3 = 2x$$
$$y = 2x - 3$$

The inverse is $f^{-1}(x) = 2x - 3$. Sketching the graphs:

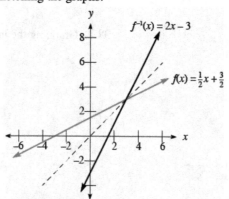

4. Graphing the function and its inverse (which is not a function):

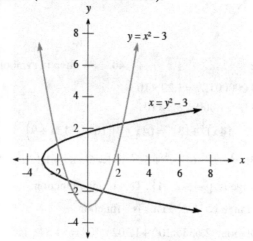

---

5. Solving for x:

$$\log_5 x = 2$$
$$x = 5^2 = 25$$

6. Solving for x:

$$\log_x 7 = 3$$
$$x^3 = 7$$
$$x = \sqrt[3]{7}$$

7. Graphing the function:

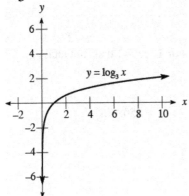

8. Graphing the function:

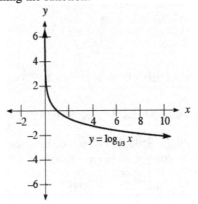

9. Evaluating the logarithm:

$$x = \log_9 3$$
$$9^x = 3$$
$$3^{2x} = 3^1$$
$$2x = 1$$
$$x = \frac{1}{2}$$

10. Evaluating the logarithm: $\log_7 35 = \dfrac{\ln 35}{\ln 7} \approx 1.83$

11. Evaluating the logarithm: $\log 14{,}500 \approx 4.16$

12. Evaluating the logarithm: $\log 0.0203 \approx -1.69$

13. Evaluating the logarithm: $\ln 56.3 \approx 4.03$

14. Evaluating the logarithm: $\ln 0.034 \approx -3.38$

15. Expanding the logarithm: $\log_7 \dfrac{4x^3}{y} = \log_7 2^2 + \log_7 x^3 - \log_7 y = 2\log_7 2 + 3\log_7 x - \log_7 y$

16. Expanding the logarithm: $\log \dfrac{\sqrt[3]{x}}{y^2 \sqrt{z}} = \log \dfrac{x^{1/3}}{y^2 z^{1/2}} = \log x^{1/3} - \log y^2 - \log z^{1/2} = \dfrac{1}{3}\log x - 2\log y - \dfrac{1}{2}\log z$

17. Writing as a single logarithm: $\dfrac{1}{3}\log_2 x + 5\log_2 y = \log_2 x^{1/3} + \log_2 y^5 = \log_2\left(x^{1/3}y^5\right) = \log_2\left(y^5 \sqrt[3]{x}\right)$

18. Writing as a single logarithm: $\dfrac{1}{4}\log_3 x - \log_3 y + 3\log_3 z = \log_3 x^{1/4} - \log_3 y + \log_3 z^3 = \log_3\left(\dfrac{x^{1/4} z^3}{y}\right)$

19. Solving for x:
$$\log x = 5.3819$$
$$x = 10^{5.3819} \approx 240{,}935.059$$

20. Solving for x:
$$\log x = -2.4531$$
$$x = 10^{-2.4531} \approx 0.004$$

21. Solving for x:

$$3^x = 4$$
$$\ln 3^x = \ln 4$$
$$x\ln 3 = \ln 4$$
$$x = \frac{\ln 4}{\ln 3} \approx 1.262$$

22. Solving for x:

$$9^{4x-1} = 27$$
$$3^{2(4x-1)} = 3^3$$
$$8x - 2 = 3$$
$$8x = 5$$
$$x = \frac{5}{8}$$

23. Solving for x:

$$\log_6 x + \log_6 3 = 1$$
$$\log_6 3x = 1$$
$$3x = 6^1$$
$$3x = 6$$
$$x = 2$$

24. Solving for x:

$$\log_3 x + \log_3 (x - 26) = 3$$
$$\log_3 (x^2 - 26x) = 3$$
$$x^2 - 26x = 3^3$$
$$x^2 - 26x - 27 = 0$$
$$(x - 27)(x + 1) = 0$$
$$x = 27, -1$$

The solution is 27 (–1 does not check).

25. Finding the pH: $pH = -\log(7.3 \times 10^{-6}) \approx 5.14$

26. Using the compound interest formula: $A = 300\left(1 + \dfrac{0.09}{2}\right)^{2 \cdot 6} = 300(1.045)^{12} \approx \$508.76$

There will be \$508.76 in the account after 6 years.

27. Using the compound interest formula:

$$500\left(1 + \frac{0.06}{2}\right)^{2t} = 2500$$
$$\left(1 + \frac{0.06}{2}\right)^{2t} = 5$$
$$\ln(1.03)^{2t} = \ln 5$$
$$2t \ln 1.03 = \ln 5$$
$$t = \frac{\ln 5}{2 \ln 1.03} \approx 27.2 \text{ years}$$

It will take 27.2 years for the account to reach \$2,500.

28. Yes, this function is one-to-one.
29. No, since both $x = 2$ and $x = 4$ have been assigned the value 0, the function is not one-to-one.
30. Yes, this function is one-to-one.
31. Yes, this function is one-to-one.
32. This is not a function, so it cannot be one-to-one.
33. Since this function does not pass the horizontal line test, it is not one-to-one.

Chapter 9
Conic Sections

9.1 Circles

1. Using the distance formula: $d = \sqrt{(6-3)^2 + (3-7)^2} = \sqrt{9+16} = \sqrt{25} = 5$

3. Using the distance formula: $d = \sqrt{(5-0)^2 + (0-9)^2} = \sqrt{25+81} = \sqrt{106}$

5. Using the distance formula: $d = \sqrt{(-2-3)^2 + (1+5)^2} = \sqrt{25+36} = \sqrt{61}$

7. Using the distance formula: $d = \sqrt{(-10+1)^2 + (5+2)^2} = \sqrt{81+49} = \sqrt{130}$

9. Solving the equation:
$$\sqrt{(x-1)^2 + (2-5)^2} = \sqrt{13}$$
$$(x-1)^2 + 9 = 13$$
$$(x-1)^2 = 4$$
$$x - 1 = \pm 2$$
$$x - 1 = -2, 2$$
$$x = -1, 3$$

11. Solving the equation:
$$\sqrt{(x-3)^2 + (5-9)^2} = 5$$
$$(x-3)^2 + 16 = 25$$
$$(x-3)^2 = 9$$
$$x - 3 = \pm 3$$
$$x - 3 = -3, 3$$
$$x = 0, 6$$

13. Solving the equation:
$$\sqrt{(2x+1-x)^2 + (6-4)^2} = 6$$
$$(x+1)^2 + 4 = 36$$
$$(x+1)^2 = 32$$
$$x + 1 = \pm\sqrt{32}$$
$$x + 1 = \pm 4\sqrt{2}$$
$$x = -1 \pm 4\sqrt{2}$$

15. The equation is $(x-3)^2 + (y+2)^2 = 9$.

17. The equation is $(x+5)^2 + (y+1)^2 = 5$.

19. The equation is $x^2 + (y+5)^2 = 1$.

21. The equation is $x^2 + y^2 = 4$.

23. The center is (0,0) and the radius is 2.

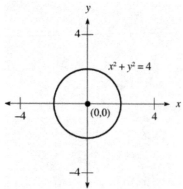

25. The center is (1,3) and the radius is 5.

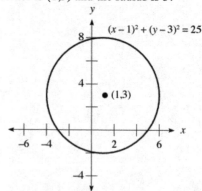

27. The center is (−2,4) and the radius is $2\sqrt{2}$.

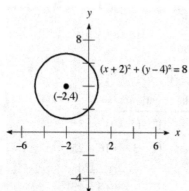

29. The center is (−2,4) and the radius is $\sqrt{17} \approx 4.1$.

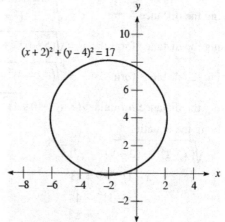

31. Completing the square:
$$x^2 + y^2 + 2x - 4y = 4$$
$$\left(x^2 + 2x + 1\right) + \left(y^2 - 4y + 4\right) = 4 + 1 + 4$$
$$\left(x + 1\right)^2 + \left(y - 2\right)^2 = 9$$
The center is (−1,2) and the radius is 3.

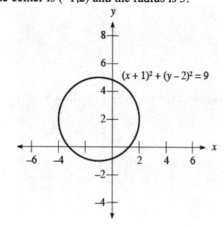

33. Completing the square:
$$x^2 + y^2 - 6y = 7$$
$$x^2 + \left(y^2 - 6y + 9\right) = 7 + 9$$
$$x^2 + \left(y - 3\right)^2 = 16$$
The center is (0,3) and the radius is 4.

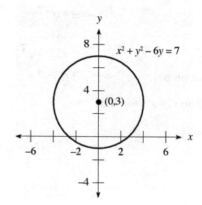

35. Completing the square:
$$x^2 + y^2 + 2x = 1$$
$$\left(x^2 + 2x + 1\right) + y^2 = 1 + 1$$
$$\left(x+1\right)^2 + y^2 = 2$$

The center is $(-1,0)$ and the radius is $\sqrt{2} \approx 1.4$.

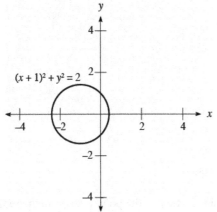

37. Completing the square:
$$x^2 + y^2 - 4x - 6y = -4$$
$$\left(x^2 - 4x + 4\right) + \left(y^2 - 6y + 9\right) = -4 + 4 + 9$$
$$\left(x-2\right)^2 + \left(y-3\right)^2 = 9$$

The center is $(2,3)$ and the radius is 3.

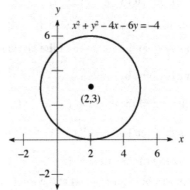

39. Completing the square:
$$x^2 + y^2 + 2x + y = \frac{11}{4}$$
$$\left(x^2 + 2x + 1\right) + \left(y^2 + y + \frac{1}{4}\right) = \frac{11}{4} + 1 + \frac{1}{4}$$
$$\left(x+1\right)^2 + \left(y + \frac{1}{2}\right)^2 = 4$$

The center is $\left(-1, -\frac{1}{2}\right)$ and the radius is 2.

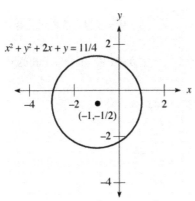

41. Completing the square:
$$4x^2 + 4y^2 - 4x + 8y = 11$$
$$x^2 + y^2 - x + 2y = \frac{11}{4}$$
$$\left(x^2 - x + \frac{1}{4}\right) + \left(y^2 + 2y + 1\right) = \frac{11}{4} + \frac{1}{4} + 1$$
$$\left(x - \frac{1}{2}\right)^2 + \left(y+1\right)^2 = 4$$

The center is $\left(\frac{1}{2}, -1\right)$ and the radius is 2.

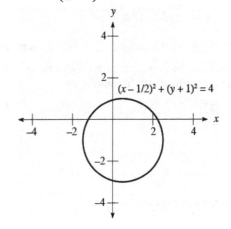

43. The equation is $\left(x-3\right)^2 + \left(y-4\right)^2 = 25$.

45. The equations are:

$$A: \left(x - \frac{1}{2}\right)^2 + (y-1)^2 = \frac{1}{4}$$

$$B: (x-1)^2 + (y-1)^2 = 1$$

$$C: (x-2)^2 + (y-1)^2 = 4$$

47. The radius is given by: $r = \sqrt{(3-0)^2 + (4-0)^2} = \sqrt{9+16} = \sqrt{25} = 5$

So the equation of the circle is $x^2 + y^2 = 25$.

49. The radius is 3, so the equation of the circle is $x^2 + y^2 = 9$.

51. The radius is given by: $r = \sqrt{(-1-4)^2 + (3-3)^2} = \sqrt{25+0} = \sqrt{25} = 5$

So the equation of the circle is $(x+1)^2 + (y-3)^2 = 25$.

53. The radius is given by: $r = \sqrt{(1+2)^2 + (-3-5)^2} = \sqrt{9+64} = \sqrt{73}$

So the equation of the circle is $(x+2)^2 + (y-5)^2 = 73$.

55. The center will be on the y-axis at the midpoint of the two y-intercepts, which is the point $(-3,0)$. So the radius of the circle is 4, and its equation is $x^2 + (y-2)^2 = 16$.

57. The radius of the circle is $\sqrt{18} = 3\sqrt{2}$, so the circumference and area are given by:

$$C = 2\pi\left(3\sqrt{2}\right) = 6\pi\sqrt{2} \qquad\qquad A = \pi\left(3\sqrt{2}\right)^2 = 18\pi$$

59. First complete the square:

$$x^2 + y^2 + 4x + 2y = 20$$
$$\left(x^2 + 4x + 4\right) + \left(y^2 + 2y + 1\right) = 20 + 4 + 1$$
$$(x+2)^2 + (y+1)^2 = 25$$

The radius of the circle is 5, so the circumference and area are given by:

$$C = 2\pi(5) = 10\pi \qquad\qquad A = \pi(5)^2 = 25\pi$$

61. Finding the distance from the starting point $(0,0)$: $d = \sqrt{(5-0)^2 + (3-0)^2} = \sqrt{25+9} = \sqrt{34} \approx 5.8$ blocks

Yes, the child is within the 6 block search area.

63. The x-coordinate of the center is $x = 500$, the y-coordinate of the center is $12 + 120 = 132$, and the radius is 120. Thus the equation of the circle is $(x - 500)^2 + (y - 132)^2 = 120^2$.

65. Solving the equation:

$$y^2 = 9$$
$$y = \pm\sqrt{9} = \pm 3$$

67. Solving the equation:

$$-y^2 = 4$$
$$y^2 = -4$$
$$y = \pm\sqrt{-4} = \pm 2i$$

69. Solving the equation:

$$-x^2 = 9$$
$$x^2 = -9$$
$$x = \pm\sqrt{-9} = \pm 3i$$

71. Dividing: $\dfrac{4x^2 + 9y^2}{36} = \dfrac{4x^2}{36} + \dfrac{9y^2}{36} = \dfrac{x^2}{9} + \dfrac{y^2}{4}$

73. To find the x-intercept, let $y = 0$:

$$3x - 4(0) = 12$$
$$3x - 0 = 12$$
$$3x = 12$$
$$x = 4$$

To find the y-intercept, let $x = 0$:

$$3(0) - 4y = 12$$
$$0 - 4y = 12$$
$$-4y = 12$$
$$y = -3$$

75. Substituting $x = 3$:

$$\frac{3^2}{25} + \frac{y^2}{9} = 1$$
$$\frac{9}{25} + \frac{y^2}{9} = 1$$
$$\frac{y^2}{9} = \frac{16}{25}$$
$$y^2 = \frac{144}{25}$$
$$y = \pm\sqrt{\frac{144}{25}} = \pm\frac{12}{5} = \pm 2.4$$

9.2 Parabolas

1. The vertex is $(-1, -3)$. Graphing the parabola:

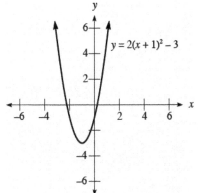

3. The vertex is $(4, 2)$. Graphing the parabola:

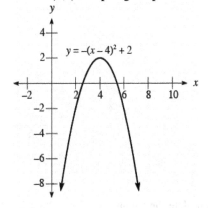

5. The vertex is $(2, 1)$. Graphing the parabola:

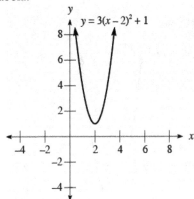

7. First complete the square: $y = x^2 + 3x - 5 = \left(x^2 + 3x + \dfrac{9}{4}\right) - \dfrac{9}{4} - 5 = \left(x + \dfrac{3}{2}\right)^2 - \dfrac{29}{4}$

The vertex is $\left(-\dfrac{3}{2}, -\dfrac{29}{4}\right)$. Graphing the parabola:

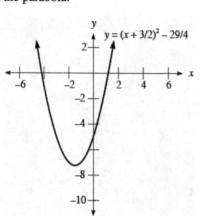

9. First complete the square: $y = -x^2 + 4x + 3 = -\left(x^2 - 4x + 4\right) + 4 + 3 = -\left(x - 2\right)^2 + 7$

The vertex is $(2, 7)$. Graphing the parabola:

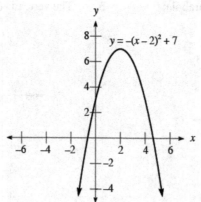

11. First complete the square: $y = 2x^2 + 8x + 5 = 2\left(x^2 + 4x + 4\right) - 8 + 5 = 2\left(x + 2\right)^2 - 3$

The vertex is $(-2, -3)$. Graphing the parabola:

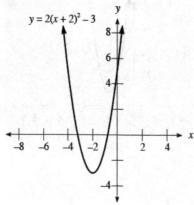

13. The vertex is (–5,–2). Graphing the parabola:

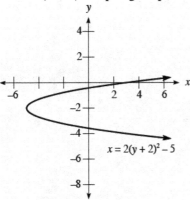

$x = 2(y + 2)^2 - 5$

15. The vertex is (3,–3). Graphing the parabola:

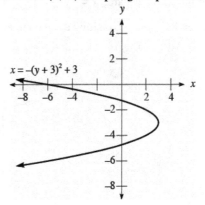

$x = -(y + 3)^2 + 3$

17. The vertex is (5,2). Graphing the parabola:

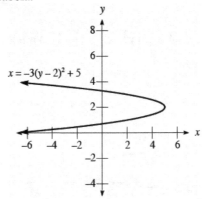

$x = -3(y - 2)^2 + 5$

19. First complete the square: $x = y^2 + 4y + 7 = \left(y^2 + 4y + 4\right) - 4 + 7 = \left(y + 2\right)^2 + 3$

The vertex is $\left(3, -2\right)$. Graphing the parabola:

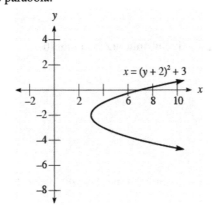

$x = (y + 2)^2 + 3$

21. First complete the square: $x = -y^2 - 4y + 3 = -\left(y^2 + 4y + 4\right) + 4 + 3 = -(y+2)^2 + 7$

The vertex is $(7, -2)$. Graphing the parabola:

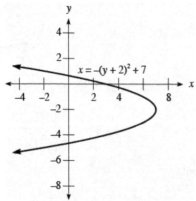

$x = -(y+2)^2 + 7$

23. First complete the square: $x = -3y^2 + 6y - 4 = -3\left(y^2 - 2y + 1\right) + 3 - 4 = -3(y-1)^2 - 1$

The vertex is $(-1, 1)$. Graphing the parabola:

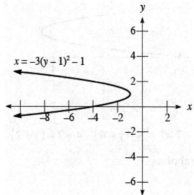

$x = -3(y-1)^2 - 1$

25. The parabola has the form $y = a(x-2)^2 - 1$. Substituting the point $(0,0)$:

$$0 = a(0-2)^2 - 1$$
$$4a = 1$$
$$a = \frac{1}{4}$$

So the equation is $y = \frac{1}{4}(x-2)^2 - 1$.

27. The parabola has the form $y = a(x+2)^2 + 3$. Substituting the point $(-1,0)$:

$$0 = a(-1+2)^2 + 3$$
$$a = -3$$

So the equation is $y = -3(x+2)^2 + 3$.

29. The parabola has the form $x = a(y-1)^2 - 4$. Substituting the point $(0,0)$:

$$0 = a(0-1)^2 - 4$$
$$a = 4$$

So the equation is $x = 4(y-1)^2 - 4$.

31. The parabola has the form $x = a(y+5)^2 + 3$. Substituting the point $(0,-2)$:

$$0 = a(-2+5)^2 + 3$$
$$9a = -3$$
$$a = -\frac{1}{3}$$

So the equation is $x = -\frac{1}{3}(y+5)^2 + 3$.

33. The parabola has the form $y = a(x-3)^2 + 8$. Substituting the point $(0,0)$:

$$0 = a(0-3)^2 + 8$$
$$9a = -8$$
$$a = -\frac{8}{9}$$

So the equation is $y = -\frac{8}{9}(x-3)^2 + 8$.

35. The parabola has the form $y = a(x-1)^2 - 3$. Substituting the point $(4,0)$:

$$0 = a(4-1)^2 - 3$$
$$9a = 3$$
$$a = \frac{1}{3}$$

So the equation is $y = \frac{1}{3}(x-1)^2 - 3$.

37. The parabola has the form $x = a(y-2)^2 + 4$. Substituting the point $(0,-1)$:

$$0 = a(-1-2)^2 + 4$$
$$9a = -4$$
$$a = -\frac{4}{9}$$

So the equation is $x = -\frac{4}{9}(y-2)^2 + 4$.

39. The parabola has the form $x = a(y+4)^2 - 7$. Substituting the point $(0,-2)$:

$$0 = a(-2+4)^2 - 7$$
$$4a = 7$$
$$a = \frac{7}{4}$$

So the equation is $x = \frac{7}{4}(y+4)^2 - 7$.

41. Finding the number of computers:

Apple: $0.27(15{,}000) = 4{,}050$ students   Dell: $0.24(35{,}000) = 8{,}400$ students

43. **a.** The vertex is at $(80, 70)$ and the landing position is at $(160, 0)$.

b. The general form of the equation is $y = -a(x - 80)^2 + 70$.

c. Using the point $(0, 0)$:

$$0 = -a(0 - 80)^2 + 70$$
$$-6400a = -70$$
$$a = \frac{7}{640}$$

The equation is $y = -\frac{7}{640}(x - 80)^2 + 70$.

45. Solving the equation:

$$(x + 4)^2 + 3 = 12$$
$$(x + 4)^2 = 9$$
$$x + 4 = \pm 3$$
$$x + 4 = -3, 3$$
$$x = -7, -1$$

47. Solving the equation:

$$(y - 1)^2 - 6 = 19$$
$$(y - 1)^2 = 25$$
$$y - 1 = \pm 5$$
$$y - 1 = -5, 5$$
$$y = -4, 6$$

49. To find the x-intercepts, substitute $y = 0$:

$$\frac{x^2}{9} + \frac{0}{16} = 1$$
$$\frac{x^2}{9} = 1$$
$$x^2 = 9$$
$$x = \pm 3$$

To find the y-intercepts, substitute $x = 0$:

$$\frac{0}{9} + \frac{y^2}{4} = 1$$
$$\frac{y^2}{4} = 1$$
$$y^2 = 4$$
$$y = \pm 2$$

51. To find the x-intercepts, substitute $y = 0$:

$$\frac{x^2}{5} + \frac{0}{16} = 1$$
$$\frac{x^2}{5} = 1$$
$$x^2 = 5$$
$$x = \pm\sqrt{5}$$

To find the y-intercepts, substitute $x = 0$:

$$\frac{0}{5} + \frac{y^2}{16} = 1$$
$$\frac{y^2}{16} = 1$$
$$y^2 = 16$$
$$y = \pm 4$$

53. Substituting $x = 1$:

$$\frac{1}{9} + \frac{y^2}{16} = 1$$
$$\frac{y^2}{16} = \frac{8}{9}$$
$$y^2 = \frac{128}{9}$$
$$y = \pm\sqrt{\frac{128}{9}} = \pm\frac{8\sqrt{2}}{3}$$

55. Substituting $y = 1$:

$$\frac{x^2}{25} + \frac{1}{4} = 1$$
$$\frac{x^2}{25} = \frac{3}{4}$$
$$x^2 = \frac{75}{4}$$
$$x = \pm\sqrt{\frac{75}{4}} = \pm\frac{5\sqrt{3}}{2}$$

9.3 Ellipses

1. Graphing the ellipse:

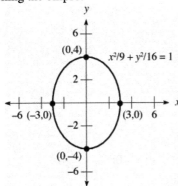

$x^2/9 + y^2/16 = 1$

3. Graphing the ellipse:

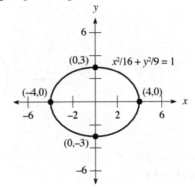

$x^2/16 + y^2/9 = 1$

5. Graphing the ellipse:

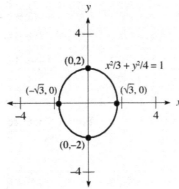

$x^2/3 + y^2/4 = 1$

7. The standard form is $\dfrac{x^2}{25} + \dfrac{y^2}{4} = 1$. Graphing the ellipse:

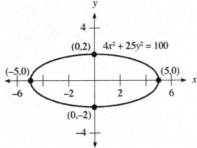

$4x^2 + 25y^2 = 100$

9. The standard form is $\dfrac{x^2}{16} + \dfrac{y^2}{2} = 1$. Graphing the ellipse:

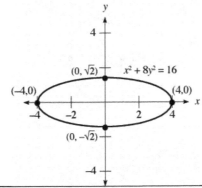

$x^2 + 8y^2 = 16$

11. The standard form is $\dfrac{x^2}{4} + \dfrac{y^2}{3} = 1$. Graphing the ellipse:

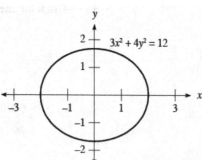

13. For the x-intercepts, set $y = 0$:
$$0.4x^2 = 3.6$$
$$x^2 = 9$$
$$x = \pm 3$$

For the y-intercepts, set $x = 0$:
$$0.9y^2 = 3.6$$
$$y^2 = 4$$
$$y = \pm 2$$

15. For the x-intercepts, set $y = 0$:
$$\dfrac{x^2}{0.04} = 1$$
$$x^2 = 0.04$$
$$x = \pm 0.2$$

For the y-intercepts, set $x = 0$:
$$\dfrac{y^2}{0.09} = 1$$
$$y^2 = 0.09$$
$$y = \pm 0.3$$

17. For the x-intercepts, set $y = 0$:
$$\dfrac{25x^2}{9} = 1$$
$$x^2 = \dfrac{9}{25}$$
$$x = \pm \dfrac{3}{5}$$

For the y-intercepts, set $x = 0$:
$$\dfrac{25y^2}{4} = 1$$
$$y^2 = \dfrac{4}{25}$$
$$y = \pm \dfrac{2}{5}$$

19. For the x-intercepts, set $y = 0$:
$$\dfrac{4x^2}{9} = 1$$
$$x^2 = \dfrac{9}{4}$$
$$x = \pm \dfrac{3}{2}$$

For the y-intercepts, set $x = 0$:
$$\dfrac{25y^2}{16} = 1$$
$$y^2 = \dfrac{16}{25}$$
$$y = \pm \dfrac{4}{5}$$

21. Graphing the ellipse:

23. Completing the square:

$$4x^2 + y^2 - 4y - 12 = 0$$
$$4x^2 + (y^2 - 4y + 4) = 12 + 4$$
$$4x^2 + (y-2)^2 = 16$$
$$\frac{x^2}{4} + \frac{(y-2)^2}{16} = 1$$

Graphing the ellipse:

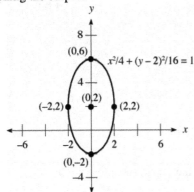

25. Completing the square:

$$x^2 + 9y^2 + 4x - 54y + 76 = 0$$
$$(x^2 + 4x + 4) + 9(y^2 - 6y + 9) = -76 + 4 + 81$$
$$(x+2)^2 + 9(y-3)^2 = 9$$
$$\frac{(x+2)^2}{9} + \frac{(y-3)^2}{1} = 1$$

Graphing the ellipse:

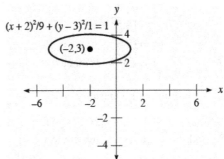

27. Substituting $y = 4$:

$$\frac{x^2}{25} + \frac{4^2}{16} = 1$$
$$\frac{x^2}{25} + 1 = 1$$
$$\frac{x^2}{25} = 0$$
$$x = 0$$

29. Substituting $x = 3$:

$$\frac{3^2}{25} + \frac{y^2}{16} = 1$$
$$\frac{9}{25} + \frac{y^2}{16} = 1$$
$$\frac{y^2}{16} = \frac{16}{25}$$
$$y^2 = \frac{256}{25}$$
$$y = \pm\frac{16}{5}$$

31. Substituting $y = -3$:

$$\frac{x^2}{25} + \frac{(-3)^2}{16} = 1$$
$$\frac{x^2}{25} + \frac{9}{16} = 1$$
$$\frac{x^2}{25} = \frac{7}{16}$$
$$x^2 = \frac{175}{16}$$
$$x = \pm\frac{5\sqrt{7}}{4}$$

33. The major axis length was 8.

35. The curve is an ellipse with $a = \dfrac{615}{2} = 307.5$ and $b = \dfrac{510}{2} = 255$, so the equation is $\dfrac{x^2}{307.5^2} + \dfrac{y^2}{255^2} = 1$.

37. The curve is an ellipse with $a = 9$ and $b = \dfrac{6}{2} = 3$, so the equation is $\dfrac{x^2}{3^2} + \dfrac{y^2}{9^2} = 1$, or $\dfrac{x^2}{9} + \dfrac{y^2}{81} = 1$.

39. Substituting $a = 4$ and $c = 3$:
$$4^2 = b^2 + 3^2$$
$$16 = b^2 + 9$$
$$b^2 = 7$$
$$b = \sqrt{7} \approx 2.65$$
The width should be approximately $2(2.65) = 5.3$ feet wide.

41. **a.** The room is an ellipse with $a = \dfrac{35}{2} = 17.5$ and $b = \dfrac{29}{2} = 14.5$, so the equation is $\dfrac{x^2}{17.5^2} + \dfrac{y^2}{14.5^2} = 1$.

b. Substituting $a = 17.5$ and $b = 14.5$:
$$a^2 = b^2 + c^2$$
$$17.5^2 = 14.5^2 + c^2$$
$$c^2 = 17.5^2 - 14.5^2 = 96$$
$$c = \sqrt{96} \approx 9.8 \text{ feet}$$

c. Finding the eccentricity: $e = \sqrt{\dfrac{17.5^2 - 14.5^2}{17.5^2}} = \sqrt{\dfrac{96}{306.25}} \approx 0.560$

43. Subtracting: $\$717{,}405{,}900 - \$529{,}021{,}800 = \$188{,}384{,}100$

45. To find the x-intercepts, substitute $y = 0$:
$$\frac{x^2}{9} - \frac{0}{4} = 1$$
$$\frac{x^2}{9} = 1$$
$$x^2 = 9$$
$$x = \pm 3$$

To find the y-intercepts, substitute $x = 0$:
$$\frac{0}{9} - \frac{y^2}{4} = 1$$
$$-\frac{y^2}{4} = 1$$
$$y^2 = -4$$
$$y = \pm 2i$$
There are no y-intercepts.

47. To find the x-intercepts, substitute $y = 0$:
$$\frac{0}{5} - \frac{x^2}{9} = 1$$
$$-\frac{x^2}{9} = 1$$
$$x^2 = -9$$
$$x = \pm 3i$$
There are no x-intercepts.

To find the y-intercepts, substitute $x = 0$:
$$\frac{y^2}{5} - \frac{0}{9} = 1$$
$$\frac{y^2}{5} = 1$$
$$y^2 = 5$$
$$y = \pm\sqrt{5}$$

49. Substituting $y = 1$:
$$\frac{x^2}{9} - \frac{1}{16} = 1$$
$$\frac{x^2}{9} = \frac{17}{16}$$
$$x^2 = \frac{153}{16}$$
$$x = \pm\sqrt{\frac{153}{16}} = \pm\frac{3\sqrt{17}}{4}$$

51. Substituting $x = -7$:
$$\frac{49}{25} - \frac{y^2}{4} = 1$$
$$-\frac{y^2}{4} = -\frac{24}{25}$$
$$y^2 = \frac{96}{25}$$
$$y = \pm\sqrt{\frac{96}{25}} = \pm\frac{4\sqrt{6}}{5}$$

Landmark Review

1. Using the distance formula: $d = \sqrt{(0-5)^2 + (2-2)^2} = \sqrt{25+0} = \sqrt{25} = 5$

2. Using the distance formula: $d = \sqrt{(1-3)^2 + (2-1)^2} = \sqrt{4+1} = \sqrt{5}$

3. Using the distance formula: $d = \sqrt{(3-0)^2 + (3-4)^2} = \sqrt{9+1} = \sqrt{10}$

4. Using the distance formula: $d = \sqrt{(4-0)^2 + (2-0)^2} = \sqrt{16+4} = \sqrt{20} = 2\sqrt{5}$

5. The equation is $(x+4)^2 + (y-3)^2 = 4$.

6. The equation is $x^2 + (y-3)^2 = 25$.

7. The center is $(0,0)$ and the radius is 3.

8. The center is $(-3,2)$ and the radius is $\sqrt{5}$.

9. The vertex is $(-3,-2)$. Graphing the parabola:

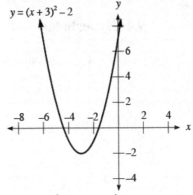

$y = (x+3)^2 - 2$

10. First complete the square: $x = 2y^2 - 4y - 2 = 2(y^2 - 2y + 1) - 2 - 2 = 2(y-1)^2 - 4$

    The vertex is $(-4,1)$. Graphing the parabola:

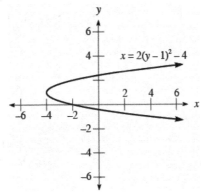

$x = 2(y-1)^2 - 4$

11. Graphing the ellipse:

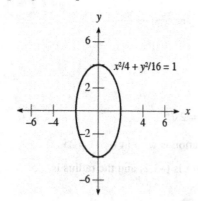

$x^2/4 + y^2/16 = 1$

12. The standard form is $\dfrac{x^2}{9} + \dfrac{y^2}{16} = 1$. Graphing the ellipse:

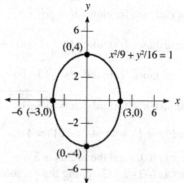

$x^2/9 + y^2/16 = 1$

9.4 Hyperbolas

1. Graphing the hyperbola:

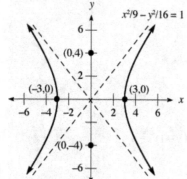

$x^2/9 - y^2/16 = 1$

2. Graphing the hyperbola:

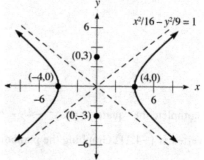

$x^2/16 - y^2/9 = 1$

5. Graphing the hyperbola:

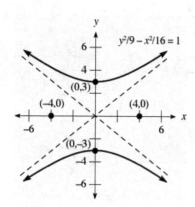

$y^2/9 - x^2/16 = 1$

7. Graphing the hyperbola:

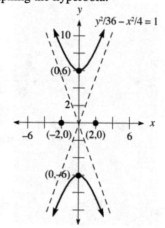

$y^2/36 - x^2/4 = 1$

9. The standard form is $\dfrac{x^2}{4} - \dfrac{y^2}{1} = 1$. Graphing the hyperbola:

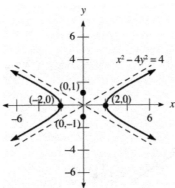

11. The standard form is $\dfrac{y^2}{9} - \dfrac{x^2}{16} = 1$. Graphing the hyperbola:

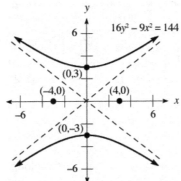

13. For the x-intercepts, set $y = 0$:
$$0.4x^2 = 3.6$$
$$x^2 = 9$$
$$x = \pm 3$$

For the y-intercepts, set $x = 0$:
$$-0.9y^2 = 3.6$$
$$y^2 = -4$$
$$y = \pm 2i$$

There are no y-intercepts.

15. For the x-intercepts, set $y = 0$:
$$\dfrac{x^2}{0.04} = 1$$
$$x^2 = 0.04$$
$$x = \pm 0.2$$

For the y-intercepts, set $x = 0$:
$$-\dfrac{y^2}{0.09} = 1$$
$$y^2 = -0.09$$
$$y = \pm 0.3i$$

There are no y-intercepts.

17. For the x-intercepts, set $y = 0$:
$$\dfrac{25x^2}{9} = 1$$
$$x^2 = \dfrac{9}{25}$$
$$x = \pm \dfrac{3}{5}$$

For the y-intercepts, set $x = 0$:
$$-\dfrac{25y^2}{4} = 1$$
$$y^2 = -\dfrac{4}{25}$$
$$y = \pm \dfrac{2}{5}i$$

There are no y-intercepts.

19. For the x-intercepts, set $y = 0$:

$$-\frac{4x^2}{9} = 1$$
$$x^2 = -\frac{9}{4}$$
$$x = \pm\frac{3}{2}i$$

There are no x-intercepts.

For the y-intercepts, set $x = 0$:

$$\frac{25y^2}{16} = 1$$
$$y^2 = \frac{16}{25}$$
$$y = \pm\frac{4}{5}$$

21. Graphing the hyperbola:

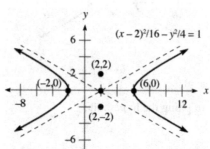

$(x - 2)^2/16 - y^2/4 = 1$

23. Completing the square:

$$9y^2 - x^2 - 4x + 54y + 68 = 0$$
$$9(y^2 + 6y + 9) - (x^2 + 4x + 4) = -68 + 81 - 4$$
$$9(y + 3)^2 - (x + 2)^2 = 9$$
$$\frac{(y + 3)^2}{1} - \frac{(x + 2)^2}{9} = 1$$

Graphing the hyperbola:

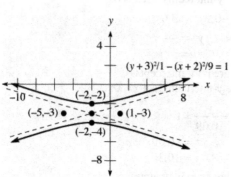

$(y + 3)^2/1 - (x + 2)^2/9 = 1$

25. Completing the square:

$$4y^2 - 9x^2 - 16y + 72x - 164 = 0$$
$$4(y^2 - 4y + 4) - 9(x^2 - 8x + 16) = 164 + 16 - 144$$
$$4(y - 2)^2 - 9(x - 4)^2 = 36$$
$$\frac{(y - 2)^2}{9} - \frac{(x - 4)^2}{4} = 1$$

Graphing the hyperbola:

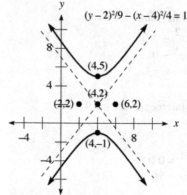

$(y - 2)^2/9 - (x - 4)^2/4 = 1$

27. Substituting $y = 4$:

$$\frac{x^2}{25} - \frac{4^2}{16} = 1$$
$$\frac{x^2}{25} - 1 = 1$$
$$\frac{x^2}{25} = 2$$
$$x^2 = 50$$
$$x = \pm 5\sqrt{2}$$

29. Substituting $x = 3$:

$$\frac{3^2}{25} - \frac{y^2}{16} = 1$$
$$\frac{9}{25} - \frac{y^2}{16} = 1$$
$$-\frac{y^2}{16} = \frac{16}{25}$$
$$y^2 = -\frac{256}{25}$$
$$y = \pm\frac{16}{5}i$$

There is no real solution.

31. Substituting $y = -3$:

$$\frac{x^2}{25} - \frac{(-3)^2}{16} = 1$$

$$\frac{x^2}{25} - \frac{9}{16} = 1$$

$$\frac{x^2}{25} = \frac{25}{16}$$

$$x^2 = \frac{625}{16}$$

$$x = \pm\frac{25}{4}$$

33. The asymptotes are $y = \frac{4}{5}x$ and $y = -\frac{4}{5}x$.

35. The slopes of the asymptotes are $\pm\frac{4}{3}$. Using the point-slope formula with the point $(-1, 2)$:

$$y - 2 = \frac{4}{3}(x+1)$$

$$y - 2 = \frac{4}{3}x + \frac{4}{3}$$

$$y = \frac{4}{3}x + \frac{10}{3}$$

$$y - 2 = -\frac{4}{3}(x+1)$$

$$y - 2 = -\frac{4}{3}x - \frac{4}{3}$$

$$y = -\frac{4}{3}x + \frac{2}{3}$$

37. The curve is a hyperbola with $a = \frac{24}{2} = 12$ and $b = \frac{50}{2} = 25$, so the equation is $\frac{x^2}{12^2} - \frac{y^2}{25^2} = 1$, or $\frac{x^2}{144} - \frac{y^2}{625} = 1$.

39. Since $4^2 + 0^2 = 16$ and $0^2 + 5^2 = 25$, while $0^2 + 0^2 = 0$, only $(0,0)$ is a solution.

41. Multiplying: $(2y+4)^2 = (2y)^2 + 2(2y)(4) + 4^2 = 4y^2 + 16y + 16$

43. Solving for x:

$$x - 2y = 4$$

$$x = 2y + 4$$

45. Simplifying: $x^2 - 2(x^2 - 3) = x^2 - 2x^2 + 6 = -x^2 + 6$

47. Simplifying: $x^2 - 4(x^2 + 2) = x^2 - 4x^2 - 8 = -3x^2 - 8$

49. Factoring: $5y^2 + 16y + 12 = (5y+6)(y+2)$

51. Factoring: $2y^2 - 8 = 2(y^2 - 4) = 2(y+2)(y-2)$

53. Solving the equation:

$$y^2 = 4$$

$$y = \pm\sqrt{4} = \pm 2$$

55. Solving the equation:

$$-x^2 + 6 = 2$$

$$-x^2 = -4$$

$$x^2 = 4$$

$$x = \pm\sqrt{4} = \pm 2$$

9.5 Nonlinear Systems of Equations and Inequalities

1. Graphing the inequality:

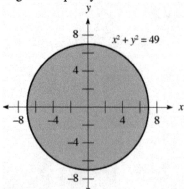

3. Graphing the inequality:

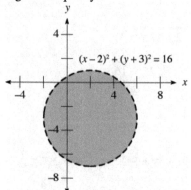

5. Graphing the inequality:

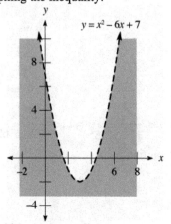

7. Graphing the inequality:

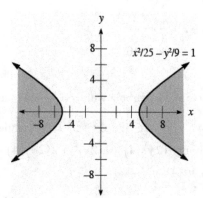

9. Graphing the inequality:

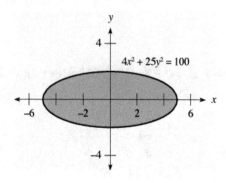

11. Graphing the inequality:

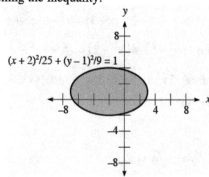

13. Graphing the inequality $\dfrac{x^2}{9} - \dfrac{y^2}{16} \geq 1$:

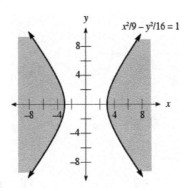

15. Completing the square:
$$9x^2 + 4y^2 + 36x - 8y + 4 < 0$$
$$9\left(x^2 + 4x + 4\right) + 4\left(y^2 - 2y + 1\right) < -4 + 36 + 4$$
$$9(x+2)^2 + 4(y-1)^2 < 36$$
$$\frac{(x+2)^2}{4} + \frac{(y-1)^2}{9} < 1$$

Graphing the inequality:

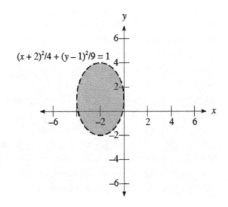

17. Completing the square:
$$9y^2 - x^2 + 18y + 2x > 1$$
$$9\left(y^2 + 2y + 1\right) - \left(x^2 - 2x + 1\right) > 1 + 9 - 1$$
$$9(y+1)^2 - (x-1)^2 > 9$$
$$\frac{(y+1)^2}{1} - \frac{(x-1)^2}{9} > 1$$

Graphing the inequality:

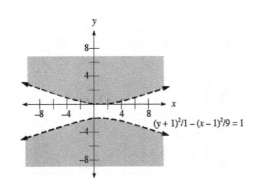

19. Solving the second equation for y yields $y = 3 - 2x$. Substituting into the first equation:

$$x^2 + (3 - 2x)^2 = 9$$
$$x^2 + 9 - 12x + 4x^2 = 9$$
$$5x^2 - 12x = 0$$
$$x(5x - 12) = 0$$
$$x = 0, \frac{12}{5}$$
$$y = 3, -\frac{9}{5}$$

The solutions are $(0,3), \left(\frac{12}{5}, -\frac{9}{5}\right)$.

21. Solving the second equation for x yields $x = 8 - 2y$. Substituting into the first equation:

$$(8 - 2y)^2 + y^2 = 16$$
$$64 - 32y + 4y^2 + y^2 = 16$$
$$5y^2 - 32y + 48 = 0$$
$$(y - 4)(5y - 12) = 0$$
$$y = 4, \frac{12}{5}$$
$$x = 0, \frac{16}{5}$$

The solutions are $(0,4), \left(\frac{16}{5}, \frac{12}{5}\right)$.

23. Adding the two equations yields:

$$2x^2 = 50$$
$$x^2 = 25$$
$$x = -5, 5$$
$$y = 0$$

The solutions are $(-5,0), (5,0)$.

25. Adding the two equations yields:

$$x^2 + \left(x^2 - 3\right)^2 = 9$$
$$x^2 + x^4 - 6x^2 + 9 = 9$$
$$x^4 - 5x^2 = 0$$
$$x^2\left(x^2 - 5\right) = 0$$
$$x = 0, -\sqrt{5}, \sqrt{5}$$
$$y = -3, 2, 2$$

The solutions are $(0,-3), \left(-\sqrt{5}, 2\right), \left(\sqrt{5}, 2\right)$.

27. Substituting into the first equation:

$$x^2 + \left(x^2 - 4\right)^2 = 16$$
$$x^2 + x^4 - 8x^2 + 16 = 16$$
$$x^4 - 7x^2 = 0$$
$$x^2\left(x^2 - 7\right) = 0$$
$$x = 0, -\sqrt{7}, \sqrt{7}$$
$$y = -4, 3, 3$$

The solutions are $(0,-4), \left(-\sqrt{7}, 3\right), \left(\sqrt{7}, 3\right)$.

29. Substituting into the first equation:

$$3x + 2\left(x^2 - 5\right) = 10$$
$$3x + 2x^2 - 10 = 10$$
$$2x^2 + 3x - 20 = 0$$
$$(x + 4)(2x - 5) = 0$$
$$x = -4, \frac{5}{2}$$
$$y = 11, \frac{5}{4}$$

The solutions are $(-4,11), \left(\frac{5}{2}, \frac{5}{4}\right)$.

31. Substituting into the first equation:
$$-x+1 = x^2 + 2x - 3$$
$$x^2 + 3x - 4 = 0$$
$$(x+4)(x-1) = 0$$
$$x = -4, 1$$
$$y = 5, 0$$
The solutions are $(-4,5)$, $(1,0)$.

33. Substituting into the first equation:
$$x - 5 = x^2 - 6x + 5$$
$$x^2 - 7x + 10 = 0$$
$$(x-2)(x-5) = 0$$
$$x = 2, 5$$
$$y = -3, 0$$
The solutions are $(2,-3)$, $(5,0)$.

35. Adding the two equations yields:
$$8x^2 = 72$$
$$x^2 = 9$$
$$x = \pm 3$$
$$y = 0$$
The solutions are $(-3,0)$, $(3,0)$.

37. Solving the first equation for x yields $x = y + 4$. Substituting into the second equation:
$$(y+4)^2 + y^2 = 16$$
$$y^2 + 8y + 16 + y^2 = 16$$
$$2y^2 + 8y = 0$$
$$2y(y+4) = 0$$
$$y = 0, -4$$
$$x = 4, 0$$
The solutions are $(0,-4)$, $(4,0)$.

39. Adding the two equations:
$$3x^2 = 8$$
$$x^2 = \frac{8}{3}$$
$$x = \pm\sqrt{\frac{8}{3} \cdot \frac{3}{3}} = \pm\frac{2\sqrt{6}}{3}$$

Substituting to find y: $y = 7 - x^2 = 7 - \left(\pm\frac{2\sqrt{6}}{3}\right)^2 = 7 - \frac{8}{3} = \frac{13}{3}$

The solutions are $\left(\frac{2\sqrt{6}}{3}, \frac{13}{3}\right)$ and $\left(-\frac{2\sqrt{6}}{3}, \frac{13}{3}\right)$.

41. Setting the two equations equal:
$$x^2 - 3 = x^2 - 2x - 1$$
$$-3 = -2x - 1$$
$$2x = 2$$
$$x = 1$$
$$y = 1^2 - 3 = -2$$
The solution is $(1,-2)$.

43. Adding the two equations:
$$8x^2 = 80$$
$$x^2 = 10$$
$$x = \pm\sqrt{10}$$
Substituting to find y:
$$4\left(\pm\sqrt{10}\right)^2 + 5y^2 = 40$$
$$40 + 5y^2 = 40$$
$$5y^2 = 0$$
$$y = 0$$
The solutions are $\left(-\sqrt{10},0\right)$ and $\left(\sqrt{10},0\right)$.

45. Graphing the inequality:

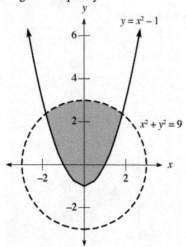

47. Graphing the inequality:

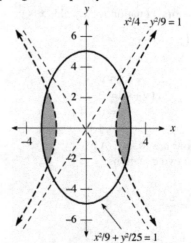

49. There is no intersection.

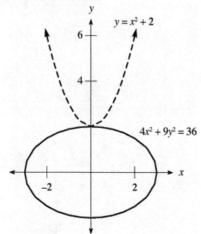

51. Graphing the inequality:

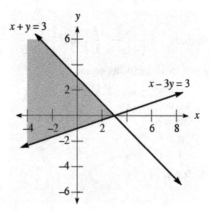

53. Graphing the inequality:

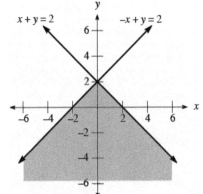

55. Graphing the inequality:

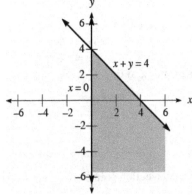

57. Graphing the inequality:

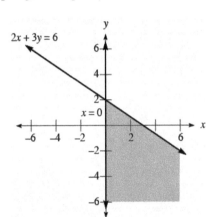

59. Graphing the inequality:

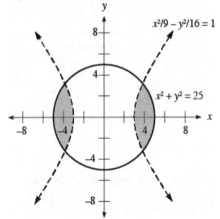

61. Graphing the inequality:

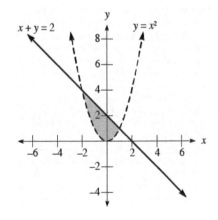

63. The system of equations is:

$$x^2 + y^2 = 89$$
$$x^2 - y^2 = 39$$

Adding the two equations yields:

$$2x^2 = 128$$
$$x^2 = 64$$
$$x = \pm 8$$
$$y = \pm 5$$

The numbers are either 8 and 5, 8 and –5, –8 and 5, or –8 and –5.

65. **a.** Subtracting the two equations yields:
$$(x+8)^2 - x^2 = 0$$
$$x^2 + 16x + 64 - x^2 = 0$$
$$16x = -64$$
$$x = -4$$
Substituting to find y:
$$(-4)^2 + y^2 = 64$$
$$y^2 + 16 = 64$$
$$y^2 = 48$$
$$y = \pm\sqrt{48} = \pm 4\sqrt{3}$$
The intersection points are $\left(-4, -4\sqrt{3}\right)$ and $\left(-4, 4\sqrt{3}\right)$.

   b. Subtracting the two equations yields:
$$x^2 - (x-8)^2 = 0$$
$$x^2 - x^2 + 16x - 64 = 0$$
$$16x = 64$$
$$x = 4$$
Substituting to find y:
$$4^2 + y^2 = 64$$
$$y^2 + 16 = 64$$
$$y^2 = 48$$
$$y = \pm\sqrt{48} = \pm 4\sqrt{3}$$
The intersection points are $\left(4, -4\sqrt{3}\right)$ and $\left(4, 4\sqrt{3}\right)$.

67. Evaluating: $f(-4) = 3(-4) - 7 = -12 - 7 = -19$

69. Evaluating: $f\big(g(-4)\big) = f\big((-4)^2 - 4\big) = f(12) = 3(12) - 7 = 36 - 7 = 29$

71. Evaluating: $f(2) - g(2) = \left[3(2) - 7\right] - \left[2^2 - 4\right] = -1 - 0 = -1$

73. Evaluating: $\dfrac{g(4) - g(2)}{4 - 2} = \dfrac{\left(4^2 - 4\right) - \left(2^2 - 4\right)}{4 - 2} = \dfrac{12 - 0}{2} = 6$

75. Evaluating: $\dfrac{f\big(g(3)\big) - f\big(g(1)\big)}{3 - 1} = \dfrac{f(5) - f(-3)}{3 - 1} = \dfrac{8 - (-16)}{2} = \dfrac{24}{2} = 12$

77. Evaluating: $\dfrac{g\big(f(-1)\big) - g\big(f(-4)\big)}{-1 - (-4)} = \dfrac{g(-10) - g(-19)}{-1 + 4} = \dfrac{96 - 357}{3} = \dfrac{-261}{3} = -87$

Chapter 9 Review

1. Using the distance formula: $d = \sqrt{(-1-4)^2 + (6+6)^2} = \sqrt{25+144} = \sqrt{169} = 13$

2. Using the distance formula: $d = \sqrt{(2+4)^2 + (-5-3)^2} = \sqrt{36+64} = \sqrt{100} = 10$

3. Solving the equation:
$$\sqrt{(-5-2)^2 + (y-4)^2} = 5\sqrt{2}$$
$$(-7)^2 + (y-4)^2 = \left(5\sqrt{2}\right)^2$$
$$(y-4)^2 + 49 = 50$$
$$(y-4)^2 = 1$$
$$y-4 = \pm 1$$
$$y-4 = -1, 1$$
$$y = 3, 5$$

4. The equation is $(x+4)^2 + (y-2)^2 = 36$.

5. Finding the radius: $r = \sqrt{(9)^2 + (12)^2} = \sqrt{81+144} = \sqrt{225} = 15$. The equation is $x^2 + y^2 = 225$.

6. The center is $(0, -5)$ and the radius is $\sqrt{9} = 3$.

7. Completing the square:
$$x^2 + y^2 - 6x + 10y = 2$$
$$\left(x^2 - 6x + 9\right) + \left(y^2 + 10y + 25\right) = 2 + 9 + 25$$
$$(x-3)^2 + (y+5)^2 = 36$$

The center is $(3, -5)$ and the radius is $\sqrt{36} = 6$.

8. This is a circle with center $(3, -1)$ and radius = 4. Graphing the circle:

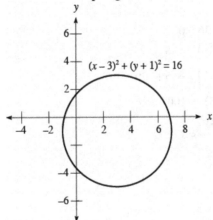

$(x-3)^2 + (y+1)^2 = 16$

9. Graphing the ellipse:

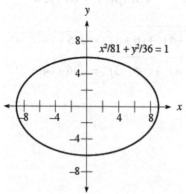

$x^2/81 + y^2/36 = 1$

10. The standard form is $\dfrac{x^2}{9} - \dfrac{y^2}{81} = 1$. Graphing the hyperbola:

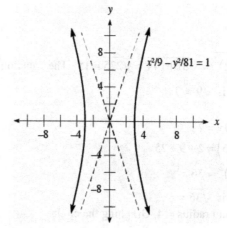

$x^2/9 - y^2/81 = 1$

11. Completing the square:

$$36x^2 + 144x + 4y^2 - 24y + 36 = 0$$
$$36\left(x^2 + 4x\right) + 4\left(y^2 - 6y\right) = -36$$
$$25\left(x^2 + 4x + 4\right) + 4\left(y^2 - 6y + 9\right) = -36 + 100 + 36$$
$$25(x+2)^2 + 4(y-3)^2 = 100$$
$$\dfrac{(x+2)^2}{4} + \dfrac{(y-3)^2}{25} = 1$$

Graphing the ellipse:

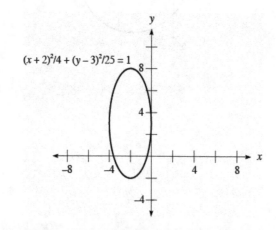

$(x+2)^2/4 + (y-3)^2/25 = 1$

12. Graphing the inequality:

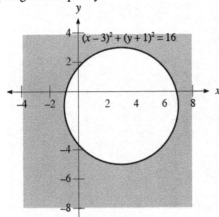

13. Graphing the inequality:

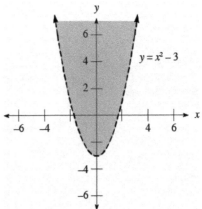

14. Solving the second equation for y yields $y = 5 - 5x$. Substituting into the first equation:

$$x^2 + (5 - 5x)^2 = 25$$
$$x^2 + 25 - 50x + 25x^2 = 25$$
$$26x^2 - 50x = 0$$
$$2x(13x - 25) = 0$$
$$x = 0, \frac{25}{13}$$
$$y = 5, -\frac{60}{13}$$

The solutions are $(0,5), \left(\frac{25}{13}, -\frac{60}{13}\right)$.

15. Substituting into the first equation:

$$x^2 + \left(x^2 - \frac{5}{2}\right)^2 = \frac{25}{4}$$
$$x^2 + x^4 - 5x^2 + \frac{25}{4} = \frac{25}{4}$$
$$x^4 - 4x^2 = 0$$
$$x^2(x^2 - 4) = 0$$
$$x = 0, -2, 2$$
$$y = -\frac{5}{2}, \frac{3}{2}, \frac{3}{2}$$

The solutions are $\left(0, -\frac{5}{2}\right), \left(-2, \frac{3}{2}\right), \left(2, \frac{3}{2}\right)$.

16. Graphing the solution set:

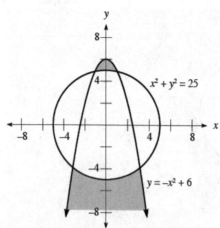

17. This is a circle with center $(0,0)$ and radius 9, so the correct graph is A.

18. The standard form is $\dfrac{x^2}{9} + \dfrac{y^2}{81} = 1$. This is an ellipse with width 6 and height 18, so the correct graph is D.

19. The standard form is $\dfrac{x^2}{9} - \dfrac{y^2}{9} = 1$. This is a hyperbola with width 6 and height 6, so the correct graph is C.

20. The standard form is $\dfrac{x^2}{81} + \dfrac{y^2}{9} = 1$. This is an ellipse with width 18 and height 6, so the correct graph is B.

21. This is a circle with center $(-3,2)$ and radius 5, so the equation is $(x+3)^2 + (y-2)^2 = 25$.

22. This is an ellipse with center $(3,1)$, width 12 and height 8, so the equation is $\dfrac{(x-3)^2}{36} + \dfrac{(y-1)^2}{16} = 1$.

23. This is a hyperbola with center $(0,0)$, width 6 and height 10, so the equation is $\dfrac{y^2}{25} - \dfrac{x^2}{9} = 1$.

Chapter 9 Cumulative Review

1. Simplifying: $\dfrac{-3-5}{6-7} = \dfrac{-8}{-1} = 8$

2. Simplifying: $\dfrac{3(-2)+4(-5)}{-8-5} = \dfrac{-6-20}{-13} = \dfrac{-26}{-13} = 2$

3. Simplifying: $\dfrac{19a^4 b^{-7}}{38a^{-3}b^4} = \dfrac{1}{2}a^{4+3}b^{-7-4} = \dfrac{1}{2}a^7 b^{-11} = \dfrac{a^7}{2b^{11}}$

4. Simplifying: $\dfrac{x^{5/3}y^2}{x^{1/6}y^{5/6}} = x^{5/3-1/6}y^{2-5/6} = x^{3/2}y^{7/6}$

5. Simplifying: $\dfrac{36x^3 y^2 - 12x^2 y^3 + 18x^4 y}{6x^2 y} = \dfrac{36x^3 y^2}{6x^2 y} - \dfrac{12x^2 y^3}{6x^2 y} + \dfrac{18x^4 y}{6x^2 y} = 6xy - 2y^2 + 3x^2$

6. Simplifying: $\dfrac{y^2 + 7y + 12}{y^2 - 9} = \dfrac{(y+3)(y+4)}{(y+3)(y-3)} = \dfrac{y+4}{y-3}$

7. Simplifying: $\log_6 36 = \log_6 6^2 = 2$

8. Simplifying: $\log_2 8 = \log_2 2^3 = 3$

9. Factoring: $ab^3 - b^3 + 4a - 4 = b^3(a-1) + 4(a-1) = (a-1)(b^3 + 4)$

10. Factoring: $7x^2 - 20x - 3 = (7x+1)(x-3)$

11. Solving the equation:
$$4 + 2(3x - 8) - 7x = 3$$
$$4 + 6x - 16 - 7x = 3$$
$$-x - 12 = 3$$
$$-x = 15$$
$$x = -15$$

12. Solving the equation:
$$6 - 7(2x + 1) = -8$$
$$6 - 14x - 7 = -8$$
$$-14x - 1 = -8$$
$$-14x = -7$$
$$x = \frac{1}{2}$$

13. Solving the equation:
$$(x - 2)(x + 5) = 8$$
$$x^2 + 3x - 10 = 8$$
$$x^2 + 3x - 18 = 0$$
$$(x + 6)(x - 3) = 0$$
$$x = -6, 3$$

14. Solving the equation:
$$1 - \frac{3}{x} = \frac{10}{x^2}$$
$$x^2\left(1 - \frac{3}{x}\right) = x^2\left(\frac{10}{x^2}\right)$$
$$x^2 - 3x = 10$$
$$x^2 - 3x - 10 = 0$$
$$(x + 2)(x - 5) = 0$$
$$x = -2, 5$$

15. Solving the equation:
$$t - 6 = \sqrt{t + 14}$$
$$(t - 6)^2 = t + 14$$
$$t^2 - 12t + 36 = t + 14$$
$$t^2 - 13t + 22 = 0$$
$$(t - 2)(t - 11) = 0$$
$$t = 2, 11$$
The solution is 11 (2 does not check).

16. Solving the equation:
$$\sqrt{6x - 3} = -3$$
$$6x - 3 = (-3)^2$$
$$6x - 3 = 9$$
$$6x = 12$$
$$x = 2 \quad \text{(does not check)}$$
There is no solution to the equation.

17. Solving the equation:
$$(7x + 2)^2 = -48$$
$$7x + 2 = \pm\sqrt{-48}$$
$$7x + 2 = \pm 4i\sqrt{3}$$
$$7x = -2 \pm 4i\sqrt{3}$$
$$x = \frac{-2 \pm 4i\sqrt{3}}{7}$$

18. Solving the equation:
$$(x - 6)^2 = -5$$
$$x - 6 = \pm\sqrt{-5}$$
$$x - 6 = \pm i\sqrt{5}$$
$$x = 6 \pm i\sqrt{5}$$

19. Solving the inequality:
$$|3x + 6| + 1 > 7$$
$$|3x + 6| > 6$$

$$3x + 6 > 6 \qquad \text{or} \qquad 3x + 6 < -6$$
$$3x > 0 \qquad\qquad\qquad 3x < -12$$
$$x > 0 \qquad\qquad\qquad x < -4$$

The solution set is $x < -4$ or $x > 0$. Graphing the solution set:

20. Solving the inequality:

$$|4x-7|-3<10$$
$$|4x-7|<13$$
$$-13<4x-7<13$$
$$-6<4x<20$$
$$-\frac{3}{2}<x<5$$

The solution set is $-\frac{3}{2}<x<5$. Graphing the solution set:

21. Graphing the inequality:

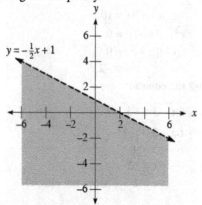

22. Graphing the inequality:

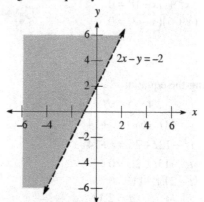

23. Graphing the parabola:

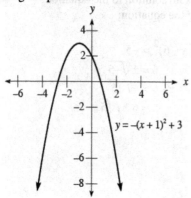

24. Graphing the parabola:

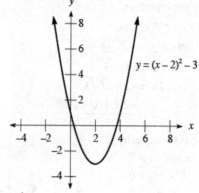

25. Multiplying: $\dfrac{y^2-3y}{2y^2+12y+10}\cdot\dfrac{2y+10}{y^2-5y+6}=\dfrac{y(y-3)}{2(y+1)(y+5)}\cdot\dfrac{2(y+5)}{(y-2)(y-3)}=\dfrac{y}{(y+1)(y-2)}$

26. Multiplying: $\dfrac{x^2-9}{x^2-2x-15}\cdot\dfrac{x^2-3x-10}{x^3+x^2-2x}=\dfrac{(x+3)(x-3)}{(x+3)(x-5)}\cdot\dfrac{(x-5)(x+2)}{x(x+2)(x-1)}=\dfrac{x-3}{x(x-1)}$

27. Multiplying: $(3-2i)(1+5i)=3+15i-2i-10i^2=3+13i+10=13+13i$

28. Multiplying: $(5+i)(6-8i)=30-40i+6i-8i^2=30-34i+8=38-34i$

29. Rationalizing the denominator: $\dfrac{3}{\sqrt{5}-\sqrt{2}}=\dfrac{3}{\sqrt{5}-\sqrt{2}}\cdot\dfrac{\sqrt{5}+\sqrt{2}}{\sqrt{5}+\sqrt{2}}=\dfrac{3\left(\sqrt{5}+\sqrt{2}\right)}{5-2}=\dfrac{3\left(\sqrt{5}+\sqrt{2}\right)}{3}=\sqrt{5}+\sqrt{2}$

30. Rationalizing the denominator:

$$\frac{3\sqrt{10}}{2\sqrt{10}+1} = \frac{3\sqrt{10}}{2\sqrt{10}+1} \cdot \frac{2\sqrt{10}-1}{2\sqrt{10}-1} = \frac{60-3\sqrt{10}}{40-1} = \frac{3\left(20-\sqrt{10}\right)}{39} = \frac{20-\sqrt{10}}{13}$$

31. Finding the inverse:

$$\frac{1-y}{3} = x$$
$$1-y = 3x$$
$$-y = 3x-1$$
$$y = -3x+1$$

The inverse function is $f^{-1}(x) = -3x+1$.

32. Finding the inverse:

$$5y+2 = x$$
$$5y = x-2$$
$$y = \frac{x-2}{5}$$

The inverse function is $f^{-1}(x) = \frac{x-2}{5}$.

33. Evaluating: $x = 10^{3.2164} \approx 1{,}645.89$

34. Evaluating: $\log_{17} 13 = \frac{\log 13}{\log 17} \approx 0.91$

35. Solving for x:

$$2mn-1 = nx+4$$
$$2mn-5 = nx$$
$$x = \frac{2mn-5}{n}$$

36. Solving for y:

$$S = 3x^2 + 5xy - 2y$$
$$S - 3x^2 = 5xy - 2y$$
$$S - 3x^2 = y(5x-2)$$
$$y = \frac{S-3x^2}{5x-2}$$

37. Finding the slope: $m = \frac{2-4}{-6-5} = \frac{-2}{-11} = \frac{2}{11}$

38. Solving for y:

$$5x-6y = 18$$
$$-6y = -5x+18$$
$$y = \frac{5}{6}x - 3$$

The slope is $\frac{5}{6}$ and the y-intercept is -3.

39. Finding the value: $f(16) = -\frac{5}{4}(16) + 2 = -20 + 2 = -18$

40. Evaluating:

$$C(15) = 60\left(\frac{1}{2}\right)^{15/15} = 60\left(\frac{1}{2}\right) = 30 \qquad C(30) = 60\left(\frac{1}{2}\right)^{30/15} = 60\left(\frac{1}{2}\right)^2 = 15$$

41. Finding the equation:

$$(x-4)(2x-1) = 0$$
$$2x^2 - x - 8x + 4 = 0$$
$$2x^2 - 9x + 4 = 0$$

42. Finding the equation:

$$(3t+4)(8t-1) = 0$$
$$24t^2 - 3t + 32t - 4 = 0$$
$$24t^2 + 29t - 4 = 0$$

43. Finding the composition: $(f \circ g)(x) = f(3-x) = 2(3-x) + 5 = 6 - 2x + 5 = -2x + 11$

44. Finding the composition: $(g \circ f)(x) = g(9-x^2) = 3(9-x^2) + 2 = 27 - 3x^2 + 2 = -3x^2 + 29$

45. Computing: $-7 + (-3-2) = -7 - 5 = -12$

46. Computing: $(-7+4) - 8 = -3 - 8 = -11$

47. The variation equation is $y = kx$. Substituting $y = 36$ and $x = 12$:

$$36 = 12k$$
$$k = 3$$

So $y = 3x$. Substituting $x = 7$: $y = 3(7) = 21$

48. The variation equation is $y = \dfrac{k}{x^2}$. Substituting $y = 2$ and $x = 4$:

$$2 = \frac{k}{4^2}$$
$$2 = \frac{k}{16}$$
$$k = 32$$

So $y = \dfrac{32}{x^2}$. Substituting $x = 5$: $y = \dfrac{32}{5^2} = \dfrac{32}{25}$

49. Let x represent the gallons of 40% solution and y represent the gallons of 90% solution. The system of equations is:

$$x + y = 50$$
$$0.4x + 0.9y = 0.85(50)$$

Multiply the first equation by –0.4:

$$-0.4x - 0.4y = -20$$
$$0.4x + 0.9y = 42.5$$

Adding yields:

$$0.5y = 22.5$$
$$y = 45$$
$$x = 50 - 45 = 5$$

The mixture should contain 5 gal of 40% solution and 45 gal of 90% solution.

50. Let x represent the gallons of 10% solution and y represent the gallons of 70% solution. The system of equations is:

$$x + y = 8$$
$$0.1x + 0.7y = 0.55(8)$$

Multiply the first equation by –0.1:

$$-0.1x - 0.1y = -0.8$$
$$0.1x + 0.7y = 4.4$$

Adding yields:

$$0.6y = 3.6$$
$$y = 6$$
$$x = 8 - 6 = 2$$

The mixture should contain 2 gal of 10% solution and 6 gal of 70% solution.

51. Finding the percentage: $0.42(425{,}382) = 178{,}660$ people

52. If 63% can introduce themselves, then $100\% - 63\% = 37\%$ cannot introduce themselves.

Finding the percentage: $0.37(5{,}347{,}265) = 1{,}978{,}488$ people

Chapter 9 Test

1. Using the distance formula: $d = \sqrt{(-4-0)^2 + (-6+3)^2} = \sqrt{16+9} = \sqrt{25} = 5$

2. Using the distance formula: $d = \sqrt{(-2-6)^2 + (4-0)^2} = \sqrt{64+16} = \sqrt{80} = 4\sqrt{5}$

3. Solving the equation:

$$\sqrt{(4-6)^2 + (y-3)^2} = 2\sqrt{5}$$
$$(-2)^2 + (y-3)^2 = \left(2\sqrt{5}\right)^2$$
$$(y-3)^2 + 4 = 20$$
$$(y-3)^2 = 16$$
$$y-3 = \pm 4$$
$$y-3 = -4, 4$$
$$y = -1, 7$$

4. The equation is $(x-3)^2 + (y+1)^2 = 16$.

5. Finding the radius: $r = \sqrt{(-12)^2 + (5)^2} = \sqrt{144+25} = \sqrt{169} = 13$. The equation is $x^2 + y^2 = 169$.

6. The center is $(0,1)$ and the radius is $\sqrt{36} = 6$.

7. Completing the square:

$$x^2 + y^2 - 4x + 8y = -11$$
$$\left(x^2 - 4x + 4\right) + \left(y^2 + 8y + 16\right) = -11 + 4 + 16$$
$$(x-2)^2 + (y+4)^2 = 9$$

The center is $(2,-4)$ and the radius is $\sqrt{9} = 3$.

8. This is a circle with center $(-2,2)$ and radius $= 3$. Graphing the circle:

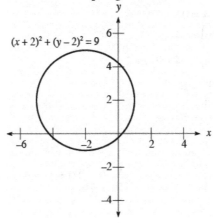

$(x+2)^2 + (y-2)^2 = 9$

9. Graphing the ellipse:

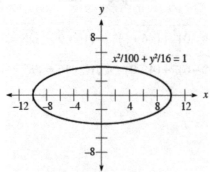

10. The standard form is $\dfrac{x^2}{16} - \dfrac{y^2}{64} = 1$. Graphing the hyperbola:

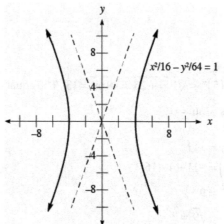

11. Completing the square:

$$25x^2 - 100x + 4y^2 + 8y + 4 = 0$$
$$25\left(x^2 - 4x\right) + 4\left(y^2 + 2y\right) = -4$$
$$25\left(x^2 - 4x + 4\right) + 4\left(y^2 + 2y + 1\right) = -4 + 100 + 4$$
$$25(x-2)^2 + 4(y+1)^2 = 100$$
$$\dfrac{(x-2)^2}{4} + \dfrac{(y+1)^2}{25} = 1$$

Graphing the ellipse:

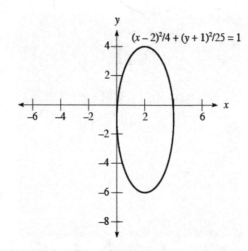

12. Graphing the inequality:

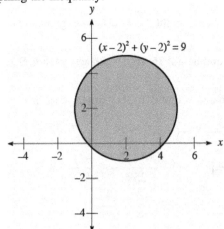

13. Graphing the inequality:

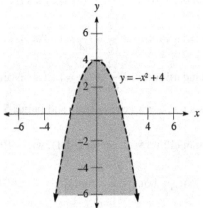

14. Solving the second equation for *y* yields $y = x - 4$. Substituting into the first equation:

$$x^2 + (x-4)^2 = 16$$
$$x^2 + x^2 - 8x + 16 = 16$$
$$2x^2 - 8x = 0$$
$$2x(x-4) = 0$$
$$x = 0, 4$$
$$y = -4, 0$$

The solutions are $(0, -4), (4, 0)$.

15. Substituting into the first equation:

$$x^2 + (x^2 - 7)^2 = 9$$
$$x^2 + x^4 - 14x^2 + 49 = 9$$
$$x^4 - 13x^2 - 40 = 0$$
$$(x^2 - 8)(x^2 - 5) = 0$$
$$x = \pm\sqrt{5}, \pm 2\sqrt{2}$$
$$y = -2, 1$$

The solutions are $\left(-\sqrt{5}, -2\right), \left(\sqrt{5}, -2\right), \left(-2\sqrt{2}, 1\right), \left(2\sqrt{2}, 1\right)$.

16. Graphing the solution set:

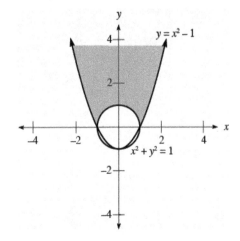

17. This is a circle with center (0,0) and radius 8, so the correct graph is A.

18. The standard form is $\dfrac{x^2}{4} - \dfrac{y^2}{1} = 1$. This is a hyperbola with width 4 and height 2, so the correct graph is D.

19. The standard form is $\dfrac{x^2}{16} + \dfrac{y^2}{64} = 1$. This is an ellipse with width 8 and height 16, so the correct graph is B.

20. The standard form is $\dfrac{x^2}{64} + \dfrac{y^2}{16} = 1$. This is an ellipse with width 16 and height 8, so the correct graph is C.

21. This is a circle with center (2,1) and radius 5, so the equation is $(x-2)^2 + (y-1)^2 = 25$.

22. This is an ellipse with center (–1,1), width 10 and height 6, so the equation is $\dfrac{(x+1)^2}{25} + \dfrac{(y-1)^2}{9} = 1$.

23. This is a hyperbola with center (0,0), width 20 and height 16, so the equation is $\dfrac{y^2}{64} - \dfrac{x^2}{100} = 1$.